About Pearson

Pearson is the world's learning company, with presence across 70 countries worldwide. Our unique insights and world-class expertise comes from a long history of working closely with renowned teachers, authors and thought leaders, as a result of which, we have emerged as the preferred choice for millions of teachers and learners across the world.

We believe learning opens up opportunities, creates fulfilling careers and hence better lives. We hence collaborate with the best of minds to deliver you class-leading products, spread across the Higher Education and Test Preparation spectrum.

Superior learning experience and improved outcomes are at the heart of everything we do. This product is the result of one such effort.

Your feedback plays a critical role in the evolution of our products and you can contact us - reachus@pearson.com. *We look forward to it.*

TRISHNA'S

PEARSON IIT FOUNDATION

PHYSICS

CLASS

8

TRISHNA'S

PEARSON IIT FOUNDATION

PHYSICS

CLASS 8

Fourteenth Edition

Pearson

Photo Credits

Chapter 1 Opener: Pixel-Shot / Shutterstock
Chapter 2 Opener: Stephanie Swartz / Shutterstock
Chapter 3 Opener: designua / 123RF
Chapter 4 Opener: Menno van der Haven / Shutterstock
Chapter 5 Opener: scyther5 / Shutterstock
Chapter 6 Opener: Todja / Shutterstock
Chapter 7 Opener: Haydar Sinanc / Shutterstock
Chapter 8 Opener: BESTWEB / Shutterstock
Chapter 9 Opener: nemoris / 123RF
Chapter 10 Opener: Flegere / Shutterstock
Chapter 11 Opener: lassedesignen / Shutterstock

ISBN 978-93-7136-697-7

First Impression

Published by Pearson India Education Services Pvt. Ltd, CIN: U72200TN2005PTC057128.

Head Office: 1st Floor, Berger Tower, Plot No. C-001A/2, Sector 16B, Noida - 201 301, Uttar Pradesh, India.

Registered Office: 6th Floor, Tower A, Unit A and B, International Tech Park, CapitaLand, Chennai, 200 Feet Radial Road, Zamin Pallavaram, Old Pallavaram, Chennai – 600117, Tamil Nadu India.

Website: in.pearson.com, Email: companysecretary.india@pearson.com

Compositor: SKY Composition Services
Printed in India

Brief Contents

Contents

Preface

"If you have a great ambition, take as big a step as possible in the direction of fulfilling it. The step may only be a tiny one, but trust that it may be the largest one possible for now."

Mildred McAfee

The *Pearson IIT Foundation* Series has been created keeping in mind the learner's ambition to excel in a competitive examination like IIT-JEE. The series can be used in addition to the books being studied in school to attain that extra edge required to strengthen the concepts and prepare well for future endeavours.

Why Start Early with Pearson IIT Foundation

Classes VI to X are the base years of a learner's academic life. In these years learner explore their interests and determine the goals they wish to attain. *Pearson IIT Foundation* series is filled with interactive learning that not only nurtures a learner's interest in science and mathematics but also strengthens their concepts.

The series uses real-life examples and application-based problems to teach theoretical concepts. The objective of this series is to help learners cultivate an analytical mind.

Most of the lessons to be learnt are introduced to the learners in the books for class VI. As they get promoted to higher classes, new topics are added to these lessons. This additive method helps the learners' span their learning over four standards, from VI-X. Thus, learners are not overwhelmed by the introduction of completely new lessons every time they are promoted to a new class.

While their learning is being spanned across five years, so is their ability to resolve doubts for further conceptual clarity. For instance, they can use concepts learnt in class VI to solve questions in class VII. If, in case, they get stuck while answering a question, the learners can infer for themselves that they might be lacking in conceptual clarity. They can then approach their teachers, requesting them to explain the concept once again. This helps the learner to clarify their concepts while revising the lessons previously learnt.

Since classes VI-X are deemed to be a student's formative years, we, at Pearson, aim to provide a foundation level course which serves more than just a standard curriculum.

Here is how it makes a difference to a learner's overall learning...

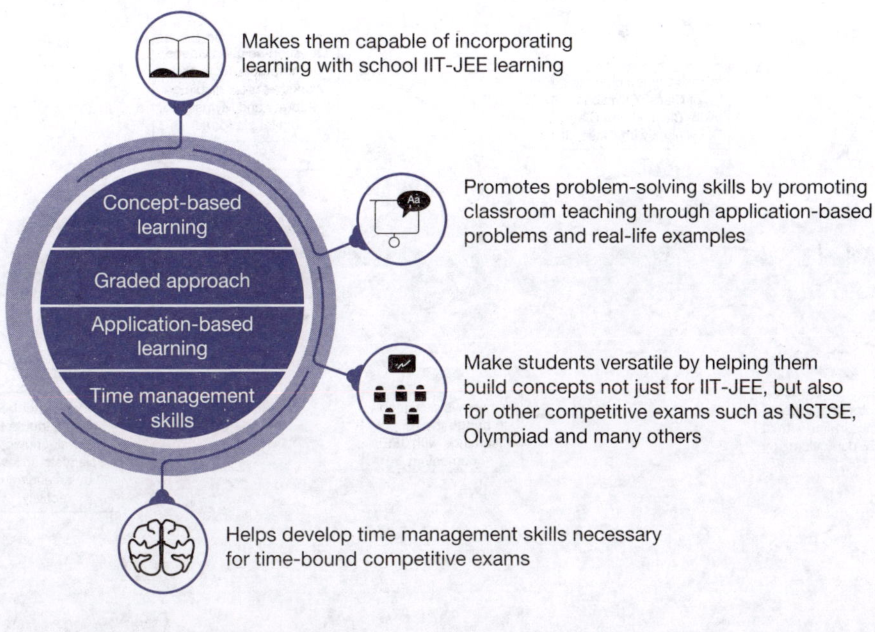

Other Uses of the Series

Instead of limiting themselves to IIT-JEE, a learner can also use this series to prepare for several other competitive examinations such as NSTSE, National and International Olympiads, NEET, BITSAT, etc. This series offers a level of concept learning that empowers learners to handle the challenging nature of questions posed in these examinations. Moreover, this will also allow the learners to have an early insight into their key strengths as well as improvement areas and help them work on themselves.

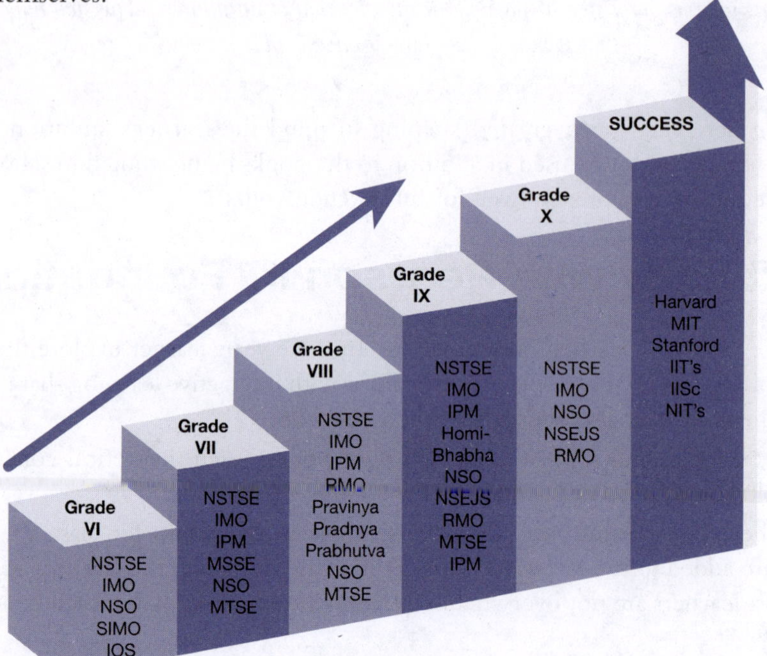

[IMO: International Mathematics Olympiad; NSO: National Science Olympiad, IOS: International Olympiad of Science, NSTSE: National Level Science Talent Search Examination, MTSE: Maharashtra Talent Search Examination, RMO: Regional Mathematical Olympiad, PPP: Pravinya Pradnya Prabhutva, NSEJS: National Standard Examination in Junior Science, IIT: Indian Institute of Technology, IISc: Indian Institute of Science, NIT: National Institute of Technology.]

Highlights of the Series

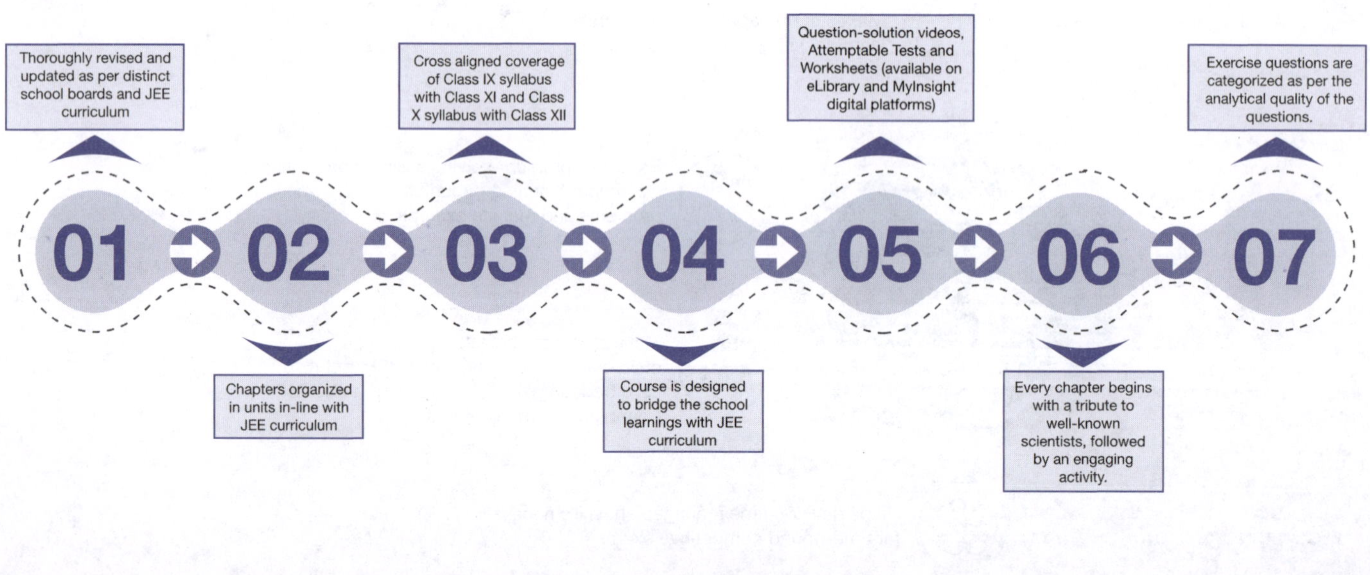

Pearson IIT Foundation series provides a perfect blend of learning through theory and practice questions with a fusion of school and JEE curriculum. It is imperative to note that this series would be as profound as you want it to be. Therefore, to get maximum benefit from this book, we recommend following the given study plan.

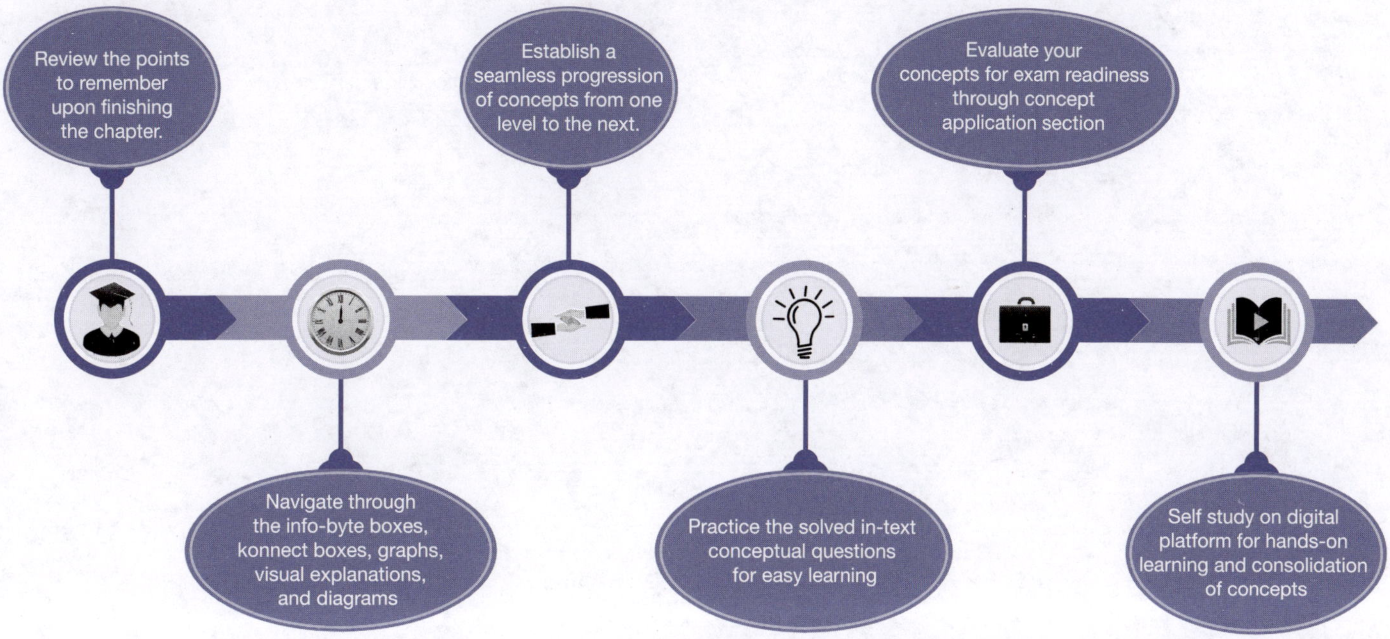

To provide a graded learning approach, the exercise part of each chapter is categorized by using four icons for question tagging. The question categorization helps the learners assess their own problem-solving and analytical skills and motivates them to improve to reach their objectives.

The following icons are used to categorize the questions with specific meanings:

Real-life Situations Questions: 

Analytical Questions: 

Conceptual Questions: 

Value-based Questions: 

With this refined and well-tuned course from Pearson, students will become more confident when they enter the competitive world for actual IIT-JEE preparation. The effort put in today will transform into a valuable asset, contributing to success in future competitive examinations.

Chapter Insights

Remember

Before beginning this chapter, you should be able to:

- know the methods involved in application of science—aim, observation, measurement, systematization and inference.

Remember section will help them to memorize and review the previous learning on a particular topic

Key points will help the students to identify the essential points in a chapter

Remember

Before beginning this chapter, you should be able to:

- know the methods involved in application of science—aim, observation, measurement, systematization and inference.

- define physical quantities and system of units,

Scientific Crypt

A Tribute to Pierre Vernier (1580–1637)

Pierre Vernier was taught mathematics and science by his father who was a lawyer and an engineer. His father introduced him to the work of Claviers and Brahe. This great scientist was born in Franche-Comte (Free country) which was under the control of the Spanish Habsburgs.

Vernier held various official positions in government such as, military engineer for the Habsburgs and director-general of the treasury in Dole and Basancon, the capital of Franche-Comte. He also held various posts in the Government of Spain. Much of the time he worked as an engineer, working on the fortifications of various cities.

Like other scientists, vernier also worked on cartography and on surveying. His interest in surveying led to the development of instruments used for surveying. His famous publication is La construction, l'usage, et les propriete's du Quadrant nouveau de mathematiques (1631). In this, vernier gives a table of sines and a method for deriving the angles of a triangle if its sides are known. In this he also describes his most famous invention, 'Vernier callipers', an instrument meant to measure the length accurately.

Scientific Crypt provides information about well-known scientists related to the chapter. The engaging activity is also given in the form of a crossword to keep the learners interested.

INTRODUCTION

Physics deals with nature and its laws. It describes laws of nature quantitatively and qualitatively. This description involves measurement of various physical quantities like height, weight, time, etc. To understand the importance of measurements, let us take few examples. To decide who is the winner in a running race, the time taken by runners to cover a certain distance is measured. Similarly, to determine the mileage of a vehicle, the distance travelled by it is measured. Thus, the measurement of quantities play an important role in our everyday life. In this chapter, we make an attempt to identify different physical quantities and associate them with proper units. We will also discuss some important techniques used for measuring physical quantities.

Introduction section helps to lay the foundation of the following chapter and leads the way for further learning

Definitions of Units

1. **Metre:** Initially metre was defined as one ten-millionth part of the distance on the Earth from the pole to the equator. As per the modern definition, one metre is the length of a certain platinum-iridium rod maintained at 0°C and kept in the International Bureau of Weights and Measures at Sevres near Paris.

   (OR)

   One metre is 1,650,763.73 times the wavelength of orange light emitted by a krypton atom at normal pressure.
2. **Kilogram:** One kilogram is the mass of a certain lump made from an alloy of platinum-iridium maintained at 0°C in the International Bureau of weights and measures.
3. **Second:** One second is defined as $(1/86,400)^{th}$ part of the mean solar day. As per the modern definition, one second is the time taken by a cesium atom (Cs^{133}) to complete 9,192,631,770 vibrations.

Concepts are explained in a well-structured and lucid manner

Konnect boxes are some add-on information of related topic

Konnect

Vernier Callipers can measure internal and external dimensions with high accuracy. They can typically measure up to 0.02mm of accuracy.

Info Bytes!

Parallax error is the error that is caused in the apparent position of the object due to the viewing angle that is other than the angle which is perpendicular to the object.

Info bytes are interesting trivia and facts that engage young minds and keep the grey cells ticking!

EXAMPLE 2.6 A car moves along a straight path with variable velocity as shown in the figure. When the car is at position A, its velocity is 10 m s^{-1} and when it is at position B, its velocity is 20 m s^{-1}. If the car takes 5 seconds of time to move from A to B, find the acceleration of the car.

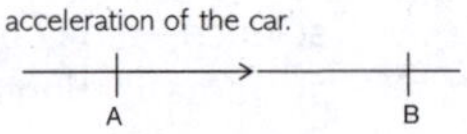

SOLUTION

Initial velocity of the car at position $A = u = 10 \text{ m s}^{-1}$

Final velocity of the car at position $B = v = 20 \text{ m s}^{-1}$

The change in velocity of the car, $\Delta v = v - u = 20 \text{ m s}^{-1} - 10 \text{ m s}^{-1}$

$= 10 \text{ m s}^{-1}$

The time taken for the car to move from A to B, $\Delta t = 5$ s

$\therefore$ Acceleration of the car, $a = \dfrac{\Delta v}{\Delta t} = \dfrac{10 \text{ m s}^{-1}}{5 \text{ s}}$

$= 2 \text{ m s}^{-2}$

Examples are given in the form of in-text exercises to reinforce the concepts learnt in a particular chapter

Illustrative examples solved in a logical and step-wise manner

POINTS TO REMEMBER

- ✔ The quantities that can be measured are called physical quantities.
- ✔ A quantity which is independent of other quantities is called fundamental quantity.
- ✔ A quantity which is dependent on other physical quantities and can be derived from the fundamental quantities is called derived quantity.
- ✔ The unit of a fundamental quantity like mass or length is called fundamental unit.
- ✔ The unit of a derived quantity like volume or velocity is called derived unit.
- ✔ A system which defines the fundamental units, in comparison with which a fundamental quantity can be expressed is referred to as system of units.
- ✔ Vernier calliper is an instrument which uses a combination of two scales, main scale and vernier scale.
- ✔ Area is the extent or measure of a surface. The S.I. unit of area is m^2 and 1 m^2 = 10000 cm^2.
- ✔ Measuring jar is graduated in millilitres and used to measure the volume of liquids in millilitres.
- ✔ Burette has a nozzle vent at the bottom with a screw system and graduated in millilitres and is used to take the desired amount of a liquid.
- ✔ Mass is the amount of matter contained in a body. It is a fundamental quantity and its unit in S.I. system is kilogram (kg).
- ✔ The density of a substance is defined as the mass per unit volume. The unit of density in

Points to remember summarises the concepts and topics presented in each chapter

CLASSROOM WING

Practice Questions

Very Short Answer Type Questions

Directions for questions 1 to 8:
Fill in the blanks.

1. If the principle used to construct a vernier calli-per is N V.S.D. = (N – 2) M.S.D., its least count is

12. Define relative density.

13. If the main scale of vernier calliper is graduated in mm and the vernier scale has 20 divisions, then what is the least count?

...at is the relation between litre and the C.G.S. and S.I. units of volume?

Short Answer Type Questions

26. What are the characteristics of a standard unit?

27. List the fundamental quantities along with their units in S.I. system.

28. Define least count. Describe the method to find the least count of a vernier calliper.

Essay Answers Type Questions

44. Explain the need for standards and systems of units in measurements.

45. Explain the principle of vernier. Draw a neat diagram of a vernier calliper showing the various parts

Different typologies of questions have been included in the *Classroom Wing* which help students to develop the problem-solving skill

Competition Wing has been integrated chapter-wise in the exercise part to prepare students for various competitive examinations.

Graded as per complexity: Level 1; Level 2; and Level 3

COMPETITION WING

Practice Questions

Level 1: Apply your Concepts

Directions for questions 1 to 12:
State whether the following statements are true or false...

15. On dropping 10 lead shots into a measuring jar containing a liquid, the level of the liquid in the jar ...ed from 40 cm^3 to 100 cm^3. Then, the volume ... lead shot is ________.

Level 2: Review your Concepts

48. Taking 1 ly (light year) = 9.3×10^{15} m and one day = 86400 s, express the speed of light (= 3×10^8 ms^{-1}) as ly (day)$^{-1}$ and speed of sound in air (= 330 ms^{-1}) as ly day^{-1}. Also find the ratio of those two values.

49. The amount of heat absorbed by a body while raising its temperature is given by the equation: $Q = ms\,\theta$

Level 3 : Assess Your Concepts

67. A vernier calipers has two sliding jaws with scales marked as shown in the figure. When a brass rod of length 5.23 cm was held between the jaws, the zero of jaw A was found to lie between the 34th and 35th

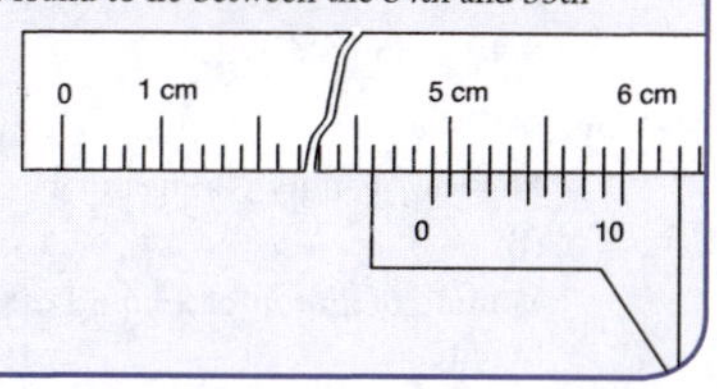

28. Define least count. Describe the method to find the least count of a vernier calliper.

29. A vernier calliper has 20 divisions on the vernier scale. One centimetre on the main scale is divided into 20 equal parts. Find the least count of this instrument.

30. While measuring the length of a copper rod using a vernier calliper, the zero of the vernier scale wa... found to be between 4.6 cm and 4.7 cm on the main scale. The 6th division of the vernier scale is found to coincide with a division on the main scale. Find the length of the rod if the least count is 0.01 cm.

31. A vernier scale has 10 divisions. It slides over the main scale, whose 1 M.S.D. is 1.0 mm. If the number of divi...

34. How do you measure the area of a... plane figure? Describe the graphica... the area of a leaf.

35. Describe a method to determine ... single drop of water.

33. A vernier calliper has 10 divisions on the vernier scale. If one centimetre of main scale is divided into 5 equal parts, find the best possible least count of the given vernier calliper.

34. How do you measure the area of an irregular shaped plane figure? Describe the graphical method to find the area of a leaf.

35. Describe a method to determine the volume of a single drop of water.

The icons are used for categorisation of the questions in Classroom Wing and Competition Wing

JEE-NEET SPECIAL WING

Practice Questions

Multiple-Answer Type Questions

Directions for questions 1 to 5:
Select one or more correct alternative(s) from the given choices.

1. A unit should have the following characteristics:
   (a) It should be well defined.
   (b) It should be irreproducible.
   (c) It should be changeable.
   (d) It should be of measurable size.

3. The least count of a meter scale is
   (a) 0.1 cm (b) 0.001 cm
   (c) 1 mm (d) 0.01 mm

4. Which of the measuring devices is used to take fixed amount of liquids?
   (a) Measuring jar (b) Measuring flask
   (c) Pipette (d) Burette

5. 1 Joule =

JEE-NEET Special Wing is curated specifically for targeted preparation of JEE and NEET examinations

Hints and Explanations

Classroom Wing

Very Short Answer Type Questions

1. L.C = 1 M.S.D. – 1 V.S.D.
   = 1 mm – 0.8 mm
   = 0.2 mm

2. 129×10^{-5}

3. 7850 kg m^{-3}

20. $\eta = \frac{Fx}{Av}$

$\frac{Nm}{m^2 \times \frac{m}{s}} = \frac{Ns}{m^2}$

21. The ratio of mass to volume is density.

22. Principle of moment.

Hints and Explanations for key questions of classroom wing, competition wing and JEE-NEET special wing along with highlights on the common mistakes that students usually make in the examinations

Competition Wing

Level 1: Apply your Concepts

13. Relative density = $\frac{\text{density of substance}}{\text{density of water}}$

$0.9 = \frac{d}{1}$

$\therefore d = 0.9 \text{ g cm}^{-3} = 900 \text{ kg m}^{-}$

= 9.85 mm

$\therefore$ Radius (R) = $\frac{9.85}{2}$ mm

14. $1 \text{ kg m}^{-1} \text{ s}^{-2} = \frac{1000 \text{ g}}{(100 \text{ cm})} \text{s}^{-2}$

$= 10 \text{ g cm}^{-1} \text{ s}^{-2}$

20. (A) $\rightarrow b$
Physical quantity is a measurabl
(B) $\rightarrow a$
Volume of a drop of a liquid ca burette.
I $\rightarrow d$
The SI unit of instantaneous sp
(D) $\rightarrow c$
Acceleration is defined as the rat

36. 1 M.S.D. = 0.5 mm
Number of vernier scale divisio
$\therefore$ Least count = $\frac{1 \text{ M.S.D.}}{N} = \frac{0.}{}$

JEE-NEET Special Wing

Multiple-Answer Type Questions

1. Unit should be reproducible and unchangeable.
Hence, the correct option is (a) and (d).

2. Temperature and time are fundamental quantities.
Hence, the correct option is (c) and (d).

3. LC of meter scale = 0.1 cm = 1 mm
Hence, the correct option is (a) and (c).

4. Measuring jar is used to measure the volume of liquid in millilitres.
Burette is used to take the desired amount of a liquid.
Hence, the correct option is (b) and (c).

5. Joule is the unit of work and energy.
Work = F×S
$\therefore$ Its unit is N m
But since F= ma
$N = \text{kg m s}^{-2}$
$\therefore$ Unit of work is $\text{kg m}^2 \text{s}^{-2}$.
Hence, the correct option is (b) and (c).

Comprehension-Based Questions

6. The smallest measurement that can be accurately made by an instrument is least count.
Hence, the correct option is (b).

7. L.C= $\frac{1 \text{ M.S.D.}}{\text{No. of V.S.D's}}$
Hence, the correct option is (c).

8. The principle of vernier is to make 'N' vernier scale divisions equal to (N – 1) main scale divisions.
Hence, the correct option is (a).

9. The observed measurement from a vernier calliper is given by M. S. R + (V. C. D×L. C).
Hence, the correct option is (a).

10. Each division of vernier scale is smaller than each main scale division.
Hence, the correct option is (c).

Match the Column

11. **Choice (b) follows.**
Units of some of the quantities in S.I. system are given.
The SI unit of **Time** is **second.**
The SI unit of **Temperature** is **Kelvin.**
The SI unit of **Luminous intensity** is **Candela.**
The SI unit of **Electric current** is **Ampere.**
The SI unit of **Amount of substance** is **Mole.**
A - e, B - d, C – a, D – b, E - c

DW

WORKSHEET
CHAPTER 2: DYNAMICS

Directions for questions from 1 to 5:
Select the correct alternative from the following options.

1. A bullet of mass 100 g moving with a velocity of 100 m s^{-1} is stopped by a plank. If the bullet travels a distance of 10 cm in the plank before it comes to rest, find the average force exerted by the plank.
(a) 100 N (b) 1000 N
(c) 2500 N (d) 5000 N

2. Find the power developed by an engine in filling water

a rough surface, the total work done by the frictional force is zero.

8. The orbital velocity of a satellite is inversely proportional to the radius of the orbit.

9. When a stone is tied to a string and rotated in a circular path, the work done by the tension of the string is zero.

10. A satellite revolving in an orbit closer to the surface of the earth has more speed than one which is moving in an orbit of higher radius.

DW: Downloadable worksheets supplementing textual exercises for hand-on learning

AT

AI Assessments ×

Which of the following is larger unit of density?

- ○ g m^{-3}
- ○ g km^{-3}
- ○ kg m^{-3}
- ◉ g cm^{-3}

Questions 1 of 4 Next

AT: Attemptable Tests for assessing understanding of concepts and getting a clear picture of your exam readiness

48. Taking 1 ly (light year) = 9.3×10^{15} m and one = 86400 s, express the speed of light (= 3×10^{8} ms as ly $(\text{day})^{-1}$ and speed of sound in air (= 330 ms^{-1} ly day^{-1}. Also find the ratio of those two values.

49. The amount of heat absorbed by a body while rais its temperature is given by the equation:
Q = ms θ,
here Q is the amount of heat, *m* is the mass of body, s is the specific heat capacity and θ is the

Video icon: Audio and visual learning to difficult questions for effective learning and retention

Measurements

CHAPTER

1

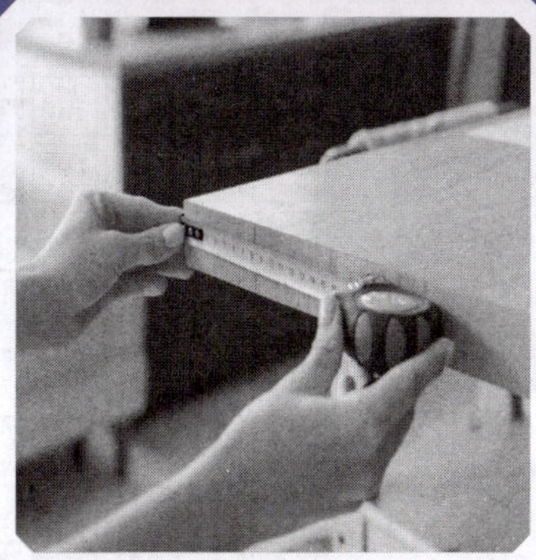

Key Ideas

After completing this chapter, you should be able to:

- ✦ understand different physical quantities and different systems of units.
- ✦ recognize the importance of accuracy of measurements.
- ✦ understand the use of vernier callipers to measure lengths.
- ✦ study the methods of determining physical quantities like area, volume, mass and density.
- ✦ find the relation between various physical quantities.

Remember

Before beginning this chapter, you should be able to:

- ☛ know the methods involved in application of science—aim, observation, measurement, systematization and inference.
- ☛ define physical quantities and system of units, measurement of some physical quantities, difference between mass and weight.
- ☛ define density of a solid and liqiud, variation in density of liquids and gases with temperatures.

Scientific Crypt

A Tribute to Pierre Vernier (1580–1637)

Pierre Vernier was taught mathematics and science by his father who was a lawyer and an engineer. His father introduced him to the work of Claviers and Brahe. This great scientist was born in Franche-Comte (Free country) which was under the control of the Spanish Habsburgs.

Vernier held various official positions in government such as, military engineer for the Habsburgs and director-general of the treasury in Dole and Basancon, the capital of Franche-Comte. He also held various posts in the Government of Spain. Much of the time he worked as an engineer, working on the fortifications of various cities.

Like other scientists, vernier also worked on cartography and on surveying. His interest in surveying led to the development of instruments used for surveying. His famous publication is La construction, I'usage, et les propriete's du Quadrant nouveau de mathematiques (1631). In this, vernier gives a table of sines and a method for deriving the angles of a triangle if its sides are known. In this he also describes his most famous invention, 'Vernier callipers', an instrument meant to measure the length accurately.

Crossword

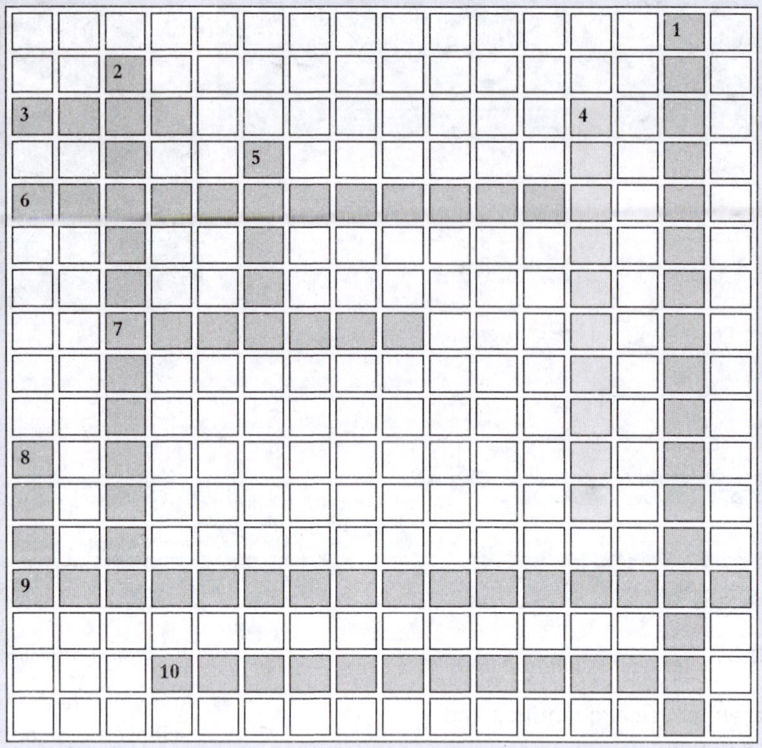

Across

3. Well-defined standard quantity.

6. A sliding frame of vernier callipers.

7. Device that has a nozzle vent at the bottom with a screw system.

9. The ratio of density of substance to the density of water.

10. Unit of derived quantity.

Down

1. Quantity that is measurable.

2. The balance that can measure mass upto 1 microgram.

4. Time taken by cesium atom to complete 9192631770 vibrations.

5. One ten millionth part of the distance on the earth from pole to equator.

8. Amount of matter contained in an object.

INTRODUCTION

Physics deals with nature and its laws. It describes laws of nature quantitatively and qualitatively. This description involves measurement of various physical quantities like height, weight, time, etc. To understand the importance of measurements, let us take few examples. To decide who is the winner in a running race, the time taken by runners to cover a certain distance is measured. Similarly, to determine the mileage of a vehicle, the distance travelled by it is measured. Thus, the measurement of quantities play an important role in our everyday life. In this chapter, we make an attempt to identify different physical quantities and associate them with proper units. We will also discuss some important techniques used for measuring physical quantities.

Physical Quantities

The quantities that can be measured are called **physical quantities.** For example, mass, length, volume, area, etc. In order to measure any physical quantity, the quantity is compared with a known standard quantity. This well defined standard quantity is called unit. The unit **kilogram** (kg) is defined as the mass of a certain platinum-iridium block kept at the international bureau of weights and measures. Now, any body having the same mass as this lump is said to have a mass of 1 kg and a body having double the mass as this lump is said to have a mass of 2 kg and so on.

Characteristics of a Unit

A unit used to measure a physical quantity should have the following characteristics:

1. It should be well-defined.
2. It should be reproducible.
3. It should be unchangeable.
4. It should be of measurable size.

Info Bytes!

In order to express any physical quantity, we need to state its numerical value and the unit.

Based on their independency from other quantities, physical quantities can be classified into two categories.

Fundamental Quantity

A quantity which is independent of other quantities is called **fundamental quantity.** Mass, length, time, electric current, temperature, luminous intensity and the amount of substance are the fundamental quantities.

Konnect

Units are standardized measurements, like the meter or the second, which scientists around the world use to ensure consistency.

Fundamental Unit

The unit of a fundamental quantity like mass or length is called **fundamental unit.**

Example: kilogram, metre, second, ampere, kelvin, candela and mole.

Derived Quantity

A quantity which is dependent on other physical quantities and can be derived from the fundamental quantities is called **derived quantity.** Area, volume, density, force and velocity are some examples of derived quantities.

Derived Unit

The unit of a derived quantity like volume or velocity is called **derived unit.**

Example: m s^{-1}, g cm^{-3}, m s^{-2}, etc.

System of Units

A system which defines the fundamental units, in comparison with which a fundamental quantity can be expressed is referred to as **system of units.** Different systems have been developed over a period of time.

The following systems of units are in common use:

1. **F.P.S. system:** In this system, the units of mass, length and time are in pound, foot and second, respectively.
2. **C.G.S. system:** In this system, the units of mass, length and time are in gram, centimetre and second, respectively.
3. **M.K.S. system:** In this system, the units of mass, length and time are in kilogram, metre and second, respectively.
4. **S.I.—(Systeme International d'unites):** This system is an extended version of M.K.S system. This system has seven fundamental and two supplementary quantities. In this system the units of metre, kilogram and second have been redefined for more accuracy. As of today S.I. system is accepted and is used all over the world for scientific work.

Table 1.1 Units and their symbols of fundamental quantities in various systems of units

	Fundamental Quantity	(System of Units)			
		C.G.S.	F.P.S.	M.K.S.	S.I.
1.	Length	centimetre (cm)	foot (ft)	metre (m)	metre (m)
2.	Mass	gram (g)	pound	kilogram (kg)	kilogram (kg)
3.	Time	second (s)	second (s)	second (s)	second (s)
4.	Amount of substance	–	–	–	mole (mol)
5.	Intensity of light	–	–	–	candela (cd)
6.	Strength of electric current	–	–	–	ampere (A)
7.	Temperature	–	–	–	kelvin (K)

Definitions of Units

1. **Metre:** Initially metre was defined as one ten-millionth part of the distance on the Earth from the pole to the equator. As per the modern definition, one metre is the length of a certain platinum-iridium rod maintained at 0°C and kept in the International Bureau of Weights and Measures at Sevres near Paris.

   (OR)

   One metre is 1,650,763.73 times the wavelength of orange light emitted by a krypton atom at normal pressure.
2. **Kilogram:** One kilogram is the mass of a certain lump made from an alloy of platinum-iridium maintained at 0°C in the International Bureau of weights and measures.
3. **Second:** One second is defined as $(1/86,400)^{th}$ part of the mean solar day. As per the modern definition, one second is the time taken by a cesium atom (Cs^{133}) to complete 9,192,631,770 vibrations.

Measurement of Length

Different instruments are used for measuring length depending upon the length being measured. For measuring the length of a room, width of a road, length of a piece of cloth, etc., which are larger quantities, measuring tapes may be used. But while measuring smaller lengths, like the diameter of a rod or wire, the length of a small rod, the thickness of a lamination sheet, etc., more accurate instruments need to be used. Vernier calliper is one such instrument.

Least count of an instrument is the smallest measurement that the instrument can make accurately. The least count of a metre scale is 0.1 cm.

Info Bytes!

The longest distance ever measured with high precision is the Earth-Moon distance using lasers and retroreflectors left by Apollo missions!

Metre Scale

Metre scale is graduated in millimetres, i.e., its least count is 1 mm. While measuring the length of any object using a scale, the observations should be taken by keeping the eye vertically above the ends of the object. This avoids the parallax error.

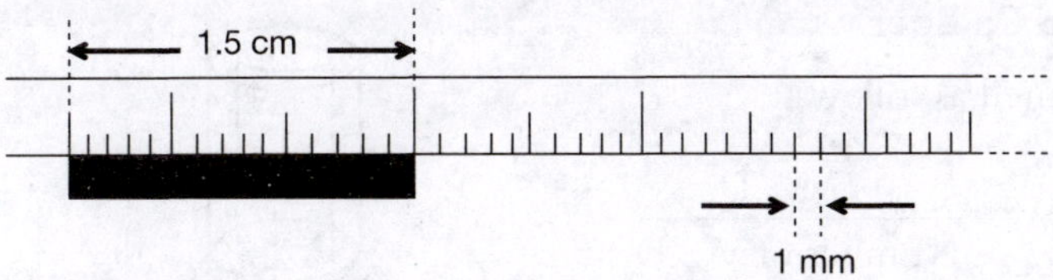

Figure 1.1 Measuring length of a rod using a scale

Info Bytes!

Parallax error is the error that is caused in the apparent position of the object due to the viewing angle that is other than the angle which is perpendicular to the object.

To measure the length of a rod or diameter of a sphere, etc., the objects can be held between two blocks as shown in Fig. 1.2 (i) and Fig. 1.2 (ii).

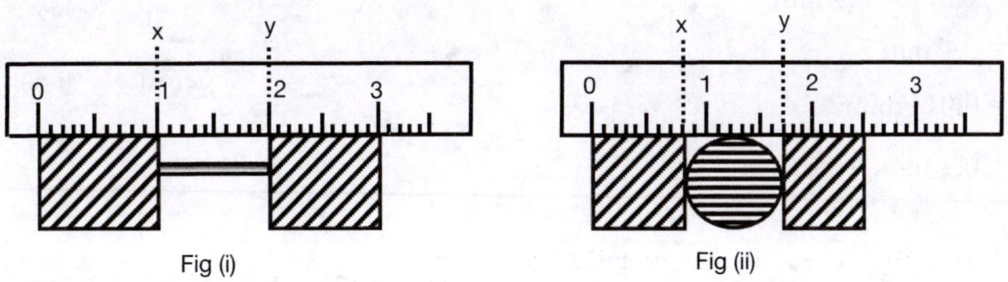

Figure 1.2 Measuring length of (i) a rod and (ii) diameter of a sphere using a scale and blocks

The readings x and y correspond to the positions of the two edges that hold the object.

Length of rod $= y - x = 2\text{ cm} - 1\text{ cm} = 1\text{ cm}$.

Diameter of sphere $= y - x = 1.7\text{ cm} - 0.8\text{ cm} = 0.9\text{ cm}$.

Vernier Callipers

Vernier callipers is an instrument which uses a combination of two scales, main scale and vernier scale sliding over each other, such that the least count of the instrument is less than the least count of the main scale.

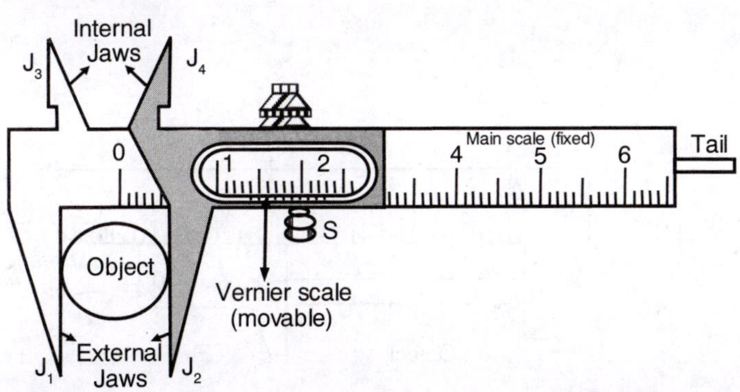

Figure 1.3 Measuring length of an object using Vernier callipers

Konnect

Vernier Callipers can measure internal and external dimensions with high accuracy. They can typically measure up to 0.02mm of accuracy.

The principle of a vernier is to make 'N' vernier scale divisions equal to $(N - 1)$ main scale divisions.

Description of Vernier Callipers

A typical vernier calliper consists of a steel strip which is generally marked in centimetres and millimetres along the lower edge. This scale is known as the main scale. The end of the main scale is provided with the fixed jaws, J_1 (external jaw) on the lower side and J_3 (internal jaw) on the upper side. A sliding frame with graduations marked on the lower side slides over the main steel strip; this scale is known as the vernier scale.

Generally, the vernier scale of a standard vernier calliper is provided with 10 graduations to coincide with 9 main scale divisions, i.e., the 10 divisions on vernier scale measure 9 mm.

The vernier frame is also provided with the movable jaws, J_2 (external jaw) on the lower side and J_4 (internal jaw) on the upper side.

To Determine the Least Count of the Vernier Calliper

The least count of a vernier calliper can be determined as follows:

For a standard vernier calliper, Least Count (L.C.) = $\frac{\text{1M.S.D.}}{\text{Number of V.S.D.s}}$

(where M.S.D is the main scale division and V.S.D is the Vernier Scale. For a standard vernier calliper, 9 M.S.D coincides with 10 M.S.D.)

Least Count (L.C.) = 1 M.S.D. – 1 V.S.D.

= 1 mm – 0.9 mm

= 0.1 mm

= 0.01 cm or

$\frac{1\text{mm}}{10}$ = 0.1 mm = 0.01 cm

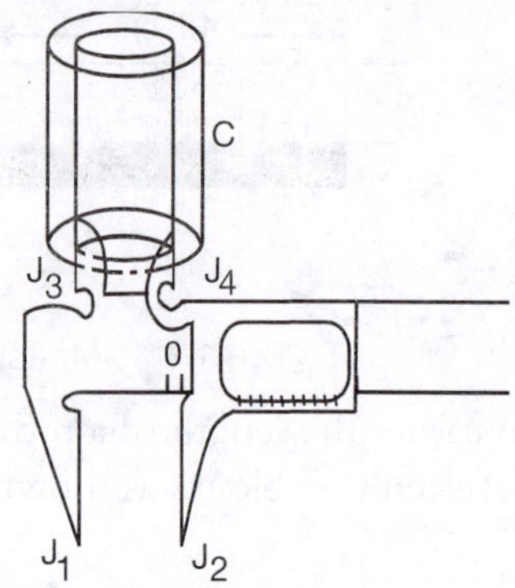

Figure 1.4 Inner diameter of a tube

Procedure for taking measurements using a vernier calliper:

1. Determine the least count of the given calliper.
2. To measure dimensions of any object, that object should be held tightly and gently between the external jaws (for external dimensions) or with internal jaws (for inner dimensions) as shown in figure 1.4.

Observations

1. **Main Scale Reading (M.S.R.):** It is the smaller of the two values of the main scale between which the zero division of vernier scale lies.
2. **Vernier Co-inciding Division (V.C.D. or *n*):** It is the vernier scale division which coincides with any one of main scale divisions. It is denoted as '*n*'.
3. **Observed reading:**

Length of the rod = $y - x$

$= (z - x) + (y - z)$

$= \text{M.S.R.} + (y - z)$

The fraction $(y - z)$ can be determined using the Vernier scale.

$$y - z = (w - z) - (w - y)$$

Let 'n' be the V.C.D.

Then,

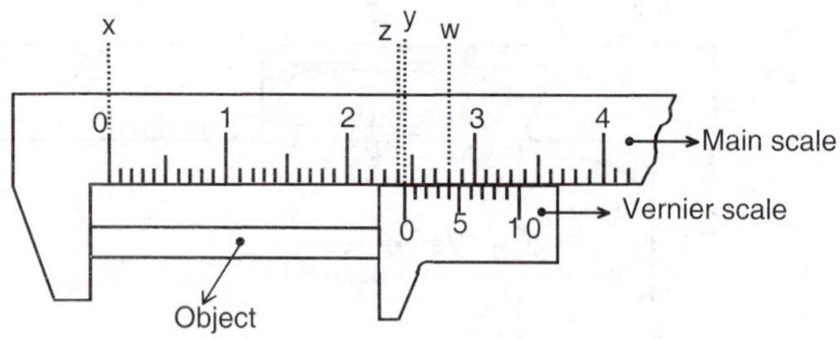

Figure 1.5 Measuring length of a rod using Vernier callipers

$$(w - z) = n \times \text{M.S.D.}$$

$$(w - y) = n \times \text{V.S.D.}$$

$$\therefore\ y - z = n(\text{M.S.D.} - \text{V.S.D.})$$

$$= n \times \text{L.C.}$$

∴ Length of the rod, $y - x = \text{M.S.R.} + n \times \text{L.C.}$

Thus, observed measurement = M.S.R. + n × L.C.

Measurement of Area

Area is the extent or measure of a surface. Area is a derived quantity and its units can be deduced from the units of length. The S.I. unit of area is m^2 and 1 m^2 = 10000 cm^2. The area of regular geometrical figures like squares, rectangles, circles, triangles, etc., can be calculated by using appropriate formulae relating the areas of these figures to their length, breadth, radius, etc. For instance, the area of a square is given by A = $(\text{side})^2$; so by knowing the measure of the side of the square, its area can be calculated.

Measurement of the Area of a Leaf

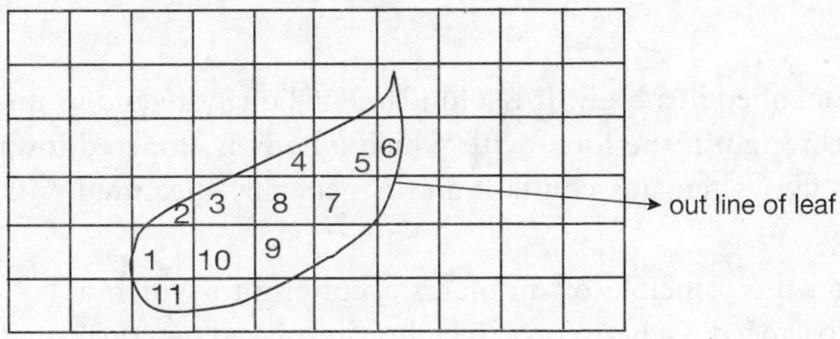

Figure 1.6 Measuring area of a leaf using graph paper

Procedure

1. Place a leaf on a graph paper and draw its outline.
2. The area of the leaf in mm^2 is the number of squares that fall within this outline.
3. Generally, the squares with half or more than half of its area within the outline are counted and others can be neglected.

   Example: In the Figure. 1.6, the squares labelled as 1, 3, 8, 7, 5, 9, 10 will be counted and remaining can be neglected. Thus, the area of leaf taken is = 7 mm^2.

Measurement of Volume

We can use a Vernier calliper (along with a beaker or a calliper or a calorimeter and a magnifying glass) to measure the internal dimensions and depth of given beaker/calorimeter and hence can also find the volume of an objetc.

Measuring Jar

Measuringjar is graduated in millilitres and used to measure the volume of liquids in millilitres.

Measuring Flask and Pipette

Measuring Flask and Pipette are used to take fixed amounts of liquids.

Burette

Burette has a nozzle vent at the bottom with a screw system and graduated in millilitres and is used to take the desired amount of a liquid.

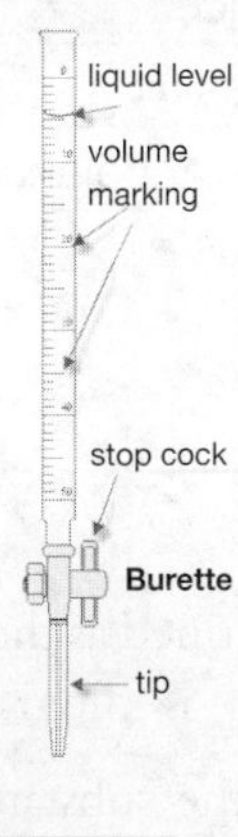

Figure 1.7 Burette

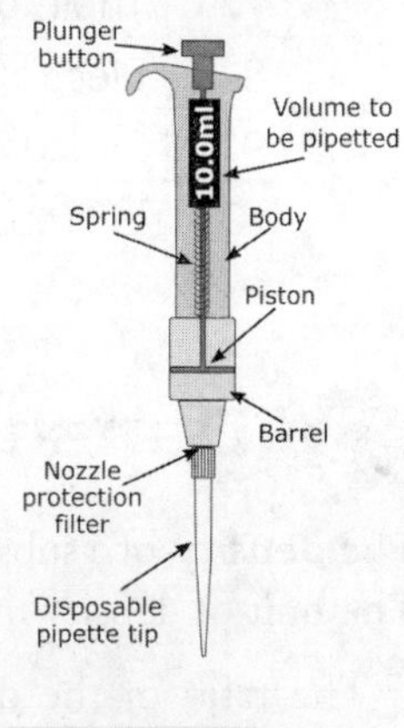

Figure 1.8 Pipette

To Determine the Volume of a Single Drop of Water

- Fill a clean burette with water, clamped upright to a stand.
- Remove air bubbles by opening the tap for some time.
- Note the level, V_1, of water in the burette.
- Allow the water to trickle slowly, drop by drop, counting the number of drops (n) at the same time.
- Close the tap after 20 cm^3 of water has been drained.
- The average volume of a drop of water $= \dfrac{20}{n}$ cm^3.

EXAMPLE 1.1 Volume of water in a pipette is 50 mL. Find the volume of a drop of water if the volume of water in the pipette is 20 mL when 75 drops of water drained out.

SOLUTION

Volume of single drop of water = (50 – 20)/75 = 0.4 mL

Measurement of Mass

Mass

Mass is the amount of matter contained in a body. It is a fundamental quantity and its unit in S.I. system is kilogram (kg). Mass is different from weight, as weight is the force with which a body is attracted towards the Earth and changes from place to place. Mass of a body always remains constant and is generally measured using a common balance.

Common balance works on the principle of moments according to which a beam remains horizontal and 'balanced', when equal weights are placed at equal distances from the point of suspension, which is at the middle of the beam. Spring balance, table balance, platform balance, roman steel yard, triple beam steel yard are a few of the other type of balances.

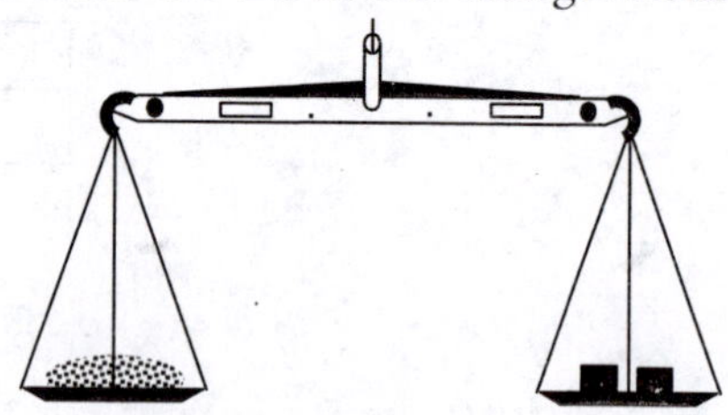

Figure 1.9 Common Dalance

Table 1.2 Applications of Different Types of Balances.

S.No.	Type	Application
1.	Spring balance	Weight of an object
2.	Compression spring balance	Weight of a person
3.	Postal balances	In post offices
4.	Table balances	In fancy shops and sweet shops
5.	Platform balances	In hardware shops, parcel offices, railway stations
6.	Roman steelyard and Danish steel yard	In hardware shops
7.	Triple beam balance	In hardware shops
8.	Electronic balances	In jewellery shops for accurate measurements of mass
9.	Single pan analytical balance	In laboratories to measure mass upto 0.1 mg
10	Microbalances	To measure mass upto 1 microgram (1 μg)

Density and Relative Density

The **density** of a substance is defined as the mass per unit volume. It is a derived quantity. The unit of density in S.I. system is kilogram per cubic metre (kg m^{-3}).

The ratio of the density of the substance to the density of water is called **relative density** or **specific gravity.** Since this is a ratio of densities, it is a mere number without any units. A specific gravity bottle is used to measure relative density.

Specific gravity bottle (density bottle) is a glass bottle with a long narrow neck and a glass stopper with a hole fitted into the neck, designed to hold a specific volume of liquid indicated on the bottle. This is used to determine the relative density of liquids.

Figure 1.10 Density Bottle

Measurement of Relative Density

To find the relative density of a liquid, the density bottle is initially filled with the liquid and then with water and the mass of the bottle in each case is noted.

We then use the following relation to find the relative density of the given liquid:

$$\text{Relative density} = \frac{\text{mass of V cm}^3 \text{ of liquid}}{\text{mass of V cm}^3 \text{ of water}}$$

The density and relative density values for some common substances are listed in the table given below:

Table 1.3 Density and relative density of some common substances.

S.No.	Substance	Density in kg m^{-3}	Relative density
1.	Water	1×10^3	1
2.	Kerosene	0.8×10^3	0.8
3.	Mercury	13.6×10^3	13.6
4.	Glass	2.5×10^3	2.5
5.	Copper	8.9×10^3	8.9
6.	Gold	19.3×10^3	19.3
7.	Hydrogen at S.T.P.	8.9×10^{-2}	8.9×10^{-5}
8.	Air at S.T.P.	1.29	1.29×10^{-3}

Info Bytes!

1000 kg/m^3
= 1 g/cm^3

Konnect

- The densest naturally occurring element is osmium, with a density of 22.59 grams per cubic centimetre.
- Relative density, also known as specific gravity, is the ratio of the density of a substance to the density of a reference substance; usually water.

POINTS TO REMEMBER

- ✔ The quantities that can be measured are called physical quantities.
- ✔ A quantity which is independent of other quantities is called fundamental quantity.
- ✔ A quantity which is dependent on other physical quantities and can be derived from the fundamental quantities is called derived quantity.
- ✔ The unit of a fundamental quantity like mass or length is called fundamental unit.
- ✔ The unit of a derived quantity like volume or velocity is called derived unit.
- ✔ A system which defines the fundamental units, in comparison with which a fundamental quantity can be expressed is referred to as system of units.
- ✔ One metre is 1,650,763.73 times the wavelength of orange light emitted by a krypton atom at normal pressure.
- ✔ One kilogram is the mass of a certain lump made from an alloy of platinum-iridium maintained at 0°C in the International Bureau of weights and measures.
- ✔ One second is defined as $(1/86,400)^{th}$ part of the mean solar day.
- ✔ Least count of an instrument is the smallest measurement that the instrument can make accurately.
- ✔ Vernier calliper is an instrument which uses a combination of two scales, main scale and vernier scale.
- ✔ Area is the extent or measure of a surface. The S.I. unit of area is m^2 and $1\ m^2 = 10000\ cm^2$.
- ✔ Measuring jar is graduated in millilitres and used to measure the volume of liquids in millilitres.
- ✔ Burette has a nozzle vent at the bottom with a screw system and graduated in millilitres and is used to take the desired amount of a liquid.
- ✔ Mass is the amount of matter contained in a body. It is a fundamental quantity and its unit in S.I. system is kilogram (kg).
- ✔ The density of a substance is defined as the mass per unit volume. The unit of density in S.I. system is kilogram per cubic metre (kg m^{-3}).
- ✔ The ratio of the density of the substance to the density of water is called relative density or specific gravity. Since this is a ratio of densities, it is a mere number without any units.
- ✔ Specific gravity bottle (density bottle) is a glass bottle with a long narrow neck and a glass stopper with a hole fitted into the neck, designed to hold a specific volume of liquid indicated on the bottle.

CLASSROOM WING

Practice Questions

Very Short Answer Type Questions

Directions for questions 1 to 8:
Fill in the blanks.

1. If the principle used to construct a vernier calliper is N V.S.D. = (N – 2) M.S.D., its least count is ________ mm. (1 M.S.D. = 1 mm and N = 10)
2. Given the density of air is 1.29 kg m^{-3}. Then, the relative density of air is ________.
3. If the mass of 100 cm^3 of iron is 785 g, then the density of iron in S.I. unit is ______.
4. A stone of density 6 g cm^{-3} can be used as a sinker in a liquid of density ________.
5. If the density of iron is 7.85 g cm^{-3} and density of water is 1000 kg m-3, then the relative density of iron is ________.
6. In a new system of units to be introduced, if the unit of length is 2 m and 2 s is considered as a unit time, then a unit speed is equal to _______.
7. The CGS unit of average speed is _________.
8. **The** density of gold is 19 g cm^{-3}. Then, the relative density is _________.

Directions for questions 9 to 25:
Answer the following questions.

9. For a given vernier caliper, one M.S.D. = 1/10 cm and the number of divisions of vernier scale is = 20. What is the least count of the vernier caliper?
10. What is the least count of the following instruments?
    (a) Metre scale
    (b) Wall clock
    (c) Celsius thermometer
    (d) Vernier calliper
11. Which jaws of the vernier calliper are used to find the internal diameter of a hollow cylinder?
12. Define relative density.
13. If the main scale of vernier calliper is graduated in mm and the vernier scale has 20 divisions, then what is the least count?
14. What is the relation between litre and the C.G.S. and the S.I. units of volume?
15. What type of balances are used in laboratories?
16. What are 'derived quantities'? Give examples.
17. Write the relation between V.S.D and M.S.D with respect to standard vernier calipers?
18. Define second.
19. Define the least count of an instrument.
20. The viscous force in the case of a liquid is given by, $F = \eta A \frac{v}{x}$.
    Where A = area, v = velocity, x = distance and η is a constant. What is the unit of η?
21. Define density.
22. What is the principle used in common balance?
23. What is the relation between the C.G.S. and the S.I. unit of area?
24. Name a convenient unit to be used for measuring the following quantities:
    (a) Distance between two cities
    (b) Length of a room in your house
    (c) Height of Qutab Minar
    (d) Thickness of a single hair
    (e) Diameter of a tea cup
25. Write the physical quantity which has Candela as its unit.

Short Answer Type Questions

26. What are the characteristics of a standard unit?

27. List the fundamental quantities along with their units in S.I. system.

28. Define least count. Describe the method to find the least count of a vernier calliper.

29. A vernier calliper has 20 divisions on the vernier scale. One centimetre on the main scale is divided into 20 equal parts. Find the least count of this instrument.

30. While measuring the length of a copper rod using a vernier calliper, the zero of the vernier scale was found to be between 4.6 cm and 4.7 cm on the main scale. The 6th division of the vernier scale is found to coincide with a division on the main scale. Find the length of the rod if the least count is 0.01 cm.

31. A vernier scale has 10 divisions. It slides over the main scale, whose 1 M.S.D. is 1.0 mm. If the number of divisions to the left side of the zero of the vernier scale on the main scale is 49 and the 8th vernier scale division coincides with the main scale, calculate the length in centimetres.

32. When a vernier calliper is used to measure external and internal diameters of an aluminium tube, the observations were made as follows:

For external diameter:

Main scale reading = 2.2 cm

Vernier coinciding division = 4

For inner diameter:

Main scale reading = 1.8 cm

Vernier coinciding division = 8

If the least count of vernier calliper is 0.1 mm, find the thickness of the wall of the tube.

33. A vernier calliper has 10 divisions on the vernier scale. If one centimetre of main scale is divided into 5 equal parts, find the best possible least count of the given vernier calliper.

34. How do you measure the area of an irregular shaped plane figure? Describe the graphical method to find the area of a leaf.

35. Describe a method to determine the volume of a single drop of water.

36. A piece of iron has dimensions 3 cm × 15 cm × 20 cm. If its mass is 7020 g, calculate the density of iron in S.I. system.

37. Calculate the mass of a body in S.I. system whose volume is 2 cm^3 and the density is 0.52 g cm^{-3}.

38. Taking the value of the acceleration due to gravity as 10 m s^{-2}, find its value in km h^{-2}.

39. The surface area of a sphere is 1000 cm^2. Find its surface area in S.I. system.

40. Express 1 g cm^{-3} in S.I. units. Which of these two units—C.G.S or S.I., is a bigger unit?

41. While measuring the length of an object, using vernier calliper, the M. S. R and V. C. D. were observed to be 22 and 8, respectively. If 1 M. S. D. = 1/2 mm and L. C. = 0.05 mm, calculate the length of the object.

42. Mention the various systems of fundamental units.

43. One centimeter of main scale of a vernier calliper is divided into 10 equal parts. M.S.R and V.C.D observed while measuring the length of an object are 3 and 4, respectively. Then, calculate the length of the object in mm. (Take number of division on vernier scale as 10).

Essay Answers Type Questions

44. Explain the need for standards and systems of units in measurements.

45. Explain the principle of vernier. Draw a neat diagram of a vernier calliper showing the various parts.

46. Describe a vernier calliper and explain the method by which the inner diameter of a hollow cylinder is determined.

47. (a) Draw neat labelled diagrams of a pipette and a burette.

(b) Draw neat labelled diagrams of a vernier calliper showing the positions of external and internal jaws in the measurement of exterior and interior dimensions.

COMPETITION WING

Practice Questions

Level 1: Apply your Concepts

Directions for questions 1 to 12:
State whether the following statements are true or false.

1. Length, mass, time are derived quantities.
2. If impulse = force × time and the S.I. unit of force is newton (N), then the S.I. unit of impulse is newton second.
3. CGS, FPS, SI, MKS are system of fundamental units.
4. 1,650,763.73 is the number of waves of orange light that will be emitted by krypton in 10 m.
5. 1kg = 1000g.
6. A standard unit should not change with respect to time but may change from place to place.
7. The zeroth division of a vernier scale lies between the 40th and 41st main scale divisions. Then, the M.S.R. = 4 cm if 1 M.S.D. = 1 mm.
8. Given that 1 M.S.D. of a vernier calliper is 1 mm and its least count is 0.025 mm, then the number of divisions in the vernier calliper is 25.
9. Given that 1 M.S.D. of a vernier calliper is 1 mm and it's least count is 0.001 cm then the number of vernier scale divisions is 100.
10. In a vernier calipers, if 1 M.S.D. = 0.1 cm and the least count is 0.1 mm, then 1 V.S.D. = 0.9 mm
11. The lower meniscus should be taken into consideration while reading the level of mercury in a burette.
12. Pipette is used to take a desired volume of liquid.

Directions for questions 13 to 19:
Fill in the blanks.

13. If the relative density of ice is 0.9, its density is _________ kg m^{-3}.
14. The unit of pressure is Pascal in the SI system. If 1 pascal is equal to 1 kg $m^{-1}s^{-2}$, then 1 Pascal = _________ g cm^{-1} s^{-2}.
15. On dropping 10 lead shots into a measuring jar containing a liquid, the level of the liquid in the jar increased from 40 cm^3 to 100 cm^3. Then, the volume of each lead shot is _________.
16. While finding the internal diameter of a pipe using a vernier calipers, the M.S.R. = 18 mm, the vernier scale coinciding division is 3. If the least count of the instrument is 0.1 mm, then the internal radius is _______ mm.
17. If 10 cm is taken as unit of length, then the height of a person 1.78 m tall in the new system of units is _______ units.
18. If the volume of 1 kg of oil, at a given temperature, is 1000 cm^3, then the volume 1000 kg oil at the same temperature is _________.
19. The least count of a vernier calipers X is 0.01 cm. If the number of divisions on the vernier scale of another vernier calipers Y is double of that in X, then the least count of Y is ______ mm. (In both instruments 1 M.S.D. = 1mm)

Direction for question 20:
Match the entries in Column A with the appropriate ones in Column B.

20. Match the statements of Column A with those of Column B.

Column A	Column B
(A) Physical quantity	(a) Volume of a drop of liquid
(B) Burette	(b) Measurable quantity
(C) Instantaneous speed	(c) Rate of change of velocity
(D) Acceleration	(d) m s^{-1}

Directions for questions 21 to 47:
For each of the questions, four choices have been provided. Select the correct alternative.

21. If the unit of mass is doubled and the units of length and time are halved, how much is 20 N of force in new units? (1N = 1 kg m s^{-2})

(a) 0.5 N
(b) 5 new units of force
(c) 5 N
(d) 0.5 new units of force

22. Which among the following physical quantities does not possess a unit?

(a) Area (b) Volume
(c) Density (d) Specific gravity

23. Which of the following is not a derived quantity?

(a) The area of floor of a room
(b) The height of a room
(c) The volume of air in a room
(d) The weight of air in a room

24. While measuring the diameter of a sphere using a vernier calipers the main scale reading was found to be p while the vernier coinciding division was q. If the least count of the instrument is r, then the radius of the sphere is given by the expression ________.

(a) $p + q + r$ (b) $\frac{qr + p}{2}$
(c) $p + qr$ (d) $\frac{pr + q}{2}$

25. Which of the following equations is true with reference to a vernier calipers?

(a) Least count = 1 M.S.D. − 1 V.S.D.
(b) 1 M.S.D. = (L.C.) × number of divisions on the Vernier scale
(c) If the least count is 0.1 mm, then

$$1 \text{ M.S.D.} = \frac{N}{10} \text{mm}$$

(d) All the above

26. The CGS unit of average speed is ________.

(a) m s^{-1} (b) cm s^{-1}
(c) ft s^{-1} (d) km h^{-1}

27. To determine the diameter of a rod a student wound a thread 5 times a round the rod and measured the length of thread as 156 mm on a metre scale. Using this value he calculated the diameter of the rod. If the actual diameter of the rod is 9.94 mm, what is the error that could result in the method followed by the student? $\left(\text{Take } \pi = \frac{22}{7}\right)$.

(a) + 0.01 mm (b) − 0.01 mm
(c) + 0.02 mm (d) − 0.02 mm

28. In a vernier calliper 1 M.S.D. = 0.1 cm and the least count is 0.05 mm. If the reading on this vernier calipers while taking a measurement is 12.8 mm, then the vernier coinciding division is ______.

(a) 20 (b) 4
(c) 8 (d) 16

29. Which of the following is true about the density of a substance?

(a) It is a derived quantity.
(b) The unit of density in S.I. system is kilogram per cubic metre.
(c) The density of a substance can be measured if the mass of the substance for a certain volume is known.
(d) All the above

30. The main scale readings of a vernier callipers (1 M.S.D. = 1 mm) having least count 0.01 cm for the internal and external diameters of a hollow tube are 11 mm and 12 mm. The minimum thickness of the tube is _____.

(a) 1 mm (b) 0. 1 mm
(c) 0.05 mm (d) 0.5 mm

31. The following information is noted in respect of two vernier callipers A and B.

Vernier calipers	1 M.S.D.	No. of divisions on vernier scale
A	1 mm	20
B	3 mm	30

If N V.S.D. = (N − 1) M.S.D. in both the vernier callipers, then which of the following statements is true?

(a) The least count of A is less than that of B.
(b) The least count of B is 0.01 cm.

(c) The largest measurement that can be made between 10 mm and 11 mm with the vernier caliper A is 10.95 mm.

(d) All the above.

32. Three cylindrical flasks A, B and C of diameter 50 mm, 75 mm and 100 mm, respectively have graduation marked in mm and are used for measurement of volume of liquid. Which of the following statements is correct?

(a) A is more accurate than B and C

(b) C has better least count than B

(c) The least counts of all three are the same.

(d) B has better least count than A.

33. R.D. of '*x*' and '*y*' are 3 and 2, respectively. Then, the density of '*x*' with respect to that of '*y*' is ______.

(a) 6 (b) 5

(c) 1.5 (d) 1

34. The initial and final readings of a burette while draining out 50 drops of a liquid are 10 mL and 40 mL, respectively. Then, the volume of each drop is ______.

(a) 0.6 mL (b) 0.06 cm^3

(c) 6×10^{-2} litres (d) 6×10^{-6} m^3

35. If the ratio of density of ice to that of wood is (9/8) and the relative density of ice is 0.9, then the density of wood is ______ kg m^{-3}.

(Take density of water = 10^3 kg m^{-3})

(a) 0.8 (b) 800

(c) 8×10^3 (d) 80

Directions for questions 36 and 37:

These questions are based on the information given in the figure below.

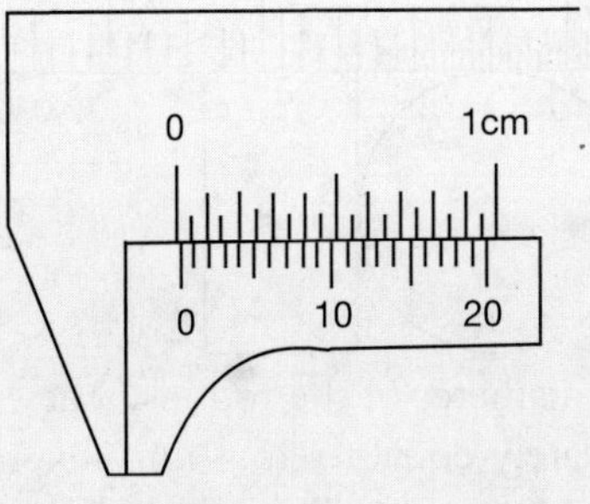

36. The least count of the vernier calipers shown in the figure is ______.

(a) 0.25 mm (b) 0.025 mm

(c) 0.025 cm (d) 250 μm

37. The zero error of the vernier calipers shown in the figure is ______.

(a) + 100 μm (b) + 0.01 cm

(c) 0.1 mm (d) All the above.

38. Assertion (A): A physical quantity which can be described with both magnitude and direction is called as a vector quantity.

Reason (R): All vector quantities are derived quantities.

(a) A and R are correct and R is the correct explanation for A

(b) A and R are correct but R is not the correct explanation for A

(c) A is correct but R is incorrect.

(d) Both A and R are incorrect.

39. A vernier callipers has positive zero error of 0.05 mm. While finding the diameter a cylinder, the MSR is 9 mm and the VCD is 9. If the least count of the vernier calliper is 0.1 mm, the area of cross-section of the cylinder is ______ mm^2.

(a) 76.2 (b) 19.1

(c) 23.6 (d) 26.5

40. If there are '*N*' number of vernier scale divisions (V.S.D.) and *N* V.S.D. = (*N* − 2) M.S.D., find the value of L.C. in terms of '*N*'.

(a) $\dfrac{1\text{M.S.D.}}{\text{N}}$ (b) $\dfrac{2\text{M.S.D.}}{\text{N}}$

(c) $\dfrac{(N-2)\text{M.S.D.}}{N}$ (d) $\dfrac{N\text{M.S.D.}}{2}$

41. Assertion (A): The mass of 150 m^3 of iron is greater than the mass of 150 m^3 of wood.

Reason (R): The density of iron is less than the density of wood.

(a) A and R are correct and R is the correct explanation of A.

(b) A and R are correct but R is not the correct explanation of A.

(c) A is correct but R is wrong.

(d) Both A and R are wrong.

42. Write the following steps in a sequential order to show that the volume of a liquid displaced by a solid, which is insoluble and completely immersed in a liquid, increases with increase in the volume of the solid.

(A) The displaced liquid is collected in a beaker and its volume is measured with the help of a measuring cylinder.

(B) Different objects such as glass, stone, etc., of different volumes are immersed in different liquids such as water, kerosene, etc.

(C) The phenomenon is observed at different places and different times.

(D) It is observed that the volume of displaced liquid increases as the volume of the solid increases.

(a) A D B C (b) C B A D
(c) B A C D (d) B D C A

43. Arrange the following steps in the proper sequence to calculate the volume of an irregular-shaped stone.

(A) Immerse the stone into the vessel and note the difference in the volume of the liquid.

(B) Take a stone (irregular shaped) and a measuring cylindrical jar.

(C) Pour a liquid like water into the jar and note the volume of the liquid.

(D) The volume of the stone is equal to the increase in the volume of the liquid.

(a) CBAD (b) BCDA
(c) ABCD (d) DCAB

44. If the smallest measurement that can be measured by using a scale is 0.1 mm, then the length of 1 m in the scale is divided into _______ equal parts.

(a) 1000 (b) 5000
(c) 10000 (d) 50000

45. An atlas of India is drawn by taking scale 100 cm = 15000 km. If the actual distance between the cities of Bhopal and Cochin is 1500 km, the distance between the two places in the atlas will be _______ cm.

(a) 10 (b) 1
(c) 10000 (d) 1000

46. Which of the following is true with respect to a standard vernier callipers?

(a) N main scale divisions = $(N - 1)$ vernier scale divisions.

(b) N vernier scale divisions = $(N - 1)$ main scale divisions.

(c) N vernier scale divisions = $(N + 1)$ main scale divisions.

(d) None of these.

47. The zeroth divisions of the vernier and main scales of a standard vernier callipers coincide, then

(a) the external jaws are in contact with each other.

(b) there is some distance between the internal jaws.

(c) Both (a) and (b).

(d) Neither (a) nor (b).

Level 2: Review your Concepts

48. Taking 1 ly (light year) = 9.3×10^{15} m and one day = 86400 s, express the speed of light (= 3×10^8 ms^{-1}) as ly (day)$^{-1}$ and speed of sound in air (= 330 ms^{-1}) as ly day^{-1}. Also find the ratio of those two values.

49. The amount of heat absorbed by a body while raising its temperature is given by the equation:

$Q = ms\,\theta$,

here Q is the amount of heat, m is the mass of the body, s is the specific heat capacity and θ is the rise in temperature. Determine the S.I. unit and C.G.S. units of the specific heat capacity, given that the C.G.S. unit of heat is erg and S.I. unit is joule.

50. A ruler marked in inches is used to measure the diameter of a rod as shown in the figure below.

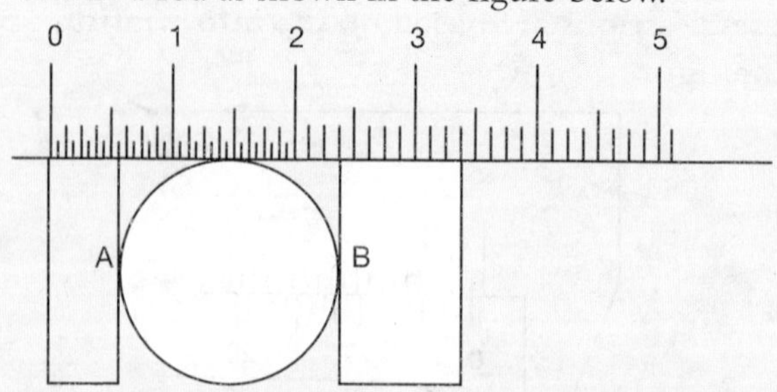

Find the diameter of the rod in inches. If one inch is approximately equal to 25.4 mm, express this diameter in cm (correct to 2 decimal places).

51. In a vernier calliper, 2 cm on main scale is divided into 20 equal parts and 1 V. S. D is equal to 0.9 mm. What is the least count of the vernier calliper?

52. According to Newton's law of gravitation, the force F between two bodies of masses m_1 and m_2 placed at a distance of 'r' from each other is given as

$$F = G \times \frac{m_1 \times m_2}{r^2}$$

where G is the universal gravitational constant. Find the units of G in both C.G.S. and S.I. system.

53. A student took the least count of a vernier calliper as 0.01 mm instead of 0.01 cm and found that the length of a copper rod was 4.909 cm. If one M.S.D. = 1 mm, then find

(1) the main scale reading

(2) the vernier coinciding division

(3) the correct length of the rod

54. The internal jaws of a vernier calipers were held tightly inside a hollow tube when the zero of the vernier scale showed a reading of 1.9 cm and the 18th division on the vernier scale was coinciding with a division on the main scale. The thickness of the wall of the tube is 1 mm. If 1 M.S.D. = 1 mm and the number of divisions on the vernier scale is 20, find the outside diameter of the hallow tube.

55. Find the area of the shaded region in the given figure:

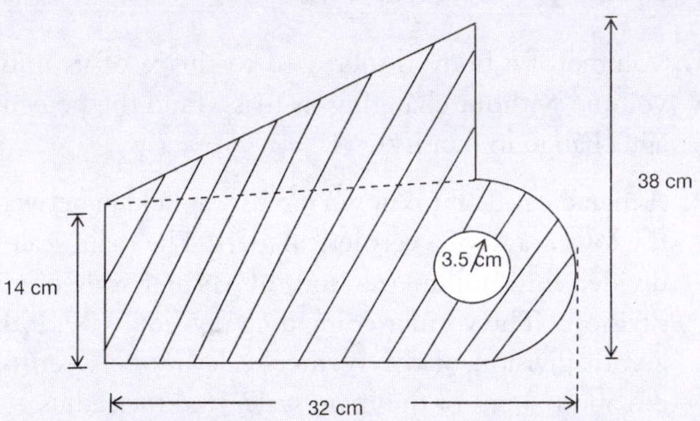

56. A height gauge (an instrument used to measure accurately the heights of the parts of machinery) is to be constructed using a main scale marked in centimetres and millimetres.

(i) What is the minimum length of the vernier scale if the required least count is 0.001 cm?

(ii) What least count can be achieved if the number of vernier scale divisions cannot be more than 50?

57. An irregular shaped crystal was dropped into a liquid of density 800 kg m^{-3} and the overflowing liquid was collected and weighed. If the mass of the liquid collected is 120 g and the mass of the crystal is 360 g, find the relative density of the crystal.
(Density of water = 1000 kg m^{-3}).

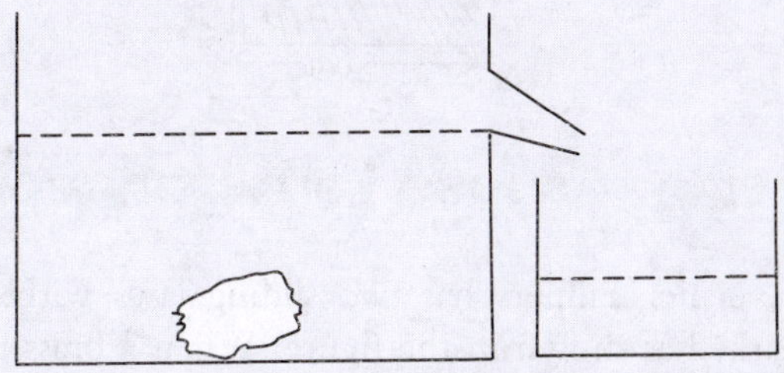

58. To find the volume of an irregularly shaped wooden piece, a sinker made of steel (relative density = 7.85) having a mass of 157 g was used. If the levels of water before and after immersing the sinker—wood combination are 102 mL and 170 mL, respectively, find the volume of the wooden piece.

59. On heating, the length, the breadth and the height of a cuboid structure was increased by 20%, 10% and 5% respectively. If the original volume of the structure is 1000 cm^3, determine the increase in its volume.

60. Two spheres made of different materials have their masses in the ratio of 1 : 2. If the diameter of the first sphere is equal to the radius of the second sphere, then determine the ratio of their densities.

$$\left(\text{volume of sphere} = \frac{4}{3}\pi r^3\right)$$

61. A vernier calipers has 25 divisions on the vernier scale. An object is held between the external jaws of this instrument. If the zeroeth division of the vernier scale is to the left of the 32nd division of the main scale and the 20th division of the vernier scale coincides with a main scale division, determine the measurement of the object. (Take 1 M.S.D. = 0.5 mm).

62. If the length of a body is to be measured accurately upto 0.05 mm using a vernier calliper with main scale divisions equal to 0.5 mm, how many divisions should be engraved on the vernier scale?

63. While measuring the length of a copper rod using a vernier callipers, the zero of the vernier scale was found to be between 4.6 cm and 4.7 cm on the main scale. The 6th division of the vernier scale is found to coincide with a division on the main scale. Find the length of the rod if the least count is 0.01 cm.

64. Find the area of shaded region in the figure given below.

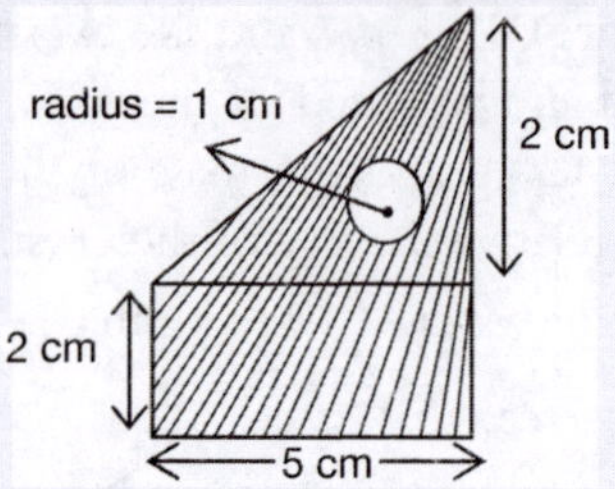

65. When an object is immersed into water, the volume of the water displaced is 200 cm^3. What is the relative density, if the mass of the object is 400 g?

66. A king ordered a goldsmith to prepare a crown with 1 kg pure gold. The relative density of pure gold is given as '19'. Is it possible to find the adulteration if the goldsmith adds some impurity in making the crown. If so how? Explain.

Level 3 : Assess Your Concepts

67. A vernier calipers has two sliding jaws with scales marked as shown in the figure. When a brass rod of length 5.23 cm was held between the jaws, the zero of jaw A was found to lie between the 34th and 35th main scale division with the 3rd division on the vernier scale coinciding with a main scale division. Find the M.S.R. and V.C.D. for the vernier scale on jaw B.

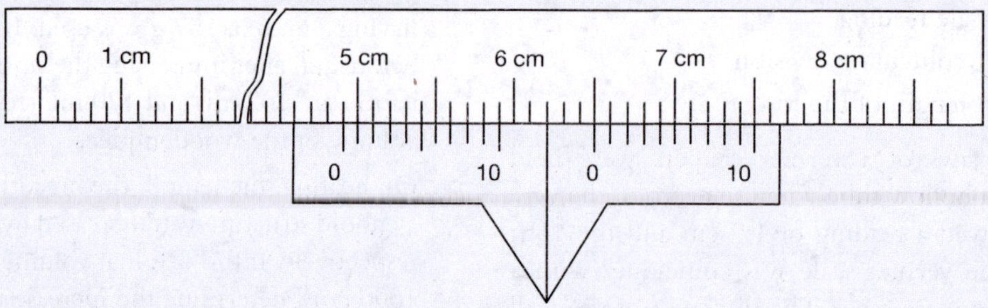

68. Two metal blocks A and B were placed on the two pans of a common balance and the beam of the balance was horizontal. However, when the blocks were interchanged and block B was placed in the left pan and block A in the right pan, the beam was not balanced and tilted down towards the left. Discuss the various factors that could be the cause of this. Are the masses of the two blocks equal?

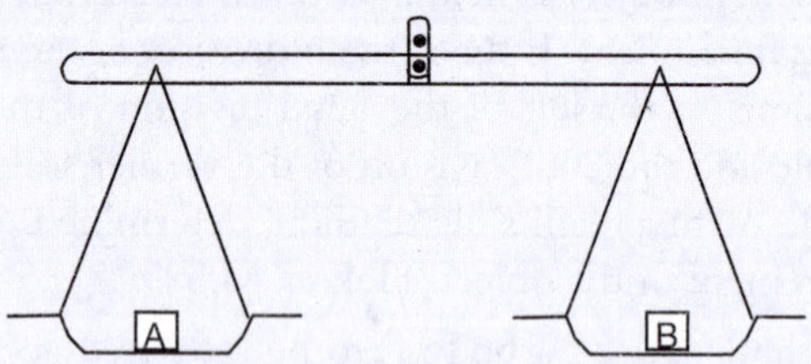

69. 100 ml of liquid A (density = 1200 kg m^{-3}) and 100 g of liquid B (density = 0.8 g cm^{-3}) are mixed to form a homogeneous mixture. Assuming that the two liquids do not chemically react with each other, find the density of the resultant mixture.

70. If the number of divisions on the vernier scale of a standard vernier calliper is N, then N is always equal to $(N - 1)$ main scale divisions. Would the vernier calliper be rendered useless if N is equal to fewer number of main scale divisions, for example $N = (N - 3)$ M.S.D.? Why? How would the least count calculations be modified?

71. Volume of a body is increased to thrice of its initial volume without changing its mass. Find the percentage change in density.

72. A metallic rod of unknown radius was held in between the lower jaws of a vernier callipers. The main scale is divided into millimetres and the vernier scale has 50 divisions. The vernier coinciding division is 39. If the zeroth division of the vernier scale lies between 6.3 cm and 6.4 cm of the main scale, find the radius.

73. In a vernier callipers 15 vernier scale divisions correspond to 14 main scale divisions and one main scale division is equal to 1.5 mm. An object is held between the external jaws of the given vernier callipers. If the zeroth division of the vernier scale is to the left of the 20th division of the main scale, find the measurement of the object; if the 14th division of the vernier scale coincides with the main scale division.

74. A cylinder of unknown radius was held between the lower jaws of a vernier caliper. The main scale is divided into millimeters and vernier scale has 20 divisions. The vernier coinciding division is 16. If the zeroth division of the vernier scale lies between 12.3 cm and 12.4 cm of the main scale, the calculate radius in mm.

75. When 100 drops of a liquid P is added into a liquid Q the volume of the liquid in the container which is initially filled with liquid Q doubled. Determine density of the mixture if density of the liquids P and Q are 1.5 g cm^{-3} and 1.3 g cm^3 respectively.

76. A Fortin's barometer has a main scale and a vernier scale to measure the atmospheric pressure. The main scale graduations are in mm. If 49 main scale divisions coincide with 50 vernier divisions, find the least count of the instrument, in Pa. (Given pressure exerted by 76 cm column of mercury = 10^5 Pa)

77. Find the area of the shaded region in the figure given below.

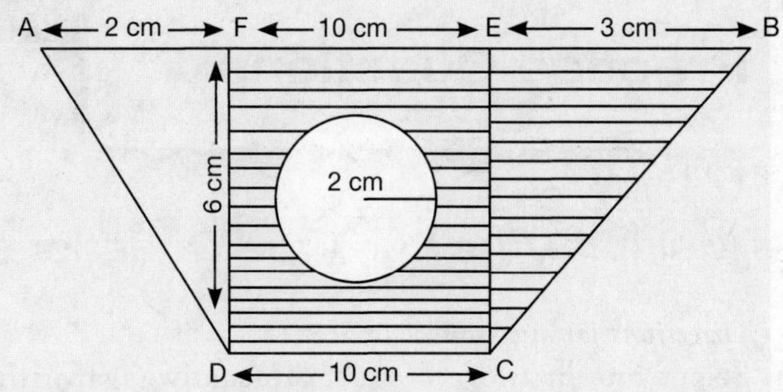

78. Siri placed two objects A and B of volumes 100 cm^3 and 400 cm^3 in two pans of a common balance and she was surprised because the two pans balanced with each other. Find the density of object A if the density of object B is 20 kg m^{-3} and clear the doubt raised by Siri.

79. Relative density of a sphere of mass 88 kg is 194.481. Find its total surface area.

AT

JEE-NEET SPECIAL WING

Practice Questions

Multiple-Answer Type Questions

Directions for questions 1 to 5:
Select one or more correct alternative(s) from the given choices.

1. A unit should have the following characteristics:
(a) It should be well defined.
(b) It should be irreproducible.
(c) It should be changeable.
(d) It should be of measurable size.

2. Identify the derived quantities
(a) Absolute temperature
(b) Time
(c) Velocity
(d) Volume

3. The least count of a meter scale is
(a) 0.1 cm (b) 0.001 cm
(c) 1 mm (d) 0.01 mm

4. Which of the measuring devices is used to take fixed amount of liquids?
(a) Measuring jar (b) Measuring flask
(c) Pipette (d) Burette

5. 1 Joule = ______
(a) $Vs^{-1}A$
(b) N m
(c) kg m^2 s^{-2}
(d) N m^{-2}

Comprehension-Based Questions

Directions for questions 6 to 10:
These questions are based on the following information.

Vernier Callipers

A vernier calliper, named after Pierre Vernier, is a measuring instrument used to measure the external and internal dimensions of an object. It consists of two jaws - a fixed jaw for outer measurements and a moveable jaw for internal measurements. It is a tool that is useful to measure spherical and cylindrical objects and can measure very small distances accurate to 0.1 mm.

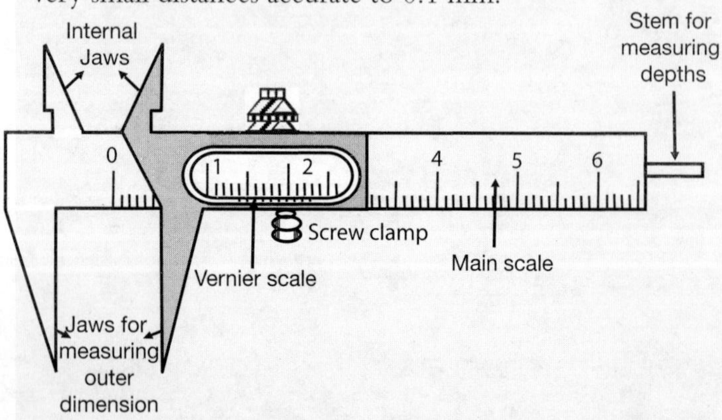

6. The smallest measurement that can be accurately made by an instrument is
(a) Precision
(b) Least count
(c) milli meter
(d) None of these

7. The Least Count of a vernier callipers can be determined by
(a) L. C = 1 M.S. D × 1 V. S. D
(b) $L.C = \frac{1\,V.S.D}{1\,M.S.D}$
(c) $L.C = \frac{1\,M.S.D}{No.\,of\,V.S.D'S}$
(d) $L.C = \frac{No.\,of\,V.S.D'S}{1\,M.S.D}$

8. The principle of vernier is to make 'N' vernier scale divisions equal to ______ main scale divisions.
(a) (N - 1) (b) (N + 1)
(c) $(N - 1)^2$ (d) $(N + 1)^2$

9. The observed measurement from a vernier calliper is given by

(a) M. S. R + (V. C. D×L. C)

(b) $\frac{M.S.R}{(V.C.D \times L.C)}$

(c) L. C (M. S. D - V. C. D)

(d) V. C. D + (M. S. R×L. C)

10. Which of the following statements is false about vernier callipers?

(a) The main scale of vernier calliper is stationary.

(b) Observations should be taken at right angles.

(c) Each division of vernier scale is bigger than each main scale division.

(d) The value of lowest main scale division is 1 mm.

Match the Column

Directions for question 11:

The question is based on the following information.

System of Units

A system which defines a set of related units in comparison with which a physical quantity can be expressed is called a system of units. This includes base units and derived units and also certain rules relating them. Over a period of time different systems have been developed. Some of them which are in common use are:

(i) F. P. S. system
(ii) C. G. S. system
(iii) M. K. S. system
(iv) S. I. system

As of today, widely accepted and commonly used system of unit all over the world for scientific work is S.I. system.

11. Match the values in List - I with those in List - II:

List - I	List - II
A. Time	a. candela
B. Temperature	b. ampere
C. Luminous intensity	c. mole
D. Electric current	d. kelvin
E. Amount of substance	e. second

(a) A - b, B - c, C - d, D - e, E - a

(b) A - e, B - d, C – a, D – b, E - c

(c) A - a, B - e, C - b, D - a, E - c

(d) A - d, B - e, C - b, D - a, E - c

Answer Keys

Crossword

Across

3. Unit 6. Vernier scale 7. Burette 9. Specific gravity 10. Derived unit

Down

1. Physical quantity 2. Micro balance 4. One second 5. Metre 8. Mass

Classroom Wing

Very Short Answer Type Questions

1. 0.2 mm 2. 129 × 10−5 3. 7850 kg m−3 4. $d_{sinker} > d_{liquid}$ 5. 7.85
6. 1 ms^{-1} 7. cm s^{-1} 8. 19 9. 0.05 mm 11. 0.2 mm
20. Ns/m^2 25. Luminous intensity 29. 0.25 mm 30. 4.66 cm
31. 49.08 cm 32. 1.8 mm 33. 0.02 cm 36. 7.8×10^3 kg m^{-3} 37. 1.04×10^{-3} kg
38. 1.296×10^5 km h^{-2} 39. 0.1 m^2 40. 1000 kg m^{-3}. S.I.

Competition Wing

Level 1: Apply your Concepts

1. False 2. True 3. True 4. False 5. True
6. False 7. True 8. False 9. True 10. True
11. False 12. False 13. 900 kg m^{-3} 14. 10 g cm^{-1} s^{-2} 15. 6 cm^3
16. 9.15 17. 17.8 18. 10^6 cm^3 19. 0.05 mm
20. A : b, B : a, C : d, D : c 21. (b) 22. (d) 23. (b)
24. (b) 25. (d) 26. (b) 27. (b) 28. (d)
29. (d) 30. (c) 31. (d) 32. (a) 33. (c)
34. (a) 35. (b) 36. (b) 37. (d) 38. (c)
39. (a) 40. (b) 41. (c) 42. (c) 43. (b)
44. (c) 45. (a) 46. (b) 47. (a)

Level 2: Review your Concepts

48. 0.929×10^6 50. $1\frac{13}{16}$ inch, 4.60 cm 53. M.S.R. = 49 mm, V.C.D. = 9, Original reading = 49.9 mm
51. 0.1 mm 54. 21.9 mm 55. 688.5 cm^2 56. (i) 9.9 cm, (ii) 0.02 mm
57. 2.4 59. 386 cm^3 60. 4 : 1 61. 15.9 mm 62. N = 10
63. 4.66 cm 64. 11.86 cm^2 65. **2**

Level 3 : Assess Your Concepts

67. M.S.R. = 10.2 cm, V.C.D. = 6 69. $\frac{44}{45}$ g cm^{-3} 71. $\frac{200}{3}$% 72. 31.89 mm
73. 2.99 cm 74. 61.9 mm 75. 1.4g cm^{-3} 76. 2.63 Pa 77. 56.44 cm^2
78. 0.08g cm^{-3} 79. 0.029 m^2

JEE-NEET Special Wing

Multiple-Answer Type Questions

1. (a) and (d) 2. (c) and (d) 3. (a) and (c) 4. (b) and (c) 5. (b) and (c)

Comprehension-Based Questions

6. (b) 7. (c) 8. (a) 9. (a) 10. (c)

Match the Column

11. (b)

For answer key of Classroom wing and Competition wing, refer to Hints and Solutions

Hints and Explanations

Classroom Wing

Very Short Answer Type Questions

1. L.C = 1 M.S.D. – 1 V.S.D.
   = 1 mm – 0.8 mm
   = 0.2 mm
2. 129×10^{-5}
3. 7850 kg m^{-3}
4. Given: d_{sinker} = 6 g cm^{-3} = 6000 kg m^{-3}
   d_{liquid} = 2000 kg m^{-3} = 2 g cm^{-3}.
   Here $d_{sinker} > d_{liquid}$
5. 7.85
6. 1 ms^{-1}
7. Average speed $= \dfrac{\text{Total distance}}{\text{Total time taken}}$
   Its CGS unit is cm s^{-1}.
8. Relative density of gold is 19.
9. 1 M.S.D = 0.1 cm = 1 mm
   $N = 20$
   $$\text{L.C.} = \frac{1\text{MSD}}{N} = \frac{1\text{mm}}{20} = 0.05 \text{ mm}$$
10. (a) 1 mm (b) 1 second
    (c) 1°C (d) 0.1 mm
11. Internal jaws
12. The ratio of density of substance to density of water at 4°C.
13. LC = 0.05 mm
14. 1 litre = 1000 cm^3 = 10^{-3} m^3
15. Single pan analytical balance
16. Quantities that depend on other quantities for their derival. Examples are density, force, etc.
17. N V.S.D. = (N – 1) M.S.D.
18. The time taken by a cesium atom (Cs–133) to complete 9, 192, 631, 770 vibrations.
19. The smallest measurement that can be made accurately.
20. $\eta = \dfrac{Fx}{Av}$
    $$\frac{Nm}{m^2 \times \frac{m}{s}} = \frac{Ns}{m^2}$$
21. The ratio of mass to volume is density.
22. Principle of moment.
23. 1 cm^2 = 10^{-4} m^2
24. (a) km (b) feet
    (c) m (d) mm
    (e) cm
25. Candela is the unit of luminous intensity.

Short Answer Type Questions

Note: This is how you should frame your answer covering.

26. (1) Well defined (2) Reproducible
    (3) Unchangeable (4) Measurable size
27. (1) Length—m
    (2) Mass—kg
    (3) Time—s
    (4) Amount of substance—mol
    (5) Intensity of light—cd
    (6) Strength of electric current—A
    (7) Temperature—K
28. (1) Smallest measurement made by an instrument accurately.
    (2) L. C.= 1 M. S. D. – 1 V. S. D.
29. 0.25 mm
30. 4.66 cm
31. 49.08 cm
32. 1.8 mm
33. 0.02 cm
34. (1) Rules while counting the squares.
    (2) Units
35. Method using burette
36. 7.8×10^3 kg m^{-3}
37. 1.04×10^{-3} kg

38. 1.296×10^5 km h^{-2}

39. 0.1 m^2

40. 1000 kg m^{-3}. S.I.

41. Given: 1 M.S.D $= \frac{1}{2}$ mm;

V.C.D = 8; L. C = 0.05 mm;

M.S.R = 22 M.S.D $= 22 \cdot \frac{1}{2}$ mm = 11 mm

l = M.S.R + (V.C · L.C)

= 11 mm + (8 · 0.05 mm)

= (11 + 0.40) mm = 11.40 mm.

42. CGS, FPS, SI, MKS.

43. $1\text{MSD} = \frac{1\text{cm}}{10} = 0.1$ cm = 1 mm

$\text{L.C.} = \frac{1\text{MSD}}{N} = \frac{1\text{mm}}{10} = 0.1$ mm

M.S.R = 3

V.C.D = 4

l = M.S.R + (V.C.D · L.C.)

= 3 mm + 4 · 0.1 mm

= 3.4 mm.

Essay Answer Type Questions

Note: This is how you should frame your answer covering.

44. (1) Definition of measurement.
    (2) Definition of physical quantity.
    (3) Definition of unit.
    (4) Uniformity in units.
    (5) Consistency of measurements.

45. (1) Relation between M.S.D. and V.S.D.
    (2) Definition of L.C.
    (3) Equal gap between the jaws.
    (4) Divisions on the main scale in mm/cm.
    (5) Divisions on the vernier scale.

46. (1) Names of parts.
    (2) Function of each part.
    (3) Relation between M.S.D. and V.S.D.
    (4) Definition of M.S.R.
    (5) Definition of least count.
    (6) Observed reading = M.S.R. + (n × L.C.)

47. (a) (1) Graduations in the burette begins at its top.

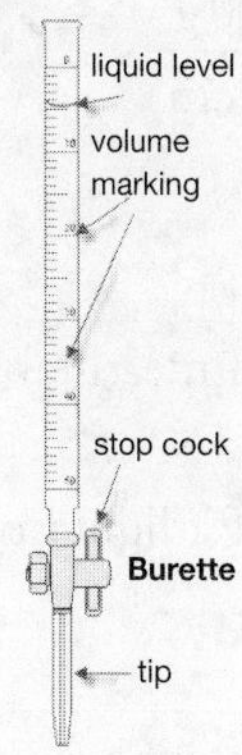

(2) No graduations, on the pippette.

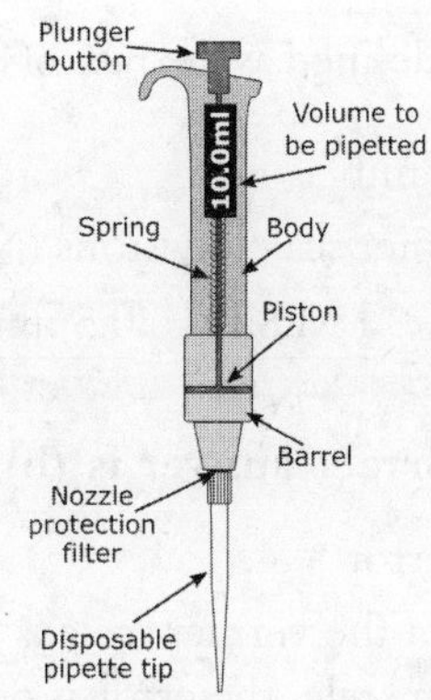

(b) (1) Main scale divisions in mm and cm.
(2) 10 V.S.D. = 9 mm
(3) Gap between the exterior jaws = gap between the interior jaws.

Competition Wing

Level 1: Apply your Concepts

13. Relative density $= \dfrac{\text{density of substance}}{\text{density of water}}$

$0.9 = \dfrac{d}{1}$

$\therefore\ d = 0.9 \text{ g cm}^{-3} = 900 \text{ kg m}^{-3}$

14. $1 \text{ kg m}^{-1}\text{ s}^{-2} = \dfrac{1000\text{ g}}{(100\text{ cm})}\text{s}^{-2}$

$= 10 \text{ g cm}^{-1}\text{ s}^{-2}$

20. (A) → *b*

Physical quantity is a measurable quantity.

(B) → *a*

Volume of a drop of a liquid can be measured using a burette.

I → *d*

The SI unit of instantaneous speed is $m\ s^{-1}$.

(D) → *c*

Acceleration is defined as the rate of change of velocity.

36. 1 M.S.D. = 0.5 mm

Number of vernier scale divisions (N) = 20.

$\therefore$ Least count $= \dfrac{1\text{ M.S.D.}}{N} = \dfrac{0.5\text{ mm}}{N} = 0.025$ mm

Hence, the correct answer is (b).

37. VCD for zero error = 4.

Since the zero of the vernier scale is to the right of the zero of the main scale, the error is positive.

$\therefore$ zero error = + *n* × L.C

= + 4 × 0.025 mm

= + 0.100 mm

= + 0.01 cm = + 100 μm

Hence, the correct answer is (d).

38. All vector quantities need not be derived quantities. For example, displacement is a vector quantity but it is not a derived quantity. The statement given as a reason is incorrect. But the assertion is correct.

Hence, the correct answer is (c).

39. Zero error = 0.05 mm

⇒ Zero correction = – 0.05 mm

MSR = 9 mm, VCD = 9

L.C = 0.1 mm

Diameter = MSR + (V.C.D) × L.C + Z.C

= 9 mm + 9 × 0.1 + (– 0.05)

= 9.85 mm

$\therefore$ Radius (R) $= \dfrac{9.85}{2}$ mm

Area of cross section $= \pi r^2 = \dfrac{22}{7}\left(\dfrac{9.85}{2}\right)^2$

$= 76.2 \text{ mm}^2$

Hence, the correct answer is (a).

40. Number of V.S.D. = *N*.

Given: N V.S.D. = (*N* – 2) M.S.D.

N.V.S.D. = N.M.S.D. – 2 M.S.D.

N.M.S.D. – N.V.S.D. = 2 M.S.D.

N (1 M.S.D. – 1 V.S.D.) = 2 M.S.D.

L.C. $= \dfrac{2\text{ M.S.D.}}{\text{N}}$

Hence, the correct answer is (b).

41. The mass of 150 m^3 of iron is greater than the mass of 150 m^3 of wood. Because, the density of iron is greater than the density of wood. But the reason given is density of iron is less than the density of wood. So, A is correct and R is incorrect.

Hence, the correct answer is (c).

42. Take different objects such as glass, stone, etc., of different volumes and immerse in different liquids such as water, kerosene, mercury, etc. (B).

The displaced liquid is collected in a beaker and its volume is measured with the help of a measuring cylinder (A).

This phenomenon is observed at different places and different times (C).

It is found that the volume of displaced liquid increases as the volume of the object increases (D).

Hence, the correct answer is (c).

43. Take a stone (irregular shape) and a measuring jar. Fill the vessel with liquid and water and immerse the stone in it. The difference in the volume of the liquid is equal to the volume of the stone.

Hence, the correct answer is (b).

44. Smallest measurement = 0.1 mm = 0.1×10^{-3} m = 10^{-4} m

So, the length of 1 m is divided into $\dfrac{1}{10^{-4}}$ equal parts, that is 10^4 = 10000

Hence, the correct answer is (c).

45. Scale: 100 cm = 15000 km

1500 km = 10 cm

Hence, the correct answer is (a).

46. For a standard vernier callipers N vernier scale divisions = (N – I) main scale divisions

Hence, the correct answer is (b).

47. If the zeroth division of the vernier callipers main scales of a standard vernier callipers coincide, then the external jaws are in contact with each other.

Hence, the correct answer is (a).

Level 2: Review your Concepts

Note: This is how you should frame your answer covering.

48. $V_{air} = 330\ ms^{-1} = \dfrac{330 \times 86400}{9.3 \times 10^{15}} = 3065806.5 \times 10^{-15}$

$= 3 \times 10^{-9}\ \ell y\ (day)^{-1}$

$C = 3 \times 10^{8}\ ms^{-1} = \dfrac{3 \times 10^{8} \times 86400}{9.3 \times 10^{15}}\ \ell y\ (day)^{-1}$

$= 2.787 \times 10^{-3}$

$\text{Ratio} = \dfrac{C}{V} = \dfrac{2.787 \times 10^{-3}}{3 \times 10^{-9}} = 0.929 \times 10^{6}$

49. (i) S.I. unit of heat is 1 J (= 1 kg $m^2\ s^{-2}$) and its CGS unit is 1 erg (= 1 g $cm^2\ s^{-2}$)

(ii) erg $g^{-1}\ {}^0C^{-1}$, J $kg^{-1}\ K^{-1}$

50. (i) 0 inch to 2 inch = 32 division

2 inch to 3 inch = 8 division

(ii) $1\dfrac{13}{16}$ inch, 4.60 cm

51. Given: 1 M. S. D = $\dfrac{2cm}{20} = \dfrac{20mm}{20}$ = 1 mm;

1 V.S.D = 0.9 mm

L.C = 1 M.S.D – 1 V.S.D

= 1 mm – 0.9 mm

= 0.1 mm.

52. Express 'G' in terms of *F*, *r*, m_1 and m_2. If C.G.S. unit of *F*, *r*, and *m* are dynes, cm and g, respectively, then on substituting these values, is it possible to obtain C.G.S. unit of 'G'?

If S.I. units of *F*, *r* and *m* are N, *m* and kg, respectively, then on substituting these values, is it possible to obtain S.I. unit of 'G'?

53. The value of 1 M.S.D. = 1mm (given)

The correct least count of vernier calliper is 0.01 cm.

Then what is the formula of the least count $\left(\text{L.C.} = \dfrac{1\ \text{M.S.D.}}{N}\right)$

How many divisions are present on the vernier scale?

The formula for the length of a vernier calipers is ℓ = M.S.R. + V.C. × L.C.--- (1)

Is the value measured by the student a mistake?

What is its value?

Then, the value of MSR is = 4.9 cm.

Then, what is the value of V.C.D.?

⇒ By inserting the values of M.S.R., V.C.D. and L.C. in (1), the correct length of the rod is obtained.

M.S.R. = 49 mm, V.C.D. = 9, Original reading = 49.9 mm

54. Outside diameter = Inside diameter + (2 × thickness)

21.9 mm

55. Area of triangle = $\dfrac{1}{2}$(base) × (height)

Area of a circle = πr^2

Area of a semi circle = $\dfrac{1}{2}\pi r^2$

Total Area = Area of triangle + Area of rectangle – Area of circle

Total area = [(1/2) × 25 × 24] + [14 × 25] – [3.14 × 3.5^2]

Total area = 300 + 350 – 38.465 = 611.535 cm^2

56. (i) The formula for L.C. of an apparatus

= 1 M.S.D. – 1 V.S.D. = $\dfrac{1.\text{M.S.D.}}{N}$

Then, what is the number of divisions present on vernier scale?

Then, the value of 1 V.S.D. = 1 M.S.D. – L.C.

If the value of N is 50, and 1 M.S.D. = 1 mm, then what is the value of L.C.?

Minimum length of the vernier scale = 9.9 cm

(ii) Least count = 0.02 mm

57. Relative density = $\dfrac{\text{Density of a substance}}{\text{Density of water}}$ = 2.4

58. Volume = $\dfrac{\text{mass}}{\text{density}}$

Will wooden piece float on water?

The relative density of the sinker = 7.85

So, the density of the sinker = 7.85 g cm^{-3}.

Given the mass of the sinker = 157 g.

Then, the volume of the sinker = $\frac{d}{m}$

Now, given the the volume of (sinker + wooden piece), we can find the volume of the sinker.

Also calculate, what is the change in the volume of water due to the immersion of sinker and the wooden piece? Then, find the volume of the wooden piece.

59. New volume = (1.2 l × 1.1 b × 1.05 h)

Original volume = lbh

Original volume, lbh = 1000 cm^3

New volume = 1.386 lbh = 1.386 × 1000 = 1386 cm3

Change in volume = 1386 – 1000 = 386 cm^3

60. Density = $\frac{\text{mass}}{\text{volume}}$

$$\frac{d_1}{d_2} = \frac{\frac{m_1}{v_1}}{\frac{m_2}{v_2}} = \frac{m_1}{m_2} \times \frac{v_2}{v_1} =$$

$$= \frac{m_1}{m_2} \times \frac{\frac{4}{3}\pi r_2^3}{\frac{4}{3}\pi r_1^3} = \frac{m_1}{m_2} \times \left(\frac{r_2}{r_1}\right)^3 = 4:1$$

61. Given,

MSR = 31 × 0.5 = 15.5 mm

VCD = 20

LC = 1 MSD/No. of VSDs = 0.5/25 = 0.02 mm

Total Reading = MSR + (VCD × LC)

= 15.5 + (20×0.02) = 15.9 mm

62. Given, L.C. of vernier calipers = 0.05 mm.

1 M.S.D. of the V.C. = 0.5 mm

Then, the formula for least count, L.C.=$\frac{\text{1M.S.D.}}{\text{N}}$

This means, N=$\frac{\text{1M.S.D.}}{\text{L.C.}}$

From the above formula, find the number of V.S.D., (N)

N = 10

63. M.S.R= 4.6 cm = 46 mm

V.C.D = 6

L.C = 0.01 cm = 0.1 mm

I = M.S.R + (V.C.D × L.C)

= 46 + 6 × 0.1 = 46.6 mm = 4.66 cm.

64. Area = $2 \times 5 + \frac{1}{2} \times 5 \times 2 - \left(\frac{22}{7}\right)(1)^2$

$= 10 + 5 - \left(\frac{22}{7}\right)$

∴ 15 – 3.14 = 11.86 cm^2

65. V = 200 cm^3

Mass = 400 g

Density $= \frac{\text{Mass}}{\text{Volume}} = \frac{400}{200} = 2 \text{ gcm}^{-2}$

∴ Relative density = 2

66. The mass of the crown can be measured by using a balance that can measure the mass more accurately. The volume of the crown can be found by immersing it in an overflow jar and measuring the volume of water over flown. Once the mass of the crown and its volume are known, its density can be calculated. If the calculated density of the crown is 19 g cm^{-3} (since relative density of gold is given as 19), the crown is made of pure gold. Otherwise it can be concluded that the crown is made with adulterated gold.

Level 3: Assess Your Concepts

Note: This is how you should frame your answer covering.

67. Length or diameter = [difference of the observed readings on the two jaws with the object held] – [difference of the observed readings when the jaws are closed].

M.S.R. = 10.2 cm

V.C.D. = 6

68. According to principle of moments, the anti clockwise moments should balance the clockwise moments.

i.e., weight in the left pan × perpendicular distance of the weight in the left pan from the point of suspension = weight in the right pan × perpendicular distance of the weight in the right pan from the point of suspension.

69. Density of mixture = $\frac{\text{total mass}}{\text{total volume}}$

$= \frac{44}{45} \text{ g cm}^{-3}$

70. What is least count?

Should the value of least count be large or small?

Will the accuracy of the vernier calipers be increased by decreasing the value of the least count?

The least count, L.C.$=\frac{1\text{M.S.D.}}{N}$ = 1 M.S.D. − 1 V.S.D. (1)

Given the principle of vernier is N V.S.D. = (N − 1) M.S.D.

This implies that, 1 V.S.D.$=\left(\frac{N-1}{N}\right)$M.S.D. (2)

On substituting (2) in (1), find the value of L.C.

Consider, if N V.S.D. = (N − 3) M.S.D.

$\Rightarrow$ 1 V.S.D.$=\left(\frac{N-3}{N}\right)$M.S.D (3)

Substituting (3) in (1), find the value of L.C.

In which case is the L.C. is the least?

71. Given, $v_1 = v, v_2 = 3v$

$m_1 = m, m_2 = m$

$d_1 = d, d_2 = ?$

$d_1 = \frac{m_1}{v_1} = \frac{m}{v}$

$d_2 \frac{m_2}{v_2} = \frac{m}{3v}$

$d_2 = \frac{m}{3v}$

$\therefore d_2 = \frac{1}{3} d_1$

$\Delta d = d_2 - d_1 = d - \frac{d}{3} = \frac{3d - d}{3} = \frac{2d}{3}$

% change in density $= \frac{\Delta d}{d_1} \times 100 = \frac{2d}{3 \times d} \times 100$

$= \frac{200}{3}\%$

72. Number of V.S.D., N = 50

V.C.D. = 39

M.S.R. = 6.3 cm = 63 mm

Diameter of the metallic rod = 2R = M.S.R + V.C.D × L.C.

$\Rightarrow R = \frac{\text{M.S.R.+V.C.D} \times \text{L.C.}}{2}$

L.C. of the vernier callipers, L.C.

$= \frac{1\text{M.S.D}}{N} = \frac{1 \text{ mm}}{50} = \frac{0.1}{5} = 0.02\text{mm}$

Diameter = 65 mm + 39 × 0.02 mm

= (63 + 0.78) mm

D = 63.78 mm (or) D = 6.378 cm

∴ Radius of the given rod,

$R = \frac{D}{2} = \frac{6.378}{2} = 3.189 \text{ cm} = 31.89 \text{ mm}$

73. Given, 1 M.S.D. = 1.5 mm

Number of V.S.D's = 15 ⇒ N = 15

L.C. of the vernier callipers,

$L.C. = \frac{1\ M.S.D.}{N} = \frac{1.5 \text{ mm}}{15}$

⇒ L.C. = 0.1 mm

Given M.S.R. = 19 × 1.5 mm = 28.5 mm

Given vernier coincidence, V.C. = 14

Measurement of length of given object

= M.S.R. + V.C. × L.C. = 28.5 mm + 14 × 0.1 mm

= 28.5 mm + 1.4 mm

= 29.9 mm = 2.99 cm

74. 1 M.S.D. = 1 mm

$N = 20$

V.C.D. = 16

M.S.R. = 12.3 cm = 123 mm

= M.S.R. + V.C.D. × L.C

$= 123 + 16 \times \frac{1}{20}$

= 123.8 mm

∴ Radius = 123.8 = 61.9 mm

75. Density of P, $d_P = 1.5 \text{ g cm}^{-3}$.

Density od Q, $d_Q = 1.3 \text{ g cm}^{-3}$.

Density of the mixture (d_m)

$= \frac{\text{mass of P + mass of Q}}{\text{Volume of P + Volume of Q}}$

$\Rightarrow d_m = \frac{m_p + m_Q}{V_p + V_Q} = \frac{d_p \times V_p + d_Q \times V_Q}{V_p + V_Q}$

But $V_P = V_Q = x$

$\therefore d_m = \frac{d_p \times x + d_Q \times x}{2x} = \frac{d_p + d_Q}{2}$

$= \frac{1.5 + 1.3}{2} = \frac{2.8}{2} = 1.4 \text{g cm}^{-3}$

76. Length of one main scale division = 1 mm.

Number of vernier scale divisions, $N = 50$.

$\therefore$ Least count of the vernier scale

$$= \frac{1\text{ mm}}{50} = 0.02\text{ mm} = 2\times10^{-3}\text{cm}$$

Given 76 cm column of mercury exerts 10^5 Pa pressure.

$\therefore$ Pressure exerted by 2×10^{-3} cm column of mercury

$$= \frac{2\times10^{-3}\times10^5}{76}\text{Pa}$$

$$= \frac{50}{19}\text{Pa} = 2.63\text{ Pa}$$

77. Area of trapezium ABCD $= \frac{1}{2}\times h(a+b)$

$$= \frac{1}{2}\times 6(10+15) = 75\text{ cm}^2.$$

Area of $\Delta AFD = \frac{1}{2}\times 2\times 6 = 6\text{cm}^2.$

Area of circle $= \pi r^2 = 3.14\times2\times2 = 12.56\text{ cm}^2.$

Area of shaded region $= 75 - 6 - 12.56 = 56.44\text{ cm}^2.$

78. Given, $m_1 = m_2 = m$

$v_1 = 100\text{ cm}^3, v_2 = 400\text{ cm}^{-3}$

$d_A = ?\ d_B = 20\text{ kg m}^{-3} = 20\times10^{-3}\text{g cm}^{-3}$

$m_B = d_B v_B = 20\times10^{-3}\times400 = 8 = 8\text{ g}$

$m_A = 8\text{ g}$

$m_A = d_A v_A$

$$d_A = \frac{m_A}{v_A} = \frac{8}{100} = 0.08\text{ g cm}^{-3}$$

79. Mass = 88 kg, relative density = 194.481

$$V = \frac{88}{194481}$$

$$\frac{4}{3}\pi r^3 = \frac{88}{194481}$$

$$r^3 = \frac{88}{194481}\times\frac{3}{4}\times\frac{7}{22}$$

$$r^3 = \frac{1}{9261}$$

$$r = \frac{1}{21}$$

$$\text{TSA} = 4\pi r^2 = 4\times\frac{22}{7}\times\frac{1}{21}\times\frac{1}{21} = \frac{88}{3087}$$

$$= 0.0285\text{ m}^3 = 0.029\text{ m}^2.$$

JEE-NEET Special Wing

Multiple-Answer Type Questions

1. Unit should be reproducible and unchangeable.
Hence, the correct option is (a) and (d).

2. Temperature and time are fundamental quantities.
Hence, the correct option is (c) and (d).

3. LC of meter scale = 0.1 cm = 1 mm
Hence, the correct option is (a) and (c).

4. Measuring jar is used to measure the volume of liquid in millilitres.
Burette is used to take the desired amount of a liquid.
Hence, the correct option is (b) and (c).

5. Joule is the unit of work and energy.
Work = F×S
∴ Its unit is N m
But since F= ma
$N = kg\ m\ s^{-2}$
∴ Unit of work is $kg\ m^2\ s^{-2}$.
Hence, the correct option is (b) and (c).

Comprehension-Based Questions

6. The smallest measurement that can be accurately made by an instrument is least count.
Hence, the correct option is (b).

7. $L.C = \dfrac{1\ M.S.D.}{\text{No. of V.S.D's}}$
Hence, the correct option is (c).

8. The principle of vernier is to make 'N' vernier scale divisions equal to (N – 1) main scale divisions.
Hence, the correct option is (a).

9. The observed measurement from a vernier calliper is given by M. S. R + (V. C. D×L. C).
Hence, the correct option is (a).

10. Each division of vernier scale is smaller than each main scale division.
Hence, the correct option is (c).

Match the Column

11. **Choice (b) follows.**
Units of some of the quantities in S.I. system are given.
The SI unit of **Time** is **second.**
The SI unit of **Temperature** is **Kelvin.**
The SI unit of **Luminous intensity** is **Candela.**
The SI unit of **Electric current** is **Ampere.**
The SI unit of **Amount of substance** is **Mole.**
A - e, B - d, C – a, D – b, E - c

Kinematics

CHAPTER

2

Key Ideas

After completing this chapter, you should be able to:

- understand the difference between rest and motion, scalars and vectors, geometrical representation of a vector.
- acquire knowledge about distance and displacement, speed and its different types.
- understand velocity and various kinds of velocity, the difference between acceleration and retardation.
- use equations of motion to solve problems and find the nature of motion of the bodies by using s – *t* and v – *t* graphs.

Remember

Before beginning this chapter, you should be able to:

- learn about different types of motion and to classify the motions of various bodies.
- define different types of speed, velocity, acceleration and their applications.

Scientific Crypt

A Tribute to Albert Einstein (1879—1955)

Albert Einstein was born on March 14, 1879 at Ulm, Württemberg, Germany in a Jewish family. His father, Hermann Einstein, was an engineer and a salesman and his mother was Pauline Einstein. This German-born theoretical physicist with his 'theory of general relativity' brought revolution in physics and he is often considered as 'father of modern physics'. Belonging to the classification of scientists and thinkers, his exceptional intelligence and originality has made the word 'Einstein' synonymous with genius.

At the age of five, Einstein received a magnetic compass from his father and then he developed a great interest to know about the invisible forces of nature. Einstein was a calm, patient child and completed elementary education from a catholic elementary school. Einstein, right from childhood, spent long hours reading books and his uncle gave him books on science(s), mathematics and philosophy which helped in his intellectual growth. He joined Federal Polytechnic Institute after his secondary school education and even taught in the same polytechnic in 1900. Later, he joined a Swiss Patent Office and there he got an opport-unity to examine others' applications. In 1905, he obtained the doctorate degree from the University of Zurich for his theory about molecular dimensions and in the same year he published four papers explaining photoelectric effect, relativity, movement of molecules and equivalence of matter and energy (E = mc2). He received noble prize for the photoelectric effect. He became American citizen in 1940. He forewent the chance to became the President of Israel and continued his research work. He taught physics at the institute for advanced study, Princeton, U.S till his death in 1955.

Crossword

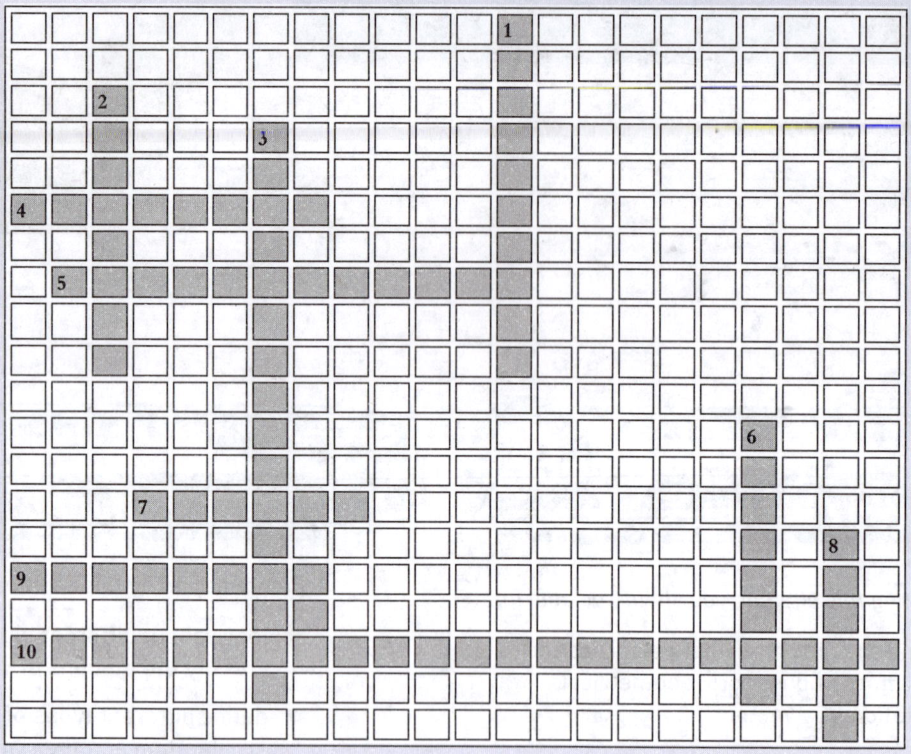

Across

4. Helps to find distance covered by the vehicle.
5. Area covered under the curve of v-t graph.
7. Physical quantity that completely specified by means of a numerical value and a unit.
9. Study of motion of bodies by considering the cause of motion.
10. Slope at any point in s-t graph.

Down

1. Acceleration of the body is negative.
2. Rate of change of displacement of a body.
3. Ratio of total displacement and total time taken.
6. The length of the actual path of the journey.
8. Deceleration of a body is a type of physical quantity.

INTRODUCTION

In day to day life, we go through the action of forces and their effects. The branch of physics which deals with the effect of forces on bodies is called mechanics.

Mechanics is classified into statics and dynamics.

Statics: It deals with bodies at rest under the action of forces.

Dynamics: Dynamics deals with bodies under motion and it is further classified into kinematics and kinetics.

Kinematics: It deals with the motion of bodies without considering the cause of motion.

Kinetics: It deals with the motion of bodies considering the cause of their motion.

Rest and Motion: An object is said to be at rest if its position does not change with respect to its surroundings with the passage of time. e.g., a clock hanging on the wall, a suitcase in a train.

An object is said to be in motion as long as its position changes with respect to its surroundings.

Example: A moving train, rotation of the Earth about its axis.

Motion is Relative: Consider two persons in a lift. Let the lift move upwards. The two persons are not in motion with respect to each other. But for a person outside the lift, the two persons are in motion. Hence, motion is relative.

In our study of mechanics we shall refer to bodies or objects as particles. An object is said to be a particle (point object) if its dimensions are negligible. For example, in planetary motion around the sun, different planets can be approximated to be particles as the distance travelled by them is very large compared to their dimensions.

Scalars and Vectors

All physical quantities can be classified into scalars or vectors. Quantities that can be completely specified by means of a numerical value and a unit are called **physical quantities**, and thus quantities which are said to have only magnitude are called **scalars**, e.g., mass, distance, time, speed, density and temperature.

Physical quantities that can be defined only if both magnitude and direction are specified are called **vectors**, e.g., displacement, force, velocity, acceleration, etc.

Example: Consider a person moving in the eastern direction in a straight path from A to B. At position B he takes a left turn and moves along a straight line to another position C which is due north as shown in the Figure 2.1.

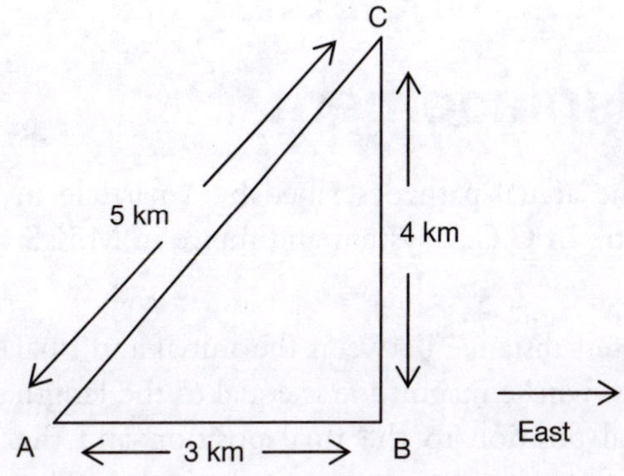

Figure 2.1 Path covered by a person starting from A and ended at C

If lengths of AB and BC are 3 km and 4 km, respectively, the distance travelled by the body from A to C is given by $AB + BC = 3\text{ km} + 4\text{ km} = 7\text{ km}$.

To measure this distance (the actual length of the path travelled) no direction is to be considered as it is not important in which direction it is covered. The magnitude gives the total description of the physical quantity and thus it is a scalar. The initial and final positions of the person being A and C, respectively, the net displacement (change in position) of the person is given by AC (the length of the shortest path between the two positions). The magnitude (length) of AC is 5 km which can be obtained by using Pythagorean theorem. This displacement is in the direction from A to C. Thus, to measure displacement, the direction also needs to be specified along with the magnitude. Specifying only one cannot give the complete description of the quantity. Thus, the physical quantities such as displacement are vectors.

Geometrical Representation of a Vector

A vector can be represented by a line segment with an arrow head.

- The length of the line segment (AB) is proportional to the magnitude of the vector.

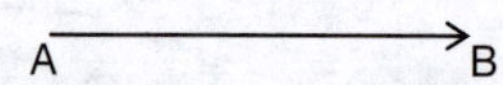

- The arrow head indicates the direction of the vector.

Consider a man walking along a straight path from P to Q, the length of the path between the two positions being 100 m. Then, this displacement is represented by a directed line segment PQ as shown in the figure.

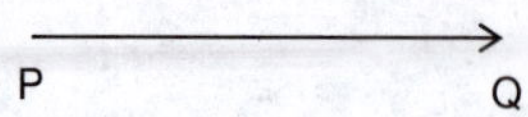

The direction of the displacement is shown by the arrow and its magnitude is given by the length of the line segment drawn to scale. For example, if the length of the line segment PQ is chosen as 5 cm, the scale considered for drawing the line segment is 1 cm = 20 m. Instead if the length of the line segment is chosen to be 4 cm, the scale considered for drawing the line segment is 1 cm = 25 m.

An arrow or a short line is drawn above the quantity to represent a vector.

Example: $\vec{F}, \vec{a}, \overrightarrow{AB}, \overrightarrow{EF}$, etc.

Table 2.1 Difference between scalar quantity and vector quantity

Scalar Quantity	Vector Quantity
They have only magnitude.	Both magnitude and direction are needed to define vectors.
Addition or subtraction of scalar quantities can be done by simple arithmetical means.	Special vector addition rules are needed for adding or subtracting vectors.

Info Bytes!

In print, vectors are printed in boldface, e.g., **F**, **a**, **AB**, **EF**, etc.

Distance and Displacement

Distance is defined as the length of the actual path described by a particle in motion. The unit of distance is centimetre in C.G.S. system and metre in M.K.S. or S.I. system.

Displacement is defined as the shortest distance between the initial and final positions of a body. It is a vector quantity, whose magnitude is equal to the length of the straight line path from the initial position to the final position and the direction is along the straight line drawn from the initial to the final position. The magnitude of displacement is expressed in centimetres (cm) in C.G.S. system and in metres (m) in M.K.S. and S.I. system.

Info Bytes!

Distance travelled by a car is measured by an odometer.

The distance travelled by a particle depends on the path traced by the particle, whereas the displacement of a particle in motion is independent of the path traced and depends only on the initial and final positions of the particle.

Consider a particle moving along the path *ABCD* as shown in Figure 2.2.

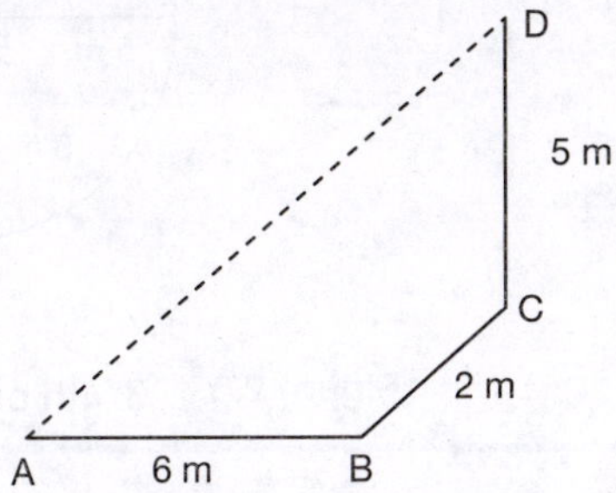

Figure 2.2 Dotted lines represents displacement of the particle

The distance travelled by the particle = 6 + 2 + 5 = 13 m. The displacement is the vector $\overrightarrow{AD}$, whose magnitude is the length of the line segment *AD*.

> **Konnect**
>
> 1. The distance covered by a body is always greater than or equal to the magnitude of displacement.
> 2. The distance travelled and magnitude of displacement of a particle will be equal if the particle travels along the shortest path from the initial to the final position without change in direction of motion.
> 3. $\overrightarrow{AB} \neq \overrightarrow{BA}$, as for $\overrightarrow{AB}$ the initial position is A and final position is B and for $\overrightarrow{BA}$ the initial position is B and final position is A.

EXAMPLE 2.1

A hunter hears that a deer is 3 km away from his campsite. Is it possible for the hunter to find the deer with the given information?

SOLUTION

It is not possible to locate the deer, as the hunter doesn't know the direction in which to search for the deer. Thus, the information about distance alone is not sufficient to determine the position of the deer.

EXAMPLE 2.2

A horse is tied to a rope of length 5 m and the other end of the rope is tied to a pole. Find the displacement and the distance travelled by the horse in the following cases:

(i) When the horse makes half revolution along a circular path.

(ii) When it makes one full revolution.

(iii) When it makes $\frac{3}{4}$ th of the revolution.

SOLUTION

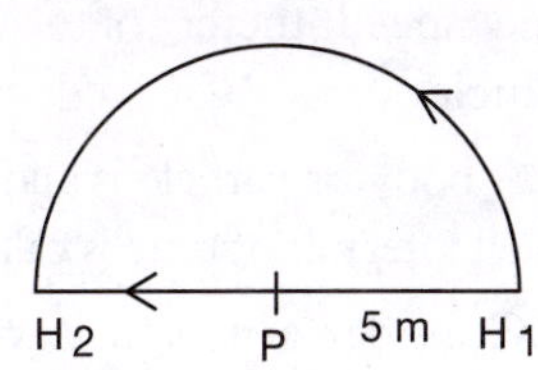

Figure 2.3 Half revolution done by the horse

(i) Half revolution along the circular path (Figure 2.3).

Distance travelled by the horse $= \frac{2\pi r}{2} = \pi r = \pi \times 5 = 5\pi$ m.

Displacement of the horse = diameter of the circular path, $\overrightarrow{H_1 H_2}$ = 10 m from H_1 to H_2

(ii) When the horse makes full revolution (Figure 2.4)

Distance travelled by the horse = circumference of the circular path

$= 2\pi r = 2\pi \times 5 = 10\,\pi$ m

Displacement of the horse = zero (Since initial and final position of the horse coincide)

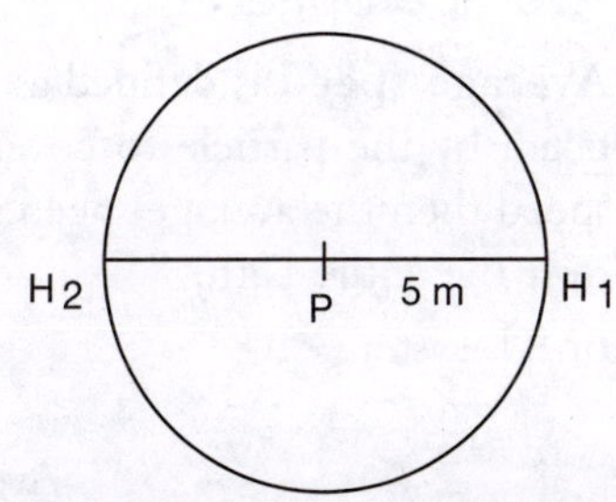

Figure 2.4 Full revolution done by the horse

(iii) When the horse makes $\frac{3}{4}$ th of the revolution (Figure 2.5)

Distance travelled by the horse $= \frac{3}{4}$ th of the circumference of the circle $= \frac{3}{4}(2\pi r)$

$$= \frac{3}{2} \times \pi \times 5 = \frac{15}{2}\pi = 7.5\ \pi\text{m}.$$

Displacement of the horse = $\overrightarrow{H_1 H_2}$

$|\overrightarrow{H_1 H_2}|$ = shortest distance between H_1 and H_2

$= \sqrt{5^2 + 5^2} = \sqrt{25+25} = \sqrt{50}$

$= 5\sqrt{2}$ m along H_1 to H_2.

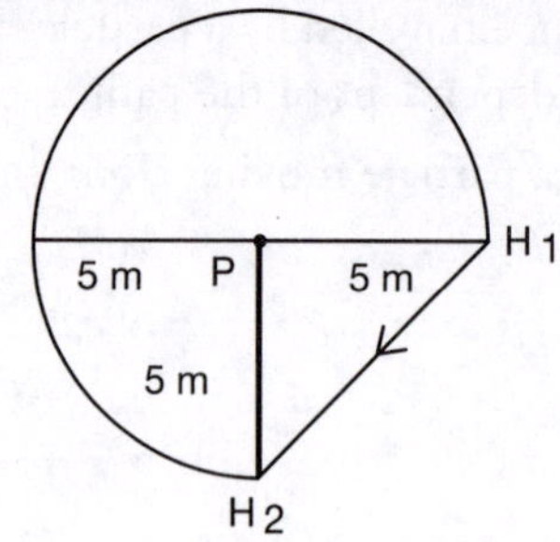

Figure 2.5 3/4th of the revolution by the horse

Speed

Speed is defined as the rate at which a particle covers a distance along a given path. It is given by the ratio of distance travelled to the time taken.The unit of speed is cm s^{-1} in C.G.S. system and m s^{-1} in M.K.S. or S.I. system.

$$\text{Speed} = \frac{\text{Distance travelled (s)}}{\text{Time (t)}} = \frac{s}{t}$$

Info Bytes!

- Since distance travelled is a scalar, the speed of a particle is also a scalar.
- The speed of light is approximately 299,792,458 meters per second, making it the universal speed limit according to Einstein's theory of relativity.

Types of Speed

Instantaneous Speed

The speed of a particle at a given instant is known as **instantaneous speed.** The speedometer of a vehicle indicates the instantaneous speed of the vehicle.

A body or particle is said to possess uniform speed if it travels equal distances in equal intervals of time is called **uniform speed.**

Consider a person travelling from A to B through O (Figure 2.6). If he walks at a constant rate of 1 m s^{-1}, i.e., for every 1 s if he travels 1 m, then the person is said to possess uniform speed.

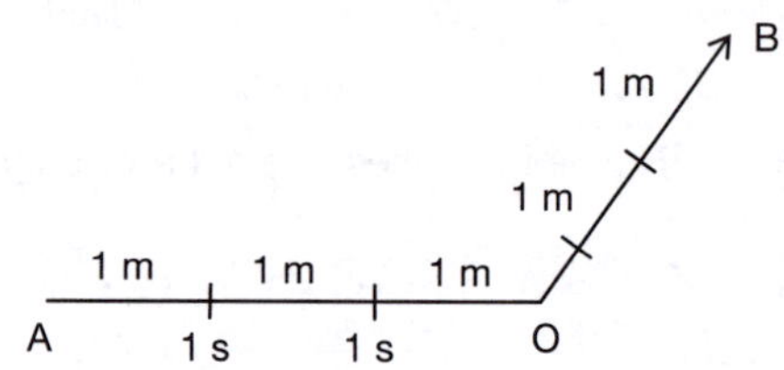

Figure 2.6 Uniform speed maintained by a person from A to B

If the instantaneous speed of a particle changes with time, then the body is said to be moving with variable speed.

Average Speed

Average speed is defined as the ratio of the total distance travelled to the total time taken by the particle to cover that distance. When a particle moves with a variable speed then the average speed is used to describe the mean speed with which it travels over the entire path.

Konnect

Uniform speed indicates that the instantaneous speed of particle remains the same throughout the motion.

$$\text{Average speed} = \frac{\text{Total distance}}{\text{Total time}}$$

Velocity

Velocity is displacement of a body in unit time or rate of displacement.

It is a vector quantity. S.I. unit of velocity is m s^{-1} and or C.G.S. unit of velocity is cm s^{-1}.

$$\text{Velocity} = \frac{\text{displacement}}{\text{time}}$$

$$\vec{V} = \frac{\vec{s}}{t}$$

Konnect

If you throw a ball straight up and catch it at the same point, the ball's average velocity for the whole trip is zero!

Consider a person moving 3 km east of A. He then turns North and moves 4 km in total time 2 hours as shown in the Figure 2.7.

$\vec{s}$ = Displacement = $\overrightarrow{AC}$ = 5 km along $\overrightarrow{AC}$.

$$\text{Velocity} = \frac{\vec{s}}{t} = \frac{5}{2} = 2.5 \text{ km h}^{-1} \text{ along } \overline{AC}.$$

Time = 2 hours

$$\therefore \text{ Speed} = \frac{\text{Distance}}{\text{time}} = \frac{7 \text{ km}}{2} = 3.5 \text{ km h}^{-1}.$$

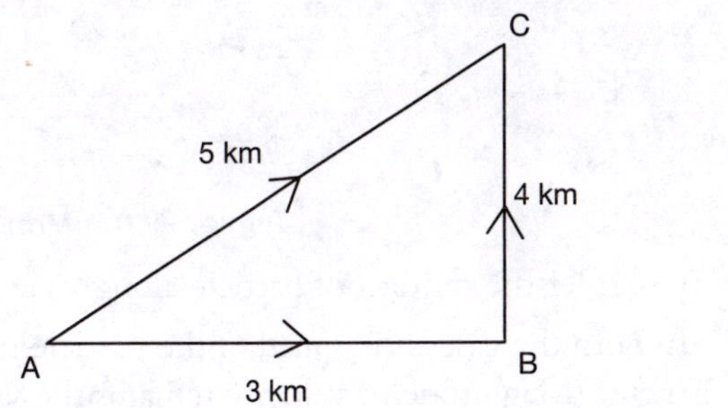

Figure 2.7 A person moving from A to C through B

Types of Velocities

Uniform and Non-Uniform Velocity

A body in motion is said to move with uniform velocity if it has equal displacements in equal intervals of time, however small these intervals may be. If a body covers unequal displacements in equal intervals of time (or equal displacements in unequal intervals of time), it is said to be moving with non-uniform velocity.

Activity: To Observe and Understand Uniform Motion

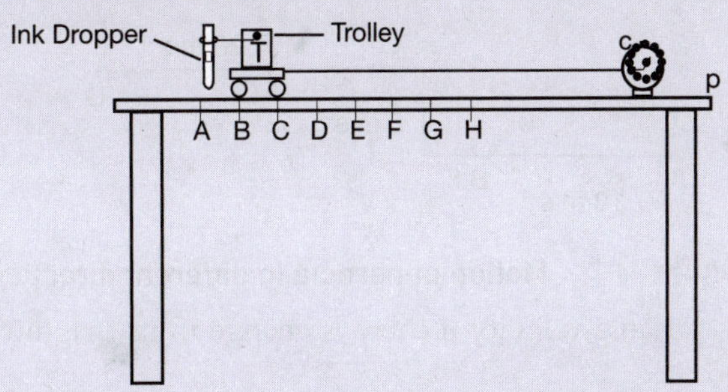

Figure 2.8 A trolley with an ink dropper

The following activity involves observing a body moving with uniform velocity:

1. Arrange a trolley (T) with an ink dropper attached to it as shown in the Figure 2.8.
2. Tie one end of a thread to the trolley and the other end to the central shaft of the seconds hand of a clock.
3. As the trolley driven by the clock moves forward, drops of ink fall on a white paper placed on the table, at regular intervals.
4. Measure the distance between successive drops and note down the time intervals between the drops.

It is observed that $\frac{\text{distance between the drops}}{\text{time}}$ = constant.

Hence, it can be concluded that the body is moving with uniform velocity.

Consider a body moving along a straight line as shown in Figure 2.9 where AB = 10 m. If the body covers 1 m in every 1 s, then the velocity is uniform.

Consider the motion of a particle from A to C as shown in Figure 2.10 (i). The particle travels at a rate of 10 m s^{-1} from A to B and again at 10 m s^{-1} from B to C.

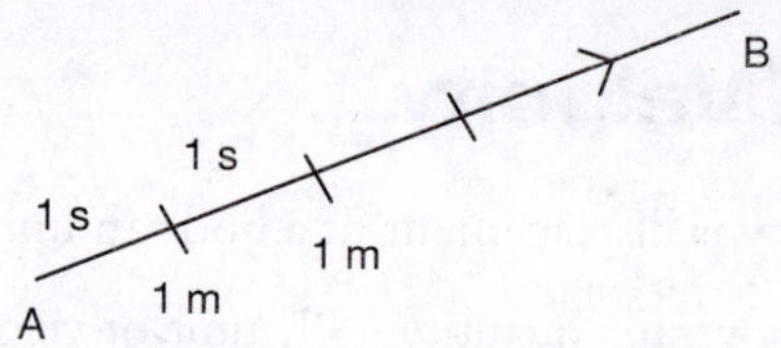

Figure 2.9 Speed and magnitude of velocity is the same along the linear path.

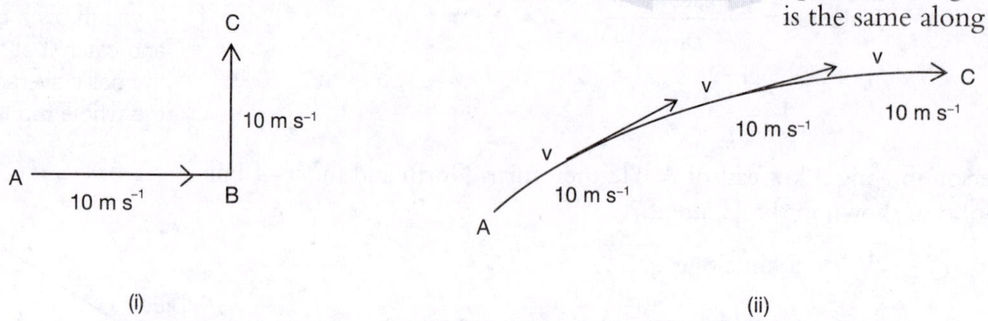

Figure 2.10 Motion of a particle in (i) straight and in (ii) curved path

Consider the motion of particle along a curve as given in Figure 2.10 (ii).

In both the cases, the speed of the particle remains constant but the velocity changes since the direction of the velocity changes. (Magnitude of velocity remains the same.)

The motion of particle is as shown below with the varying speed from A to D. Here, the velocity of the particle is not uniform since the magnitude of velocity changes though the direction remains the same.

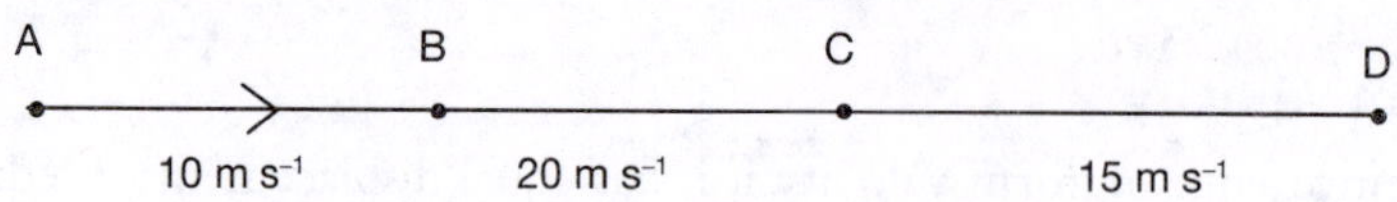

Figure 2.11 Motion of particle in same direction

Examine the motion of a particle as shown below. It is seen that the magnitude and direction of velocity changes. Hence, the velocity is not uniform.

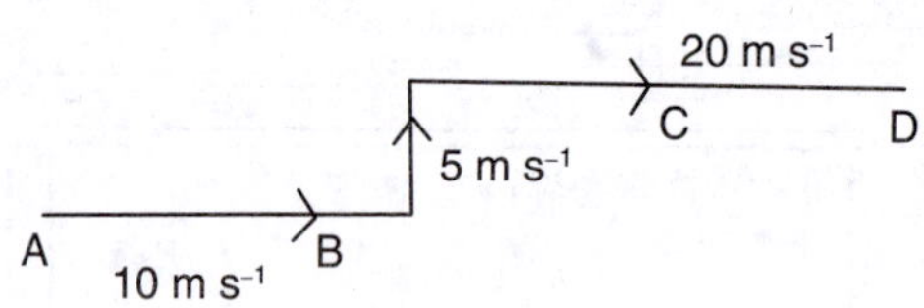

Figure 2.12 Motion of particle in different direction

Thus, the particle is said to possess variable velocity if there is change in its magnitude or direction or both.

Instantaneous Velocity

The velocity of a particle at a given instant of time is called its **instantaneous velocity**. The direction of the instantaneous velocity is along the tangent to the path at that instant. Instantaneous velocity of the particle changes if the body is travelling with variable velocity.

> **Info Bytes!**
>
> 1 km = 1000 m
>
> 1 hour = 3600 s.
>
> $$1 \text{ km h}^{-1} = \frac{1000 \text{ m}}{3600 \text{ s}} = \frac{5}{18} \text{ m s}^{-1}$$

Average Velocity

Average velocity is the ratio of total displacement to total time taken.

$$\text{Average velocity} = \frac{\text{Total displacement}}{\text{Total time}}$$

$$\text{Average velocity, } \overrightarrow{V_{avg}} = \frac{s}{t}$$

EXAMPLE 2.3

A tower clock has its hour hand 20 cm long. At what speed and at what velocity does the tip of the hour hand move in a three-hour duration?

SOLUTION

Length of the hour hand of the clock = 20 cm

During a three-hour duration, the tip of the hour hand moves between two diametrically opposite positions. Thus, the distance moved by the tip of the minute hand is equal to half the circumference of the circular path along which the tip moves = $1/4(2\pi r)$, where '*r*' is the length of the hour hand.

$\therefore$ Distance = $\frac{1}{4} \times 2 \times 22/7 \times 20$ cm = 31.43 cm. (rounded to two decimal places)

Displacement of the tip of the hour hand is equal to the arc length for a quarter circle, as the starting and ending points are not diametrically opposite. This means the displacement is equal to the calculated distance = 31.43 cm.

The time of travel of the tip of the hour hand, t = 3 hours = $3 \times 60 \times 60$ s = 10800 s

Speed of the hour hand = Distance/time

= 31.43 cm/10800 s = 31.43/10800 = 0.00291 cm s^{-1}

$\therefore$ Velocity of the minute hand = Displacement/time

= 31.43 cm/10800 s = 0.00291 cm s^{-1}

(Note: In this particular case, since the tip's movement in the 3-hour duration forms an arc rather than a straight line, the speed and velocity have the same values.)

EXAMPLE 2.4

A car moving at a speed of 60 ms^{-1} slows down to 20 ms^{-1} in 4 seconds. Find its retardation.

SOLUTION

Initial velocity of the car, u = 60 m/s.

Final velocity of the car, v = 20 m/s.

Time taken by the car to slow down, t = 4 s

$\therefore$ Retardation of the car, $a = (v - \underline{u})/t = (20–60)/4 = -10\ ms^{-2}$.

Hence, retardation of the car = 10 m/s^2.

EXAMPLE 2.5

A motorbike accelerates uniformly at 6 ms^{-2} from rest. Find its velocity at the end of 3 seconds.

SOLUTION

Given the acceleration of the motorbike, a = 6 ms^{-2}.

Initial velocity of the motorbike, u = 0 ms^{-1}.

Time interval, t = 3 s.

$\therefore$ Final velocity of the motorbike, $v = u + at$

= 0 + (6)(3)

= 18 ms^{-1}.

Acceleration

A particle moving with variable velocity is said to possess acceleration. When a particle executes non-uniform motion, its velocity changes. **Acceleration** is defined as the rate of change of velocity. The unit of acceleration is cm s^{-2} in C.G.S. system and m s^{-2} in S.I. system.

$$\text{Acceleration} = \frac{\text{Change in velocity}}{\text{time}}$$

$$\text{Mathematically acceleration, } \vec{a} = \frac{\vec{v} - \vec{u}}{t}$$

where 'u' is the initial velocity, 'v' is the final velocity.

Considering only the rectilinear motion, we can replace the vector quantities by scalar quantities.

Thus, $$a = \frac{v - u}{t}$$

Konnect

Acceleration doesn't just mean speeding up; it can also refer to slowing down (deceleration) or changing direction.

EXAMPLE 2.6 A car moves along a straight path with variable velocity as shown in the figure. When the car is at position A, its velocity is 10 m s^{-1} and when it is at position B, its velocity is 20 m s^{-1}. If the car takes 5 seconds of time to move from A to B, find the acceleration of the car.

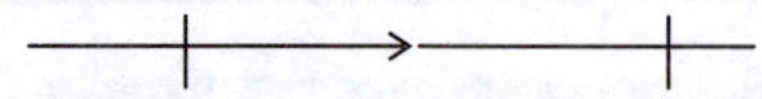

SOLUTION

Initial velocity of the car at position $A = u = 10 \text{ m s}^{-1}$

Final velocity of the car at position $B = v = 20 \text{ m s}^{-1}$

The change in velocity of the car, $\Delta v = v - u = 20 \text{ m s}^{-1} - 10 \text{ m s}^{-1}$

$= 10 \text{ m s}^{-1}$

The time taken for the car to move from A to B, $\Delta t = 5$ s

$\therefore$ Acceleration of the car, $a = \frac{\Delta v}{\Delta t} = \frac{10 \text{ m s}^{-1}}{5 \text{ s}}$

$= 2 \text{ m s}^{-2}$

EXAMPLE 2.7 The driver of a passenger train moving at a speed of 90 km h^{-1} observes a goods train at rest on the same track at a distance of 250 m and immediately applies the brakes. What should be the minimum retardation of the passenger train so as to avoid collision of the two trains?

SOLUTION

The initial velocity of the passenger train, $u = 90 \text{ km h}^{-1}$.

$$= 90 \times \frac{5}{18} \text{ m s}^{-1} = 25 \text{ m s}^{-1}.$$

The final velocity of the passenger train, $v = 0 \text{ m s}^{-1}$.

The distance that can be travelled by the passenger train in coming to rest position, s = 250 m.

Let 't' be the time taken by the passenger train to come to rest. Then, the total distance travelled by the train, s = (Average velocity)×(time).

$$\Rightarrow s = \left(\frac{v+u}{2}\right)t$$

$$\Rightarrow 250 = \left(\frac{0+25}{2}\right)t$$

$$\Rightarrow t = 20 \text{ s}$$

Let 'a' be the acceleration of the passenger train, then $a = \frac{v-u}{t}$

$$= \frac{0-25}{20} = \frac{-25}{20}$$

$$= -1.25 \text{ m s}^{-2}.$$

Hence, retardation of the passenger train is 1.25 m s^{-2}.

Equations of Motion

There are three important equations of motion, namely:

$$v = u + at$$

$$s = ut + \frac{1}{2}at^2$$

$$v^2 = u^2 + 2as$$

where 'u' is initial velocity, 'v' is final velocity, 'a' is uniform acceleration and 's' is the displacement of the body.

EXAMPLE 2.8 A train moving at a speed of 100 m s^{-1} comes to rest in 5 seconds. Find its retardation.

SOLUTION

Initial velocity of the train, u = 100 m s^{-1}.

Final velocity of the train, v = 0 m s^{-1}.

Time taken by the train to come to rest, t = 5 s

∴Acceleration of the train, $a = \frac{v-u}{t} = \frac{0-100}{5} = -20 \text{ m s}^{-2}$

Hence, retardation of the train = 20 m s^{-2}.

EXAMPLE 2.9 A car accelerates uniformly at 4 m s^{-2} from rest. Find its velocity at the end of 5 seconds.

SOLUTION

Given acceleration of the car, a = 4 m s^{-2}.

Initial velocity of the car, u = 0 m s^{-1}.

Time interval, t = 5 s.

∴ Final velocity of the car, $v = u + at$

$$= 0 + (4)\,(5)$$

$$= 20 \text{ m s}^{-1}$$

Konnect

1. Since velocity is a vector, acceleration is also a vector.
2. If the velocity of the particle increases with respect to time ($v > u$), the acceleration is said to be positive.
3. If the velocity of the particle decreases with respect to time, the acceleration is said to be negative, and is referred to as 'deceleration' or 'retardation'.
4. When the motion of a particle is such that there are equal changes in velocity in equal intervals of time, then it is said to be moving with 'uniform acceleration', e.g., a body falling under the influence of gravity.
5. The acceleration of a body falling under the influence of Earth's gravitational force is called 'acceleration due to gravity' and is represented by the letter 'g'.
6. The direction of the acceleration due to gravity is always downward (towards and normal to the surface of Earth). The magnitude of 'g' varies from place to place but is constant at a given place. The average value of 'g' at sea level is 9.8 m s^{-2} in S.I. system and 980 cm s^{-2} in C.G.S. system.
7. When a body moves with uniform acceleration, its average velocity can be calculated by using the expression, $V_{average} = \frac{u+v}{2}$ where 'u' and 'v' are its initial and final velocities for a given time interval.

Graphical Representation of Motion

Motion of a body can be represented by graphs. These give the visual representation of motion of the body. There are three types of graphs, namely $s - t$, $v - t$ and $a - t$ graphs. $s - t$ is displacement time or position time, $v - t$ is velocity time and $a - t$ is acceleration-time graph. Here, we discuss $s - t$ and $v - t$ graphs.

Displacement–Time Graph

In this graph, displacement is plotted along y-axis and time along x-axis.

Example:

Time in (s)	0	1	2	3	4	5
Displacement in (m)	0	5	10	15	20	25

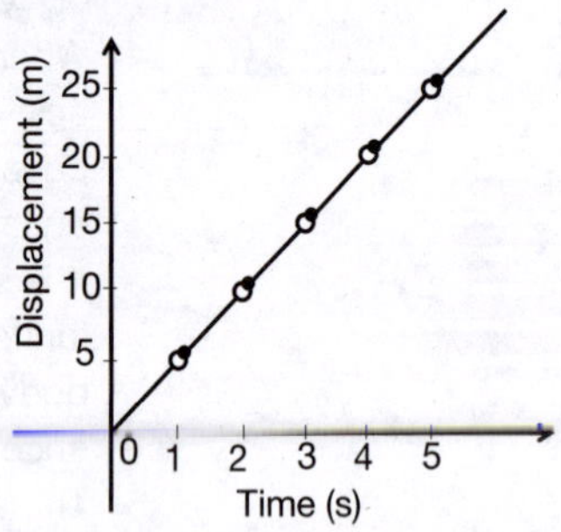

Figure 2.13 Graphical representation of data given in the above table

Info Bytes!

A straight, inclined line on a displacement-time graph indicates constant velocity, while a curve indicates acceleration.

Konnect

Equations of motion are applicable to a body moving with uniform acceleration.

Significance of Displacement—Time Graph

1. Displacement of a particle at any instant of time can be determined.
2. Nature of motion of the particle can be studied.
3. Slope of the graph at any point gives the instantaneous velocity of the body.

Velocity–Time Graph

If velocity is plotted along y-axis and time along x-axis, then the graph is called v–t graph.

Example:

Time (min)	0	1	2	3	4	5	6	7	8
Velocity (m s^{-1})	5	10	15	20	20	20	15	10	5

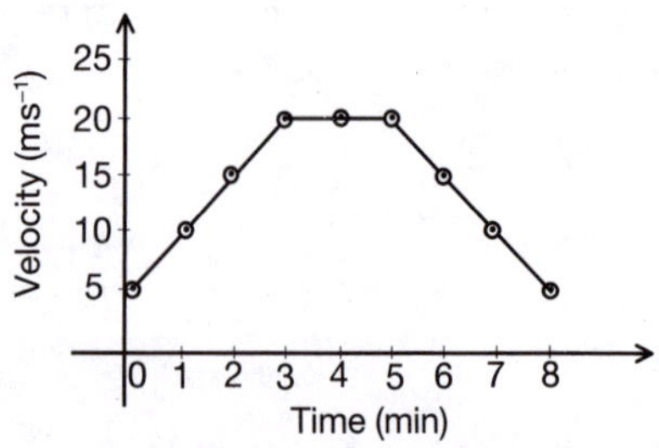

Figure 2.14 Graphical representation of data given in the above table

Significance of *V*—T Graph

1. Nature of motion of body can be determined.
2. Slope of the linear part of the curve gives the acceleration.
3. Area under the curve gives the displacement of the body.
4. Velocity at any instant can be found out.

Info Bytes!

The area under a velocity-time graph can be used to calculate the object's displacement.

POINTS TO REMEMBER

- ✔ Quantities that can be completely specified by means of a numerical value and a unit are called physical quantities.
- ✔ Quantities which are said to have only magnitude are called scalars.
- ✔ Physical quantities that can be defined only if both magnitude and direction are specified are called vectors.
- ✔ Distance is defined as the length of the actual path described by a particle in motion.
- ✔ Displacement is defined as the shortest distance between the initial and final positions of a body.
- ✔ Speed is defined as the rate at which a particle covers a distance along a given path.
- ✔ The speed of a particle at a given instant is known as instantaneous speed.
- ✔ A body or particle is said to possess uniform speed if it travels equal distances in equal intervals of time is called uniform speed.
- ✔ Average speed is defined as the ratio of the total distance travelled to the total time taken by the particle to cover that distance.
- ✔ Velocity is displacement of a body in unit time or rate of displacement.
- ✔ Average velocity is the ratio of total displacement to total time taken.
- ✔ The velocity of a particle at a given instant of time is called its instantaneous velocity.
- ✔ Acceleration is defined as the rate of change of velocity.

CLASSROOM WING

PRACTICE QUESTIONS

Very Short Answer Type Questions

Directions for questions 1 to 10:
Fill in the blanks.

1. If a body is moving with uniform velocity, then its acceleration is ________.

2. The average value of acceleration due to gravity at sea level is ______ m s^{-2}.

3. Speedometer of a vehicle measures its _____ speed.

4. The ratio of the total distance travelled by a body to the total time taken is known as its _____.

5. The slope of a displacement-time graph is _______.

6. A car attains a velocity of 20 m s^{-1} in 2.5 s. If initially it had been at rest, its acceleration must be ______.

7. Rate of decrease in the magnitude of velocity is also known as ______.

8. The displacement–time graph of a body is shown in the figure below. The part of the graph that represents the uniform motion of the body is _____ .

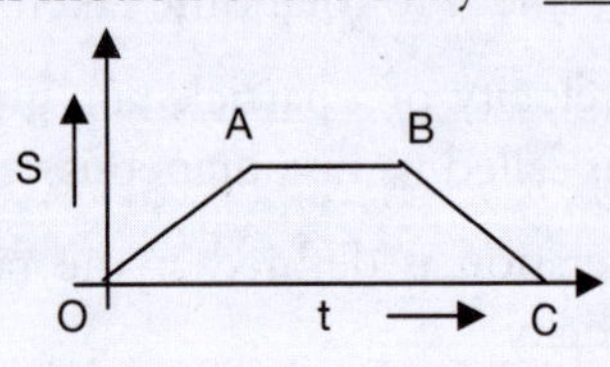

9. A bus moves by 8 m from its position of rest in 2 s, along a straight road. If it covers 10 m in the next second, it is moving with__________.

10. A body is moving in a straight path, then its instantaneous speed is _______ instantaneous velocity and its average speed is _______ its average velocity.

Directions for questions 11 to 25:
Answer the following questions.

11. Motion and rest are relative. How do you justify this?

12. You are walking towards India Gate. Is India Gate at rest with respect to you or in motion with respect to you?

13. Define scalar quantities and vector quantities. Give some examples.

14. A particle moved 5 m towards east and then moved 8 m towards west. What is the total distance travelled and the magnitude of displacement?

15. Define distance, displacement, speed, velocity and acceleration.

16. Why is displacement referred to as a vector quantity?

17. When does a particle in motion have uniform speed?

18. When does a particle in motion have non-uniform velocity?

19. What is instantaneous velocity?

20. Convert the following speeds into m s^{-1}.
    (a) 18 km h^{-1} (b) 63 km h^{-1}
    (c) 99 km h^{-1} (d) 108 km h^{-1}

21. Convert the following speeds into km h^{-1}.
    (a) 2 m s^{-1} (b) 10 m s^{-1}
    (c) 12.5 m s^{-1} (d) 15 m s^{-1}

22. What is the acceleration of a particle moving with uniform velocity?

23. A person on a rotating platform of radius 7 m, makes 3 rotations in 4 min. What is the magnitude of the displacement of the person (in m)?

24. What are the different types of graphs that can be drawn to represent the motion of a particle?

25. A person starts from his house on his bike at 9 a.m. and returns to his house at 8 p.m. If the odometer reading at 9 a.m. is 4700 km and the average speed of the bike is 20 km h^{-1}, then calculate the odometer reading of the bike at 8 p.m. in km.

Short Answer Type Questions

26. Explain briefly what is mechanics and mention the different branches of mechanics.

27. An athlete completes a running track of length 330 m in 40 s and comes back to his original position. Find the average velocity of the athlete.

28. A race horse runs straight north and covers a distance of 12 m, then turns east and travels a distance of 5 m. Draw the diagram showing the displacements and from the figure, calculate the net displacement of the horse.

29. Redraw the following figure to scale and find out the distance and displacement of a particle moving along the path $A - B - C - D$.

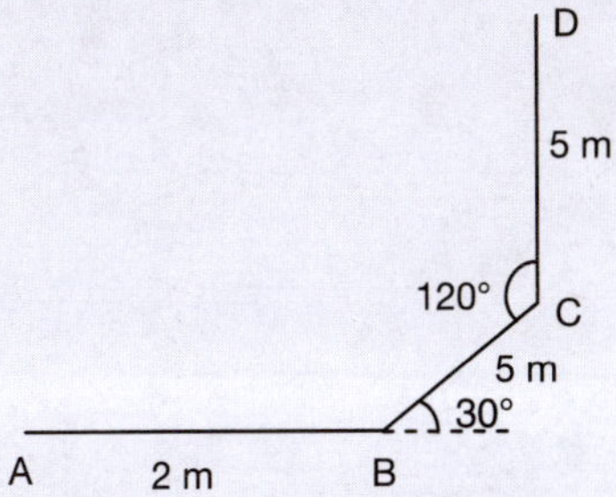

30. Tabulate the differences between distance and displacement.

31. A crow picks up pebbles and puts them into a pot which is 10 m away from the pot. In doing so, it makes 5 trips within 80 seconds. What is the average speed of the crow?

32. Differentiate between speed and velocity.

33. Write short notes on instantaneous speed and instantaneous velocity. Give examples.

34. Write short notes on uniform speed and uniform velocity. Give examples.

35. A bike starting from rest picks up a velocity of 72 km h^{-1} over a distance of 40 m. Calculate its acceleration.

36. Explain, with an example, how a particle moving with uniform speed has variable velocity.

37. A string of 5cm, fixed to a nail, had a pencil tied to other end. If the time taken to draw a semi circle and a complete circle with the pencil is 2 seconds and 4 seconds, respectively, find the speed and velocity
    (a) to draw semi circle.
    (b) to draw complete circle.

38. A bus starts from the rest and moves with a uniform acceleration 2 m s^{-2} for 10 s. What will be the average velocity of the bus?

39. A particle travelled along a semi-circular path $A - C - B$ as shown in the figure below. The radius of the semi-circular path is 7 m.

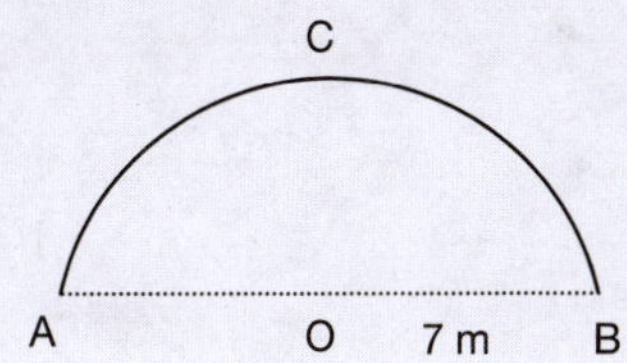

    (a) Find the distance travelled by the particle.
    (b) Find the displacement (magnitude and direction).
    (c) What would be these quantities if the particle completes the circle?

40. In the previous question, find the speed and velocity in each case if the time taken
    (a) to travel from A to B is 11 s.
    (b) to complete the circle is 22 s.

41. What are the different branches of mechanics?

42. A ball is rolling with a velocity 20 m s^{-1} on a cement floor and stops in 10 s. What is the acceleration produced by the ball?

43. A fan blade of length 1/3 m moving with uniform velocity makes 1000 rotations in 20 s. Calculate the average velocity of the fan at the end of 20 s.

Essay Answer Type Questions

44. A toy car moves along the length and breadth of a rectangle as shown in the figure given below. If the length of the rectangle is 4 m, then find the ratio of displacement to distance covered by the car.

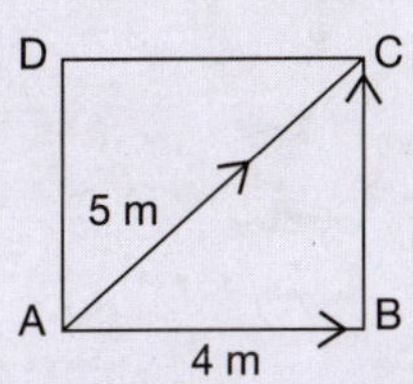

45. A cyclist moves the first-half of the distance with 10 km h^{-1} speed and the second-half of the distance with speed V km h^{-1}. If the average speed of the cycle is 15 km h^{-1}, then calculate the value of V in km h^{-1}.

46. A particle moving along a straight line has instantaneous velocities during the first 5 seconds as given below. Draw a velocity–time graph.

Time (t) (in s)	0	1	2	3	4	5
Velocity (v) (in m s^{-1})	0	2.5	5	7.5	10	12.5

47. Draw a displacement–time graph for the data given below with respect to a particle moving in a straight line.

Time (t) (in s)	0	1	2	3	4
Displacement(s) (in m)	0	5	20	45	80

48. In the previous question, calculate the acceleration in each time interval and plot acceleration–time graph. Does the particle have uniform velocity or uniform acceleration?

COMPETITION WING

PRACTICE QUESTIONS

Level 1: Apply your Concepts

Directions for questions 1 to 12:
State whether the following statements are true or false

1. Statics and dynamics are different branches of mechanics.
2. A branch that deals with motion of bodies without considering the cause of motion is called statics.
3. An arrow head is used to represent scalar quantities.
4. The length of the line in geometrical representation of a vector signify magnitude of vector.
5. A body is first displaced by 5 m and then by 12 m in different directions. The minimum displacement it can have is 7.
6. Uniform speed is a vector quantity.
7. For a body moving along a circular path the average velocity and average speed can never be equal.
8. A body can have constant speed and still have varying velocity.
9. The magnitude of average velocity is always equal to the average speed.
10. Velocity–time graph cannot be used to find instantaneous velocity.
11. Average velocity can be calculated by taking the average of initial and final velocities for a given time interval irrespective of type of acceleration.
12. The travel of a train from one station to another is an example of translatory motion.

Directions for questions 13 to 19:
Fill in the blanks

13. An aeroplane is moving with a uniform velocity of 800 km h^{-1}, then its instantaneous velocity will be _____ the average velocity. Hence, its acceleration is equal to _______.
14. The ratio of the total displacement of a body to the total time taken is ______.
15. The velocity–time graph of a body moving with uniform velocity is a straight line parallel to ________.
16. A body moving with constant speed has zero acceleration only when the particle is in ______ dimensional motion.
17. The average speed of a bus in its whole journey when it travels a given distance between two places with a speed of 20 km hr^{-1} and returns back with a speed of 12 km hr^{-1} is ________.
18. When a body has unequal displacements in equal intervals of time, it is said to be moving with ______.
19. When a particle moves in a straight line from point A to point B the distance covered is ________ the magnitude of the displacement.

Direction for question 20:
Match the entries given in Column A with appropriate ones in Column B.

20. Match the statements of Column A with those of Column B.

Column A	Column B
(A) Uniform velocity derived quantity	(a) Total distance ÷ time
(B) Average speed	(b) m s^{-2}
(C) Average velocity	(c) Acceleration is zero
(D) Acceleration	(d) Ratio of total displacement to total time taken

Directions for questions 21 to 50:
For each of the questions, four choices have been provided. Select the correct alternative.

21. Which of the following graphs is not possible with respect to the velocity-time graph?

(a) 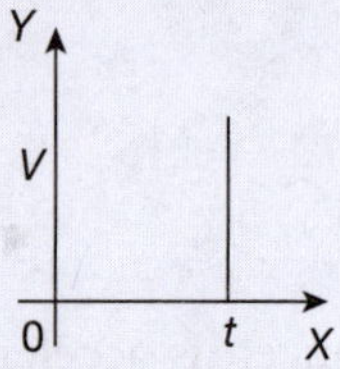

(b) 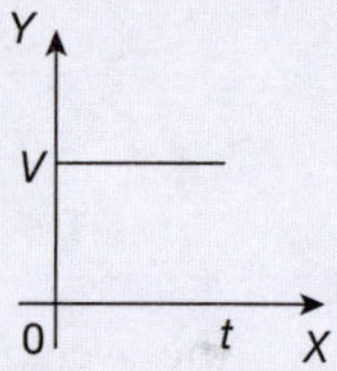

(c) 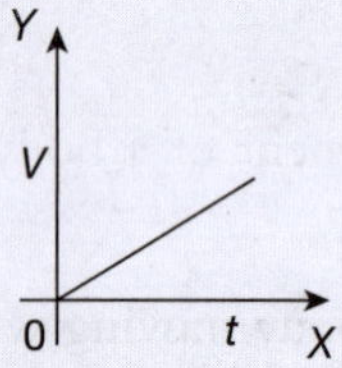

(d) 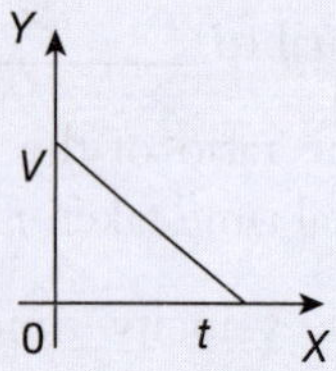

21. Two persons X and Y take 10 hours and 12 hours, respectively to travel from Bangalore to Hyderabad, then the

(a) average velocity of X is equal to the average velocity of Y.
(b) average velocity of X is less than that of Y.
(c) average velocity of X is more than that of Y.
(d) We cannot compare their velocities.

22. A car starting from rest traveling along a straight path with uniform acceleration covers S_1, S_2, and S_3 distances in the first, second and third seconds of its travel.

Then, the ratio of $\frac{(S_2 - S_1)}{(S_3 - S_2)}$ is ______.

(a) 3 : 5 (b) 1 : 2
(c) 1 : 3 (d) 1 : 1

23. The displacement–time graph of a body is shown in the figure below.

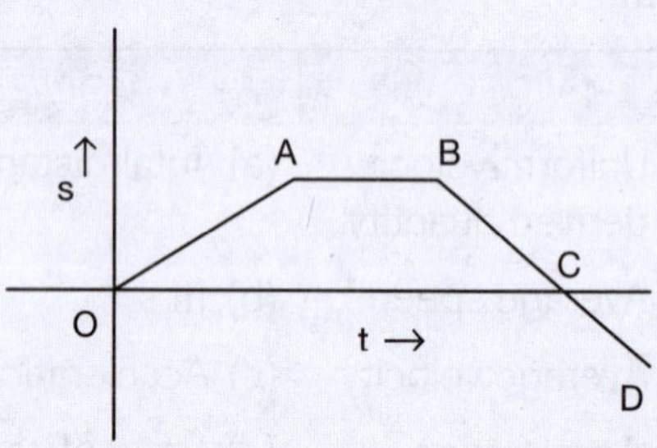

The part of the graph that represents the body at rest is :

(a) OA (b) AB
(c) BC (d) CD

24. A body is first displaced by 5 m and then by 12 m in different directions. The minimum displacement it can have is ______ m.

(a) 0 (b) 17
(c) 7 (d) 13

25. A person, seated in a bus at rest, is at rest with reference to

(a) the bus.
(b) a jeep moving in the opposite direction to the bus.
(c) the trees on the ground.
(d) both (a) and (c).

26. A body starting from rest and travelling along a straight line with an acceleration of 6 m s^{-2}, then the distance traveled by it in the 3rd second is ______ m.

(a) 27 (b) 18
(c) 15 (d) 21

27. A body starts from rest and moves along a straight line path with uniform acceleration. The ratio of velocities at t = 1s and t = 2 s is ______.

(a) 2 : 1 (b) 1 : 2
(c) $1 : \sqrt{2}$ (d) $\sqrt{2} : 1$

28. A body undergoes a displacement of 3 m in the 1st second, 4 m in the 2nd second, 5 m in the 3rd second and so on. The body is moving with a:

(a) uniform velocity
(b) uniform acceleration
(c) uniform deceleration
(d) None of these

29. 45 km h^{-1} = ______ m s^{-1}.

(a) 162 (b) 12.5
(c) 2.5 (d) 75

30. A body moving from its initial position of rest along a straight line covers 1 m in 1 s. If it covers 8 m in the next 2 s, then the body is moving with ______.

(a) uniform velocity
(b) an acceleration of 2 m s^{-2} in the first second
(c) average acceleration of 2 m s^{-2} from t = 1 s to 3 s
(d) both (b) and (c).

31. The ratio of average velocity to average speed is always ______ one.

(a) greater than
(b) less than or equal to

(c) greater than or equal to

(d) less than

32. The speedometer of a vehicle indicates its ________.

(a) instantaneous speed.

(b) average speed.

(c) instantaneous velocity.

(d) average velocity.

33. The ratio of distances traveled by two bodies A and B starting from rest moving along a straight line with equal accelerations is x, where $x \geq 1$, then

(a) time taken by body A > time taken by body B.

(b) time taken by body A < time taken by body B.

(c) time taken by body A ≥ time taken by body B.

(d) time taken by body A ≤ time taken by body B.

34. When a body moves with uniform velocity then

(a) it has zero acceleration.

(b) it moves along a straight line path.

(c) average velocity = instantaneous velocity.

(d) All the above

35. The velocity–time graph of a certain body is shown in the following graph. The part of the graph that shows deceleration of the body is

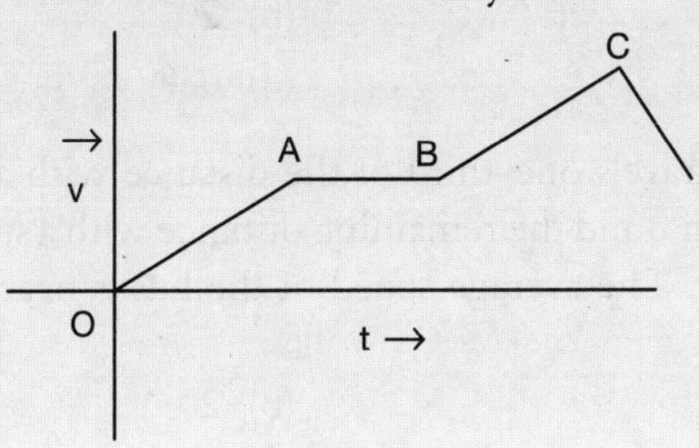

(a) OA (b) AB

(c) BC (d) CD

36. A body is moving along the curve ABC as shown in the figure and the initial and final positions are A and C, respectively. Displacement is the line joining

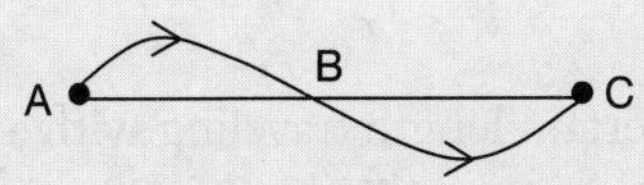

(a) initial and final position of the body.

(b) midpoint (B) and final position of the body.

(c) midpoint (B) and initial position of the body.

(d) Both (b) and (c)

37. A boy throws a ball vertically upwards and catches it after 2 seconds. Which of the following is true regarding the motion of the ball?

(i) The displacement is zero.

(ii) Magnitude of acceleration is constant.

(a) Only (i) is true.

(b) Only (ii) is true.

(c) Both (i) and (ii) are true.

(d) Both (i) and (ii) are false.

38. If a sports car at rest accelerates uniformly to a speed of 144 km h^{-1} in 5 s, it covers a distance of _____ m.

(a) 100 (b) 140

(c) 60 (d) 80

39. A hockey player hits the ball moving with a speed of 50 m s^{-1} in the same direction. Because of this, the velocity increases to 60 m s^{-1} in 0.1 s. Arrange the following steps in sequential order to calculate the acceleration of the ball.

(A) Find the initial velocity of the ball and the velocity of the ball at the end of 0.1 s after it is being hit.

(B) Write down the required equation of motion as $v = u + at$, where v, u, a and t are final velocity, initial velocity, acceleration and time, respectively.

(C) Substitute the given values in the above equation and obtain the value of a.

(D) Get the value of a as $\dfrac{v-u}{t}$

(a) BACD (b) BDAC

(c) ABCD (d) ABDC

40. The driver of a car moving with a velocity of 54 km h^{-1} applies brakes to decrease its velocity to 36 km h^{-1}. If the retardation produced by the brakes is 2.0 m s^{-2}, arrange the following steps in a sequential order to calculate the distance travelled by the car.

(A) Write down the required equation of motion as $v^2 - u^2 = 2as$ where v, u, a and s are final velocity, initial velocity, retardation and displacement, respectively.

(B) Write down the given data and convert all the values into the same system of unit.

(C) Get the value of 's' as $\dfrac{v^2-u^2}{2a}$

(D) Substitute the given values in the above equation.

(a) A B D C (b) B A C D

(c) A D B C (d) A B C D

41. **Assertion (A):** A body may have velocity and displacement in the opposite directions.

Reason (R): Velocity is distance travelled by the body in a unit time.

(a) A and R are correct and R is the correct explanation for A

(b) A and R are correct but R is not the correct explanation for A

(c) A is correct but R is incorrect.

(d) Both A and R are incorrect.

42. The $\vec{s}$ - t graph of a body is as shown in the figure. The time for which the body is in motion is ______ second.

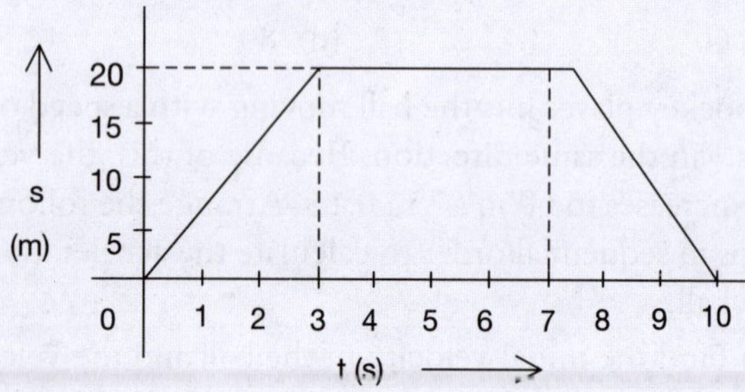

(a) 2 (b) 3

(c) 6 (d) 10

43. The motion of a body is depicted graphically as shown in the figure. The average speed of the body is __________ m s^{-1}.

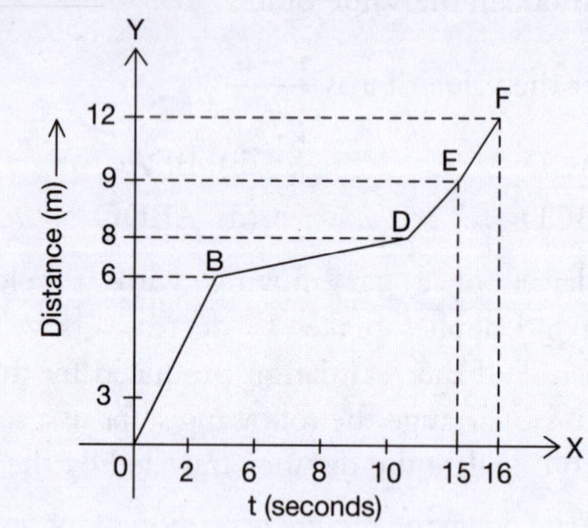

(a) 3/4 (b) 9/8

(c) 4/3 (d) 8/9

44. An object moves the first half of the total distance with a speed of 2 m s^{-1}. If the average speed of the body is 3 m s^{-1}, the speed of the body when it travelled the remaining distance is __________ m s^{-1}.

(a) 3 (b) 6

(c) 4 (d) 2

45. An electric fan rotates 100 times in 50 s. If the length of its wing from its axis of rotation is 0.5 m, then the speed of particle at the edge of the wing is ______ m s^{-1}.

(a) 2π (b) 0.5π

(c) π (d) 2

46. A person starts from a point P and travels along a path PQRP as shown in the figure. Then, the speed of the person is __________ m s^{-1}.

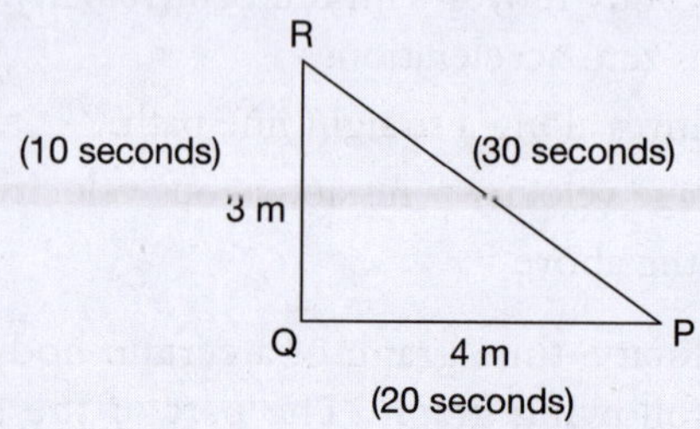

(a) 0.2 (b) 20

(c) 12 (d) 0.4

47. A bus travels one-third of the distance with a speed of 12 km h^{-1} and the remaining distance with a speed of 20 km h^{-1}. The average speed of the bus is nearly________ km h^{-1}.

(a) 14 (b) 20

(c) 12 (d) 16

Level 2: Review your Concepts

48. A car is moving at 120 km h^{-1}. On seeing a speed breaker, the driver applies the brakes and stops the car in 4 seconds. What is the value of the deceleration produced in the car?

49. A bus moving along a straight highway with a speed of 72 km h^{-1} is brought to rest within a distance of 50 m. How long does it take for the bus to stop?

50. A train of certain length traveling with a uniform speed of 36 km h^{-1} crosses a bridge of 600 m in 80 s. Find the length of the train.

51. The length of a minute hand of a clock is 3 cm. Find the average velocity of the tip of the minute hand when it moves during a time interval from 4:00 p.m. to 4:15 p.m.

52. Give examples of variable velocity, when
   (a) the magnitude is constant and the direction is changing.
   (b) the magnitude is changing and the direction remains the same.
   (c) both the magnitude and direction are changing.

53. The distance between two places A and B is 180 km by road and 120 km by air. An aeroplane takes 20 min to go from A to B whereas a deluxe bus starting at A takes 5 h to reach B. Find the average speed and average velocity by both means of transport. (Ignore the vertical ascent of aeroplane).

54. A car starting from rest and moving with uniform acceleration on a straight road travels for sometime such that the paths described by it in the last second and in the penultimate second of its motion are in the ratio 4 : 3, respectively. Calculate the total time traveled by the body.

55. On a 60 km stretch of road a cyclist travels first 20 km at a uniform speed of 20 km h^{-1}. How fast must he travel the remaining distance so that his average speed is 10 km h^{-1} for the entire trip?

56. A car starting from rest and moving along a straight path with uniform acceleration covers distances p and q in the first two successive equal intervals of time. Find the ratio of p to q.

57. A bus starts from rest and moves with an acceleration of 5 m s^{-2}. A man who is on a motorcycle, 24 m behind the bus, overtakes the bus in 2 s. If the motorcyclist moves with uniform velocity, find his velocity.

58. The dimensions (measurements) of a hall are 12 m, 4 m and 3 m, respectively. An ant starts at one corner of the hall, travels only along the edges and reaches a diagonally opposite corner, taking the shortest possible route. Find the distance travelled by the ant and its magnitude of displacement.

59. A car takes 25 s to stop after the application of brakes. What is the distance traveled by the car if the brakes produce a uniform retardation of 0.4 m s^{-2}?

60. A bus starts moving with uniform acceleration from its position of rest. It moves 48 m in 4 s. On applying the brakes, it stops after covering 24 m. Find the deceleration of the bus.

61. A bus traveling along a straight highway covers one-third of the total distance between two places with a velocity 20 km h^{-1}. The remaining part of the distance was covered with a velocity of 30 km h^{-1} for the first half of the remaining time and with velocity 50 km h^{-1} for the next half of the time. Find the average velocity of the bus for its whole journey.

62. A particle starts from rest and moves with a constant acceleration along a straight path to attain 64 m s^{-1} in t s. If at $t = (t + 3)$s the speed is 76 m s^{-1}, then find the acceleration of the particle and 't'.

Level 3: Assess Your Concepts

63. A car travels the first hour with 50 km h^{-1} and the second hour with 100 km h^{-1}. What is the average speed of the car?

64. A body travels 100 m in 10 s. Then out of A and B which is/are true?
   (A) the average velocity of the body is 10 m s^{-1} only when the body travels in a straight path.
   (B) the average speed of the body is 10 m s^{-1} irrespective of its direction of motion.

65. In the figure shown, explain the difference between $\overrightarrow{DE}$ and $\overrightarrow{ED}$.

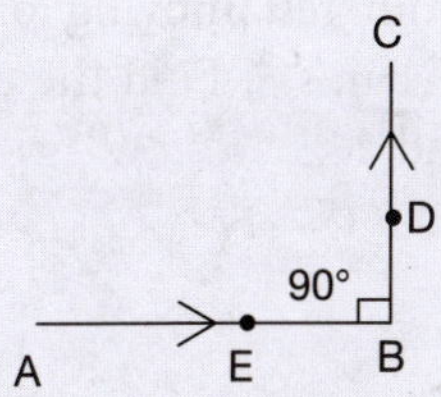

66. A police man is running with a uniform speed of 5 km h^{-1} and a thief is running with a uniform speed of 2 km h^{-1}. Is it possible to find whether the policeman can catch the thief? Explain.

67. An object moves along the path ABC as shown in the figure. Determine the displacement.

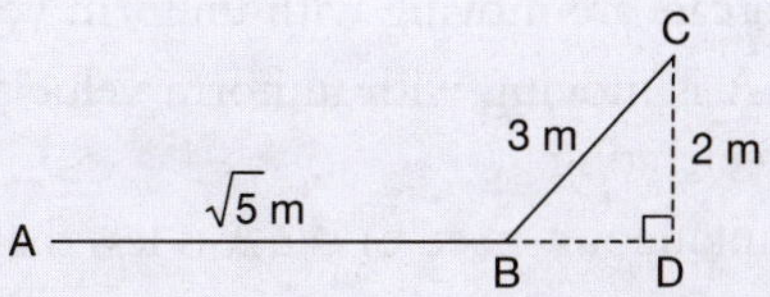

68. A policeman is running with a uniform velocity of 5 km h^{-1} towards east and a thief is running with a uniform velocity of 2 km h^{-1} towards east. Is it possible for the policeman to catch the thief? Explain

69. A car moving with a constant acceleration covers 24 m in 4 s and 21 m in the next 2 s. What is the initial velocity of the car?

70. A boy kicks a football horizontally from the roof of a building of height 6 m. If the line joining the initial position of the football and the point where it hits the ground makes an angle of 45° with the ground, then calculate the displacement of the football.

71. A pencil is tied to one end of a string of length 5 cm and the other is fixed to a nail. If the time taken to draw a half circle and a full circle with the pencil is 2 and 4 seconds, respectively, find the speed and velocity of the pencil,

(a) when half circle is drawn.

(b) when full circle is drawn.

72. A cylinder of radius 0.8 m starts rolling on horizontal surface with velocity 0.5 m s^{-1}. When the cylinder starts from rest, simultaneously an insect starts crawling from one end of the diameter to another end in a straight-line path with velocity 2 mm s^{-1}. Find the distance covered by the cylinder when the insect reaches the other end of the diameter.

73. A bullet train in Japan starting from rest accelerates uniformly at 0.5 m s^{-2} for 2 minutes. It then maintains uniform speed for 20 minutes and then retards uniformly at the rate of 0.25 m s^{-2} and comes to rest. Calculate the average speed of the train.

74. A car A has just overtaken car B which is moving in the same direction as A. Given below are few cases explaining the motion of the cars at that instant. Identify the given cases as cases that are necessarily true, cases that can be true only under certain conditions and cases that are necessarily false.

(a) The car A is accelerating and car B is decelerating.

(b) The car A is decelerating and car B is accelerating.

(c) Both cars are accelerating.

(d) Both cars are decelerating.

(e) Both cars are moving with uniform velocity.

(f) Car A is moving with uniform velocity and car B is accelerating.

(g) Instantaneous speed of car A is less than that of car B.

(h) Instantaneous speed of car B is less than that of car A.

75. A car starts moving with uniform acceleration from its position of rest and it moves 100 m in 10 s. On applying brakes, it stops after covering 50 m. Then calculate the magnitude of acceleration in the second part of its motion.

76. A vertically placed rod of length 5 m falls on the horizontal surface in 2 seconds. Find the speed and velocity of the centre of the rod.

77. An ant is moving on a straight line drawn on the paper obtained from velocity-time graph of a car starting from rest and travelswith acceleration 5 m s^{-2} for 5 seconds. Find the time taken by the ant to move from one end of the graph to another end if it moves with uniform velocity of 1 mm s^{-1} (Take 1 cm as 1 sec on x–axis and 1 cm as 10 m s^{-1} on y – axis).

78. A passenger is at a distance 10 m from a bus when the bus starts with a constant acceleration of 0.1 m s^{-2}. Then calculate the velocity with which the passenger should run towards the bus so as to catch the bus in 30 s.

79. A rod of length 2 m starts to roll on a horizontal surface as shown in figure. At the same time an ant starts moving from one end (A) of the rod to other and when the rod rolls through a distance 10 m the ant reaches the other end (B). Calculate the distance and displacement of the ant

(a) with respect to the rod.

(b) with respect to the ground.

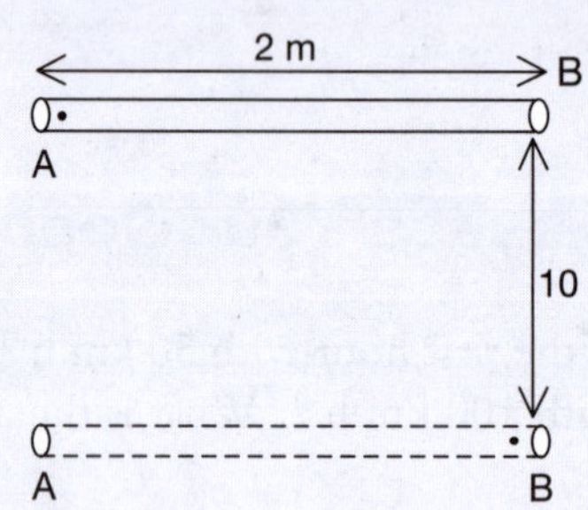

80. A person is running perpendicular to the straight railway track from 40 m distance to save a dog sleeping on the railway track at a place exactly opposite to the person. Find the minimum uniform velocity required by the person to save the dog if the distance of the front part of a train is 50 m from the person when he is at a distance of 30 m from dog and velocity of the train is 36 km h^{-1}.

81. A car started from rest moving on the straight road accelerates with 1 m s^{-2}. Find the displacement of the car in 36th second.

JEE-NEET SPECIAL WING

PRACTICE QUESTIONS

Multiple-Answer Type Questions

Directions for questions 1 to 5:
Select one or more correct alternative(s) from the given choices.

1. Which of the following are scalar quantities?
   (a) Force (b) Density
   (c) Displacement (d) Temperature

2. Given below is the velocity - time graph of a body which represents

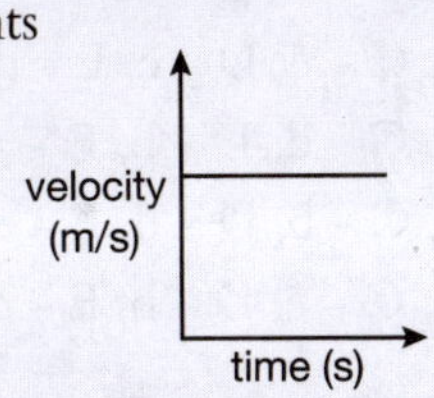

   (a) Uniform acceleration
   (b) Uniform velocity
   (c) Negative acceleration
   (d) Zero acceleration

3. Which of the following is/are incorrect statements with respect to velocity - time graph?
   (a) Nature of motion of the body can be determined.
   (b) Slope of the linear portion of the curve gives acceleration.
   (c) Area under the curve gives velocity of the body.
   (d) Distance at any instant point of time can be found.

4. The velocity of the car that accelerates uniformly at the rate of 3 m s^{-2} from rest, at the end of 7 seconds is (in m s^{-1})
   (a) 15 m s^{-1} (b) 21 m s^{-1}
   (c) 54 km h^{-1} (d) 75.6 km h^{-1}

5. An athlete is running in a circular track of radius 5 m. If he completes one full revolution, then
   (a) distance = 3.14 m (b) distance = 31.4 m
   (c) displacement = 10 m (d) displacement = zero

Comprehension-Based Questions

Directions for questions 6 to 10:
These questions are based on the following information.

Arnav is driving his car. For the first 4 seconds he increases the speed and thereafter he maintains the speed for the next 8 seconds. Afterwards, he decreased the speed for the next 6 seconds. The velocity - time graph for the motion of the car is given below.

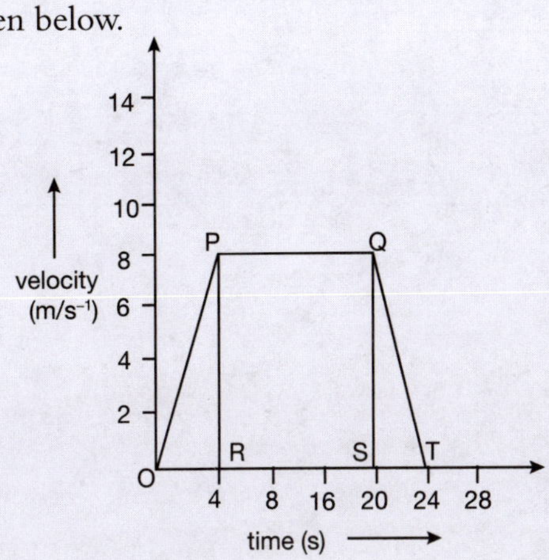

6. What type of motion is represented by OP?
   (a) Uniform acceleration
   (b) Uniform deceleration
   (c) Uniform velocity
   (d) Zero acceleration

7. For the motion of the car from O to P, its acceleration is (in m s^{-2})
   (a) 1.33
   (b) 1.56
   (c) 2
   (d) 2.11

8. The acceleration for the motion represented by PQ in the graph is (in m s^{-2})
   (a) 0.66
   (b) 1.33
   (c) 2
   (d) zero

9. The distance travelled by the car in 24 seconds is (in m)
   (a) 140
   (b) 160
   (c) 186
   (d) 204

10. The average speed with which the car moves from O to T is (in m s^{-1})
   (a) 3.32
   (b) 4.65
   (c) 5.48
   (d) 6.66

Match the Column

Directions for question 11:
The question is based on the following information.
Graphical representation of motion
Graphical representation of motion of an object gives a visual representation of motion. In the graphical representation, the independent quantity is taken along the *x*-axis and dependent quantity is taken along the y - axis. There are three types of graphs mainly to represent motion as displacement - time graph, velocity - time graph, and acceleration - time graph. The velocity - time graph for certain motions are given below:

11. Match the values in List - I with those in List - II:

List - I	List - II
A. Uniform motion	a. 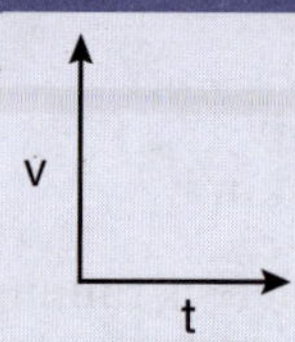
B. Uniformly accelerated motion	b. 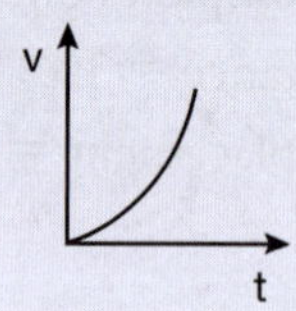
C. Uniformly decelerated motion	c. 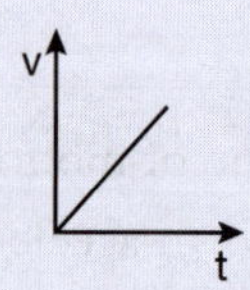
D. Non - uniformly accelerated motion	d. 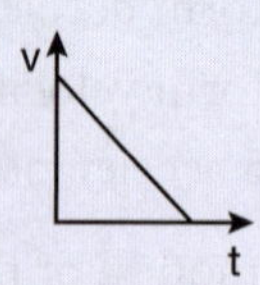
E. Object at rest	e. 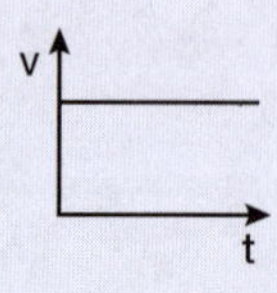

(a) A - b, B - a, C - e, D - c, E - d
(b) A - e, B - c, C - d, D - b, E - a
(c) A - a, B c, C b, D d, E - e
(d) A - d, B - a, C - e, D - b, E - c

ANSWER KEYS

Crossword

Across

4. Odometer
5. Displacement
7. Scalar
9. Dynamics
10. Instantaneous velocity

Down

1. Retardation
2. Velocity
3. Average velocity
6. Distance
8. Vector

Classroom Wing

Very Short Answer Type Questions

1. Velocity per unit time
2. $g = 9.8 \text{ m s}^{-2}$
3. Instantaneous
4. Average speed
5. Slope indicates velocity
6. 8 ms^{-2}
7. Retardation
8. OA and BC
9. 4 m/Sec^2
10. Equal to, equal to
23. Zero
25. 4920

Short Answer Type Questions

27. 0 ms^{-1}
28. 13 m along N.E
31. 1.25 m s^{-1}
35. 5 m s^{-2}
37. (a) $\frac{5\pi}{2}$ cm s^{-1}, 5 cm s^{-1} (b) $\frac{5\pi}{2}$ cm s^{-1}, zero.
38. 10 ms^{-2}
39. 22 m, 14 m $\overrightarrow{AB}$, 44 m, zero.
44. Place last line from the word file given
40. 2 m s^{-1}, $\frac{14}{11}$ m s^{-1} $\overrightarrow{AB}$, 2 m s^{-1}, zero
42. -2 ms^{-2}
43. $=0/t = 0$

Essay Answer Type Questions

44. $\frac{5}{7}$
45. 30 km $\text{h}^{-1} = v$

Competition Wing

Level 1: Apply your Concepts

1. True
2. False
3. False
4. True
5. True
6. False
7. True
8. True
9. False
10. False
11. False
12. True
13. Equal to Average velocity, zero
14. Average velocity
15. x-axis
16. One
17. 15 km h^{-1}
18. Non-uniform velocity
19. Equal to
20. A : c, B : a, C : d, D : b
21. (a)
22. (d)
23. (b)
24. (c)
25. (d)
26. (c)
27. (b)
28. (b)
29. (b)
30. (d)
31. (b)
32. (a)
33. (c)
34. (d)
35. (d)
36. (a)
37. (c)
38. (a)
39. (d)
40. (c)
41. (c)
42. (c)
43. (a)
44. (b)
45. (a)
46. (a)
47. (d)

Level 2: Review your Concepts

48. 25/3 ms^2
49. t = 5 s
50. 200 m
51. 0.00471 cm s^{-1}
53. 540 km h^{-1}, 360 km h^{-1}, 36 km h^{-1}, 24 km h^{-1}
54. n = 4.5
55. 8 km h^{-1}
56. $\frac{p}{q} = \frac{1}{3}$
57. 17 m s^{-1}
59. 125 m
60. 12 m s^{-2}
61. 30 km h^{-1}
62. 4m s^{-2}, 16s

Level 3 : Assess Your Concepts

63. 75 km^{-1}
64. Both (A) and (B) are true
67. $\sqrt{24}$ m
69. 3 m s^{-1}
70. $6\sqrt{2}$ m
71. (a) $\frac{5\pi}{2}$ cm s^{-1}, 5 cm s^{-1} (b) $\frac{5}{4}$ m s^{-1}, 0
72. 400 m
73. 53.07 m s^{-1}
75. 4 ms^{-2}
76. 1.96 m s^{-1}, 1.77 m s^{-1}
77. 56 seconds
78. 1.83 m s^{-1}
79. 2 m, 2m, 12 m, $\sqrt{104}$ m
80. 7.5 m s^{-1}
81. 35.5 m

JEE-NEET Special Wing

Multiple-Answer Type Questions

1. (b) and (d)
2. (b) and (d)
3. (c) and (d)
4. (b) and (d)
5. (b) and (d)

Comprehension-Based Questions

6. (a)
7. (c)
8. (d)
9. (b)
10. (d)

Match the Column

11. (b)

For answer key of Classroom wing and Competition wing, refer to Hints and Solutions

Hints and Explanations

Classroom Wing

Very Short Answer Type Questions

1. Because acceleration is the change in velocity per unit time.

2. $g = 9.8\ m\ s^{-2}$

3. instantaneous

4. Average speed.

5. In the displacement-time graph, the slope indicates velocity.

6. $a = \frac{v-u}{t}$

   substituting $V = 20\ m\ s^{-1}$, $u = 0$, $t = 2.5$ s

   $a = \frac{20-0}{2.5} = \frac{200}{25} = 8\ m\ s^{-2}$

7. Retardation

8. OA part of displacement–time graph represents uniform velocity in positive direction while BC part of the graph represents uniform velocity in opposite direction.

9. 4 m/Sec^2

10. When a body is moving in a straight path, then its instantaneous speed is equal to instantaneous velocity and its average speed is equal to its average velocity.

11. Two persons in a moving train are at rest with respect to each other but under motion to a person outside the train.

12. In motion

13. Quantity that has only magnitude—scalar.

    Quantity that has magnitude as well as direction—vector.

14. 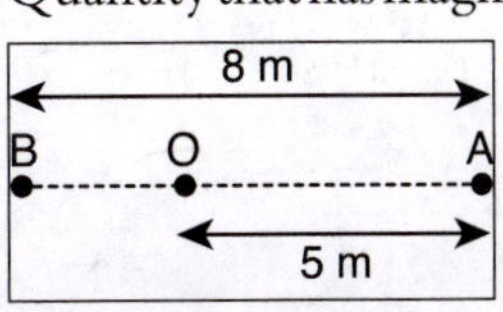

    Distance = 5 + 8 = 13 m

    Displacement = 8 – 5 = 3 m towards west.

15. The total length of the path travelled in a given time is Distance.

    The shortest distance travelled in a given time is Displacement.

    Rate of change of distance is speed

    Rate of change of displacement is velocity

    Rate of change of velocity is acceleration

16. Displacement has magnitude as well as direction.

17. When a body covers equal distances in equal intervals of time, however small the intervals of time may be.

18. When a body covers unequal displacements in equal intervals of time.

19. Rate of change of displacement such that the $\Delta t \to 0$

20. (1) $5\ m\ s^{-1}$

    (2) $17.5\ m\ s^{-1}$

    (3) $27.5\ m\ s^{-1}$

    (4) $30\ m\ s^{-1}$

21. (1) $7.2\ km\ h^{-1}$ (2) $36\ km\ h^{-1}$

    (3) $45\ km\ h^{-1}$ (4) $54\ km\ h^{-1}$

22. Zero

23. As the person comes to the same position after 4 rotations, the displacement is zero.

24. $s - t$, $v - t$, $a - t$

25. Given: $t_1 = 9$ a.m.; $t_2 = 8$ p.m.

    $\Rightarrow \otimes\ T = t_2 - t_1 = 11$ h

    Distance travelled; s = ?

    Average speed, $v = 20\ km\ h^{-1}$

    $v = \frac{s}{t}$

    $s = v \cdot t = 20 \cdot 11 = 220$ km

    Odometer reading at 8 p.m. is

    $\therefore$ 4700 + 220 = 4920.

Short Answer Type Questions

Note: This is how you should frame your answer covering.

26. (i) Branch of physics dealing with the effect of forces on bodies.

    (ii) Statics, dynamics.

27. $l = 330$ m

    $t = 40$ s

    $$\text{Average velocity}, \vec{V} = \frac{\text{Total displacment } (\vec{S})}{\text{Total time taken } (t)}$$

Here, the athlete comes back to his original position. So,

$$\vec{S} = 0$$

$$\Rightarrow \vec{V} = \frac{0}{40s} = 0 \text{ ms}^{-1}$$

28. Displacement is the shortest path from the initial to final positions.

13 m along N.E.

29. Distance depends on the path; displacement depends on the initial and final positions.

30. Distance

(i) Scalar.

(ii) Depends on path traced by the particle.

Displacement

(i) Vector.

(ii) Independent of path traced by the particle.

(iii) Depends on initial and final positions.

(iv) Shortest distance between initial and final positions.

31. Average speed $= \dfrac{\text{Total distance}}{\text{Total time}}$

1.25 m s^{-1}

32. Speed

(i) Scalar

(ii) $\dfrac{\text{Distance travelled}}{\text{Time}}$

Velocity

(i) Vector

(ii) $\dfrac{\text{Displacement}}{\text{Time}}$

33. (i) Speed of a particle at a given instant of time.

(ii) Speedometer.

(iii) Velocity of a particle at a given instant of time.

(iv) Direction of instantaneous velocity is along the tangent to the path at that instant.

34. (i) Equal distances in equal intervals of time.

(ii) Instantaneous speed remains same throughout the motion.

(iii) Equal displacements in equal intervals of time.

35. Use $v^2 = u^2 + 2as$

$a = 5 \text{ m s}^{-2}$

36. (i) Circular motion—a ceiling fan.

(ii) Magnitude of velocity, i.e., speed is constant.

(iii)Direction of motion changes continuously.

37. Speed $= \dfrac{\text{Distance}}{\text{Time}}$

Velocity $= \dfrac{\text{Displacement}}{\text{Time}}$

(a) $\dfrac{5\pi}{2}$ cm s^{-1}, 5 cm s^{-1}.

(b) $\dfrac{5\pi}{2}$ cm s^{-1}, zero.

38. Given: $u = 0$: $a = 2$ m s^{-2}: $t = 10$ s

$V = u + at = 0 + 2 \times 10 = 20$ m s^{-1}

$$\therefore \text{ Average velocity} = \frac{u+v}{2} = \frac{0+20}{2} = 10 \text{ ms}^{-1}.$$

39. Distance = length of the path.

Displacement = the shortest straight line path.

22 m, 14 m $\overrightarrow{AB}$, 44 m, zero.

40. Speed $= \dfrac{\text{Distance}}{\text{Time}}$

Velocity $= \dfrac{\text{Displacement}}{\text{Time}}$

2 m s^{-1}, $\dfrac{14}{11}$ m s^{-1} $\overrightarrow{AB}$, 2 m s^{-1}, zero.

41. Statics, Dynamics.

42. Given: $u = 20$ m s^{-1}; $V = 0$; $t = 10$ s

$$\alpha = \frac{v-u}{t} = \frac{0-20}{10} = -2 \text{ ms}^{-2}$$

43. Given: $l = \dfrac{1}{3}$ m; $n = 1000$ rotations; $t = 20$ s

$$\text{Average velocity } \vec{V} = \frac{\text{Total displacement}}{\text{Total time}}$$

$$= \frac{0}{t} = 0.$$

Essay Answer Type Questions

Note: This is how you should frame your answer covering.

44.

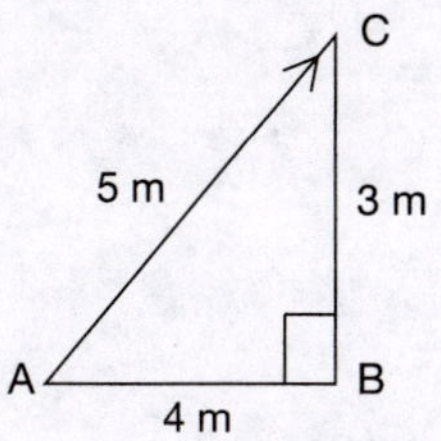

Using Pythagoras theorem,

$$AC^2 = AB^2 + BC^2$$

$$\Rightarrow BC^2 = AC^2 - AB^2$$

$$= 5^2 - 4^2$$

$$= 25 - 16 = 9$$

$$\Rightarrow BC = \sqrt{9} = 3 \text{ m}$$

Distance covered by toy car, $s = 4 + 3 = 7$ m

Displacement of the car, $\vec{s} = 5$ m.

$$\therefore \frac{\vec{s}}{s} = \frac{5}{7}$$

45. Here $v_1 = \dfrac{\frac{s}{2}}{t_1} \Rightarrow t_1 = \dfrac{\frac{s}{2}}{10} = \dfrac{s}{20}$

$$v_2 = \frac{\frac{s}{2}}{t_2} \Rightarrow t_2 = \frac{\frac{s}{2}}{2v_2}$$

$$\text{Average speed, } V = \frac{\text{Total distance}}{\text{Total time taken}}$$

$$\Rightarrow 15 = \frac{\frac{s}{2} + \frac{s}{2}}{t_1 + t_2} = \frac{s}{\frac{s}{20} + \frac{s}{2v_2}}$$

$$15 = \frac{s}{s\left(\dfrac{2v_2 + 20}{40v_2}\right)} = \frac{40v_2}{s(v_2 + 10)}$$

$$40\, v_2 = 30\, v_2 + 300$$

$$\Rightarrow v_2 = 30 \text{ km h}^{-1} = v.$$

46. Plot time on x-axis and velocity on y-axis.

47. Time along x-axis and displacement along y-axis.

48. (i) $a = \dfrac{v - u}{t}$

(ii) Time along x-axis and acceleration along y-axis.

(iii) $a = 0 \Rightarrow$ uniform velocity.

(iv) The graph is a straight line parallel to the x-axis implies uniform acceleration.

Competition Wing

Level 1: Apply your Concepts

13. When a body moves with a uniform (constant) velocity, then its instantaneous velocity will be equal to the average velocity. Hence, its acceleration is equal to zero.

20. A → c, B → a, C → d, D → b.

21. The graphs in (b), (c) and (d) are possible. (a) is not possible as nobody can have different velocities at the same time.

36. Displacement is the shortest length of the line joining the initial and final positions of the body.

Hence, the correct answer is (a).

37. The initial and final positions of the body are same. Therefore, displacement is zero and acceleration of the body is equal to the acceleration due to gravity and it is a constant.

Hence, the correct answer is (c).

38. $u = 0$

$$v = 144 \text{ km h}^{-1} = 144 \times \frac{5}{18} \text{m s}^{-1} = 40 \text{m s}^{-1}$$

$t = 5$ s

$$a = \frac{v-u}{t} = \frac{40}{5} = 8 \text{ m s}^{-2}$$

$$s = \frac{1}{2} \times 8 \times (5)^2 = 100 \text{ m}$$

Hence, the correct answer is (a).

39. Here, $u = 50\ m\ s^{-1}$; $v = 60\ m\ s^{-1}$; $t = 0.1\ s$; (i)

Using the equation of motion, $V = u + at$ (ii)

From the above equation, $\alpha = \dfrac{v-u}{t}$ (iii)

$$\Rightarrow \alpha = \frac{60-50}{0.1} = 100 \text{ms}^{-2} \quad \text{(iv)}$$

Hence, the correct answer is (c).

40. Given

$$u = 54 \text{ km h}-1 = 54 \times \frac{5}{18} = 15 \text{ m s}^{-1}$$

$$V = 36 \text{ km h}^{-1} = 36 \times \frac{5}{18} = 10 \text{ m s}^{-1}$$

$a = -2.0 \text{ m s}^{-1}$

Using $v^2 - u^2 = 2as$ (a)

$$s = \frac{v^2 - u^2}{-2a} (c)$$

$$s = \frac{100 - 225}{-4} (c)$$

$s = 125/4 = 31.25$ m

Hence, the correct answer is (c).

41. $\text{Velocity} = \dfrac{\text{displacement}}{\text{time}}$

The displacement and the velocity need not be in the same direction. *Example:* SHM

Hence, A is correct; R is incorrect.

Hence, the correct answer is (c).

42. From the graph it is clear that, from the instant $t = 3$ s to the instant $t = 7$ s, the displacement of the body is constant. This implies that the body is at rest for 4 seconds of time. Thus, the body is in motion for 6 seconds (10 – 4 = 6)

Hence, the correct answer is (c).

43. From the graph:

The total distance moved by the body = OF = 12 m.

The total time taken = 16 s.

$$\text{Average speed} = \frac{\text{total distance}}{\text{total time}} = \frac{12}{16} \text{ms}^{-1} = \frac{3}{4} \text{ ms}^{-1}$$

Hence, the correct answer is (a).

44. Let the total distance be 2d.

Then, $$\frac{d}{t_1} = 2 \quad (1)$$

$$\frac{d}{t_2} = x;$$

$$\frac{2d}{t_1 + t_2} = 3 \Rightarrow d = \frac{3(t_1 + t_2)}{2} \quad (2)$$

From (1) and (2),

$$2t_1 = 3\frac{(t_1 + t_2)}{2} \Rightarrow 4t_1 = 3t_1 + 3t_2$$

$$t_1 = 3t_2 \therefore \frac{d}{t_1/3} = x \Rightarrow \frac{3d}{t_1} = x$$

From (1),

$3(2) = x$

$x = 6 \text{ m s}^{-1}$

Hence, the correct answer is (b).

45. Radius of the circular path covered by the fan = 0.5 m. The number of rotations per second = 100.

$$\text{Speed} = \frac{\text{distance}}{\text{time}} = \frac{100 \times (2\pi r)}{50}$$

$$= \frac{100 \times 2\pi \times 0.5}{50} = 2\,\pi \text{ ms}^{-1}$$

Hence, the correct answer is (a).

46.

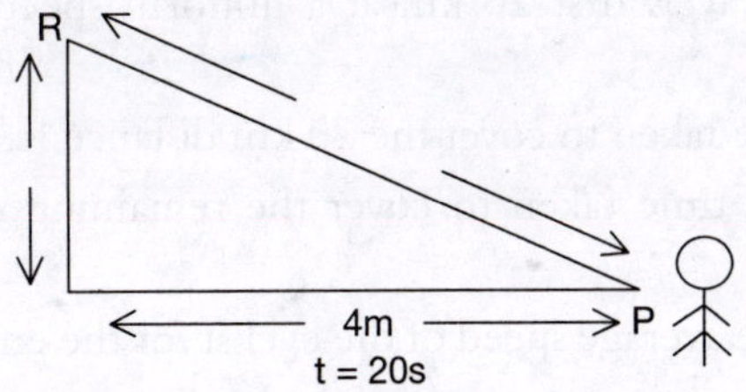

From the given figure, by Pythagorous theorem

$PR^2 = PQ^2 + RQ^2$

$PR^2 = 4^2 + 3^2$

$PR^2 = 16 + 9$

$PR = \sqrt{25} \Rightarrow PR = 5 \text{ m}$

Average speed

$$= \frac{\text{total distance}}{\text{total time}} = \frac{4\text{m} + 3\text{m} + 5\text{m}}{20\text{s} + 10\text{s} + 30\text{s}}$$

$$= \frac{12\text{m}}{60\,s} = 0.2 \text{ m s}^{-1}$$

Hence, the correct answer is (a).

47. $t_1 = \dfrac{\frac{1}{3}d}{12} \qquad t_1 = \dfrac{d}{36}\text{s}$

$t_2 = \dfrac{\frac{2}{3}d}{20}, \qquad t_2 = \dfrac{d}{30}\text{s}$

$$\text{Total time, } t = t_1 + t_2 = \frac{d}{36} + \frac{d}{30} = d\left(\frac{1}{36} + \frac{1}{30}\right)$$

$$= d\left(\frac{5+6}{180}\right) = d\left(\frac{11}{180}\right)s$$

$$\text{Average speed} = \frac{\text{Total distance}}{\text{Total time}} = \frac{d}{\frac{11d}{180}}$$

$$= \frac{180}{11} = 16.4 \text{km h}^{-1}$$

Hence, the correct answer is (d).

Level 2: Review your Concepts

Note: This is how you should frame your answer covering.

48. $u = 120 \text{ km h}^{-1} = 120 \times \dfrac{5}{18} = \dfrac{100}{3}\text{ms}^{-1}$

$V = 0 \text{ km h}^{-1} = \text{m s}^{-1}$

$t = 4$ s

$$\alpha = \frac{V - u}{t} = \frac{0 - \frac{100}{3}}{4} = -\frac{100}{12} = -\frac{25}{3}\text{ms}^{-2}$$

$\therefore$ Deceleration = 25/3 m s^2.

49. Given, Speed of the bus, u = 20 m s^{-1}

Distance travelled by the bus before coming to rest, s = 50 m

Final velocity, v = 0

Using $\quad v^2 - u^2 = 2as$

We get, $\quad 0 - (20)^2 = 2 \times a \times 50 \Rightarrow a = -4 \text{ m s}^{-2}$

Now, using $\quad v = u + at$

We get, $\quad 0 = 20 - 4t \qquad \Rightarrow t = 5$ s

50. Given, Speed of the train, v = 36 km h^{-1}

$= 36 \times \dfrac{5}{18} = 10 \text{ m s}^{-1}$

Length of the bridge, L = 600 m

Time taken, t = 80 s

Using, Speed $= \dfrac{\text{Distance}}{\text{Time}} \Rightarrow$ Distance = Speed × Time

Distance travelled by the train in 80 s = 10 × 80 = 800 m

Then the length of the train = 800 – 600 = 200 m

51. Given, Length of the minute hand, r = 3 cm

when the minutes hand moves during a time interval from 4:00 p.m. to 4:15 p.m., its position is exactly perpendicular to previous position as shown in figure.

Then the displacement between the positions of the tip of the minute hand $= \sqrt{3^2 + 3^2} = 3\sqrt{2}$

Time taken = 15 minutes = 15 × 60 = 900 s

Now, average velocity $= \frac{3\sqrt{2}}{900} = 0.00471\,\text{cm s}^{-1}$

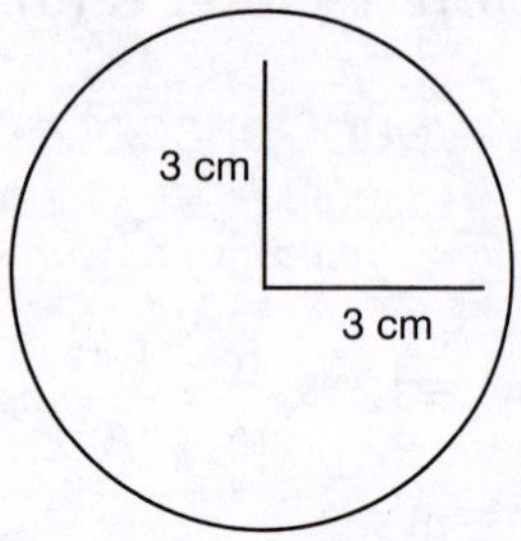

52. (a) A particle executing circular motion with uniform speed.

(b) A freely falling body or a body projected up.

(c) Consider a vehicle moving on a busy road.

53. Given, Distance between two places A and B (by road) = 180 km

Distance between two places A and B (by air) = 120 km

Time taken by an aeroplane to travel from A to B – 20 min $= \frac{1}{3}$ h

Time taken by a bus to travel from A to B = 5 h

For aeroplane: $\text{Avg. speed} = \frac{\text{Total distance}}{\text{Tatal time}}$

$$= \frac{180}{\frac{1}{3}} = 540\,\text{km h}^{-1}$$

$$\text{Avg. velocity} = \frac{\text{Total displacement}}{\text{Tatal time}}$$

$$= \frac{120}{\frac{1}{3}} = 360\,\text{km h}^{-1}$$

For Bus: $\text{Avg. speed} = \frac{\text{Total distance}}{\text{Total time}}$

$$= \frac{180}{5} = 36\,\text{km h}^{-1}$$

$$\text{Avg. velocity} = \frac{\text{Total displacement}}{\text{Total time}}$$

$$= \frac{120}{5} = 24\,\text{km h}^{-1}$$

54. Given, Initial velocity of the car, u = 0

Ratio of distance travelled in n^{th} second to that in $(n+1)^{th}$ second,

$S_n : S_{n-1} = 4:3$ ---- (1)

We have $S_n = u + a\left(n - \frac{1}{2}\right)$ ---(2)

and $S_{n-1} = u + a\left((n-1) - \frac{1}{2}\right)$ ---(3)

Substituting (2) and (3) in (1), we get

$$\frac{n - \frac{1}{2}}{n - \frac{3}{2}} = \frac{4}{3} \Rightarrow n = 4.5$$

55. Given, Total length of the road, L = 60 km

The cyclist travels first 20 km at a uniform speed of 20 km h^{-1}.

Then the time taken to cover the 20 km distance is 1 h.

Let 't' be the time taken to cover the remaining distance, 40 km.

Given that the average speed of the cyclist for the entire trip is 10 km h^{-1}

We have, $\text{Avg. speed} = \frac{\text{Total diatance}}{\text{Total time}}$

$$\Rightarrow 10 = \frac{60}{1+t} \Rightarrow t = 5\text{h}$$

Then the velocity of the cyclist to cover the remaining distance (40 km) $= \frac{40}{5} = 8$ km h^{-1}

56. Given, Initial velocity of the car, u = 0

Car is moving with uniform acceleration.

Distance covered in the first time interval (say t), $s_1 = p$

Distance covered in the second time interval (say t), $s_2 = q$

Using $s = ut + \frac{1}{2}at^2$

We get $s_1 = \frac{1}{2}at^2 = p$

Similarly, $s_1 + s_2 = p + q = \frac{1}{2}a(2t)^2$

(for the entire time intervel, i.e., $t + t = 2t$)

$$\Rightarrow p + q = 4\left(\frac{1}{2}at^2\right) = 4p$$

$$\Rightarrow q = 4p - p = 3p \Rightarrow \frac{p}{q} = \frac{1}{3}$$

57. (i) What is the initial velocity and acceleration of the bus?

Find the distance travelled by the bus in 2 s, by using the formula, $s = ut + \frac{1}{2}at^2$ (1)

Is the distance travelled by the motorcycle equal to $(s + 24)$ *m*? (2)

Find the time taken by the motorcycle to overtake the bus.

Find the velocity of the motorcycle from the formula, distance/time.

(ii) Uniform velocity of the motorcyclist = 17 m s^{-1}

58. What are the dimensions of the hall?

If the ant moves along the edges, then find the distance?

Is the total distance equal to the sum of the lengths of the dimensions?

The displacement of the ant is a straight line joining initial and final positions of the ant.

Find the length of the diagonal of the face having 12 m and 4 m as dimensions by using the Pythagoras theorem.

Find the length of the hypotenuse drawn over this diagonal and side edge '3 m' by using the Pythagoras theorem.

59. Given, Time taken, t = 25 s

Final velocity, v = 0

Acceleration, a = – 0.4 m s^{-2}

Using v = u + at

We get, $0 = u + (-0.4)(25) \Rightarrow u = 10$ m s^{-1}

Now, distance travelled, s = avg. velocity × Time

$$= \left(\frac{u+v}{2}\right) \times t = \left(\frac{0+10}{2}\right) \times 25 = 125\text{m}$$

60. (i) What is the initial velocity of the bus?

If the bus moves 48 m in 4 s, find the velocity of the bus at the end of 4 s.

Use the formula, $s = ut + \frac{1}{2}at^2$ and $v = u + at$

When brakes are applied, the bus stops after covering 24 m.

What is the final velocity of the bus?

Then, find the deceleration of the bus by using the formula, $v^2 - u^2 = 2as$.

(ii) 12 m s^{-2}

61. Let 'x' be the total distance travelled by the bus.

One third of the distance (i.e., $\frac{x}{3}$) is covered with a velocity of 20 km h^{-1}

Then the time taken to cover one third of the distance,

$$t_1 \frac{\frac{x}{3}}{20} = \frac{x}{60} \text{h}$$

Let 't' be the time taken to cover the total distance 'x'. Then the time taken to cover the remaining (two third) distance, $t_2 = t - t_1$

For the half of the above time, i.e., $\frac{t - t_1}{2}$, the bus travels with a velocity of 30 km h^{-1}

i.e., $$\frac{t - t_1}{2} = \frac{y}{30} \quad \text{--- (1)}$$

(here 'y' is the distance covered by bus with 30 km h^{-1})

And for the remaining half of the time $\left(\text{i.e., } \frac{t - t_1}{2}\right)$, the bus travels with a velocity of 50 km h^{-1}

i.e., $$\frac{t - t_1}{2} = \frac{\left(\frac{2x}{3}\right) - y}{30} \quad ---(2)$$

(here '$\frac{2x}{3} - y$' is the distance covered by bus with 50 km h^{-1})

From (1) & (2), $$\frac{y}{30} = \frac{\left(\frac{2x}{3}\right) - y}{30} \Rightarrow y = \frac{x}{4}$$

Then $$\left(\frac{2x}{3}\right) - y = \frac{5x}{12}$$

Now, $$\text{Avg. velocity} = \frac{\text{Total distance}}{\text{Total time}} = \frac{x}{t_1 + t_2 + t_3}$$

$$t_1 = \frac{x}{60}\text{h} \quad t_2 = \frac{\frac{x}{4}}{30} \quad t_3 = \frac{\frac{5x}{12}}{50}$$

$$\text{Avg. velocity} = \frac{x}{\frac{x}{60} + \frac{x}{120} + \frac{x}{120}} = 30 \text{ km h}^{-1}$$

62. Given, initial velocity of the particle, u = 0

Final velocity of the particle at 't', v_1 = 64 m s^{-1}

Final velocity of the particle at 't + 3', v_2 = 76 m s^{-1}

Let times $t_1 = t$ and $t_2 = t + 3$

We have, Acceleration,

$$a = \frac{v_2 - v_1}{t_2 - t_1} = \frac{76 - 64}{(t+3) - t} = \frac{12}{3} = 4\,\text{m s}^{-2}$$

Using v = u + at

$$\Rightarrow t = \frac{v - u}{a} = \frac{64 - 0}{4} = 16\,\text{s}$$

Level 3: Assess Your Concepts

Note: This is how you should frame your answer covering.

63. 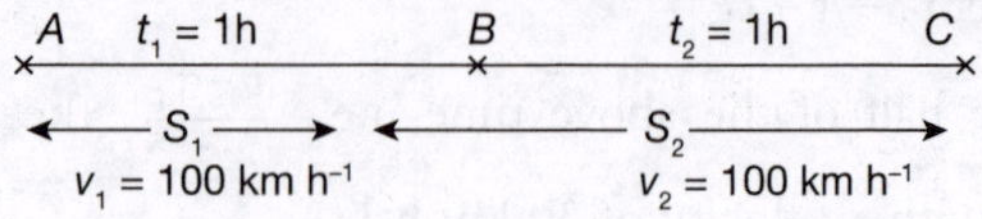

$v_1 = \frac{S_1}{t_1} \Rightarrow S_1 = v_1 t_1 = 500$ km

$v_2 = \frac{S_2}{t_2} \Rightarrow S_2 = U_2 t_2 = 100$ km

$\text{Average speed} = \frac{\text{Total distance}}{\text{Total time taken}} = \frac{S_1 + S_2}{t_1 + t_2}$

$= \frac{150}{2} = 75\,\text{kmh}^{-1}.$

64. Here the body covers 100 m in 10 *s*

The body travels in a straight path, then displacement, $\vec{S}$ =100 m and t = 10 s. The average velocity,

$\vec{V} = \frac{100\text{ m}}{10\text{ s}} = 10\,\text{ms}^{-1}$

And average speed, $= \frac{S}{t} = \frac{100\text{ m}}{10\text{ s}} = 10\text{ ms}^{-1}$

Both (A) and (B) are true.

65. $\overrightarrow{DE}$ and $\overrightarrow{ED}$ are equal in magnitude but opposite in direction.

66. Here the speed of the police man is greater than that of the thief. Since their direction of motion and initial positions are not given, we cannot find the answer from the given information.

67. 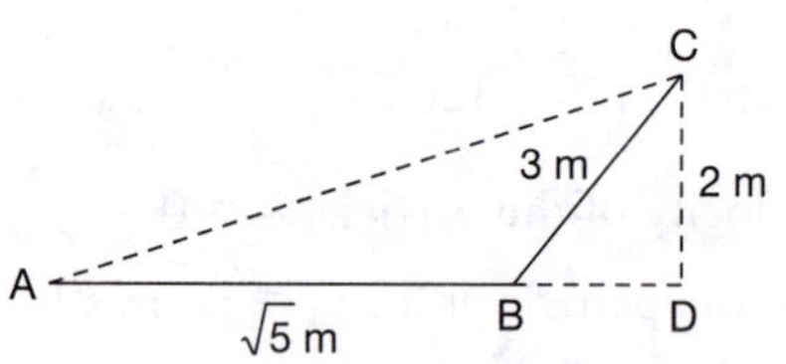

Displacement $= \overrightarrow{AC} = \sqrt{AD^2 + DC^2}$

From the right angled ΔBDC

$BC^2 = BD^2 + DC^2$

$9 = BD^2 + 4$

$BD^2 = 9 - 4$

$BD = \sqrt{5}$ m

$AD = AB + BD = \sqrt{5} = 2\sqrt{5}$ m

$\therefore \overrightarrow{AC} = \sqrt{(2\sqrt{5})^2 + 2^2} = \sqrt{4 \times 5 + 4} = \sqrt{24}$ m

68. As the velocity of policeman is greater than the velocity of the thief and both are moving in the same direction, policeman can catch the thief.

69. 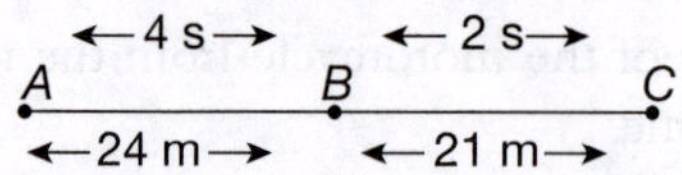

Case I: A → B

Initial velocity = u

$t = 4$ s $s = 24$ m

$S = ut + \frac{1}{2}at^2$

$24 = u \times 4 + \frac{1}{2} \times a \times 16$

$24 = 4u + 8a$

$\Rightarrow 6 = u + 2a$ (i)

Case II: A → C

Initial velocity = u

$t = 6$ s

$s = 45$ m

$s = ut + 1/2at^2$

$45 = 6u + \frac{1}{2} \times a \times 36$

$45 = 6u + 18a$

$15 = 2u + 6a$ (ii)

(ii) – 2 × (i)

$15 = 2u + 6a$

$-12 = 2u + 4a$

– – –

$3 = 2a$

$a = 1.5$

Substitute in (i), we get

$6 = u + 2a$

$6 = u + 2(1.5)$

$u = 3$

∴ Initial velocity = 3 m s^{-1}

70. 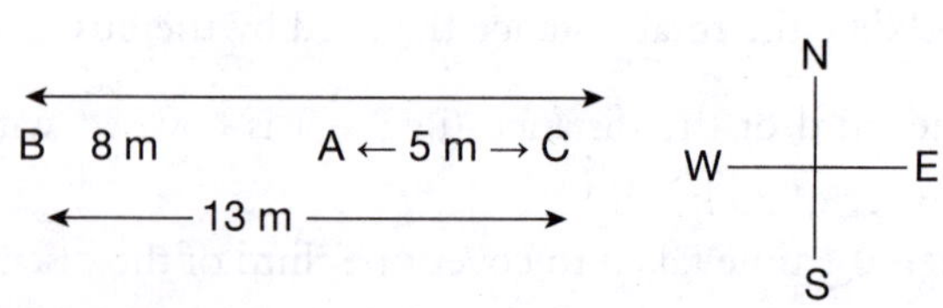

AB = height of building = 6 m

A = initial position

C = final position

As ΔABC isosceles triangle AB = BC

(AB = 6 m given)

BC = 6 m

AC = displacement

$$AC = \sqrt{AB^2 + BC^2}$$

$$= \sqrt{6^2 + 6^2} = \sqrt{72}$$

$$= \sqrt{36 \times 2} = 6\sqrt{2} \text{ m}$$

∴ Displacement is $6\sqrt{2}$ m

71. (a) Distance covered to draw half circle, $s = \pi r$

$$= \frac{22}{7} \times 5\text{cm}$$

Displacement = 2r = 2 × 5 = 10 cm

Time taken = 2 s

$$\therefore \text{Speed} = \frac{\text{Distance}}{\text{Time}} = \frac{5\pi}{2} \text{cm s}^{-1}$$

$$\text{Velocity} = \frac{\text{Displacement}}{\text{Time}} = \frac{10}{2} = 5 \text{ cm s}^{-1}$$

(b) Distance covered to draw full circle = 2π × 5 = 10π cm s^{-1}

Displacement = 0

Time taken = 4 s

$$\text{Speed} = \frac{\text{Distance}}{\text{Time}} = \frac{10}{8} = \frac{5}{4} \text{m s}^{-1}$$

Velocity = 0

72. For particle traveling through *p*,

For insect

Radius of cylinder = 0.8 m.

Displacement of insect = diameter = 1.6 m.

Velocity of insect = 2 mm s^{-1}

= 2 × 10^{-3} m s^{-1}.

$$\text{Time taken by insect} = \frac{\text{displacement}}{\text{velocity}}$$

$$= \frac{1.6}{2 \times 10^{-3}}$$

= 0.8 × 10^3

= 800 s.

For cylinder, time = 800 s.

Velocity = 0.5 m s^{-1}.

Distance = velocity × time

= 0.5 × 800 = 400 m.

73. Given, Initial velocity of the bullet train, u = 0

Acceleration of the bullet train, a = 0.5 m s^{-2}

First Part of the Motion: Time taken, t_1 = 2 min = 2 × 60 = 120 s

Then, velocity of the bullet train at t_1, v = u + at = 0 + (0.5)(120) = 60 m s^{-1}

Distance covered by the bullet train, s_1

$$= \frac{1}{2} \times 0.5 \times (120)^2 = 3600 \text{ m}$$

Second Part of the Motion: Time taken,

t_2 = 20 min = 20 × 60 = 1200 s

Distance covered by the bullet train, s_2 = 60 × 1200 = 72000 m

Third Part of the Motion: Initial velocity of the bullet train, u = 60 m s^{-1}

Final velocity of the bullet train, v = 0

Acceleration, a = – 0.25 m s^{-2}

$$\text{Using: } v^2 - u^2 = 2as \Rightarrow s_3 = \frac{v^2 - u^2}{2a}$$

$$\Rightarrow s_3 = \frac{0^2 - 60^2}{2(-0.25)} = \frac{3600}{0.5} = 7200 \text{ m}$$

Time taken by the bullet train to cover third part of the motion, $v = u + at_3$

$$\Rightarrow 0 = 60 + (-0.25)t_3$$

$$\Rightarrow t_3 = \frac{-60}{-0.25} = 240 \text{ s}$$

$$\text{Average velocity} = \frac{s_1 + s_2 + s_3}{t_1 + t_2 + t_3} = \frac{3600 + 72000 + 7200}{120 + 1200 + 240}$$

$$= \frac{82800}{1560} = 53.07 \text{ m s}^{-1}$$

74. What is instantaneous velocity?

When car *A* has just overtaken car *B*, which one has higher instantaneous velocity?

If the instantaneous velocity of *A* is greater than that of *B*, then is it a must that it should be accelerated or decelerated?

Is it not possible that both the cars have acceleration or deceleration or move with uniform velocity?

75. 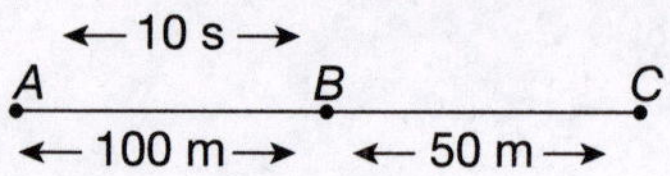

Case I: A → B

Initial velocity = $u = 0$

$t = 10$ s $S = 100$ m

By $s = ut + 1/2at^2$

$$100 = \frac{1}{2} \times a \times 100$$

$$a = 2 \text{ m s}^{-2}$$

$$V_B = u + at$$

$$= 0 + 2 \cdot 10 = 20 \text{ m s}^{-1}$$

Case II: B → C

$u = 20$ m s^{-1} $v = 0$ m s^{-1} $s = 50$ m

$$\text{By } \vec{a} = \frac{v^2 - u^2}{2s} = \frac{0^2 - 20^2}{2 \times 50}$$

$$= \frac{-400}{100} = -4$$

$$a = -4 \text{ m s}^{-2}; \ |\vec{a}| = 4 \text{ ms}^{-2}$$

76. 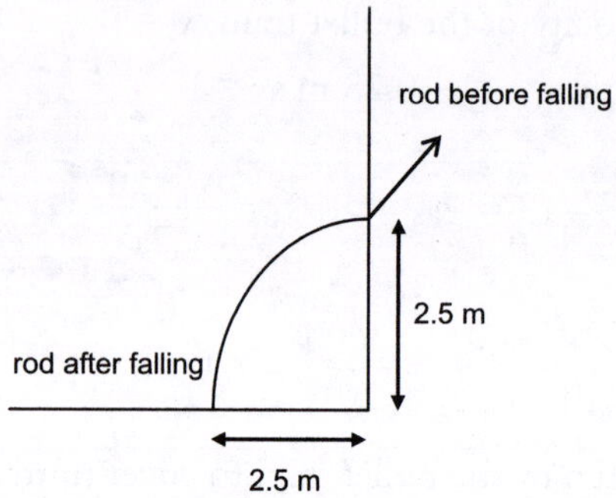

Distance covered by centre of the rod when it falls down is $= \dfrac{2\pi \times 2.5}{4} = \dfrac{5\pi}{4}$

Time = 2s

$$\text{Speed} = \frac{s}{t} = \frac{5\pi}{4 \times 2} = 1.96$$

Speed = 1.96 m s^{-1}

$$V = \frac{\sqrt{(2.5)^2 + (2.5)^2}}{2} = \frac{\sqrt{12.5}}{2} = 1.77$$

Velocity = 1.77 m s^{-1}

77. 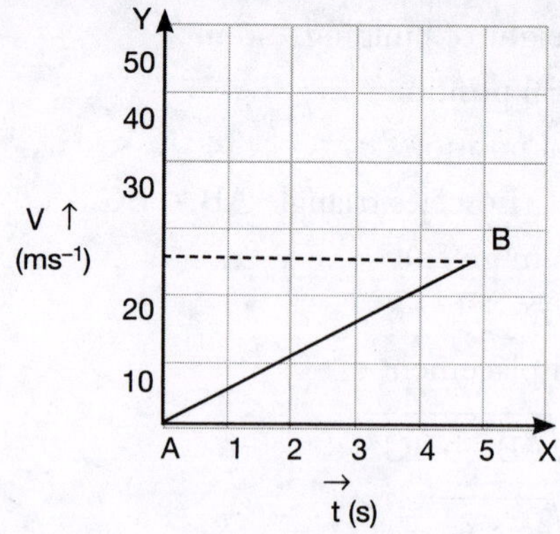

Length of the v – t graph AB is

$$AB = \sqrt{(2.5)^2 + 5^2}$$

$$= \sqrt{6.25 + 25} = \sqrt{31.25} = 5.6 \text{ cm}$$

s = 5.6 cm.

For the ant 5.6 cm = 5.6×10^{-2} m

$v = 1 \text{ mm s}^{-1} = 10^{-3} \text{ m s}^{-1}$,

$$t = \frac{s}{v} = \frac{5.6 \times 10^{-2}}{10^{-3}} = 56 \text{ s}.$$

Time taken by the ant is 56 seconds.

78. 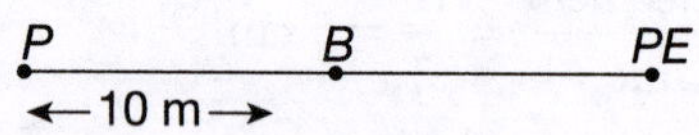

Let V be the velocity.

Then distance covered by person in time $t = Vt$ and distance covered by the bus in the same time.

$$S_b = ut + \frac{1}{2}at^2$$

$$x = \frac{1}{2} \times 0.1 \times (30)^2$$

$$= 45 \text{ m}$$

$$55 = V \times 30$$

$$V = \frac{55}{30}$$

$$= \frac{11}{6}$$

$$= 1.83 \text{ m s}^{-1}.$$

79. Distance travelled by the ant with respect to the rod = 2 m

Displacement with respect to the rod = 2 m

Distance with respect to the ground = 10 + 2 = 12 m

Displacement with respect to the ground

$= \sqrt{2^2 + 10^2} = \sqrt{4 + 100} = \sqrt{104}$ m

80.

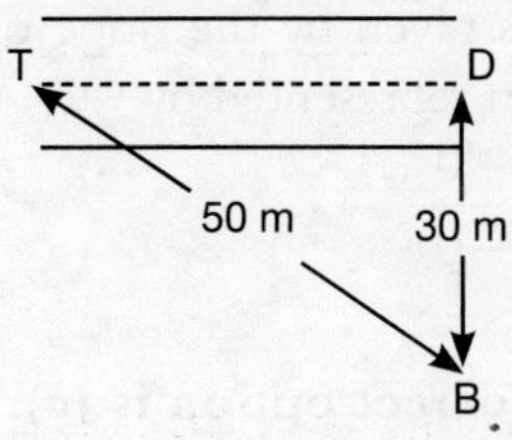

Distance between train and dog is given by DT

$= \sqrt{50^2 - 30^2} = \sqrt{1600} = 40\text{m}$

$V_t = 36$ km h^{-1} = 10 m s^{-1}

Time taken by the train to reach the dog is $t_t = \frac{40}{10} = 4$ s

Minimum velocity required by the person to save the dog is v = 30/4 = 7.5 m s^{-1}.

81. S displacement in 36 seconds is

$S_1 = ut + \frac{1}{2}at^2$

$= \frac{1}{2} \times 1 \times 36^2 = 648$ m.

Displacement in 35 seconds

$S_2 = ut + \frac{1}{2}at^2$

$= 0 + \frac{1}{2} \times 1 \times 35^2 = 612.5.$

Displacement in 36th second is = 648 – 612.5 = 35.5 m

JEE-NEET Special Wing

Multiple-Answer Type Questions

1. Scalar quantities are those which depend only on magnitude.
E.g.: - Density, temperature
Vector quantities are those which depend both on magnitude and direction.
E.g.: - Force, displacement
Hence, the correct option is (b) and (d).

2. When an object is moving with constant velocity, its acceleration would be zero.
Hence, the correct option is (b) and (d).

3. From the velocity - time graph, velocity at any instant point of time can be obtained and the displacement of the body is given by the area under the curve.
Hence, the correct option is (c) and (d).

4. $a = 3\text{ m s}^{-2}$
$u = 0$
$t = 7\text{ s}$
$v = u + at$
$= 0 + 3\times7$
$v = 21\text{ m s}^{-1}$
$= 21\times3.6$
$v = 75.6\text{ km h}^{-1}$
Hence, the correct option is (b) and (d).

5. Distance $= 2\pi r$
$= 2\times3.14\times5$
$= 31.4\text{ m}$
Displacement = zero (Initial and final points are the same)
Hence, the correct option is (b) and (d).

Comprehension-Based Questions

6. Velocity is increasing at constant rate.
Hence, the correct option is (a).

7. Acceleration is given by the slope of the v - t graph. For the motion represented by OP,
$$a = \frac{v-u}{t_2-t_1} = \frac{8-0}{4-0}$$
$= 2\text{ m s}^{-2}$
Hence, the correct option is (c).

8. The car is moving with constant velocity.
$\therefore a = 0$
Hence, the correct option is (d).

9. The distance travelled by the car is given by the area under the v -t graph.
Distance travelled = area of ΔOPR + area of PQRS + area of ΔQST
$$= \frac{1}{2}\times 4\times8 + 16\times8 + \frac{1}{2}\times 4\times 8$$
$= 16 + 128 + 16$
$= 160\text{ m}$
Hence, the correct option is (b).

10. Average speed $= \dfrac{\text{Total distance}}{\text{Total time}}$
$$= \frac{160}{24} = 6.66\text{ m s}^{-1}$$
Hence, the correct option is (d).

Match the Column

11. Choice (b) follows.
A - e, B - c, C - d, D - b, E - a

Dynamics

CHAPTER
3

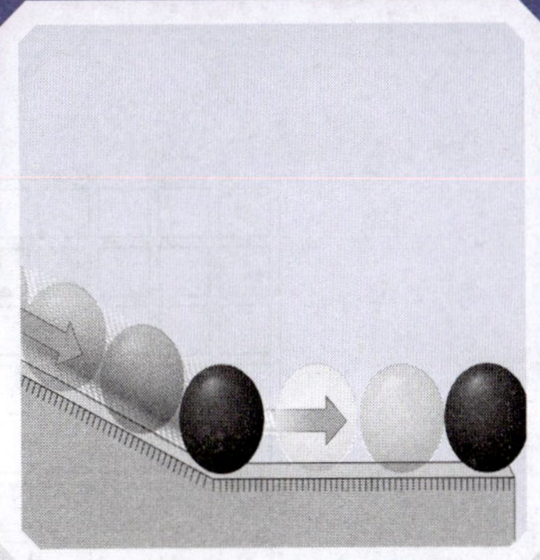

Key Ideas

After completing this chapter, you should be able to:

- classify forces, friction and types of friction, advantages and its disadvantages.
- state Newton's laws of motion and law of conversation of momentum.
- understand potential and kinetic energies and their derivations, centre of gravity, transformation of energy and law of conservation of energy.
- learn about equilibrium of bodies, levers, pulley and inclined plane.

Remember

Before beginning this chapter, you should be able to:

- know types of motion and to classify the motions of various bodies.
- understand the concept of 'speed' and kinds of speed.
- learn about different types of velocities, acceleration and their applications.

Scientific Crypt

A Tribute to Sir Isaac Newton (1643–1727)

Who discovered the concept of universal Law of Gravitation and Laws of Motion? Who invented the first practical reflecting telescope? Who along with Gottfried Leibniz was responsible for the development of calculus? Who gave the generalized binomial theorem? Surely all of us must have got it right, it is none other than Sir Issac Newton. He was a mathematician, physicist and an astronomer. He was also an alchemist and theologian. His work 'Mathematical Principles of Natural Philosophy', published in 1687, laid the foundation for most of the classical mechanics that we know today. In Physics, Newton contributed to classical mechanics, built the first practical reflecting telescope, formulated an empirical law to study the speed of sound. In mathematics, he was instrumental in the development of the concept of calculus and also contributed to the study of power series. The Epitaph written by the English poet Alexander Pope is a true tribute to Newton's accomplishments, the epitaph reads: Nature and nature's laws lay hid in night; God said "Let Newton be" and all was light. While the humble Newton remarked "I do not know what I may appear to the world, but to myself I seem to have been only like a boy playing on the sea-shore, and diverting myself in now and then finding a smoother pebble or a prettier shell than ordinary, whilst the great ocean of truth lay all undiscovered before me"..

Crossword

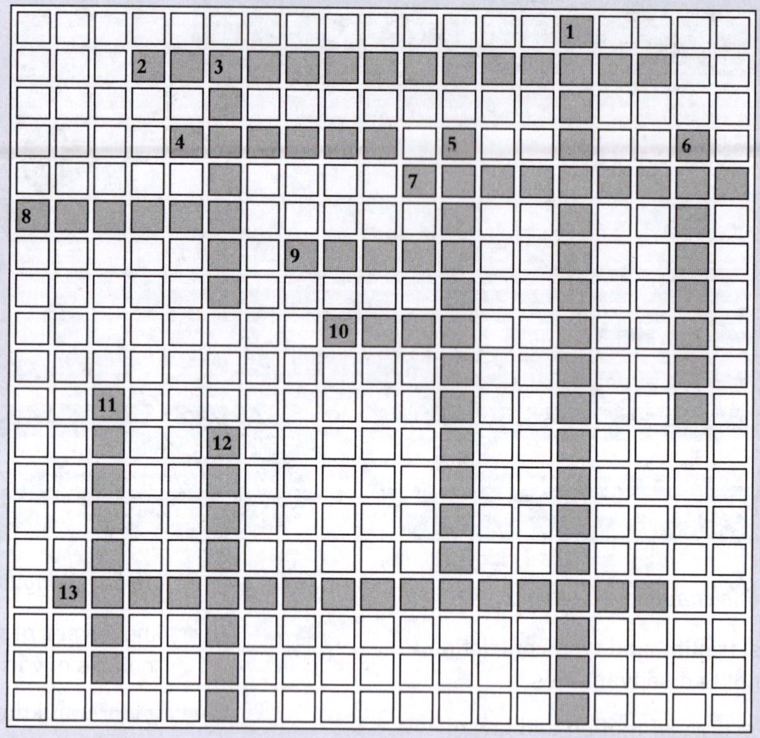

Across

2. A person jumping from a height.

4. S.I. unit of force.

7. The distance between the effort and the fulcrum.

8. The pull of the earth on a body.

9. Work done on the machine.

10. The direction of motion of the body can be changed.

13. Work done in lifting a body is stored in it.

Down

1. Rolling ball is an example.

3. Inability to change the state of a body.

5. Force which act on a body through physical contact.

6. Opposes any tendency for relative motion.

11. The centre of gravity of a triangular lamina.

12. Determines the inertia of motion of a body.

INTRODUCTION

In kinematics, we have studied the motion of an object along a straight line, without discussing the cause of its motion. In dynamics we study the cause of motion of bodies and why they move fast, or slow or remain at rest.

Force

If a pull or a push is given to a body which is static or moving with uniform velocity, then the body moves with increasing or decreasing speed. This pull or push acting on the body is known as force.

On pressing a rubber ball or a lump of clay, the rubber ball or clay gets deformed. Thus, force can be applied to change the shape and size of the body. Force can be defined as that physical cause which tends to change the state of rest or of uniform motion, or change the shape and size of the body.

Classification of Forces

Forces are classified as contact and non-contact forces.

- Forces can be applied on a body by making physical contact or otherwise.
- Forces which act on a body through physical contact are **contact forces**.
- Forces which act on a body without making any physical contact with the body are known as **non-contact forces**.

Based on their nature, forces can also be classified as:

1. Mechanical force
2. Magnetic force
3. Gravitational force
4. Electric force
5. Nuclear force

Info Bytes!

The strongest force in the universe is the strong nuclear force, which is 137 times stronger than electromagnetism.

Mechanical Force

To hit a nail into a wall, we use a hammer. Now, the force exerted by the hammer on the nail drives it into the wall. Thus, in this case, the force makes a physical contact and displaces the nail. Such a force is called contact force or in this case, it can also be called mechanical force.

Magnetic Force

Magnetic force is a non-contact force, since the iron piece experiences a force though there is no physical contact.

Place a small iron piece near a magnet. The iron piece moves towards the magnet. This force applied by the magnet is called magnetic force.

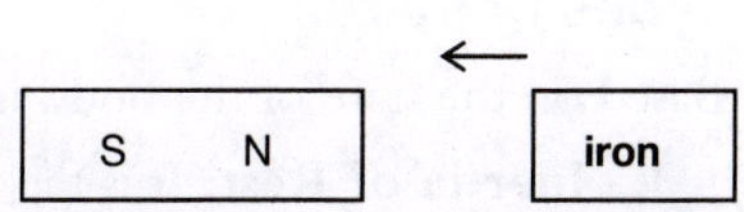

Figure 3.1 Magnet attracting an Iron piece

Gravitational Force

A ball thrown vertically upwards returns to the ground after some time. It is a non contact force. This is on account of the attractive force the Earth exerts on the ball. Similarly, the Earth also exerts an attractive force on celestial bodies such as the moon, the sun, the planets, etc. This force of attraction between any two masses is known as **gravitational force**.

Electric Force

When a glass rod is rubbed with wool, the glass rod acquires electric charge. It is a non contact force. Now, when the glass rod is brought near some pieces of paper, they cling to the glass rod. This is due to the electric force of the glass rod.

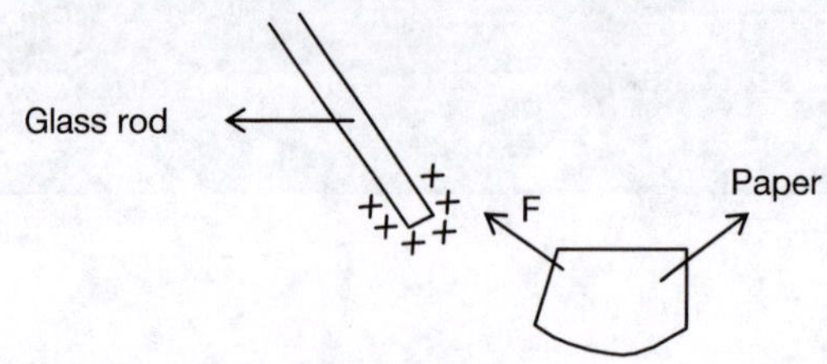

Figure 3.2 Charged glass rod attracting a paper

Nuclear Force

A **nuclear force** is a force that exists only if the interacting particles are protons or neutrons or both. It is a non contact force. It is different from gravitational and electromagnetic forces.

Newton's First Law of Motion

If a football is at rest or at a stationary position, on exerting force by kicking on it starts moving. Thus, there is a change in the state of the ball from rest to motion. Similarly, when a force is applied to a body in uniform motion, the velocity of the body tends to change its position. But if no external force acts on a body at rest or in uniform motion, the body continues to be in the same state. This forms the basis of the first law.

Every body continues to be in its state of rest or uniform motion along a straight line unless and until a net external force acts on it. Thus, one can conclude that force is a physical quantity that can change the state of rest or of motion of a body.

- If a body is observed to be at rest, then the net force acting on the body is zero.
- If a body is observed to be moving with uniform velocity, then the net force acting on the body must be zero.
- If a body is observed to be neither at rest nor in uniform motion, then the net force acting on the body is not zero.
- If the net force acting on the body is not zero, then the body is in non-uniform motion, i.e., it is neither at rest nor in uniform motion.
- If the net force acting on the body is zero, then the body must be either at rest or in uniform motion.

Inertia

This 'property of the body to continue in its state of rest or uniform motion unless acted upon by a net external force' or 'the inability of a body to change its state unless acted upon by a net external force' is known as **inertia**. This is the concept of inertia.

Types of Inertia

Based on the state of the body, inertia is classified as follows:

1. **Inertia of Rest:** It is the resistance of the body at rest to change its state of rest.

   Examples:

   (a) When books are piled one above the other and the lowest book is suddenly pulled out, the rest of the books remain intact. This is due to inertia of rest.

   (b) When the bus starts suddenly, the standing passengers in the bus tend to fall backward. When the bus is at rest, the entire body of a passenger is at rest but when the bus starts suddenly, the lower portion of the body of passenger which is in contact with the bus moves along with the bus while the upper part remains at rest due to inertia of rest. Hence, the standing passengers tend to fall backwards.

Info Bytes!

Newton's first law of motion is also known as the **law of inertia**.

2. **Inertia of Motion:** If a body is in a state of uniform motion, it continues to remain in the same state unless an external force acts on it.

   Examples:

   (a) When a boy who is running is tripped by a stone, he falls, because his feet come to rest whereas the upper portion of his body continues to move forward due to inertia of motion.

   (b) A passenger standing in a moving bus tends to fall forward when the driver of the bus suddenly applies the brakes. This is because the feet of the passenger (which are in contact with the bus) come to rest along with the bus but the upper portion of his/her body continues to move forward due to inertia of motion.

3. **Inertia of Direction:** It is the inability of a body to change its direction of motion on its own.

Example: When a car takes a sudden turn towards the left, the person seated inside it is pushed towards the right. This is because when the car takes a sharp turn it changes its direction whereas the person seated inside tends to move in the original direction due to inertia. Hence, the person is pushed towards the right (Figure 3.3).

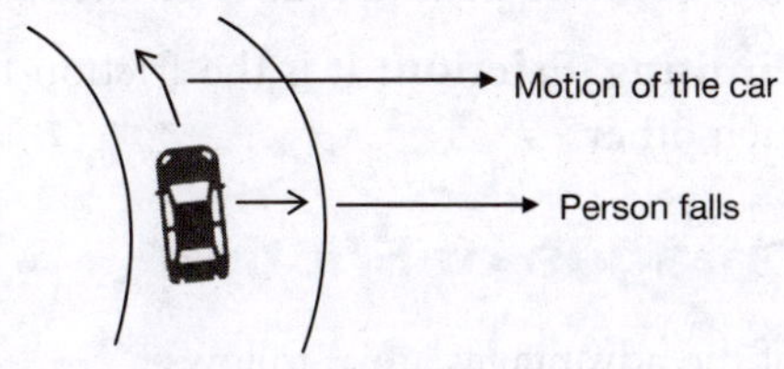

Figure 3.3 Person in the car moving along a circular path experiencing an outward force

Mass and Inertia

If a football is kicked, it moves a long way. But if an iron ball of the same size is kicked with the same force it hardly moves. This implies that the iron ball has more inertia than a football. Similarly, a greater force is required to stop a loaded truck than an empty one. Hence, a truck loaded with bricks has more inertia than an empty truck. Thus, a heavy body has more inertia than a lighter body. All objects do not offer the same resistance to change their state of rest or of uniform motion. Thus, we may conclude that the mass of a body is the measure of its inertia.

Friction

When an equal initial velocity is given to a block of wood, it travels different distances on different surfaces. On a smooth surface, it covers a longer distance than on a rough surface. When some force is applied on a body of given mass it moves through a certain distance, gradually slows down and comes to a halt. The body stops due to an opposing force acting between the body and the surface. This force is called **frictional force**. This force acts in a direction opposite to the direction of motion.

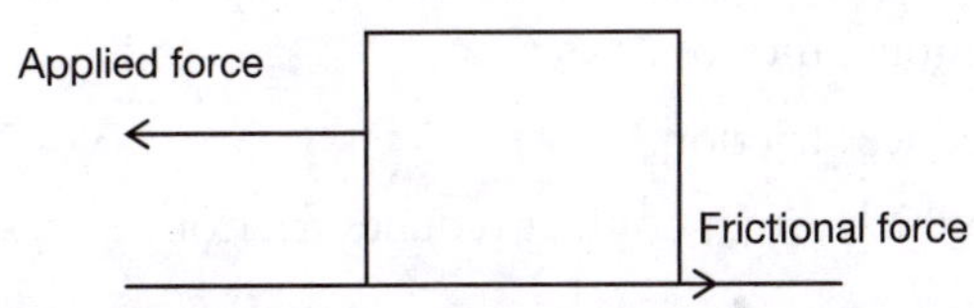

Figure 3.4 Frictional force opposing the direction of motion

Thus, **friction** is defined as the force which opposes any tendency for relative motion between bodies in contact.

Factors Affecting Frictional Force

Maximum frictional force depends on the following factors:

- Nature of the surfaces in contact. A rough surface offers greater friction than a smooth surface.
- Normal force that acts on the body.
- Nature of motion of the body (sliding or rolling).

Types of Friction

1. **Sliding Friction:** When one body slides over another, the force which opposes relative motion between them is called sliding friction.

   Example: When a book slides over a table, the friction present is sliding friction.

2. **Rolling Friction:** When a body rolls over another, the frictional force between them is called rolling friction.

   Example: Wheels of a moving car roll on the road and the friction present is rolling friction.

   It has been experimentally proved that sliding friction is greater than rolling friction. Hence, it is easier to roll a body over a surface than to slide it on the same surface.

3. **Limiting Friction:** It is the friction that is generated between the two static surfaces that come in contact with each other.

Advantages of Friction

Some of the advantages are as follows:

1. It is difficult to walk on highly smooth surfaces as we tend to skid on these surfaces. Hence, friction between our feet and the ground helps us to have a firm grip on ground and walk safely.
2. Without friction between the head of a match-stick and the lateral surface of a match-box, it is not possible to light the match stick.
3. Because of the friction between the brakes and the wheels, it is possible to stop a moving vehicle by applying brakes.

Disadvantages of Friction

Some of the disadvantages are as follows:

1. Friction between tyres of a vehicle and the road causes wear and tear in the tyres.
2. Friction between different parts of a machine gives rise to heat and more energy is needed to overcome the friction. Hence, there is loss of energy due to friction. Also, the wear and tear caused by friction may damage certain machine parts.

Methods to Reduce Friction

Friction can be reduced by using ball bearings. They are used to reduce friction in rotation or slipping of a body. A ball bearing consists of steel balls between two metal rings. After lubricating them with oil or grease, they are used in cycles and other machine parts involving rotational motion.

1. Lubricating the machine parts reduces friction.
2. Polishing the surfaces of bodies which are in contact reduces friction. Excess polishing increases friction.

Streamlining

When racing cars, aeroplanes, etc., travel cutting through air, friction is produced and this force reduces the speed. Hence, the shapes of racing cars and aeroplanes are designed so as to reduce friction.

Example: Fishes have streamlined body.

Momentum

If you have played cricket, you would have experienced that catching a ball which is moving with a higher velocity is more difficult than catching a ball which is moving with lesser velocity. Similarly, it is easier to catch a table tennis ball as compared to a cricket ball when both are dropped from the same height.

Thus, we see that moving bodies possess a physical quantity associated with their motion which determines how much force is required to bring them to rest. This quantity which depends on the mass and velocity of the moving body is called '**momentum**' and is defined as **momentum (p) = mass (m) × velocity (v)**

Units of Momentum

Since $p = mv$, units of momentum = (unit of mass) × (unit of velocity) = g cm s^{-1} (in C.G.S system) and kg m s^{-1} (in SI system)

1 kg m s^{-1} = 10^5g cm s^{-1}

Konnect

- Since mass is a scalar and velocity is a vector, momentum is a vector quantity.
- If a body is moving along a straight path, the body is said to possess 'linear momentum'.

EXAMPLE 3.1 The speeds of a snail and a squirrel are 0.5 m/s and 3 m/s, respectively. The mass of the squirrel is 1 kg and that of the snail is 0.2 kg. Which of the two has greater momentum? (Assume the speed of each to be steady.)

SOLUTION

We have seen above that,

momentum = mass × velocity

Since velocity is a vector quantity, it possesses both magnitude (speed) and direction. In the question, only the magnitude of velocity, i.e., speed, is provided. We do not have information about the direction of motion of the snail and the squirrel. Hence, it's not possible to compare their vector quantities directly. However, we can compare the magnitudes of their momenta as below:

Mass of snail = 0.2 kg.

Speed of snail = 0.5 m/s

P_{snail} = 0.2 × 0.5 = 0.1 kg m/s

Mass of the squirrel = 1 kg

Speed of the squirrel = 3 m/s

$P_{squirrel}$ = 1 × 3 = 3 kg m/s

Thus, the magnitude of the momentum of the squirrel is greater than that of the snail.

Newton's Second Law of Motion

When a force is applied to a body at rest, it is set in motion. There is change in velocity, and hence, there is change in momentum. If a greater force is applied, a greater change in velocity takes place, and hence, there will be greater change in momentum. This change in momentum give rises to Newton's second law of motion. The rate of change of momentum is directly proportional to the applied force and takes place in the direction of force. Newton's second law helps us to measure force.

Derivation of $\vec{F} = m\vec{a}$

Consider a body of mass 'm' moving along a straight line with initial velocity $\vec{u}$.

When a force 'F' is applied, it attains velocity $\vec{v}$ in time t seconds.

$$\text{Initial momentum} = \vec{P_1} = m\vec{u}$$

$$\text{Final momentum} = \vec{P_2} = m\vec{v}$$

Info Bytes!

The faster you go, the heavier you get—thanks to Newton's Second Law of Motion.

Change in momentum $= \Delta\vec{p} = \vec{P_2} - \vec{P_1}$

Rate of change of momentum $= \dfrac{\Delta\vec{p}}{\Delta t}$

$$\frac{\Delta\vec{p}}{\Delta t} = \frac{\vec{P_2} - \vec{P_1}}{t}$$

$$\frac{\Delta\vec{p}}{\Delta t} = \frac{m(\vec{v} - \vec{u})}{t}$$

Δt is the change in time

According to Newton's second law,

$$\vec{F} \propto \frac{\Delta\vec{p}}{\Delta t}$$

$$\vec{F} \propto \frac{m(\vec{v} - \vec{u})}{t}$$

But $\vec{a} = \dfrac{\vec{v} - \vec{u}}{t}$

$$F \propto ma \Rightarrow F = \text{kma}$$

where k is the constant of proportionality.

The unit of force is so defined as to make the value of k equal to one.

'A force of one unit acting on a body of one unit mass produces in it an acceleration of one unit.'

$$\vec{F} = m\vec{a}$$

Force is a vector quantity and its direction is the same as that of acceleration.

Units of Force

Absolute Unit of Force:

If $m = 1$ unit, $a = 1$ unit, then the value of $F = 1$ unit

C.G.S. unit of force is **'dyne'** and S.I. unit of force is **'newton' (N)**.

- **Dyne:** It is the force which when acting on a body of mass one gram produces in it an acceleration of 1 cm s^{-2} in its direction.

  $\therefore$ 1 dyne = 1 g × 1 cm s^{-2}

- **Newton:** It is the force which when acting on a body of mass 1 kg produces in it an acceleration of 1 m s^{-2} in its direction.

  $\therefore$ 1 newton (N) = 1 kg × 1 m s^{-2}

Relation between Newton and Dyne

$m = 1$ kg; $a = 1$ m s^{-2}

1 N = 1 kg × 1 m s^{-2}

1 N = 1000 g × 100 cm s^{-2}

1 N = 10^5 g cm s^{-2}

1 N = 10^5 dynes

EXAMPLE 3.2 What is the force exerted by a horse in pulling a carriage of mass 200 kg and accelerating at a rate of 2 m/s^2?

SOLUTION

$F = ?$

$m = 200$ kg

$a = 2 \text{ m s}^{-2}$

From Newton's second law,

$F = ma$

$\therefore F = 200 \text{ kg} \times 2 \text{ ms}^{-2} = 400 \text{ N}$

EXAMPLE 3.3 A ball of mass 5 kg is moving with an initial velocity of 8 m/s. A constant force acts for 3 s on the ball, making it come to a halt. Find the acceleration and force.

SOLUTION

$m = 5$ kg

$u = 8 \text{ m s}^{-1}$

Let the final velocity be v when the ball comes to a halt.

$t = 3$ s

$v = 0 \text{ m s}^{-1}$ (since it's stopped)

$a = ?$

$F = ?$

Using the formula from the equations of motion, $v = u + at$

$a = (v - u)/t$

$a = (0–8)/3 = –8/3 = –2.67 \text{ m/s}^2$.

The negative sign indicates that it is deceleration or retardation.

From Newton's second law,

$F = ma = 5 \times -2.67 = -13.35$ N

$\Rightarrow$ Retarding force = 13.35 N

Weight and Mass

Every body on the surface of the Earth experiences a pull towards the centre of the Earth. It is because of this pull that a body released at a certain height from the ground falls freely towards the surface of the Earth. And while falling, its velocity increases at a uniform rate, i.e., the body moves with uniform acceleration. This acceleration of a freely falling body towards the centre of the Earth, caused due to the pull of the Earth, is known as **'acceleration due to gravity'**. It is denoted by 'g'. The pull of the Earth on a body is called weight of the body, generally denoted by 'W'.

Using the relation: $F = ma$, the weight of a body can be expressed as $W = mg$, where 'W' is the force exerted on the body by the Earth.

Like force, weight is also a vector quantity and can be measured in terms of 'dyne' or 'newton'. The direction of weight of a body is always towards the centre of the Earth. Even though the mass of a given body is constant anywhere in the universe, its weight changes as the magnitude of acceleration due to gravity is not constant everywhere. Due to the same reason, the weight of a body changes from place to place on the surface of the Earth. The general value of acceleration due to gravity is taken as 980 cm s^{-2} or 9.8 m s^{-2}.

Apart from the normal C.G.S. and S.I. units of measurement which are also called absolute units of weight, gravitational units can also be used to measure weight.

In gravitational units, the weight of the body is measured in terms of 'gram weight' (g wt) or 'kilogram-weight' (kg wt)

1 g wt is the weight of a body of mass 1 gram.

$W = mg = 1 \times 980 \text{ cm s}^{-2} = 980 \text{ g cm s}^{-2} = 980$ dyne

$\therefore$ 1 g wt = 980 dyne

1 kg wt is the weight of a body of mass 1 kg.

$W = mg = 1 \text{ kg} \times 9.8 \text{ m s}^{-2} = 9.8 \text{ kg m s}^{-2} = 9.8$ Newton

Table 3.1 Difference between Mass and Weight

Mass	Weight
It is the measure of matter contained in a body.	It is the force with which a body is attracted towards the centre of the Earth.
Its magnitude does not change from place to place.	It changes with change in acceleration due to gravity.
It is measured with the help of a physical balance.	It is measured with the help of a spring balance.
It is measured in units of gram or kilogram.	It is measured in units of dyne or newton.
It is a scalar quantity.	It is a vector quantity.

Weightlessness

Weightlessness is a condition that is experienced during a free-fall in which the effect of gravity is cancelled by the internal force resulting from the orbital flight. Many a times, we also define weightlessness as zero gravity.

Example: While moving in a lift, we feel either an increase or a decrease in our weight depending upon the direction of acceleration of the lift. If the lift moves downward with an acceleration equal to 'g', then we feel weightless.

Similarly, weightlessness is experienced by a person jumping from a height. If a heavy load is placed on his head, he would not feel the weight of the load during his free fall.

Info Bytes!

Astronauts float in the space due to the phenomenon called weightlessness.

Newton's Third Law of Motion

It states that for every action there is an equal and opposite reaction Some of the examples are mentioned below, which proves Newton's Third Law of Motion..

- When we hit a table with our palm with force, we experience pain because the table exerts an equal force on the palm in the opposite direction. Hence, 'action' is our palm hitting the table and 'reaction' is the table hitting the palm.
- When a person swims, he pushes the water backwards and the water in turn pushes the person with an equal force in the forward direction.
- When stepping out of a boat near a river bank, we exert a force on the boat pushing it away from the river bank. This is known as action. The boat also exerts an equal and opposite force on us, and this force helps us to step out of the boat.

It is also clear from the above examples that action and reaction act on two different bodies.

Principle of Conservation of Mass

Principle of Conservation of Mass states that mass can be neither created nor destroyed. This can be illustrated with the help of an example. Measure the mass of a block of ice. Allow the ice to melt completely and collect the water in a beaker and now measure the mass of water collected in the beaker.

It is found that the mass of water is same as the mass of the ice block. Hence, there is no gain or loss in mass. This, in principle, is the law of conservation of mass.

Law of Conservation of Momentum

The total momentum of a system of bodies remains constant unless there is a net external force acting on the system. This can be explained by Newton's third law of Motion.

Proving Law of Conservation of Momentum by Newton's third Law

Consider two bodies A and B of masses m_1 and m_2, respectively moving with initial velocities u_1 and u_2, respectively in the same direction along a straight path where $u_1 > u_2$ (Figure 3.5). (Ignore the presence of friction) After some time the two bodies collide.

Figure 3.5 Before collision

Figure 3.6 After collision

Let 'v_1' and 'v_2' be the velocities of A and B, respectively after collision (Figure 3.6).

Then, the rate of change of momentum of 'B' due to force exerted by 'A' is

$$F_B = \frac{\Delta p_B}{\Delta t} = \frac{m_2 v_2 - m_2 u_2}{t} \quad (3.1)$$

where 't' is the time during which A and B exert force on each other.

Rate of change of momentum of 'A' due to the force exerted by 'B' is

$$F_A = \frac{\Delta p_A}{\Delta t} = \frac{m_1 v_1 - m_1 u_1}{t} \quad (3.2)$$

According to Newton's third law,

$$F_B = -F_A$$

Hence, from equations (3.1) and (3.2), we get

$$\frac{m_2 v_2 - m_2 u_2}{t} = -\left[\frac{m_1 v_1 - m_1 u_1}{t}\right]$$

$$\Rightarrow m_2 v_2 - m_2 u_2 = -m_1 v_1 + m_1 u_1$$

$$\Rightarrow m_1 u_1 + m_2 u_2 = m_1 v_1 + m_2 v_2$$

Hence, in the absence of net external force the total momentum before collision is equal to the total momentum after collision. This is the law of conservation of momentum.

Rockets

Rockets and jet planes work on the principle of Newton's third law and the law of conservation of momentum.

A rocket has chambers containing oxygen and fuel. The fuel is burnt in the presence of oxygen. The burnt gases escape with high velocity in the downward direction. This is known as action. The gas exerts an equal but opposite force on the rocket. This is the reaction. Due to this reaction, the rocket moves in the upward direction.

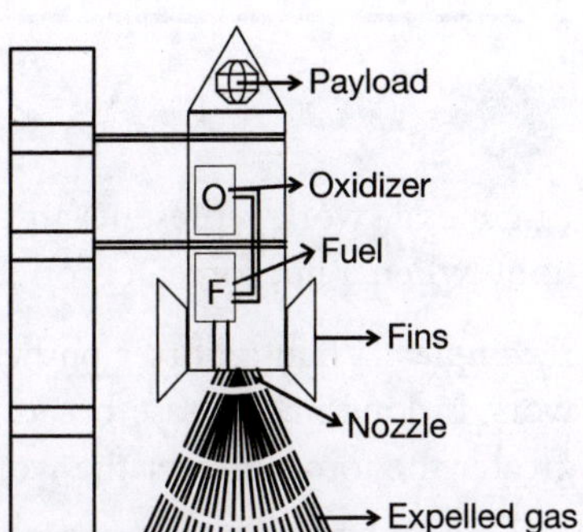

Figure 3.7 Parts of a Rocket

EXAMPLE 3.4 A car of mass 800 kg moving at a speed of 20 ms^{-1} collides with a stationary van of mass 1200 kg. After the collision, the car and van move together with a common velocity. Find the common velocity.

SOLUTION

Let the common velocity of the two bodies be 'v'.

Car

$m_1 = 800$ g

$u_1 = 20$ m s^{-1}

$v_1 = v = ?$

Van

$m_2 = 1200$ g

$u_2 = 0$ m s^{-1} (since it's stationary)

$v_2 = v = ?$

From the law of conservation of momentum,

$m_1u_1 + m_2u_2 = m_1v_1 + m_2v_2$

$800 \times 20 + 0 = 800 \times v + 1200 \times v$

$16000 = 2000\, v$

$v = 16000/2000 = 8\ ms^{-1}$

EXAMPLE 3.5 A cannon fires a shell of mass 25 kg with a velocity of 120 ms^{-1}. Due to this, the cannon recoils with a velocity of 5 ms^{-1}. Determine the mass of the cannon.

SOLUTION

Mass of the shell = m_1 = 25 kg

Initial velocity of shell, $u_1 = 0$

Final velocity of the shell, $v_1 = 120$ m s^{-1}

Mass of the cannon, m_2 = ?

Initial velocity of the cannon, $u_2 = 0$

Final velocity of the cannon = –5 ms^{-1} (negative sign indicates that its direction is opposite to that of the shell's velocity)

From the law of conservation of momentum,

$m_1u_1 + m_2u_2 = m_1v_1 + m_2v_2$

Substituting the given values,

$0 + 0 = 25 \times 120 - m_2 \times 5$

$m_2 = (25 \times 120)/5 = 600$ kg

Thus, the mass of the cannon is 600 kg.

Work

In general, work represents any physical or mental activity. But work has precise meaning in physics. **Work** is said to be done when a net force acts on a body and the body undergoes displacement.

Example: When a porter pushes a luggage trolley, work is done. But, when we push a wall, the wall does not move. No work is done in this case because there is no displacement of the wall. Work done also depends on the applied force, i.e., greater the force, greater the work done.

Thus, when a force acting on a body moves it in its direction, the work done is given by

$$\text{Work } (W) = \text{Force } (\vec{F}) \times \text{Displacement } (\vec{s})$$

Units of Work

Unit of work = (unit of force) (unit of displacement)

Thus, S.I. unit of work is newton-metre which is called 'joule' (J).

$\Rightarrow$ 1 J = 1 N $\times$ 1 m = 1 N m and C.G.S. unit of work is erg.

$\Rightarrow$ 1 erg = 1 dyne $\times$ 1 cm

Work done is a scalar quantity.

EXAMPLE 3.6 What is the work done by a horse in displacing a cart through 5 m in the direction of the force if the force applied by the horse is 10 N?

SOLUTION

Force = F = 10 N

Displacement = 5 m

Since the force and displacement are acting in the same direction, work done is given by

$\therefore$ Work = $F \times s$

= 10 × 5

$\Rightarrow$ Work done by the horse = 50 J

EXAMPLE 3.7 2 joules of work is done in displacing a stone through 0.5 m. Find the force applied on the stone.

SOLUTION

Given work, W = 2 J

Displacement, s = 0.5 m

$W = F \times s$

2 J = $F \times$ 0.5 m

$$\therefore F = \frac{2}{0.5} = 4 \text{ N}$$

Energy

Whenever we do any work, we feel tired as we expend some energy. Energy spent appears in the form of work done. **Energy** is defined as the ability of a body to do work. Energy has the same units as that of work. Energy can neither be created nor be destroyed but it can be transformed from one form to another. This is known as the law of conservation of energy.

Example: An incandescent bulb transforms electrical energy into light and heat energy.

S.I. unit of energy is 'joule', same as that of work. Since work is a scalar quantity, energy is also a scalar quantity.

Various Forms of Energy

1. Mechanical energy
2. Heat energy
3. Light energy
4. Sound energy
5. Electrical energy
6. Nuclear energy

Mechanical energy is classified further into potential energy and kinetic energy.

Mechanical energy can be easily transformed into heat energy by friction. Transforming wind energy, tidal energy and hydel energy into usable form is expensive.

During transformation, part of the energy is wasted (or transformed) into non-usable form. Thus, no process transforms energy with 100% efficiency.

It is easy to convert electrical energy into other forms and vice-versa. Electricity can be transmitted quickly from one place to another. Thus, electrical energy is considered to be the best form of energy.

Energy is obtained from different sources. Some sources of energy are renewable and some are non-renewable. Some energy sources get renewed by nature but take a long period of time. For example, wood. It takes 10 to 15 years for a tree to grow.

Centre of Gravity

You must have seen a circus artist doing a tight rope walk. Ever wondered how he manages to walk on a rope without falling down and why he stretches his hands or holds a long bamboo pole while doing so? You must also have seen a rolly-polly doll which always stands erect even if it is tilted to a side and left. These effects can be understood by the study of the concept of centre of gravity and equilibrium of bodies.

An extended body is made up of a large number of particles. In the case of rigid bodies, the relative position of these particles does not change. Each of these particles is attracted by a force towards the centre of the Earth called weight of the particle.

The weight of each particle of the body acts downwards (Figure 3.8). If w_1, w_2, w_3,.... are weights acting on particles p_1, p_2, p_3,....of the body, respectively, the resultant weight of the body is given by the sum of individual weights, $W = w_1 + w_2 + w_3 + ...$

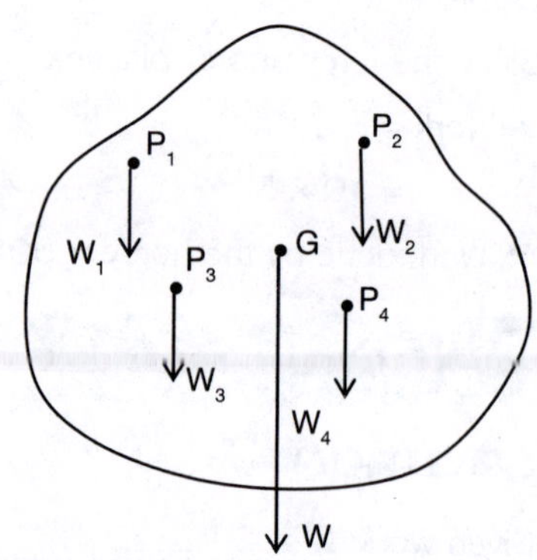

Figure 3.8 Centre of gravity

The resultant weight (W) appears to act through a fixed point irrespective of the position or the orientation of the body. This fixed point is called centre of gravity and is denoted as G. The centre of gravity of a body is defined as the point through which the weight of the body acts.

Activity

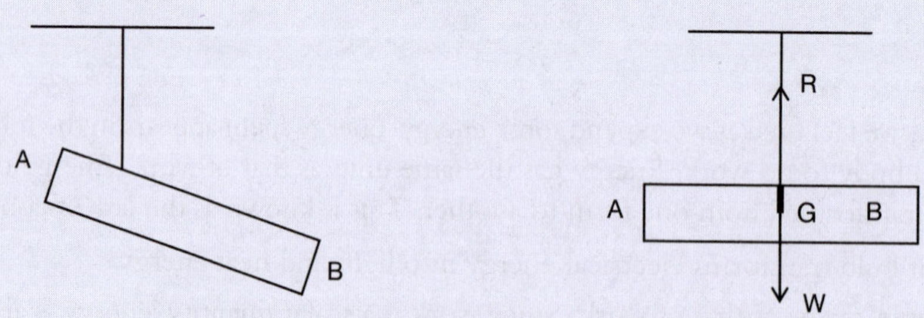

Figure 3.9 Center of gravity – Metre scale

1. Suspend a metre scale at one end by means of a string. The scale does not remain horizontal.
2. The scale remains horizontal and stable when it is suspended at the centre.

   This point on the scale is the centre of gravity of the scale. The centre of gravity may lie within the body or outside it. If a body is suspended at its centre of gravity, it remains in a balanced state. This fact can be used to test if a given point in a body is its centre of gravity or not.

Centre of Gravity of Regular Bodies

The centre of gravity of a body depends on the shape and size of the body.

1. The centre of gravity of a square lamina or a rectangular lamina is at the point of intersection of its diagonals.

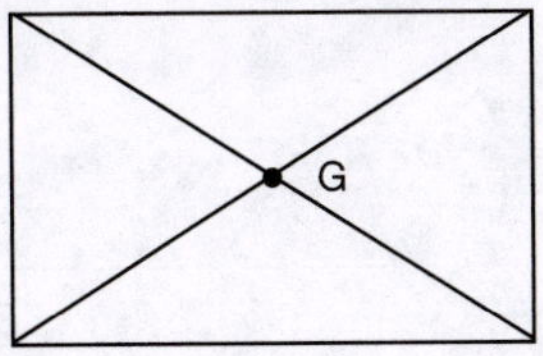

Figure 3.10 Center of gravity – Rectangular lamina

Info Bytes!

The Eiffel Tower's centre of gravity is actually below ground!

2. The centre of gravity of a circular plate lies at its centre.

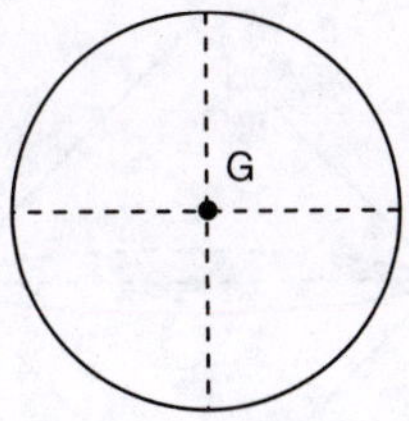

Figure 3.11 Center of gravity – Circular plate

3. The centre of gravity of a triangular lamina is at the point of intersection of its medians (centroid).

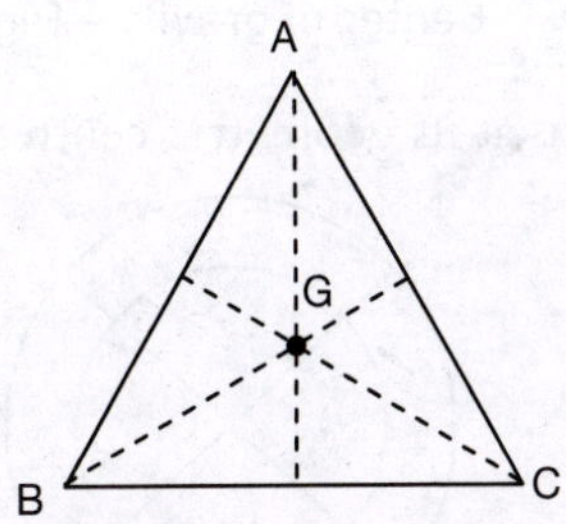

Figure 3.12 Center of gravity – Triangular lamina

4. The centre of gravity of a sphere is at the geometric centre of the sphere.

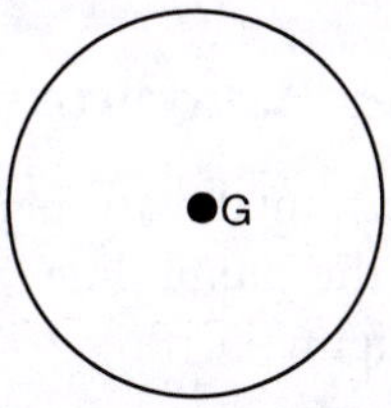

Figure 3.13 Center of gravity – Sphere

5. The centre of gravity of a solid right circular cone of height '*h*' lies on its axis at a distance ($h/4$) from its base.

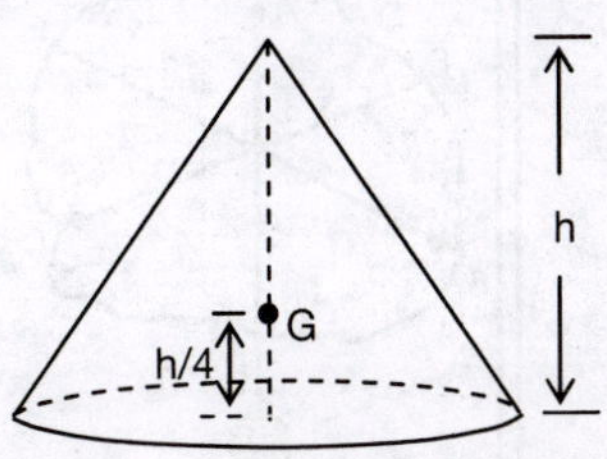

Figure 3.14 Center of gravity – Right circular cone

6. The centre of gravity of a cylinder is at the midpoint of its axis.

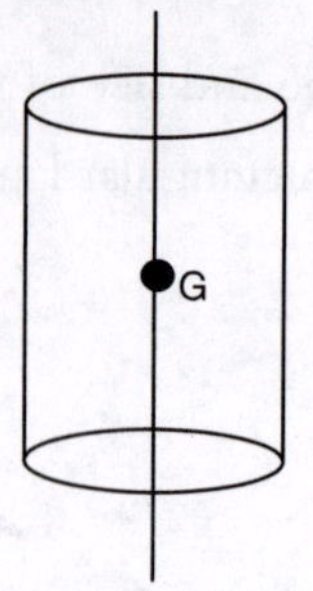

Figure 3.15 Center of gravity – Cylinder

7. The centre of gravity of two right circular cones of equal height and joined at the base is at the centre of base of either cone.

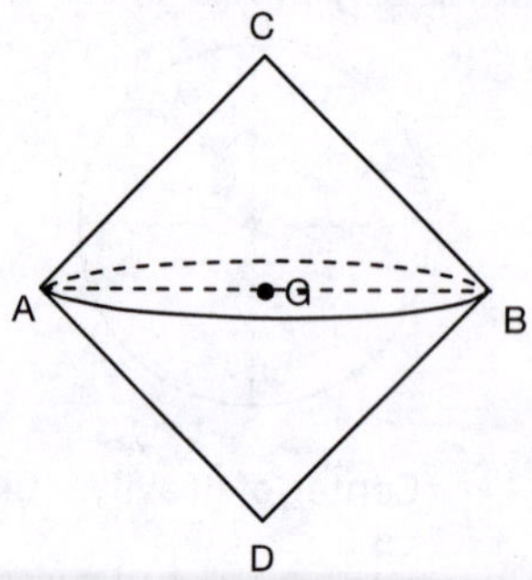

Figure 3.16 Center of gravity – Right circular cone

8. The centre of gravity of an annular ring is at its geometric centre.

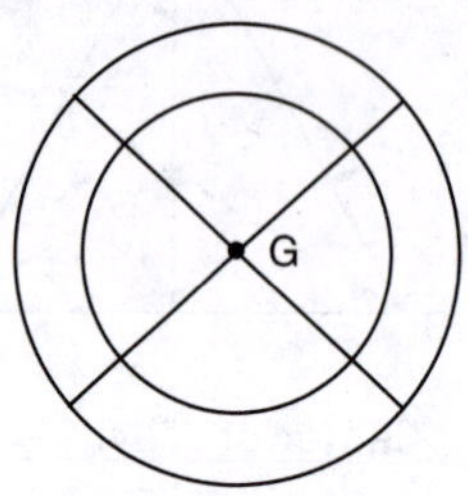

Figure 3.17 Center of gravity – Annular ring

Centre of Gravity of an Irregular Lamina

The centre of gravity of an irregular lamina is determined by suspending it at any three different points near its edge and drawing lines from the point of suspension along the plumb line. The point of intersection of the three lines gives the position of the centre of gravity, as shown in the Figure. 3.18.

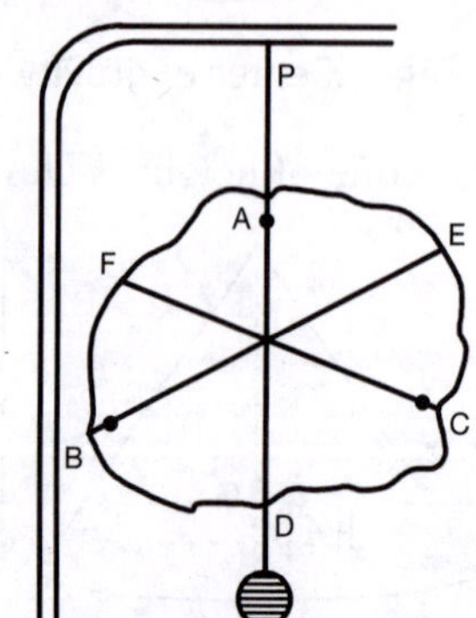

Figure 3.18 Center of gravity – Irregular shaped lamina

Stability of Bodies

Consider two cylinders *A* and *B* of equal height but having different cross-sectional areas, as shown in the Figure 3.19. On giving a slight push to both of them by applying equal forces at their top ends, it is found that the thin cylinder falls down easily whereas the thick cylinder tilts slightly but regains its original position when the applied force is removed. From this, we conclude that bodies with larger base area are more stable than bodies with smaller base area.

Now, consider two cylinders *X* and *Y* having different heights but having equal areas of cross section, as shown in the Figure 3.20.

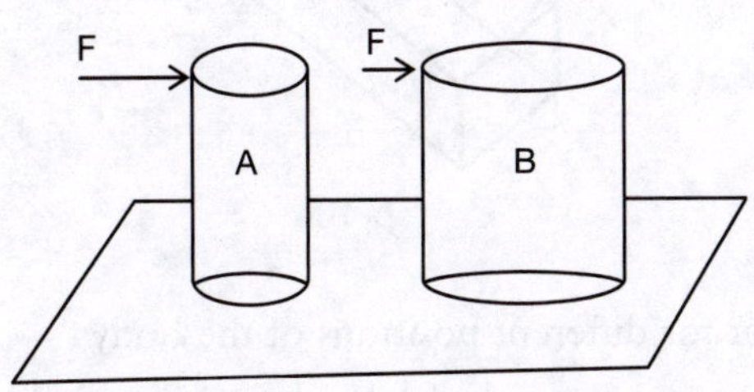

Figure 3.19 Stability of a body increases with increase in base area of a body

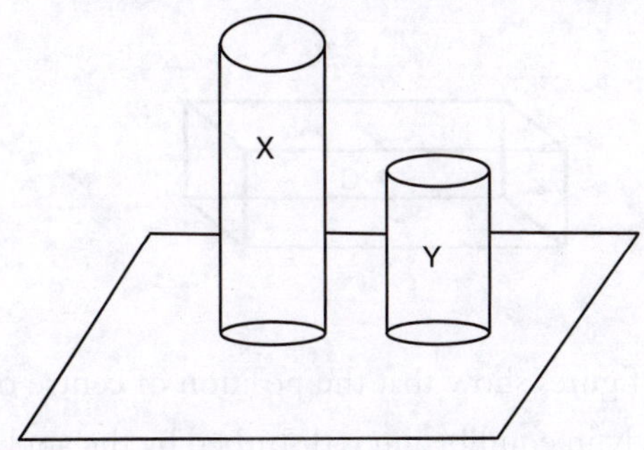

Figure 3.20 Stability of a body decreases with increase in height of the body

On applying equal forces on each of them at their top ends, the longer cylinder falls down easily as compared to the shorter one. This shows that the shorter body whose centre of gravity is at a lesser height from its base is more stable than the longer body whose centre of gravity is comparatively at a greater height from its base. The leaning tower of Pisa, one of the seven wonders of the world, is slightly tilted but it is stable. This is because the imaginary line joining the centre of gravity of the tower and the centre of the Earth falls within the base of the tower.

Thus, the stability of a body depends on

- its base area,
- the height of the centre of gravity from its base and
- the position of the centre of gravity.

Broader the base, greater is the stability. Lesser the height of the centre of gravity, greater is the stability. For example, Racing cars have a broad base and lower height of their centres of gravity from their bases and their wheels are more apart, as compared to a passenger car.

Konnect

The stability of a body increases when it has a broader base and the height of its centre of gravity from its base is lower.

Equilibrium of Bodies

A body is said to be in equilibrium if it does not experience a change in its state of rest or of uniform motion, even under the influence of external forces. For example, A book lying on the table is said to be in equilibrium because the resultant force acting on it is zero.

The force due to gravity equal to '*mg*' acts on the book in the downward direction where '*m*' is the mass of the book and the table exerts a force *R* which is equal and opposite to '*mg*'.

$\therefore R = mg$.

Thus, net force acting on the book is zero.

Example: A body moving on a smooth surface in a straight line with uniform velocity is in equilibrium as the net force acting on it is zero.

Conditions for a Body to be in Equilibrium

1. Resultant of all linear forces (forces that impart translatory motion) acting on the body should be equal to zero.
2. The resultant of all the turning effects should be equal to zero.

Kinds of Equilibrium

By position of a body, we refer to the position of the centre of gravity of that body with respect to some reference point, line or a plane surface. So, in a way the position of a body refers to the height of the centre of gravity from the base of a body, taking the base as reference plane.

Consider the following figures:

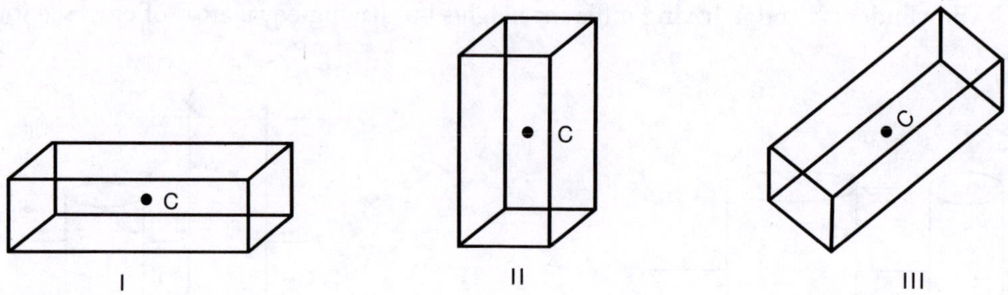

The above figures show that the position of centre of gravity is different for different positions of the body.

When a body in equilibrium is disturbed by the application of a small external force, the body may or may not return to its original position. Depending on its ability to regain its original position, we describe three states of equilibria. They are:

1. Stable equilibrium
2. Unstable equilibrium
3. Neutral equilibrium

1. **Stable Equilibrium:** A body is said to be in stable equilibrium if it regains its original position on the removal of the external force after being slightly disturbed by it. The body in stable equilibrium has minimum potential energy.

   For a body to be in stable equilibrium, the line joining the centre of gravity and the centre of the Earth must fall within the base of a body, after being disturbed by an external force. The base of the body should be broad and heavy. The heavy base lowers the position of the centre of gravity.

   A book lying on a flat table with its broad surface in horizontal position and a right circular cone lying on a surface on its base are examples of stable equilibrium.

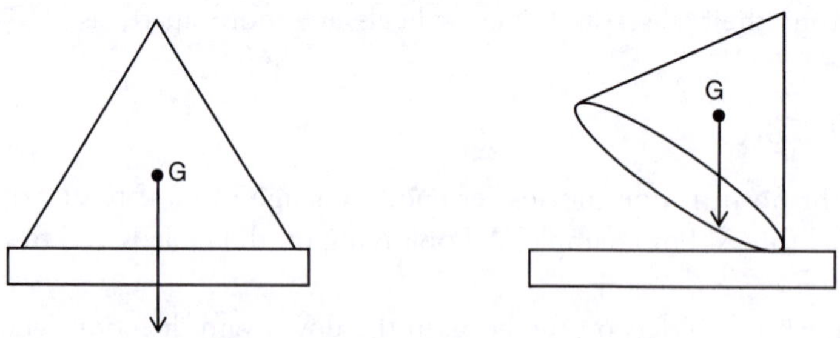

Figure 3.21 Stable equilibrium of the cone

2. **Unstable Equilibrium:** A body is said to be in unstable equilibrium when it does not regain its original position after being slightly disturbed by an external force. The body in unstable equilibrium has high potential energy.

   A body is in unstable equilibrium when, on application of an external force, the imaginary line joining its centre of gravity and the centre of the Earth falls outside its base. The base of the body should be small and the top portion of the body should be heavy as it raises the height of the centre of gravity from its base.

A bottle standing on the edge of its mouth, a cone resting on its apex, a book placed on its edge are examples of unstable equilibrium.

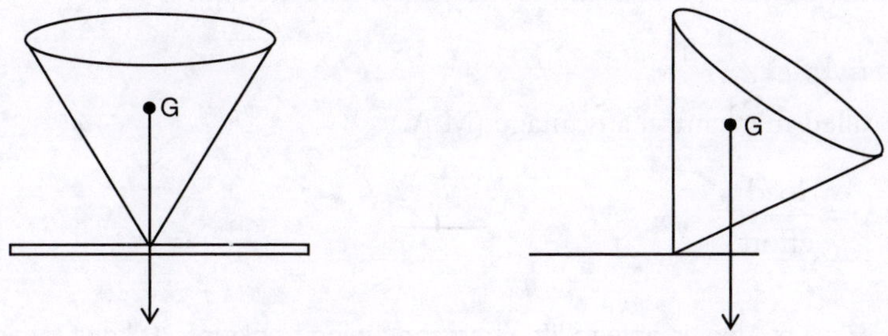

Figure 3.22 Unstable equilibrium

3. **Neutral Equilibrium:** A body is said to be in neutral equilibrium when it moves to a new place on the application of an external force and on the removal of the external force the body may or may not come back to its original place, but the height of its centre of gravity from a reference surface remains the same. When a body is in neutral equilibrium, the line joining the centre of gravity and the centre of the Earth falls within the base of body on the application of external force.

   A rolling ball, a cylinder lying on its curved surface, a cone resting on its side are some of the examples of bodies in neutral equilibrium.

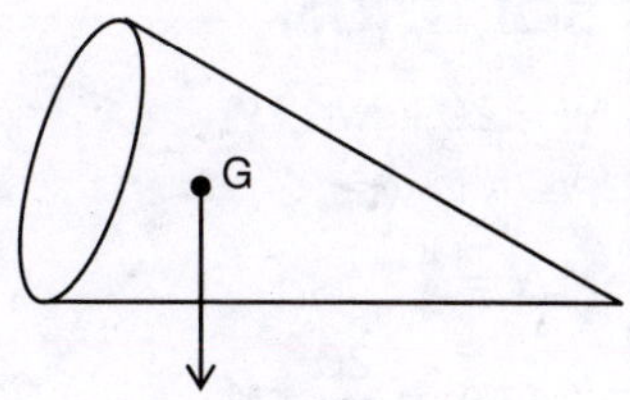

Figure 3.23 Neutral equilibrium

Practical Applications

1. **Person Walking on a Tight Rope:** A person walking on a rope is in unstable equilibrium because a little push may result in his falling down. He can walk on a tight rope without falling as long as the imaginary line joining his centre of gravity to the centre of the Earth passes through the rope.
   In order to achieve this, he holds a pole in his hands and changes the orientation of the pole in such a way that the line joining his centre of gravity and the centre of the Earth always passes through the rope.
2. **Construction of Ship and its Stability:** A ship should remain stable even at the time of a cyclone, when wind blows with high speed and tides with large energy strike it. This high stability is achieved by making the base of the ship as large as possible and lowering the height of the centre of gravity, so that it is in stable equilibrium.

Simple Machines

In order to lift heavy objects while loading or unloading a truck, to draw water from well, to climb upstairs, etc., we make use of different devices. These devices make work easier and quicker. These are called simple machines.

A **simple machine** is a device used to overcome resistance by applying a smaller force at a convenient point and the effect of this force is obtained at another point, with change in magnitude or direction or both.

Some simple machines are as follows:

1. Inclined plane
2. Pulleys
3. Wheel and axle
4. Wedge
5. Jack

The following are some terms used in understanding the working of simple machines.

Power (P)

Machine cannot do the work on its own. It works only when a force is applied on it at a convenient point. A force applied to the simple machine is called **power**. Sometimes this is also referred to as an 'effort'.

Load (W)

The force that is to be overcome by the use of a simple machine is called **load.**

Mechanical Advantage (M.A.)

The ratio of load to effort is called mechanical advantage (M.A.)

Thus, mathematically, $\text{M.A.} = \dfrac{\text{load}}{\text{effort}}$

EXAMPLE 3.8 A student is able to lift a bag containing books of 20 kgwt by applying a force of 5 kgwt. Find the mechanical advantage.

SOLUTION

W = 20 kgwt

P = 5 kgwt

M.A. = ?

$\therefore \text{M.A.} = \dfrac{20}{5} = 4$

Velocity Ratio (V.R.)

It is the ratio of distance through which the point of application of the effort moves to the distance through which the point of application of the load moves in the same interval of time.

$$\text{Velocity ratio} = \frac{\text{Displacement of the power}}{\text{Displacement of the load}}$$

Efficiency (η)

It is the ratio of work done by a machine to the work done on the machine.

Work done on the machine is also called input.

Work done by the machine is also called output.

Thus, $$\text{Thus Efficiency} = \frac{\text{Work done by the machine}}{\text{Work done on the machine}}$$

(Or)

$$\text{Efficiency} = \frac{\text{Output}}{\text{Input}}$$

Konnect

No machine can be 100% efficient due to friction.

Some times, efficiency is expressed as percentage.

Then, $$\text{Percentage efficiency} = \frac{\text{Output}}{\text{Input}} \times 100$$

Relation among Mechanical Advantage, Velocity Ratio and Efficiency

'*P*' is the effort applied to overcome a load '*W*' (Figure 3.24). The load moves through a distance *y* when the point of application of the effort moves through a distance *x*.

Work done by the effort = Work done on the machine = $P \times x$ (1) $\longrightarrow$ Input

Work done by the machine = $W \times y$ (2) $\longrightarrow$ Output

$$\therefore \text{Efficiency} = \frac{W \times y}{P \times x}$$

$$\text{Efficiency} = \frac{\frac{W}{P}}{\frac{x}{y}}$$

$$\therefore \text{Efficiency} = \frac{\text{Mechanical advantage}}{\text{Velocity ratio}}$$

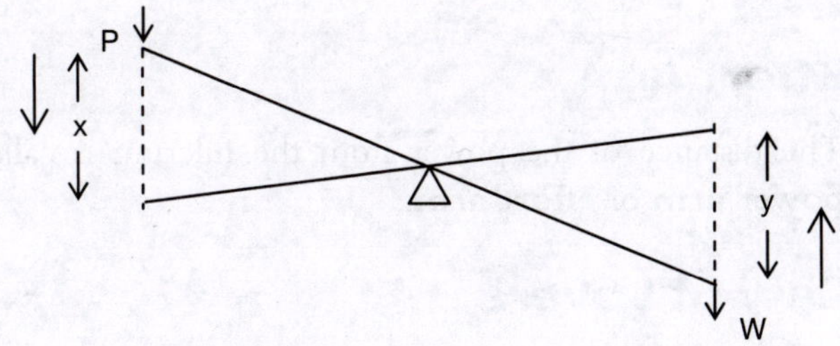

Figure 3.24 Effort applied on load W

EXAMPLE 3.9

The mechanical advantage of a machine is 4 and its velocity ratio is 5. What is its percentage efficiency?

SOLUTION

$$\text{Percentage efficiency} = \frac{\text{M.A.}}{\text{V.R.}} \times 100$$

Given M.A. = 4 and V.R. = 5

$$\therefore \text{Efficiency} = \frac{4}{5} = 0.8$$

Percentage efficiency = 0.8 × 100 = 80%

EXAMPLE 3.10

A machine is operated by a power of 50 N and the power has a downward displacement of 0.25 m in raising a load of mass 100 N through 10 cm. Calculate M.A., V.R. and efficiency.

SOLUTION

$$\text{M.A.} = \frac{\text{Load}}{\text{Power}} = \frac{100}{50} = 2$$

$$\text{V.R.} = \frac{\text{displacement of the power}}{\text{displacement of the load}}$$

$$\text{V.R.} = \frac{0.25}{0.10} = 2.5$$

$$\eta = \frac{\text{M.A.}}{\text{V.R.}} = \frac{2}{2.5} = 0.8$$

$$\therefore \eta\% = 0.8 \times 100 = 80\%$$

Levers

A **lever** consists of a straight bar or a bent bar free to turn on a pivot called fulcrum. It is used to lift a heavy load with a small power.

Load Arm

The distance of the load from the fulcrum is called **load arm**.

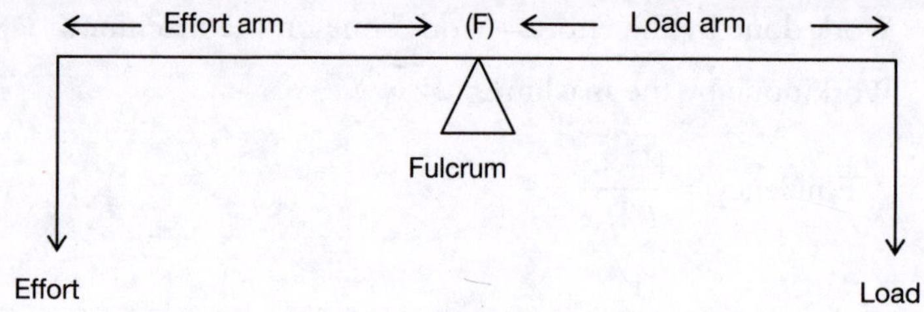

Figure 3.25 Lever

Effort Arm

The distance of the power from the fulcrum is called **power arm** or **effort arm**.

Law of Levers

It states that the product of load and load arm is equal to the product of power and the power arm.

$\Rightarrow$ **load × load arm = power × power arm**

Classification of Levers

The type of lever depends on the relative position of fulcrum, load and effort. Based on this levers are classified into three types. They are as follows:

1. First-order levers or class I lever
2. Second-order levers or class II lever
3. Third-order levers or class III lever

Info Bytes!

The longer the effort arm compared to the load arm, the easier it is to lift the load.

First Order Lever

In a first order lever, fulcrum lies between load and effort.

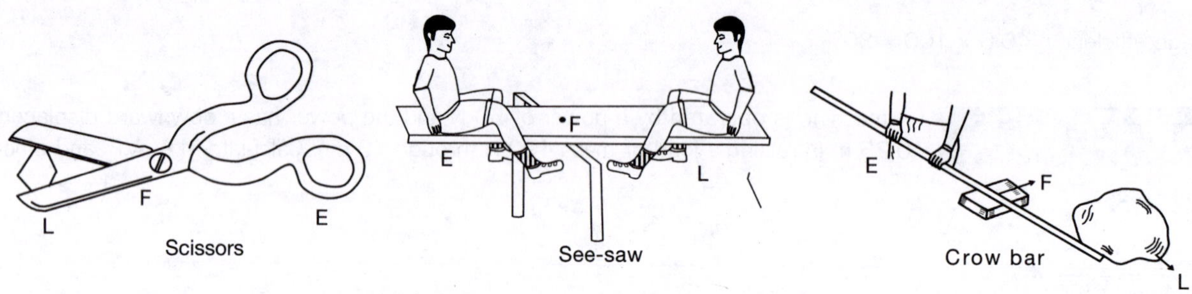

Figure 3.26 Examples of first-order levers

Second Order Lever

In this type of lever, the load lies between the fulcrum and the effort.

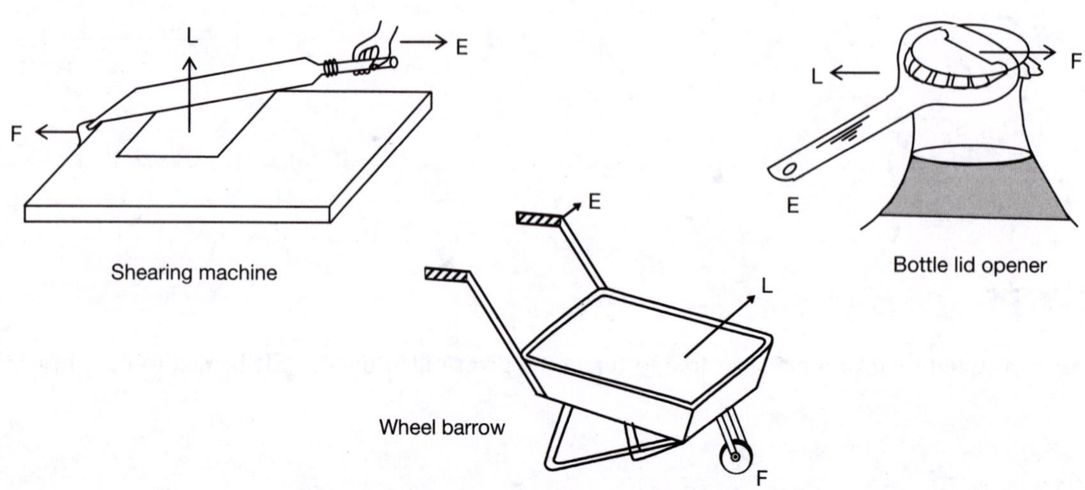

Figure 3.27 Examples of second-order levers

Third Order Lever

In this type, the effort lies between the fulcrum and the load.

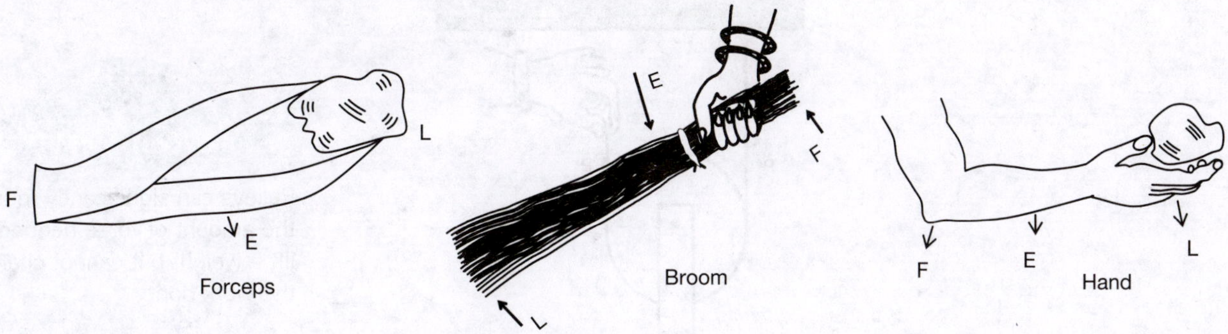

Figure 3.28 Examples of third-order levers

EXAMPLE 3.11 Why does a professional cleaner or a sweeper prefers a broom stick with large handle than a small broom stick used for household purposes?

SOLUTION

If the length of the handle is larger, the ratio of effort arm to load arm is greater and hence the mechanical advantage is greater, leading to lesser effort to accomplish the given task.

$$\text{M.A} = \frac{\text{Effort arm}}{\text{Load arm}}$$

Pulley

It is a simple machine used to alter the direction of force. It consists of a grooved wheel that can turn about an axle passing through its centre. The axle is supported by a block.

It is possible to have a

1. single fixed pulley
2. single movable pulley
3. combination of fixed and movable pulleys (block of pulleys)

Single Fixed Pulley

If the block of the pulley is fastened to a rigid support, it is called **fixed pulley**.

A rope passes over the groove of the pulley. Load is attached to one end of the rope and effort is applied at the other end. This pulley only changes the direction of the action of the force.

Example: Pulley which is used to draw water from a well.

In this type of pulley the effort applied is equal to the load. Thus, its mechanical advantage is equal to one.

$$\Rightarrow \text{Mechanical advantage} = \frac{W}{P} = 1$$

Figure 3.29 Single fixed pulley

Credit Line: *MilanB / Shutterstock*

Single Movable Pulley

In this type, one end of the string is attached to a rigid support and the string passes through the groove of the pulley.

Effort is applied to the free end of the string and the load is attached to the block of the pulley. Thus, the pulley can move up and down along with the load. The various forces acting on the pulley are as shown in the Figure 3.30.

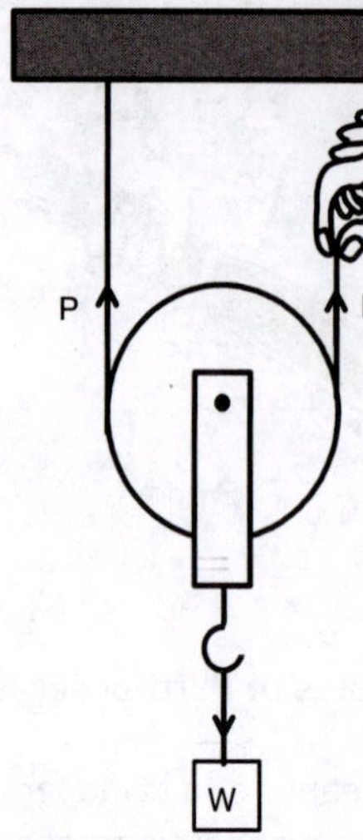

Figure 3.30 Single movable pulley

Konnect

Pulleys can significantly reduce the amount of force needed to lift a weight but cannot change the work done.

It is clear from the Fig. 3.30 that $W = P + P$ or $W = 2P$, where W and P are load and effort, respectively.

Hence, mechanical advantage of a single movable pulley.

$$= \frac{W}{P} = \frac{2P}{P} = 2 \ (\because W = 2P)$$

Block of Pulleys

In order to obtain greater mechanical advantage, a number of movable pulleys are used. In this type, the pulleys are arranged in blocks. The upper block is fixed and the lower block is movable. One such arrangement is shown in the Figure 3.31.

One end of the string is tied to the upper block and it passes over all the pulleys and the effort is applied at the free end of the string. The load is attached to the lowermost movable pulley for equilibrium of the lower block. From the Figure 3.31, it is obvious that $W = P + P + P + P + P + P$ $\Rightarrow W = 6P$ where W and P are the load and the effort, respectively.

The mechanical advantage of the arrangement is given by,

$$\text{M.A.} = \frac{W}{P} = \frac{6P}{P} = 6$$

Hence, if there are 'n' number of pulleys, then M.A. = n.

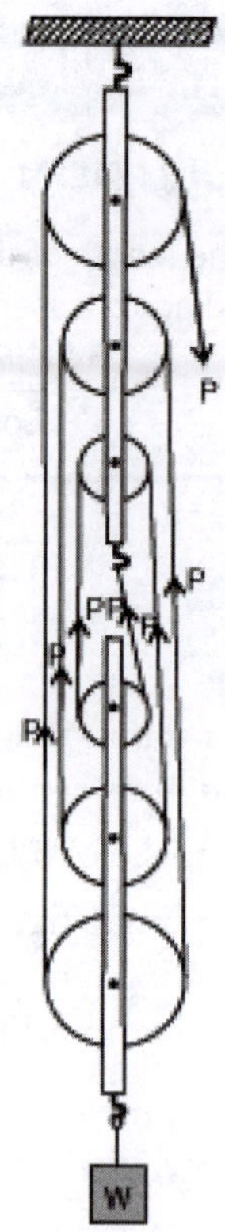

Figure 3.31 Block of pulleys

Inclined Plane

It is a simple machine used to lift a heavy load with a small effort. It is difficult to lift heavy loads vertically against gravity. Hence, inclined planes are used, so that the loads can be rolled or slided up or down with ease. This can be explained with an example below:

To lift heavy loads such as barrels or machinery, etc., to the top of a truck, a plank is laid with one end on the ground and the other end on the top of the truck. Thus, the truck can be loaded or unloaded with small power.

Staircase, over-bridges and mountain roads are also inclined planes.

Figure 3.32 Inclined plane

Credit Line: *MilanB / Shutterstock*

Experiment To find mechanical advantage of an inclined plane

Two wooden planks are joined at one end so that the inclination between them can be varied. In order to reduce friction, a glass plate is fixed on the top surface of the inclined plane. A metal roller (load = W) is tied to one end of the string and the string passes over a pulley, fixed at the top of the inclined plane. To the other end of the string a scale pan is attached (assumed to be of negligible mass).

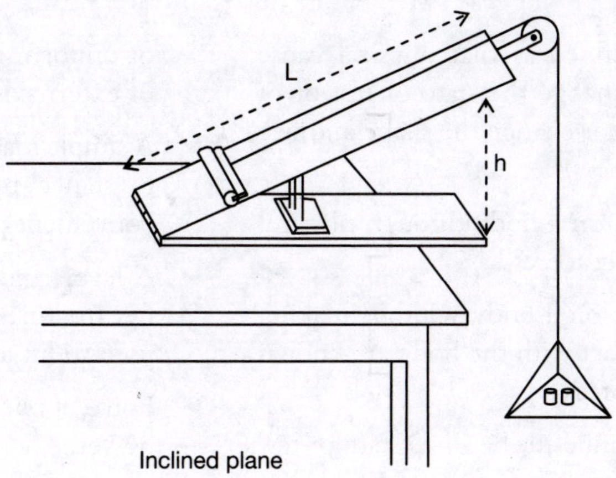

Figure 3.33 Arrangement to determine the mechanical advantage of an inclined plane

Procedure

1. Adjust the inclined plane to a certain height (h).
2. Measure the length of the inclined plane (L).
3. Suitable weights are added in the scale pan, so that the roller just ascends.
4. Note down the weight added in scale pan and this is equal to power (P) used to raise the load.

Work done on the load = $W \times h$

Work done by the effort = $P \times L$

Here, $W \times h = P \times L$

$$\Rightarrow \frac{W}{P} = \frac{L}{h}. \text{ But } \frac{W}{P} = \text{mechanical advantage (M.A.)}.$$

Thus, M.A. of an inclined plane $= \frac{L}{h}$.

Hence, for an inclined plane, the mechanical advantage $= \dfrac{\text{Length of the plane}}{\text{Height of the plane}}$

POINTS TO REMEMBER

- ✔ Force can be defined as that physical cause which tends to change the state of rest or of uniform motion, or change the shape and size of the body.
- ✔ Forces which act on a body through physical contact are contact forces.
- ✔ Forces which act on a body without making any physical contact with the body are known as non-contact forces.
- ✔ Every body continues to be in its state of rest or uniform motion along a straight line unless and until a net external force acts on it.
- ✔ Property of the body to continue in its state of rest or uniform motion unless acted upon by a net external force' is known as law of inertia.
- ✔ The body stops due to an opposing force acting between the body and the surface. This force is called frictional force.
- ✔ The rate of change of momentum is directly proportional to the applied force and takes place in the direction of force.
- ✔ This acceleration of a freely falling body towards the centre of the Earth, caused due to the pull of the Earth, is known as 'acceleration due to gravity'.
- ✔ Work is said to be done when a net force acts on a body and the body undergoes displacement.
- ✔ Energy is defined as the ability of a body to do work.
- ✔ A body is said to be in equilibrium if it does not experience a change in its state of rest or of uniform motion, even under the influence of external forces.
- ✔ A simple machine is a device used to overcome resistance by applying a smaller force at a convenient point.
- ✔ A lever consists of a straight bar or a bent bar free to turn on a pivot called fulcrum. It is used to lift a heavy load with a small power.
- ✔ Force applied to the simple machine is called power.
- ✔ The force that is to be overcome by the use of a simple machine is called load.
- ✔ The ratio of load to effort is called mechanical advantage (M.A.)
- ✔ Efficiency is the ratio of work done by a machine to the work done on the machine.
- ✔ A lever consists of a straight bar or a bent bar free to turn on a pivot called fulcrum.
- ✔ The distance of the load from the fulcrum is called load arm.
- ✔ The distance of the power from the fulcrum is called power arm or effort arm.
- ✔ Law of levers states that the product of load and load arm is equal to the product of power and the power arm.
- ✔ Pulley is a simple machine used to alter the direction of force.
- ✔ Inclined plane is a simple machine used to lift a heavy load with a small effort.

CLASSROOM WING

PRACTICE QUESTIONS

Very Short Answer Type Questions

Directions for questions 1 to 13:
Fill in the blanks.

1. ________ is the physical quantity that changes or tends to change the state of rest or of uniform motion of a body.
2. The rate of change of momentum of a body is proportional to __________.
3. When the mass of a body is kept constant, its acceleration is directly proportional to the ________ acting on it.
4. Powder is sprinkled on a carom board to reduce the ________.
5. A constant force of 2 N acts on a body for 5 seconds to change its velocity. The change in its momentum is ______________.
6. 1 newton = ________ dynes.
7. A plumb line is used to determine the center of gravity of ________ lamina.
8. A bottle standing on its base is more stable than when it stands on its neck. This is so because when it stands on the base its __________.
9. Friction in moving parts of a machine can be reduced by using _____________.
10. Bottle lid opener is an example of ______ lever
11. One S.I. unit of force is _______ times one unit of force in CGS system.
12. See-saw is an example of ________ order lever.
13. The mechanical advantage of a broomstick is ________.

Directions for questions 14 to 25:
Answer the following questions

14. Define newton.
15. Define work.
16. What is energy?
17. What is a rigid body?
18. Weightlessness experienced by astronauts on the moon or people during free fall.
19. A rod of 4 m in length is bent in the form of a square. What is the distance of the centre of gravity to any one of the vertices (in m)?
20. Give three examples of bodies in unstable equilibrium.
21. What is a simple machine?
22. (i) What is mechanical advantage?
    (ii) Define efficiency of a machine.
23. What is a lever?
24. What is a first order lever?
25. What is the use of a pulley?

Short Answer Type Questions

26. Derive $F = ma$
27. Explain the inertia of rest through some examples.
28. An empty truck of mass 1000 kg is moving at a speed of 36 km h^{-1}. It is loaded with 500 kg material on its way and again moves with the same speed. Will the momentum of the truck remain the same after loading? If not, find the momentum of the truck after loaded.
29. Distinguish between the mass and the weight of a body.
30. A railway wagon of mass 1000 kg is pulled with a force of 10000 N. What is its acceleration?

31. Explain how the position of the centre of gravity determines whether a body is in stable or unstable equilibrium.

32. To make two bodies A and B experience an equal acceleration, forces 6 N and 4 N are applied, respectively. If the bodies are combined, then to produce the same acceleration. What will be the applied force?

33. A railway engine of mass 2 tons moving at a speed of 72 km h^{-1} collides with a wagon at rest. After collision both have a common velocity of 36 km h^{-1}. Find the mass of the wagon. (1 ton = 1000 kg)

34. Find the centre of gravity of a triangular lamina, each side of which measures $9\sqrt{3}$ cm

35. State and explain the conditions necessary for equilibrium.

36. Find the effort required to lift a load of 50 kgwt using a simple machine.

37. Derive the mechanical advantage of single fixed pulley?

38. Why are passengers travelling in a double decker bus allowed to stand in a lower deck, but not in the upper deck?

39. What is the efficiency of a machine, given mechanical advantage is 2 and velocity ratio is 4?

40. Derive the mechanical advantage of single movable pulley?

41. State Newton's first law of motion.

42. Two bodies A and B moving towards each other along a straight line, coalesce after collision. At what condition the system will move in the initial direction of A?

43. A certain quantity of mercury is present in a cylindrical vessel of cross-sectional area 'A' up to a height, h. The mercury is then transferred to another cylindrical vessel of cross-sectional area 2A. What is the shift in the centre of gravity of mercury with respect to the base of the cylindrical vessels?

Essay Answer Type Questions

44. State and prove the law of conservation of momentum.

45. Obtain the relation between mechanical advantage, velocity ratio and efficiency.

46. Explain how the centre of gravity of an annular ring is determined.

47. Describe an experiment to determine mechanical advantage of an inclined plane.

48. A ball of mass 200 g moving with a speed of 2 m s^{-1} hits a wall normally and bounces back with the same speed. If the ball is in contact with the wall for 2 milliseconds, then calculate the force exerted on the ball.

COMPETITION WING

PRACTICE QUESTIONS

Level 1: Apply your Concepts

Directions for questions 1 to 5:
State whether the following statements are true or false.

1. Every body continues to be in its state of rest or of uniform motion, unless a net external force acts on it is Newton's second law of motion.
2. The inability of a body to change its state unless acted upon by a net external force is called inertia.
3. Product of mass and velocity is called momentum.
4. The line drawn in the direction of force is called line of action of that force.
5. Frictional force always acts in a direction opposite to the weight of the body.

Directions for questions 6 to 14:
Fill in the blanks.

6. Mass of a body is a ________ quantity whereas its weight is a ________ quantity.
7. ________ is the measure of inertia.
8. Newton's first law of motion is also called law of ________.
9. A wheel barrow is an example of ________ order of lever.
10. For greater stability, the position of center of gravity should be low and base area should be ________.
11. The force exerted by a body on the Earth is ________ the force exerted by the Earth on the body.
12. 'A' can finish certain work in one day and B can finish the same work in two days. The ratio of energy spent by A to that spent by B is _____.
13. Two spheres moving in opposite directions along a straight line can interchange their velocities on colliding with each other if ________.
14. A car changes its speed from 20 km h^{-1} to 50 km h^{-1}. This is possible only if ______ is applied on the car.

Direction for question 15:
Match the entries given in Column A with appropriate ones in Column B.

15. Match the statements of Column A with those of Column B.

Column A	Column B
(A) Frictional force between highly polished surfaces in contact	(a) Outside the body
(B) Interaction between protons and neutrons	(b) Increases
(C) Centre of gravity of an annular ring	(c) Decreases
(D) When a person standing on a swing sits, the height of the centre of gravity	(d) Nuclear forces
	(e) Within the body
	(f) Electromagnetic forces

Directions for questions 16 to 40:
For each of the questions, four choices have been provided. Select the correct alternative.

16. When two marbles collide, their total momentum before collision is equal to
    (a) the difference in their momentum after collision.
    (b) the average of their momentum after collision.
    (c) the square of the sum of their momentum after collision.
    (d) their total momentum after collision.
17. A nut cracker is an example of ________.
    (a) first-order lever
    (b) second-order lever
    (c) third-order lever
    (d) None of the above

18. A man standing on one leg is an example of ________.
(a) unstable equilibrium
(b) stable equilibrium
(c) neutral equilibrium
(d) Both (b) and (c)

19. The momentum of a body
(a) is associated with its motion.
(b) is a product of mass of the body and its velocity.
(c) is a vector quantity.
(d) All the above

20. The wrong statement in the following is ________.
(a) action and reaction act on two different bodies
(b) action and reaction are equal in magnitude
(c) action and reaction are opposite in direction
(d) None of the above

21. When a fast moving vehicle is stopped suddenly the person sitting in it tend to fall forward. This is due to ________.
(a) inertia of rest
(b) inertia of motion
(c) inertia of direction
(d) All the above

22. When a person jumps up,
(a) he exerts a force on the ground.
(b) the ground exerts a force on him.
(c) Both (a) and (b) are true
(d) Both (a) and (b) are false

23. When a stationary vehicle suddenly starts, the person in it tend to fall backward. This is due to
(a) inertia of rest.
(b) inertia of motion.
(c) inertia of direction.
(d) All the above

24. The mechanical advantage of tongs is
(a) always equal to one.
(b) always less than one.
(c) always greater than one.
(d) sometimes less than one and sometimes greater than one.

25. Identify the wrong statement.
The momentum of a body is
(a) the product of mass and velocity of the body.
(b) the product of force and time.
(c) the vector quantity.
(d) measured in kg m s^{-1} in S.I. system.

26. The centre of gravity of a boomerang is always situated
(a) inside the material of the body.
(b) outside the material of the body.
(c) at one of its ends.
(d) None of the above

27. An inclined plane of length 2 m is used to lift a load of 100 kgwt. The force required to lift the load is 20 kgwt. The height through which the load is lifted is ________ m
(a) 2 (b) 2.5
(c) 1.5 (d) 0.4

28. To increase the stability of an object such as ship
(a) the base area should be made large.
(b) height of its centre of gravity should be kept as low as possible.
(c) Both (a) and (b)
(d) Neither (a) nor (b)

29. A spring balance is attached to a lever of negligible mass as shown in the diagram. A body of mass 10 kgwt hangs from the lever. The reading of the spring balance is ______ kgwt.
(a) 2 (b) 5
(c) 6 (d) 3.5

30. A cone resting on its apex is an example of
(a) unstable equilibrium.
(b) stable equilibrium.
(c) neutral equilibrium.
(d) None of these

31. A constant force of 100 N acts on the body for 8 s for changing its momentum. The change of momentum of the body is ______ newton second.
(a) 400 (b) 800
(c) 200 (d) 100

32. Action and reaction

(a) always act on two different bodies.

(b) are equal in magnitude.

(c) are opposite in direction.

(d) All the above.

33. The velocity of a body changes from x m s^{-1} to y m s^{-1} in t s under the action of constant external force. Arrange the following steps in sequential order to calculate the magnitude of the external force acting on the body.

(A) Determine the change in velocity, $(y - x)$ m s^{-1}.

(B) The magnitude of an external force acting on the body is $m \times \frac{(y-x)}{t} N$.

(C) Let m be the mass of the body.

(D) The rate of change in velocity is the acceleration of the body, $(y - x/t)m$ that is, s^{-2}.

(a) BCDA (b) CBDA

(c) ABCD (d) CADB

34. An object of mass 500 g moving with a speed of 10 m s^{-1} collides with another object of mass 250 g moving with a speed of 2 m s^{-1} in the opposite direction. After collision both the objects move in the same direction with common velocity. Write the proper order of steps to find out their common velocity after collision.

(A) Calculate the total momentum of two bodies before collision as $m_1 u_1 + m_2 u_2$.

(B) Write down the given values of m_1 and m_2 in SI system.

(C) Write the expression for their total momentum after collision as $(m_1 + m_2)v$ where v is their common velocity.

(D) Assign proper signs to the initial velocities u_1 and u_2.

(E) Using law of conservation of momentum. Equate the above two expressions and determine the value of v as $\frac{m_1 u_1 + m_2 u_2}{m_1 + m_2}$

(a) B D A C E (b) B D C E A

(c) A D B C E (d) C D E B A

35. The work done to move an object of mass 2 kg to a height of 50 m from the ground is _____ J.

(g = 10 m s^{-2})

(a) 100 (b) 1000

(c) 500 (d) 5000

36. The centre of gravity of a ring is situated _____.

(a) inside the material of the ring

(b) outside the material of the ring at the centre

(c) outside the material of the ring anywhere away from the centre

(d) None of the above

37. A bottle standing on its base is more stable than when it stands on its neck. This is so because when it stands on the base its

(a) base area is more.

(b) centre of gravity is nearer to the base.

(c) centre of gravity is at the top.

(d) Both (a) and (b).

38. The mechanical advantage of a broomstick is _____.

(a) always equal to one.

(b) always less than one.

(c) always greater than one.

(d) dependent on where it is held.

39. We know, $L \times dL = E \times dE$; for a given type of lever, the effort arm is always less than loadarm, then

(a) The V.R is less than one.

(b) The M.A is less than one.

(c) The given simple machine is a third-order lever.

(d) All the above.

40. Raju while drawing water from a well with help of a fixed pulley found that he applied more force than the weight of bucket and water. Then,

(a) M.A is less than 1.

(b) efficiency of the pulley is more than 100%.

(c) V.R is equal to one.

(d) Both (a) and (c).

Level 2: Review your Concepts

41. Explain why a person falling from certain height on a hard surface gets hurt more seriously than when he falls on a soft surface.

42. A system of pulleys is used to lift a load of 1000 kg wt. If the efficiency of the pulley system is 80% and velocity ratio is 20, find the effort required to lift the load.

43. A spring balance is used to weigh an object of mass M kg hanged from the centre of a lever as shown in the figure. What is the mass of the object (in kg), if the reading shown by the spring is 60 kg wt and the lever is in equilibrium? (g = 10 m s^{-2})

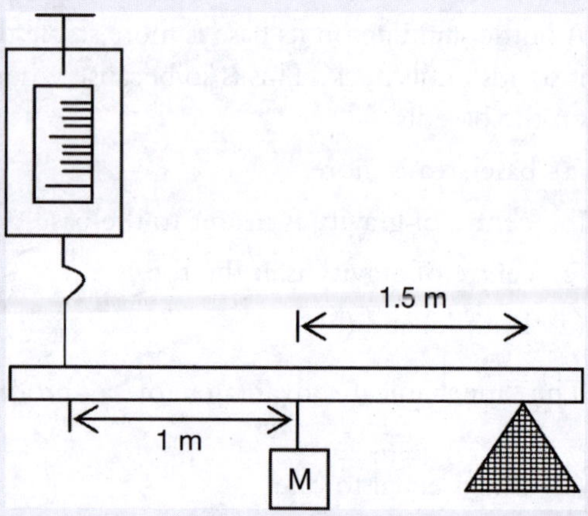

44. A rectangular cuboid whose face ABCD shown with measurements in the figure is cut into two halves diagonally (along AC or BD) and the lower-half portion is used as an inclined plane. What is the mechanical advantage of the inclined plane formed?

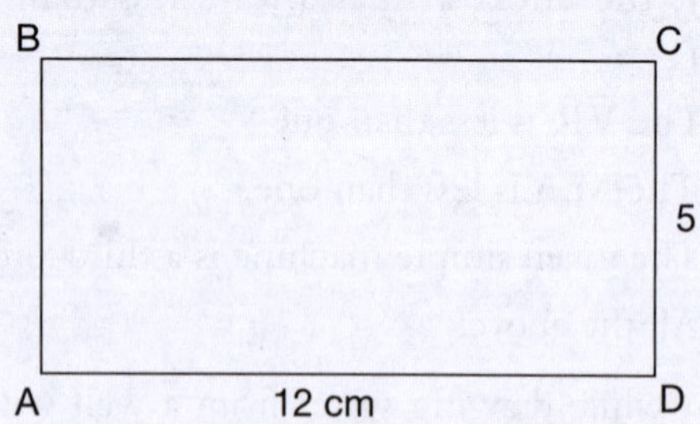

45. A crowbar is of length 3 m. Where should the fulcrum be placed along the length of the crowbar so that a boulder of 9 kg wt be lifted with it by applying an effort of 10 N? (g = 10 m s^{-2})

46. If the mass of a body is increased by 20%, then the momentum of the body remains the same. Calculate the approximate velocity.

47. Explain which of Newton's laws of motion are applicable in the following cases.

(a) A person swimming in water.

(b) A person gets hurt when jumping on the hard cement surface.

(c) A mango falls from the tree when the branch of the tree is suddenly shaken.

(d) The recoil of the gun when the bullet is fired from it.

(e) To compare accelerations produced in spheres of mass m and 2 m, when equal force is applied to them.

48. A person, sitting in a car, tries to move the car by applying force to its walls. Will the car move? Explain in detail.

49. What is the percentage change in the momentum of the body, if the mass of a body is doubled and its velocity is reduced by half?

50. Calculate the density of a cubical ice block of side 50 cm if a force 1125 N applied to it produces an acceleration of 10 m s^{-2} in it. Neglect the force of friction. Assume the ice block remains in solid state without melting.

51. To lift a body vertically up from the surface of the Earth through a certain height, 20 J of work is required. If the same body is lifted up vertically through an equal height on the surface of the Moon, then calculate the work required.

$$\left(g_{\text{moon}} = \frac{g_{\text{earth}}}{6}\right)$$

52. A load of 10 kg weight is suspended at one end of a lever which is pivoted on a fulcrum at the other end, as shown in the given figure. What should be the effort (P) (in N), if we apply the effort at the centre of the lever to balance it? (g = 10 m s^{-2})

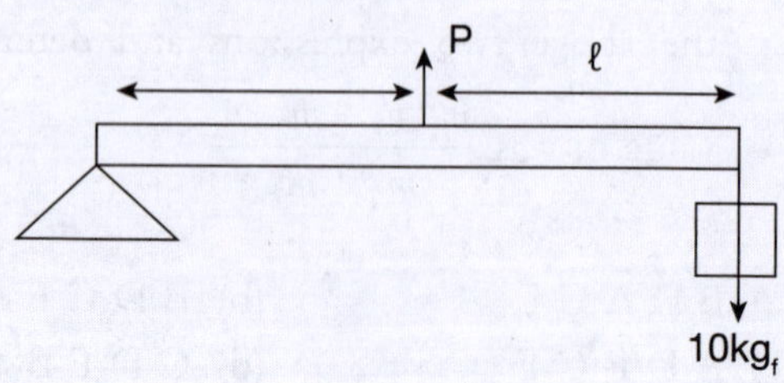

53. Find the magnitude of the force applied to a block of mass 5 kg at rest if it moves 36 m in the first 6 seconds. Neglect the force of friction.

54. A clean hole is made in a glass window pane when it is struck by a bullet fired from a gun. Whereas, the same window pane will be broken to pieces when struck by a stone of a similar size. Explain this phenomenon quoting the relevant principles.

55. A car of mass 1000 kg is moving with a certain speed. When a constant braking force 1000 N acts on it for 5s and the speed of the car reduces to half its original speed. Find the further time required to stop the car if the same constant force acts.

56. A force can produce an acceleration of 2 m s^{-2} and 6 m s^{-2} on bodies A and B, respectively, when applied individually. What is the acceleration produced (in m s^{-2}), if the bodies are combined and the same force is applied?

57. Two forces having magnitudes 3F and 2F, when act in the same direction simultaneously on a body, the net force is equal to 25 N. Find the value of F.

58. If a force of 50 N is applied on a body and it is still at rest, then find the magnitude of static frictional force acting on it.

59. Find the energy possessed by a bird of 5 kg moving at a constant height of 10 m from the ground with a speed of 2 m s^{-1}. (Take g = 10 m s^{-2}.)

60. A brick measures 12 cm × 6 cm × 3 cm. Initially, it is kept on the ground such that the rectangular surface with the smallest area is in contact with the ground and then it is placed such that the rectangular surface with the largest area touches the ground. Calculate the height of the centre of gravity from the ground in the two cases. Out of the two positions, in which case does the brick have greater stability and why?

Level 3: Assess Your Concepts

61. Two spheres of mass 10 g and 100 g each falls on the two pans of a table balance from a height of 40 cm and 10 cm, respectively. If both are brought to rest in 0.1 second, determine the force exerted by each sphere on the pans.

62. What is the efficiency of the pulleys, if the pulleys used in the following system are frictionless and the string used is massless?

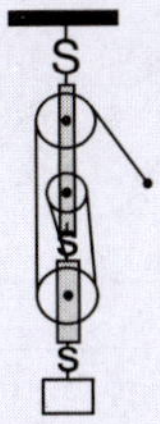

63. A hollow spherical ball is completely filled with water. But due to leakage, water continuously flows out of it and finally no water is left in the ball. Discuss the variation in the position of the center of gravity as the water leaks out.

64. Two spheres made of clay of masses 'm_1' and 'm_2' moving along a straight line in the same direction collide with each other. Their velocities just before collision are 'u_1' and 'u_2', respectively. After collision, they stick together and move with the same velocity, in the same direction, along the straight line. Find the velocity with which they move together.

65. A force 50 N acts on a block A of mass 3 kg which is in contact with a block B of mass 2 kg, as shown in the figure. Find the forces acting on A and B. Will the same forces act on A and B if instead of applying the force to A, it is applied to B?

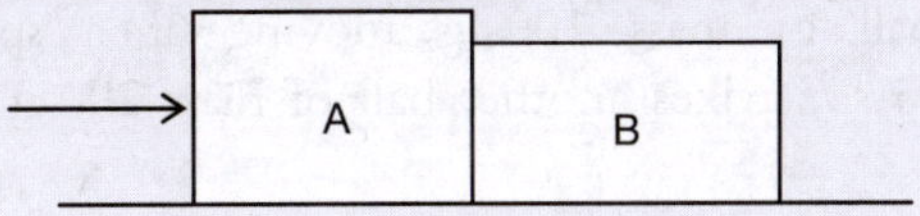

66. A physics student took a solid sphere of density 2 g cm^{-3} and radius 3.5 cm and applied a force on the sphere. If an acceleration of 1.5 cm s^{-2} is produced in it, find the amount of force applied on it.

67. A bullet of mass 50 g is fired from a gun. If the bullet acquires a velocity of 100 m s^{-1} in 0.1 second, what is the recoil force on the gun?

68. Ramu saw in a NEWS channel that a goods train of mass 200 metric ton moving with a velocity of 72 km h^{-1} collides with a passenger train of mass 300 metric ton with a velocity of 54 km h^{-1} coming in the opposite direction on the same track and both the trains move together after collision. He calculates their common velocity. Find what could be his answer.

69. A T.V. stand with wheels is placed on a trolley. What happens if the trolley starts immediately and also if trolley is suddenly stopped?

70. The physics teacher gave a rod of length 'L' units to Roy and the teacher asked Roy to find the shift in the centre of gravity when ¼ of the total length of the rod is removed. What will be the Roy's answer in terms of L?

71. A rectangular tank is completely filled with water. But due to leakage, water continuously flows out of it and finally, the tank is empty. Discuss the variation in the position of the centre of gravity as the water leaks out.

72. If a body of mass 5 kg is dragged along the frictionless inclined plane shown in the figure, then calculate the effort (p) required to drag the body. (g = 10 m s^{-2})

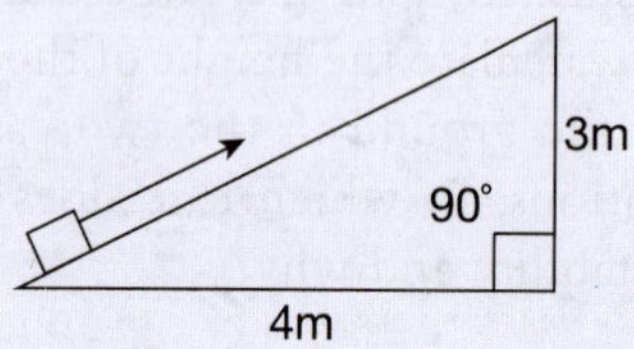

73. An inclined plane of length 6 m is used to lift a load of 42 N, by applying an effort of 7 N. Find the height of the plane.

74. A system of pulleys is used to lift a load of 1000 kgwt. If the efficiency of the pulley system is 80% and velocity ratio is 20, find the effort required to lift the load.

75. A ball of mass 100 g moving at a speed of 12 m s^{-1} strikes another ball of mass 200 g at rest. After the collision both the balls move with a common velocity. Find the common velocity

76. It is easier to pull a lawn roller than to push, why? Explain with a free body diagram.

77. A body of mass 4 kg is at rest on a horizontal surface. It is acted upon by a constant horizontal force of 20 N for 6 s. At the end of 6 s, the force ceases to act. Calculate the displacement of the body at the end of 8 s (Assume the surface is smooth).

78. A bomb of mass 'm' at rest explodes into three pieces. Two of the pieces having masses m/6 and 2m/6, were thrown off in perpendicular directions with velocities of 6 m s^{-1} and 4 m s^{-1}respectively. What is the velocity of the third piece?

79. (a) If the kinetic energy and momentum of a body of mass 'm' are 'K' and 'p' respectively, find a relation between 'm', 'K' and 'p'.

(b) Two marbles of masses 1 g and 4 g are moving with equal kinetic energies. Calculate the ratio of the magnitudes of their:

(i) velocities

(ii) momenta.

80. A motor hoists 9000 kg of limestone in one hour from a mine to a height of 120 m. If the efficiency of motor is 75%, calculate the work done by the motor (in J) and power of the motor (in HP). Take g = 10 m s^{-2}.

AT

JEE-NEET SPECIAL WING

PRACTICE QUESTIONS

Multiple-Answer Type Questions

Directions for questions 1 to 5:
Select one or more correct alternative(s) from the given choices.

1. Identify the non-contact force.
   (a) Electric force
   (b) Magnetic force
   (c) Mechanical force
   (d) Force of friction

2. If the net force acting on a body is zero, then the
   (a) body is observed to be at rest.
   (b) body is moving with uniform velocity
   (c) body is in non - uniform motion.
   (d) cannot be determined

3. What are the factors affecting frictional force?
   (a) Nature of surfaces in contact.
   (b) Normal force on the body.
   (c) Nature of motion of the body
   (d) Mass of the body.

4. Which is true according to Newton's second law of motion?
   (a) F. m $(v - u) = \Delta t$
   (b) $F = \frac{m(v-u)}{t}$
   (c) $F = ma$
   (d) $\frac{\Delta p}{\Delta t} = a$

5. The stability of a body depends on
   (a) position of centre of gravity
   (b) its density
   (c) pressure exerted by the body.
   (d) its base area.

Comprehension-Based Questions

Directions for questions 6 to 10:
These questions are based on the following information.

Simple Machines: Any device that is used to change the motion or the magnitude and direction of force applied to an object to perform work is called a simple machine. There are mainly 6 types of simple machines:

- Lever
- Pullies
- Inclined plane
- Wedges
- Axle
- Wheels

Simple machines are the simplest mechanisms that use mechanical advantage (leverage) to multiply force.

6. Power of a simple machine is also referred to as
   (a) Load (b) M. A.
   (c) Effort (d) Fulcrum

7. Identify the correct relation
   (a) Velocity ratio $= \frac{\text{Displacement of the load}}{\text{Displacement of the power}}$
   (b) Velocity ratio $= \frac{\text{Displacement of the power}}{\text{Displacement of the load}}$
   (c) Velocity ratio $= \frac{\text{Displacement of the power}}{\text{Time}}$
   (d) Velocity ratio $= \frac{\text{Displacement of the load}}{\text{Time}}$

8. Ishita lifts her school bag containing books of 28 kg w t by the application of force of 4 kg wt. The mechanical advantage will be
   (a) 4 (b) 5
   (c) 6 (d) 7

9. The velocity ratio of a machine whose mechanical advantage is 6 and efficiency to be 75% is
(a) 4
(b) 6
(c) 8
(d) 10

10. The ratio of work done by a machine to work done on the machine is
(a) Efficiency
(b) Effort
(c) Velocity ratio
(d) Load

Match the Column

Directions for question 11:
The question is based on the following information.

Levers: Levers are the most fundamental machines that is used to perform work with minimum effort. It is a simple machine that consists of a bar that rotates around a fixed point called fulcrum. Based on the position of fulcrum, effort and load, levers are classified as

- Class I lever (eg.: - scissors, see - saw, etc.)
- Class II lever (eg.: - staplers, doors, etc.)
- Class III lever (eg.: - forearm of a human, etc.)

11. Match the values in List - I with those in List - II:

List - I	List - II
A. Law of levers	a. The distance of the power from the fulcrum.
B. First order lever	b. Load lies between fulcrum and effort
C. Second order lever	c. Effort lies between fulcrum and load
D. Third order lever	d. Fulcrum lies between load and effort
E. Effort arm	e. Load × load arm = power × power arm

(a) A - e, B - d, C - b, D - c, E - a
(b) A - e, B - b, C - c, D - d, E - a
(c) A - b, B - c, C - d, D - a, E - e
(d) A - a, B - e, C - d, D - b, E - c

ANSWER KEYS

Crossword

Across

2. weightlessness
4. newton
7. power arm
8. weight
9. input
10. force
13. potential energy

Down

1. neutral equilibrium
3. inertia
5. contact force
6. friction
11. centroid
12. momentum

Classroom Wing

Very Short Answer Type Questions

1. Force
2. Force acting on it
3. Force
4. Friction
5. 10 kg m s^{-1}
6. One lakh
7. Irregular
8. Base area is more and center of gravity is low
9. Lubricants and ball bearings
10. Second order lever.
11. One lakh
12. First
13. Always less than one.
19. $\frac{1}{\sqrt{2}}$ m

Short Answer Type Questions

28. 15000 kg m s^{-1}
32. 10 N
33. 2000 kg
34. 8.1 cm from base
36. 25 kgwt
39. 50%
43. h/4 m

Competition Wing

Level 1: Apply your Concepts

1. False
2. True
3. True
4. True
5. False
6. Scalar, vector
7. Mass
8. Inertia
9. Second
10. Large
11. Equal and opposite
12. 1 : 1
13. $m_1 = m_2$
14. External force
15. A : b, B : d, C : a, D : c
16. (d)
17. (b)
18. (a)
19. (d)
20. (d)
21. (b)
22. (c)
23. (a)
24. (b)
25. (b)
26. (b)
27. (d)
28. (c)
29. (c)
30. (a)
31. (b)
32. (d)
33. (d)
34. (a)
35. (b)
36. (b)
37. (d)
38. (b)
39. (d)
40. (a)

Level 2: Review your Concepts

43. 100 kg
44. $\frac{13}{5}$
46. 17%
51. 200N
56. 1.5 ms^{-2}
57. 5 N
58. 50 N
59. 510 J

Level 3 : Assess Your Concepts

62. 1
66. 539 dyne.
67. 50 N
68. 3.6 km h^{-1}
70. $\frac{L}{8}$ units
72. 30 N = $3 \cdot 10^6$ dyne
73. 1 m
74. 62.5 kgwt
75. $4m$ s^{-1}
77. 150 m
78. 3.33 m s^{-1}
79. 2:1, 1:2
80. 1.08×10^7 J, 5.36

JEE-NEET Special Wing

Multiple-Answer Type Questions

1. (a) and (b) **2.** (a) and (b) **3.** (a), (b) and (c) **4.** (b) and (c)

5. (a) and (d)

Comprehension-Based Questions

6. (c) **7.** (b) **8.** (d) **9.** (c) **10.** (a)

Match the Column

11. (a)

For answer key of Classroom wing and Competition wing, refer to Hints and Solutions

Hints and Explanations

Classroom Wing

Very Short Answer Type Questions

1. Force
2. Force acting on it
3. Force
4. Friction
5. 10 kg m s^{-1}
6. One lakh
7. Irregular
8. Base area is more and center of gravity is low
9. Lubricants and ball bearings
10. Second order lever.
11. One lakh
12. First
13. Always less than one.
14. The force which when acting on a body of mass 1kg produces in it an acceleration of 1 m s^{-2} in its direction.
15. When a net force acts on a body and body undergoes displacement.
16. The capacity to do work.
17. An object whose relative positions of the particles in it does not change.
18. Astronauts on the moon and a person experiencing a reactional force feel their weight. But a person undergoing a free fall does not experience his weight.
19.

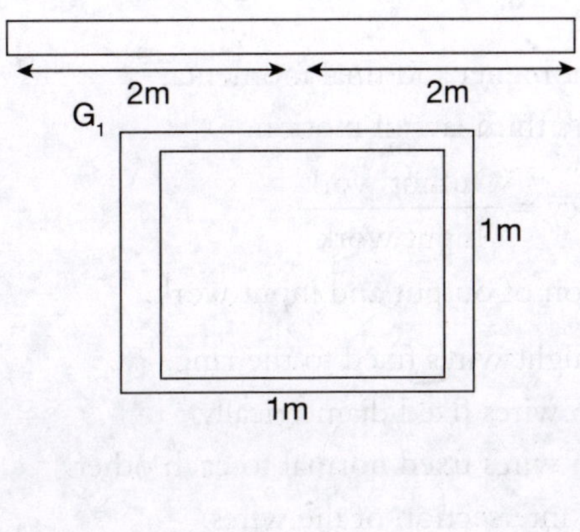

Length of diagonal = $\sqrt{1^2 + 1^2} = \sqrt{2}\,\text{m}$

$\therefore$ The required distance = $\frac{\sqrt{2}}{2} = \frac{1}{\sqrt{2}}\,\text{m}$

20. A bottle standing on the edge of its mouth, a cone resting on its apex, a book placed on its edge.
21. A device used to overcome resistance by applying a small force at a convenient point and its effect obtained at other point.
22. (i) M.A. = $\frac{\text{load}}{\text{effort}}$

    (ii) $\eta = \frac{\text{output}}{\text{input}}$
23. A lever consists of a straight bar or a bent bar free to turn on a pivot.
24. In first order level, fulcrum lies between load and effort.
25. To alter the direction of force.

Short Answer Type Questions

Note: This is how you should frame your answer covering.

26. (1) Initial momentum.
    (2) Final momentum.
    (3) Change in momentum.
    (4) Rate of change of momentum.
    (5) Newton's II Law.
27. (1) Resistance of the body to change its state of rest.
    (2) Books piled one above the other, lowest book is suddenly pulled out, rest of the books remain intact.
    (3) Bus starts suddenly, passengers standing in the bus tend to fall backward.
28. Momentum = mass × velocity

    15000 kg m s^{-1}

29. Mass

(i) Measure of matter contained.

(ii) Magnitude remains constant from place to place.

(iii) Measured using physical balance.

(iv) A scalar quantity.

(v) Measured in units of g or kg.

Weight

(i) Force with which a body is attracted towards the earth.

(ii) Changes with change in acceleration due to gravity.

(iii) Measured using spring balance.

(iv) A vector quantity.

(v) Units: dyne or newton.

30. F = ma

10 m s^{-2}

31. (1) Height of centre of gravity from base.

(2) Line joining centre of gravity to centre of earth.

32. $F = ma$. Here a is constant

$\therefore F_1 = m_1a$ and $F_2 = m_2a$

$\Rightarrow 6 = m_1a$ and $4 = m_2a$

If 'F' is a force on $m_1 + m_2$, then

$F = (m_1 + m_2)\ a = m_1a + m_2a$

$= 6 + 4 = 10$ N

33. Total momentum remains constant.

2000 kg

34. (1) Point of intersection of medians.

(2) Centroid = centre of gravity

(3) Centroid divides each median in the ratio 2 : 3

(4) Ans: 8.1 cm from base.

35. (1) Resultant of all Linear forces acting on the body should be zero.

(2) Resultant of all torques should be zero.

36. Definition of mechanical advantage

25 kgwt

37. (1) Forces acting on the pulley = load = W

(2) Mechanical advantage $= \dfrac{W}{P}$

38. Stable equilibrium.

39. The relation between efficiency, M.A. and V.R.

50%.

40. (1) Load, W = 2P

(2) M.A. $= \dfrac{W}{P}$

41. Every body continues to be in its state of rest or of uniform motion, unless a net external force acts on it.

42. According to the law of conservation of momentum,

$m_1u_1 + m_2u_2 = m_1v_1 + m_2v_2$

$\Rightarrow m_1u_1 + m_2u_2 = (m_1 + m_2)v$

The bodies A and B are moving in opposite directions. Let u_1 be taken as positive, then u_2 would be negative.

$\Rightarrow m_1u_1 - m_2u_2 = (m_1 + m_2)v$

v can be positive if $m_1u_1 > m_2u_2$

Thus, the system will move in the direction of A if its momentum before collision is more than that of B before collision.

43. The volume of mercury remains the same.

Area × height = Area × height

Let the height be h' on transferring the mercury to a new vessel.

$2A \times h' = A \times h$

$$h' = \frac{A \times h}{2A}$$

$$h' = \frac{h}{2}$$

$$\text{The shift in CG } = \frac{h}{2} - \frac{h'}{2}$$

$$= \frac{h}{2} - \frac{h}{4} = \frac{h}{4} = \frac{h}{4}\,m.$$

Essay Answer Type Questions

Note: This is how you should frame your answer covering.

44. (1) Two spheres moving along a straight path and colliding.

(2) Initial momenta and final momenta.

(3) Newton's third law of motion.

45. (1) Efficiency $= \dfrac{\text{Output work}}{\text{Input work}}$

(2) Definition of output and input work.

46. (1) Two straight wires fixed to the ring.

(2) The two wires fixed diametrically.

(3) The two wires fixed normal to each other.

(4) Point of intersection of the wires.

47. (1) Slant plank and a glass plate over it.

(2) Roller and a pulley.

(3) Weight scale and increase weights till roller starts rolling.

(4) $\text{M.A.} = \dfrac{\text{Load}}{\text{Effort}}$

48. $m = 200 \text{ g} = 0.2 \text{ kg}$

$u = -2 \text{ m s}^{-1}$

$v = 2 \text{ m s}^{-1}$

$t = 2$ millisecond

$= 2 \times 10^{-3}$ s

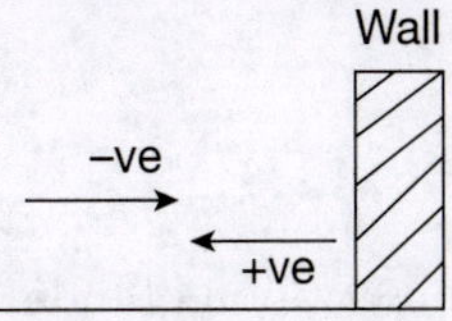

$F = ma,$

but,

$$a - \frac{v-u}{t} = \frac{2-(2)}{2\times10^{-3}} = \frac{4\times10^{3}}{2} 2\times10^{3} \text{ ms}^{-2}$$

$\therefore F = ma$

$= (0.2)\,(2 \times 10^{3}) = 400 \text{ N}$

Competition Wing

Level 1: Apply your Concepts

13. According to the law of conservation of momentum,

$m_1u_1 + m_2u_2 = m_1v_1 + m_2v_2$

But here $v_1 = u_2$, $v_2 = u_1$

Thus, $m_1u_1 + m_2u_2 = m_1u_2 + m_2u_1$

$m_1(u_1 - u_2) = m_2(u_1 - u_2)$

$\Rightarrow m_1 = m_2$

15. (A) $\rightarrow$ b The frictional force between highly polished surfaces in contact increases.

(B) $\rightarrow$ d Interaction between the protons and neutrons inside the nucleus is nuclear force.

(C) $\rightarrow$ a Centre of gravity of an annular ring lies outside the body.

(D) $\rightarrow$ c When a person standing in a swing, sits, the height of the centre of gravity of the system decreases.

31. By Newton's 2nd law

$$F = \frac{m(v-u)}{t}$$

$\Rightarrow mv - mu = F \times t$

Substituting $F = 100$ N

$t = 8$ s

$mv - mu = 100 \times 8 = 800$ N s

Hence, the correct answer is (b).

32. (a) Action and reaction always act on two different bodies.

(b) They are equal in magnitude but opposite in direction.

Hence, the correct answer is (d).

33. Let m be the mass of the body. Determine the change in velocity of the body, i.e., $(y - x)$ m s^{-1}. It takes 't's to change the velocity. So, the rate of change in velocity is $\left(\frac{y-x}{t}\right)$ m s^{-2}, which is the acceleration of the body.

The product of mass and acceleration gives the magnitude of external force acting on the body.

Hence, the correct answer is (d).

34. Given $m_1 = 500\text{ g} = \frac{1}{2}\text{kg}$, $m_2 = 250\text{ g} = \frac{1}{4}\text{kg}$ (b)

$u_1 = 10$ m s^{-1}, $u_2 = -2$ m s^{-1} (d)

Momentum before collision, $m_1\,u_1 + m_2\,u_2$

$$= \frac{1}{2} \times 10 + \frac{1}{4} \times (-2); 5 - \frac{1}{2} = \frac{9}{2}\text{Kg m s}^{-1}$$

Momentum after collision, $(m_1 + m_2)\ v = \frac{3}{4}v$ (c)

From law of conservation of momentum,

$\frac{9}{2} = \frac{3}{4}v \Rightarrow v = 6\text{m s}^{-1}$ (e)

Hence, the correct answer is (a).

35. Work done = mgh

= 2 × 10 × 50 = 1000 J

Hence, the correct answer is (b).

36. The centre of gravity of a ring is situated outside the material of the body, at the centre.

Hence, the correct answer is (b).

37. A bottle standing on the base is more stable because its base area is more and the position of the centre of gravity is as low.

Hence, the correct answer is (d).

38. A broom stick works as a lever of order three. Hence, its mechanical advantage is less than one.

Hence, the correct answer is (b).

39. $L \times dL = E \times dE \Rightarrow \frac{L}{E} = \frac{dE}{dL}$

Given $dE < dL \Rightarrow$ V. R < 1

and also MA < 1

This type of lever is a third-class lever.

Hence, the correct answer is (d).

40.

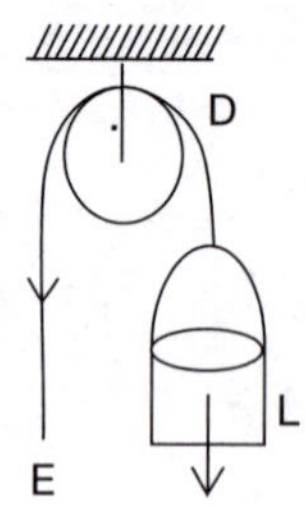

Given $E > L$

$$\text{MA} = \frac{L}{E} < 1$$

Here $\text{DE} = \text{DL} \Rightarrow \text{V.R} = \frac{\text{DE}}{\text{DL}} = 1$

We know, $n = \frac{\text{MA}}{\text{V.R}} < 1$

Therefore, efficiency is less than 100%.

Hence, the correct answer is (a).

Level 2: Review your Concepts

Note: This is how you should frame your answer covering.

41. Force exerted by hard surface on the man is more than the one exerted by soft surface.

42. You have to first find M.A. use efficiency

$$= \frac{\text{Mechanical advantage}}{\text{Velocity ratio}}$$

To find effort use, $\text{M.A.} = \frac{\text{load}}{\text{effort}}$

43. By the principle of lever,
load × load arm = power × power arm

$$\text{load} = \frac{\text{power} \times \text{power arm}}{\text{load arm}}$$

$$= \frac{60 \times 10 \times 2.5}{1.5}$$

$$= 1000 \text{ N}$$

$$\text{Mass object} = \frac{1000}{10} = 100 \text{ kg}$$

44. Mechanical advantage of an inclined plane

$$= \frac{\text{length}}{\text{height}}$$

$$= \frac{\sqrt{12^2 + 5^2}}{5} = \frac{13}{5} = 2\frac{3}{5}$$

45. Find the length of the crowbar.
Find the value of the effort from given data.
Find the value of the load from the given data.
(Covert it into S.I. units).
Now, load × load arm = effort X effort arm (1)
Substitute the values of load and effort.
Find the ratio of the load arm to effort arm from equation (1).
Here, load arm + effort arm = 3 m.
Now, find the position of the fulcrum from the load arm.
Is load arm $= \frac{1}{10}$th part of 3 m?

46. Momentum, $P = mv$

$$P_1 = P_2$$

$$m_2 = \frac{12m_1}{100}$$

$$v_2 = ?$$

$$m_1v_1 = m_2v_2$$

$$\Rightarrow v_2 = \frac{m_1v_1}{m_2}$$

$$v_2 = \frac{m_1v_1}{\frac{120}{100}m_1}$$

$$v_2 = \frac{100}{120}v_1 = 0.83v_1 = 83\% \text{ of } v_1$$

∴ The velocity should be decreased by 17%.

47. a. First law
b. Third law
c. First law
d. Third law
e. Second law

48. An internal force does not produce an acceleration. Only external force produces an acceleration.

49. **1st case:**
mass = m
velocity = v
∴ momentum, $P_1 = mv$
2nd case:
Mass = $2m$

$$\text{velocity} = v - \frac{v}{2} = \frac{v}{2}$$

$$\therefore \text{momentum}, P_2 = (2m)\left(\frac{v}{2}\right)$$

$$P_2 = (2m)\left(\frac{v}{2}\right) = mv$$

$P_1 = P_2$. Therefore, there is no change in momentum.

50. First, find mass by using formula, $F = ma$ and then substitutes mass in $m = V \times \rho$ to find density.
The doll is constructed in such a way that the line joining the center of gravity and the center of Earth fall within the base of the rolly polly doll. So, when the doll is disturbed by an external force, it wobbles and then regains its original position and thereby stable equilibrium.

51. Work done = Force × displacement

$$= mg \times h$$

Work done to lift up the body from the ground on the moon

$$= mg_{\text{moon}} \times h = \frac{mg_{\text{earth}}}{6} = \frac{20}{6} = 3.33 \text{ J}$$

52. According to the law of levers,

effort × effort arm = load × load arm

$$\text{Effort} = \frac{\text{load} \times \text{loadarm}}{\text{effortarm}}$$

$$= \frac{10 \times 10 \times 2\ell}{\ell}$$

= 200 N.

53. Using $s = ut + \frac{1}{2}at^2$, find the acceleration.

To find force, use $F = ma$

54. Which one among the following, i.e., bullet fired from a gun or a stone of similar size will have greater velocity?

From this information, which one will have more momentum?

Is inertia of motion for bullet more than that of stone?

Is the impulsive force exerted by bullet more?

In which case is the force exerted on the window pane more?

55. Find acceleration of the car by using

$F = ma$.

Find the initial speed, by using $v = u + at$

To find the further time taken to stop the vehicle, use $v = u + at$

56. Let the force be F; m_1 and m_2 be masses of 1st and 2nd bodies, respectively.

$a_1 = 2$ m s^{-2} and $a_2 = 6$ m s^{-2}

$\therefore F = m_1a_1 = m_2a_2 = ma$

where,

$m = m_1 + m_2$

$m_1 \times m_2$

$\Rightarrow 3m_2 = m_1$

$$\therefore a = \frac{F}{m} = \frac{m_1a_1}{m_1 + m_2} = \frac{m_2a_2}{m_1 + m_2}$$

$$= \frac{m_2 \times 6}{3m_2 - m_2} = \frac{6m_2}{4m_2} = 1.5 \text{ ms}^{-2}$$

57. Net force = sum of the two forces = $3F + 2F = 5F$

$$\therefore 5F = 25 \Rightarrow F = \frac{25}{5} = 5 \text{ N}$$

58. The magnitude of the force acting on the body (f) = 50 N. Due to application of this force, the body tends to move but is not set in motion, and hence, the applied force is equal in magnitude and opposite in direction to static frictional force.

Therefore, the magnitude of static frictional force acting = 50 N.

59. Given, mass, (m) = 5 kg

Height from the ground, h = 10 m

Velocity, v = 2 m s^{-1}

g = 10 m s^{-2}

The bird possesses both potential energy (PE) and kinetic energy (KE).

$\therefore$ PE = mgh

= 5 × 10 × 10 = 500 J

$$\text{KE} = \frac{1}{2}mv^2 = \frac{1}{2} \times 5 \times 2^2 = 10\text{J}$$

$\therefore$ Energy possessed by the bird = 500 + 10 = 510 J

60. (i) In first case

Height of the brick = 12 cm

Height of CG from the ground = 6 cm

(ii) In second case

Height of the brick = 3 cm

Height of CG from the ground = 1.5 cm

In the second case the brick has more stability because height of CG is small and also base area is more.

Level 3: Assess Your Concepts

Note: This is how you should frame your answer covering.

61. First find the velocity acquired by each sphere using $v^2 = u^2 + 2as$

Find the rate of change of momentum of a sphere

$$= F = \frac{m(v - u)}{t}$$

The force exerted by a sphere = weight (w) + F.

62.

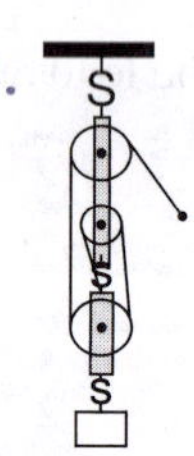

$$\text{Efficiency} = \frac{\text{Mechanical advantage}}{\text{velocity ratio}}$$

From given figure,

E = P

L = 3P

Mechanical advantage

$$= \frac{L}{E} = \frac{3P}{P} = 3$$

The number of pulleys in the system is 3. Thus, the velocity ratio (V.R.) = 3.

$$\text{Efficiency } (|) = \frac{\text{M.A}}{\text{V.R.}} = \frac{3}{3} = 1$$

64. Find the masses of two spheres made of clay.

Find the velocities of the spheres before collision from the given data.

Find the velocity of the spheres after collision.

Here, do the two spheres stick together and move with the same velocity, in the same direction, along the straight line.

Does it mean that they have a common velocity?

Then, find the law of conservation of momentum.

Using data, total momentum of bodies before collision is equal to total momen-tum after collision in a given system.

So, $m_1u_1 + m_2u_2 = m_1v_1 + m_2v_2$ (1)

Given, that, $v_1 = v_2 = v$ (common velocity)

Find the value of 'v' from equation (1).

65. Both the blocks move with the same acceleration given by

$$a = \frac{\text{Force applied on A}}{\text{Mass of A + Mass of B}}$$

The force on B is $F_B = m_B \times a$

Then, B exerts an equal but opposite force on A.

$= 50 - F_B$

66. Given, acceleration, $a = 1.5$ cm s^{-2}

Radius of sphere, $r = 3.5$ cm

Density of sphere = 2 g cm^{-3}

Force, F = (mass) (acceleration)

But mass, m = (volume) (density),

$$\text{Volume V} = \frac{4}{3}\pi r^3 = \frac{4}{3} \times \frac{22}{7} \times (3.5)^3 \text{ cm}^3$$

$$\therefore \text{m} = \frac{4}{3} \times \frac{22}{7} \times \left(\frac{7}{2}\right)^3 \times 2 = \frac{1078}{3} \text{ g}$$

$$\therefore \text{ Force, } F = \frac{1078}{3} \times 1.5 \text{ dyne} = \frac{1078}{2} = 539 \text{ dyne.}$$

67. Mass of bullet, $m = 50$ g $= 50 \times 10^{-3}$ kg

Initial velocity of the bullet, $u = 0$ m s^{-1}

Final velocity of the bullet, $v = 100$ m s^{-1}

Time, $t = 0.1$ s

Force exerted on the bullet,

$$F = ma = m\left[\frac{v-u}{t}\right]$$

$$= 50 \times 10^{-3}\left(\frac{100-0}{0.1}\right) = 50N$$

This is the action on the bullet.

Thus, reaction on the gun = 50 N

$\therefore$ The recoil force on the gun = 50 N

68.

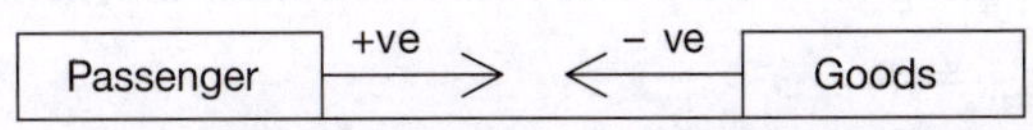

Passenger and goods trains are moving on the same track in opposite directions. Let us consider the direction of motion of passenger train as positive (left to right in the figure) and that of goods train as negative (right to left in the figure).

Mass of passenger train,

m_p = 300 metric ton = 300×10^3 kg

Velocity of passenger train before collision,

u_p = 54 kmph

$$= 54 \times \frac{5}{18} \text{ m s}^{-1} = 15 \text{m s}^{-1}$$

$\therefore$ Momentum of passenger train before collision,

$P_{ip} = 300 \times 10^3 \times 15 = 45 \times 10^5$ kg m s^{-1}

Mass of goods train,

m_g = 200 metric ton = 200×10^3 kg

Velocity of goods train before collision,

$u_g = -72$ km

$$h^{-1} = -72 \times \frac{5}{18} \text{ m s}^{-1} = -20 \text{ms}^{-1}$$

∴ Momentum of goods train before collision,

$P_{ig} = 200 \times 10^3 \times (-20) = -40 \times 10^5$ kg m s^{-1}

[Negative sign is taken, as the direction of motion of goods train is considered negative].

∴ Total momentum before collision,

$P_{i(\text{total})} = P_{ip} + P_{ig}$

$= 45 \times 10^5 + (-40 \times 10^5) = 5 \times 10^5$ kg m s^{-1}

Since total momentum is positive, both the trains after collision, move in the same direction as that of the passenger train.

Let 'v' be the magnitude of the common velocity with which both trains move together after collision.

Then, after collision, the momentum of passenger train is, $P_{fp} = m_p v$ and that of the goods train is, $P_{fg} = m_g v$.

∴ Total momentum after collision $P_{f\,(\text{total})}$

$= P_{fp} + P_{fg} = m_p v + m_g v = (m_p + m_g)\, v$

$= (300 \times 10^3 + 200 \times 10^3)\, v = 500 \times 10^3 \times v$

According to principle of conservation of momentum,

$P_{i\,(\text{total})} = P_{f\,(\text{total})}$

$\Rightarrow 5 \times 10^5 = 500 \times 10^3 \times v$

$\Rightarrow v = 1\ m\ \text{s}^{-1} = 3.6$ km h^{-1}

69. When trolley starts immediately the T.V. stand will continue to be in state of rest so it roles backwards where as when trolley is suddenly stopped the T.V. stand continues to be in state of motion so it rolles forward.

70. Original length of rod = L units

$\text{CG} = \dfrac{L}{2}$ units

New length of rod $= L - \dfrac{L}{4} = \dfrac{3L}{4}$

New position of $\text{CG} = \dfrac{3L}{8}$

Shift in $\text{CG} = \dfrac{L}{2} - \dfrac{3L}{8} = \dfrac{4L - 3L}{8} = \dfrac{L}{8}$ units

71. Initially when the tank is completely filled with water, the *CG* is at the geometric centre of the tank. But as the water leaks out, the *CG* shifts downward. When water leaks out completely such that the tank is now empty, the *CG* again reaches the geometric centre.

72. Mechanical advantage of an inclined plane

$= \dfrac{\text{length}}{\text{height}}$

By Pythagoras theorem,

$\text{Length} = \sqrt{3^2 + 4^2} = 5$ m.

Thus, mechanical advantage

$= \dfrac{\text{Load}}{\text{effort}} = \dfrac{5}{3}$

$\text{Effort} = \dfrac{\text{load} \times 3}{5}$

$= \dfrac{5 \times 10 \times 3}{5} = 30$ N $= 3 \times 10^6$ dyne

73. Given, length of the plane, $\ell = 6$ m

Load, $L = 42$ N

effort, $E = 7$ N

Let height of the plane = h

We know, $\dfrac{L}{E} = \dfrac{\ell}{h}$

$\Rightarrow h = \ell \times \dfrac{E}{L} = 6 \times \dfrac{7}{42} = 1$ m

74. Use, efficiency $= \dfrac{\text{M.A.}}{\text{V.R.}} \times 100$

Substitute

MA = ?

$80 = \dfrac{\text{MA}}{20} \times 100 \Rightarrow \text{MA} = \dfrac{80}{5} = 16$

$\text{MA} = \dfrac{\text{load}}{\text{effort}}$

$\Rightarrow \text{effort} = \dfrac{1000}{16} = 62.5$ kgwt

75. Let the common velocity of the two balls be 'v'.

1st ball	2nd ball
$m_1 = 100$ g	$m_2 = 200$ g
$u_1 = 12$ m s^{-1}	$u_2 = 0$ m s^{-1}
$v_1 = v = ?$	$v_2 = v = ?$

From law of conservation of momentum,

$m_1 u_1 + m_2 u_2 = m_1 v_1 + m_2 v_2$

$100 \times 12 + 0 = 100 \times v + 200 \times v;$

$1200 = 300\ v \Rightarrow v = \frac{1200}{300} = 4m\ s^{-1}$

76. When the roller is pulled as shown below

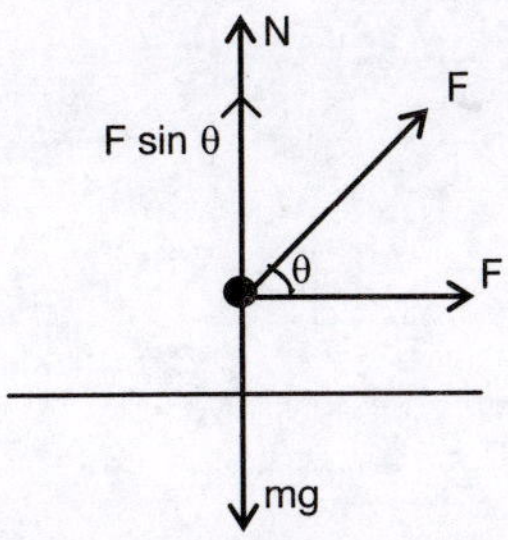

F sin θ opposes the weight of the body.

When the roller is pushed as shown below

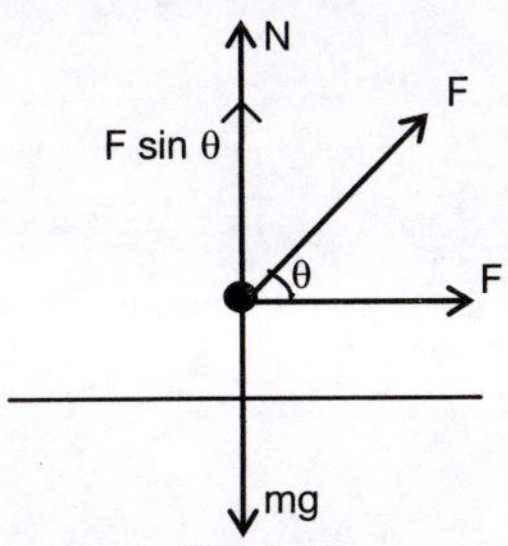

F sin θ acts in the direction of weight of the roller.

So, when roller is pulled N = mg – F sin θ

When roller is pushed

N = mg + F sin θ

Friction depends on normal reaction (N).

So, friction is more when roller is pushed.

Therefore, pulling is easier than pushing.

77. Mass of the body, m = 4 kg

Initial velocity of the body, u = 0 m/s

Force applied, F = 20 N

Time for which the force acts, t = 6 s

Acceleration of the body, $a = F/m = 20/4 = 5\ m/s^2$

Hence, velocity at the end of 6 s,

v = u + at = 0 + 5 × 6 = 30 m/s

The displacement of the body at the end of 6 s. $s_1 = ut + ½\ at^2 = 0 \times 6 + ½ \times (5) \times 62 = 90$ m

The force ceases to act at the end of 6 s. Hence, the body continues to move with the same velocity of 30 m/s.

From 6 s to 8 s, the body moves with uniform velocity of 30 m/s.

Hence, the displacement of the body from 6 s to 8 s, $s_2 = 2 \times 30 = 60$ m.

Therefore, the total displacement of the body, at the end of 8 s, $s = s_1 + s_2 = 90$ m + 60 m = 150 m.

78. $M_1 = \frac{m}{6}, m_2 = \frac{2m}{6} = \frac{m}{3}$

$\therefore m_3 = \frac{3m}{6} = \frac{m}{2}$

$v_1 = 6m\,s^{-1}\ v_2 = 4m\,s^{-1}\ v_3 = ?$

$P_3^2 = P_1^2 + P_2^2$

$P_3 = \sqrt{P_1^2 + P_2^2}$

$\frac{m}{2}v_3 = \sqrt{\left(\frac{m}{6}\times 6\right)^2 + \left(\frac{m}{3}\times 4\right)^2}$

$= \sqrt{\frac{36m^2}{36} + \left(\frac{16m^2}{9}\right)}$

$= \sqrt{\frac{36m^2 + 64m^2}{36}}$

$= \frac{m}{2}v_3 = \frac{10m}{6} \Rightarrow v_3 = \frac{2\times 5}{3}$

$v_3 = 3.33\,m\,s^{-1}$

79. (a) Mass = m

Kinetic energy, $K = ½\ mv^2$

Momentum, $p = mv \Rightarrow v = p/m$

$\Rightarrow K = ½\ m(p/m)^2 = p^2/2m$

(b) Mass of the first marble $(m_1) = 1$ g

Mass of the second marble $(m_2) = 4$ g

(i) Given kinetic energy of the both the marbles are equal. $\Rightarrow K_1 = K_2 \Rightarrow ½\ m_1 v_1^2 = ½\ m_2 v_2^2$

$\Rightarrow 1 \times v_1^2 = 4 \times v_2^2 \Rightarrow v_1 : v_2 = 2:1$

(ii) If p_1 and p_2 are the momenta of the two bodies, then we have, $p_1 : p_2 = m_1v_1 : m_2v_2 = (m_1/m_2)\times(v_1/v_2)$

$\therefore p_1 : p_2 = (1/4) \times (2/1) = 1:2$

80. Mass of limestone, m = 9000 kg

Time taken, T = 1 h = 3600 s

H = 120 m

Efficiency, η = 75%

Work required to lift the limestone against gravitational force,

$W = mgh = 9000\ kg \times 10\ m\ s^{-2} \times 120\ m = 1.08 \times 10^7\ J$

If W' is the actual work done in lifting the limestone, we have 75% of W' = W

$\Rightarrow 0.75 \times W' = 1.08 \times 10^7$

$\Rightarrow W' = 1.08 \times 10^7 \times 4/3 = 1.44 \times 10^7\ J$

Power of the motor, $P = W'/t = 1.44 \times 10^7 / 3600$

$= 0.0004 \times 10^7\ W = 4000\ W$

$= 4000 / 746\ HP = 5.36\ HP.$

JEE-NEET Special Wing

Multiple-Answer Type Questions

1. Mechanical force and frictional force are contact force.
Hence, the correct option is (a) and (b).

2. If the net force acting on the body is zero, then the body must be either at rest or in uniform motion.
Hence, the correct option is (a) and (b).

3. Friction does not depend on the mass of the body.
Hence, the correct option is (a), (b) and (c).

4. According to II law of motion, $F = \frac{dp}{dt}$

$$F = \frac{m(v-u)}{t}$$

$$F = ma \left[\because \frac{v-u}{t} = a\right]$$

Hence, the correct option is (b) and (c).

5. The stability of a body depends on its base area, position of C.G and height of C.G from its base.
Hence, the correct option is (a) and (d).

Comprehension-Based Questions

6. Power of a simple machine is also referred to as effort.
Hence, the correct option is (c).

7. Velocity ratio $= \frac{\text{displacement of the power}}{\text{displacement of the load}}$

Hence, the correct option is (b).

8. $\text{M.A} = \frac{\text{Load}}{\text{Effort}} = \frac{28}{4} = 7$

Hence, the correct option is (d).

9. Percentage efficiency $= \frac{\text{M.A}}{\text{V.R}} \times 100$

Efficiency = 0.75
M. A = 6

$$\text{V.R} = \frac{\text{M.A}}{\text{Efficiency}}$$

$$= \frac{6}{0.75}$$

$$= 8$$

Hence, the correct option is (c).

10. The ratio of work done by a machine to work done on the machine is efficiency.
Hence, the correct option is (a).

Match the Column

11. Choice (a) follows.
A - e, B - d, C - b, D - c, E - a

Hydrostatics

CHAPTER

4

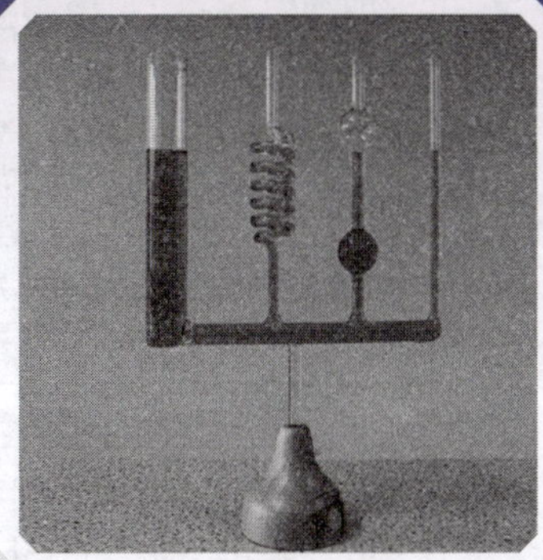

Key Ideas

After completing this chapter, you should be able to:

- state and understand the kinetic theory of matter.
- discuss the different types of pressures and understand the law of liquid pressure.
- learn the different principles associated with the study of fluid pressure and atmospheric pressure.
- understand properties of fluids like surface tension, upthrust, buoyancy, etc.

Remember

Before beginning this chapter, you should be able to:

- define motion.
- know the definitions of speed, velocity, acceleration, force and their applications in everyday life.

Scientific Crypt

A Tribute to Blaise Pascal (1623-1662)

Blaise Pascal was a French mathematician, physicist, and philosopher. His earliest mathematical work was on conic sections which he wrote at the age of 16. Pascal's development of probability theory was one of the his most influential contribution to mathematics. He invented the method of representing binomial coefficients which is now called Pascal's triangle. He is one of the first two inventors of the mechanical calculator which is capable of calculating addition and subtraction. Pascal contributed to several fields of physics, most notably the fields of fluid mechanics and pressure. His work in the fields of hydrodynamics and hydrostatics centred on the principles of hydraulic fluids. He proved that hydrostatic pressure depends not on the weight of the fluid but on the elevation difference. His inventions include the hydraulic press (using hydraulic pressure to multiply force) and the syringe. In honour of his scientific contributions, the name Pascal has been given to the SI unit of pressure and Pascal's law.

Crossword

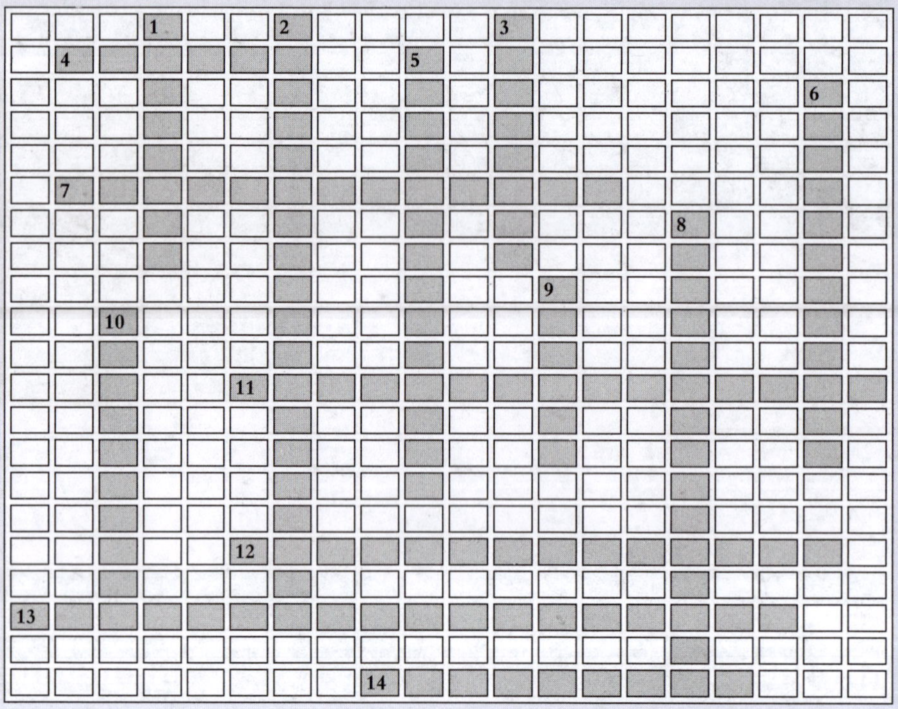

Across

4. Force acting normal to a surface.
7. The pressure of a gas present in a closed vessel.
11. The ratio of the density of a substance to the density of water at 4 °C.
12. The property of a liquid due to which its surface behaves like a stretched membrane.
13. The empty space at the top of the tube of mercury barometer.
14. The instrument used to measure the altitudes in aircraft.

Down

1. Thrust per unit area.
2. The pressure exerted by the atmospheric gases on the surface of the earth and on the surroundings.
3. The resultant thrust acting on a body immersed in a fluid in the upward direction.
5. The lines marked on the sides of the ship which indicate the depth of the ship that can be maintained safely without the danger of it sinking due to the load.
6. The device used for the measurement of the pressure of gas in a closed vessel.
8. The pressure exerted by the fluids on the sides of the vessel containing fluid.
9. SI unit of pressure.
10. The device used to measure the relative density of fluids.

INTRODUCTION

In chapter kinematics, you have studied about bodies in motion under external forces. Study of a body at rest under external forces is called statics. The bodies under consideration were solids. Matter exists in liquid and gaseous states also. Do liquids and gases react to external forces and surroundings the same way as solids do? To know the difference, we need to understand the properties of the three states of matter. This entails the study of kinetic theory of matter. In this chapter, let us delve into the behaviour of liquids and gases under external forces. Particularly our area of interest will be the study of liquids, at rest under external forces, which comes under a branch of mechanics called hydrostatics. The word 'hydro' is used as a synonym for water but in general is also used for all the liquids. Hence, the name—Hydrostatics.

Kinetic Theory of Matter

Anything which has a mass and occupies space is called **matter**. The smallest unit of matter, which can exist independently and exhibit all the physical and chemical properties of matter is called **molecule**.

The following are some of the postulates of kinetic theory of matter which would help us to understand the concepts in this chapter better.

1. The kinetic energy of molecules is directly proportional to the absolute temperature.
2. Molecules always attract each other. The force of attraction between like molecules is called **cohesive force**. The same force between unlike molecules is called **adhesive force**.

The cohesive force depends on the space between molecules called **inter-molecular space**. More the space, less is the cohesive force. In solids the cohesive force is very strong as the inter-molecular space is very less. If a force is applied to a solid, it is displaced from one place to another, but the relative positions of its molecules do not change. Hence, solids have rigidity, definite shape and volume.

When the inter-molecular force is decreased by either decreasing the pressure or increasing the temperature, a solid converts to liquid and liquid to gas. As cohesive force is less in liquids, they do not have rigidity and definite shape. However the force is strong enough to maintain the number of molecules, per unit volume, same. Hence, liquids have definite volume.

For gases, the cohesive force is extremely negligible. Hence, gases do not have rigidity, definite shape and volume.

It is clear that, molecules in liquids and gases have more freedom of movement. Hence, their relative position changes continuously. This gives liquids and gases a unique ability to 'flow' from one point to another, even when no external force is applied. This property is called 'fluidity' and thus liquids and gases together are called fluids.

Thrust and Pressure

Thrust

When we walk on sand we leave our foot prints in the sand. This is due to the weight of our body which acts normal to the surface of contact—the foot and the sand. Similarly when we want to stick a picture in a scrap book we apply a force normal to the surface of the paper. Such force acting normally on a surface is called **thrust**. Thus, the net force acting normal to a surface is called **thrust**. Thrust is a vector quantity.

Konnect

'Force' is the push or pull on an object whereas 'Thrust' is the reaction force acting on an accelerated object because of an applied force.

Units of Thrust

S.I. unit: newton (N)

C.G.S. unit: dyne

Thrust is also expressed in kgwt or gwt or kgf.

1 kgwt = 9·8 *N*

1 gwt = 980 dynes

Pressure

When we pump air into the tube of a cycle tyre we check the pressure of air inside the tube. This pressure is the thrust acting normally on a unit surface area of the walls of the tube. Thus, **pressure** is defined as the ratio of the thrust (*T*) to the area of contact (*A*) on which the thrust is acting normally. **Pressure** is a scalar quantity.

If a person lies on a sofa, the depression produced on the sofa is less compared to the depression produced when he stands on it. This is because when the person lies on the sofa, his weight acts on a larger surface, and therefore, the pressure is less. When we stand on it, the same weight acts but on a smaller area, and therefore, the pressure is more.

Info Bytes!

Pressure is a scalar quantity.

$$\text{Pressure }(p) = \frac{\text{Thurst }(T)}{\text{Area }(A)}$$

Units of Pressure

S.I. unit: N m^{-2} or Pascal (Pa)

C.G.S. unit: dynes cm^{-2}

Pressure is also expressed in $kg_f\,m^{-2}$

The meteorological unit of pressure is bar.

1 Pa = 1 N m^{-2}

1 $kg_f\,m^{-2}$ = 9·8 Pa

$$1\text{ N m}^{-2} = \frac{10^5\text{ dyne}}{10^4\text{ cm}^2}$$

1 Pa = 10 dyne cm^{-2}

1 bar ≈ 10^5 Pa

EXAMPLE 4.1 A cylindrical container with a cross-sectional area of 50 cm^2 is filled with oil. The mass of the oil is 4 kg. Determine the pressure exerted on the base of the container.

SOLUTION

Mass of oil in the container = 4 kg

∴ Weight = mg = 4 kg × 9.8 m s^{-2} = 39.2 N.

Area of the base = 50 cm^2 = 5 × 10^{-3} m^2

∴ Pressure = weight/area = 39.2N/ (5×10^{-3} m^2) = 7840 N m^{-2} = 7840 Pa

EXAMPLE 4.2

A cuboid has dimensions as shown. If the mass of the block is 2 kg, find the minimum and maximum pressure it exerts as the orientation of the body is changed.

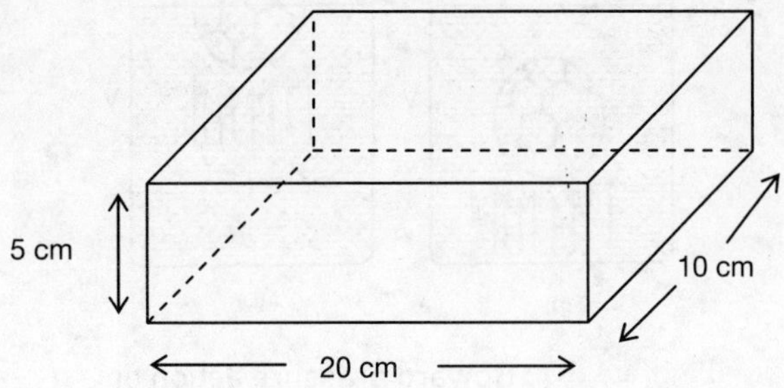

SOLUTION

The weight exerted by the block = mg

$= 2\text{ kg} \times 9.8\text{ m s}^{-2} = 19.6\text{ N}$

For the pressure to be minimum, this weight should act on maximum area and the block should be placed with the largest lateral surface on the bottom side.

$$P_{min} = \frac{19.6N}{10 \times 20 \times 10^{-4}} = 980\text{ N m}^{-2}$$

For pressure to be maximum, the area on which the weight of the block acts, should be minimum and the block should be placed with the smallest lateral surface as the bottom side.

$$P_{max} = \frac{19.6}{5 \times 10 \times 10^{-4}} = 3920\text{ N m}^{-2}$$

Fluid Pressure

As the molecules in fluids can move up, down and sideways (laterally), they continuously collide with each other and with the sides of the container. While doing so, they exert forces (thrust) on the walls of the container or any object in the fluid, from all directions. This gives rise to fluid pressure. It is clear that fluid can exert pressure in all directions.

Take a glass jar having a small opening near the base. Tie a small rubber balloon to the side opening. Pour water into the cylinder. With an increase in the level of water, the balloon starts bulging. This shows that liquids exert pressure laterally.

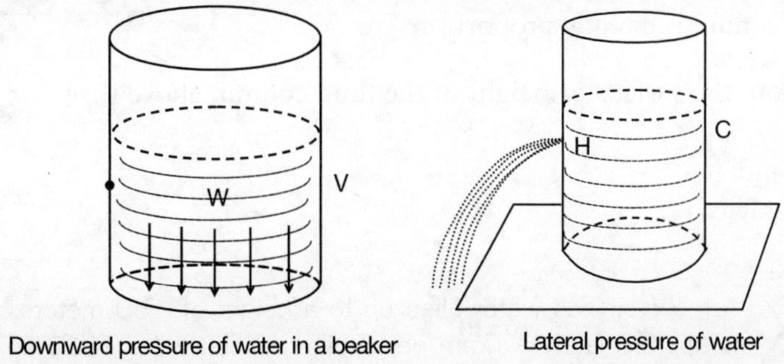

Figure 4.1 Pressure exerted by liquid increases with the height of the liquid level

The pressure exerted by the fluids on the sides of the vessel containing the fluid is called **lateral pressure.**

Take two glass jars A and B of base area 50 cm^2 and 100 cm^2, respectively. A liquid of equal mass (*m*) is taken in both the beakers. The total pressure of the liquid acting on the base of the beakers A and B is (mg/50) and (mg/100), respectively. Thus, the pressure acting on the base area of the two beakers is not equal even though the total weight of the liquid taken is equal. The pressure acting in the downward direction is called the **downward pressure**.

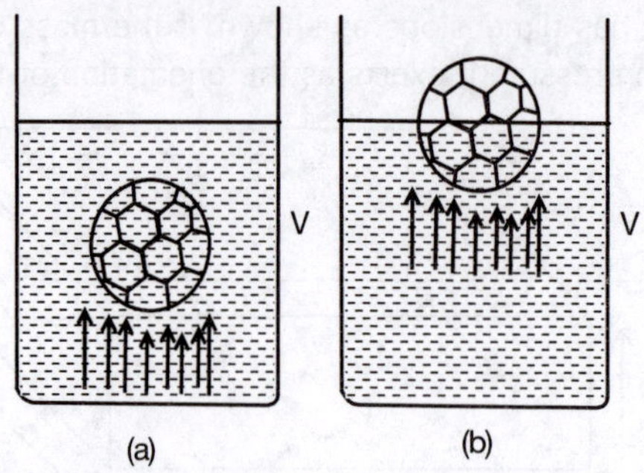

Figure 4.2 Upward pressure action on foltball immersed in water

> **Konnect**
> The pressure exerted by a fluid at a given point inside the fluid is equal in all directions.

If a rubber ball is immersed in a bucket of water, the ball is immediately pushed upward by the water and the ball starts floating on the surface of the water. This shows that water exerts pressure in the upward direction also, called **upward pressure.**

Pressure at a Point Inside a Liquid

Consider a beaker whose area of cross-section is A. Pour a liquid of density '*d*' inside the beaker. Let the height of the liquid column be '*h*'.

The weight (W) of the liquid acting normally on the base area of the beaker is the downward thrust exerted by the liquid.

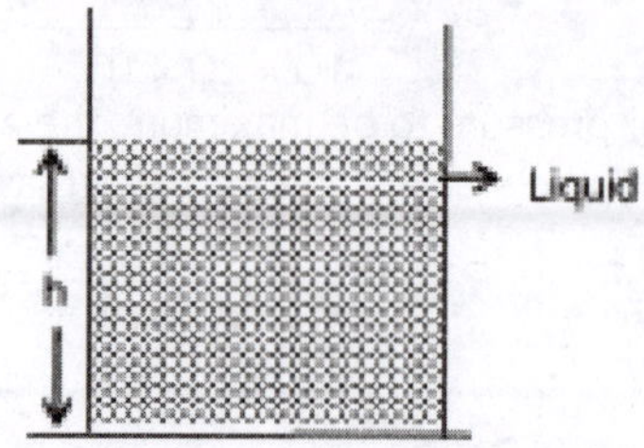

Figure 4.3 A Beaker containing liquid

$$\text{Hence, } P = \frac{W}{A}$$

$$P = \frac{mg}{A}$$

But $m = V \times d$, where V is the volume of the liquid ($= Ah$)

$$\therefore \quad m = Ahd$$

$$\text{So,} \quad p = \frac{Ahdg}{A} \Rightarrow p = hdg$$

$\therefore$ Pressure (P) = height of the liquid column (h) $\times$ density of the liquid (d) $\times$ acceleration due to gravity (g).

Thus, pressure at a point in a fluid is directly proportional to

- the depth of the point from the surface or height of the fluid column above that point
- the density of the fluid, and
- the acceleration due to gravity.

> **Konnect**
> Fluid pressure, however, is independent of the area of cross-section.

EXAMPLE 4.3 A reservoir has water filled up to a height of 150 meters. Given that the density of water is approximately 1 gram per cubic centimetre (or 1000 kg/m^3), calculate the difference in pressures acting at the following two points:

(i) Point exactly at a depth one-third of the total height.
(ii) Point two-thirds down the depth of the reservoir.

SOLUTION

Height of the reservoir = 150 meters.

Density (d) of water = 1 gram/cm^3 = 1000 kg/m^3

(i) Depth of the first point = 1/3 × 150 = 50 meters

Pressure at this point (P_1) using the formula $P = h\rho g$:

$P_1 = 50 \times 1000 \times 9.8$

$P_1 = 490 \times 10^3$ pascals

(ii) Depth of the second point = 2/3 × 150 = 100 meters

Pressure at this point (P_2) using the formula $P = h\rho g$:

$P_2 = 100 \times 1000 \times 9.8$

$P_2 = 980 \times 10^3$ pascals

Difference in pressures: $P_{diff} = P_2 - P_1 = (980 - 490) \times 10 = 490 \times 10^3$ pascals or 490 kPa.

Laws of Liquid Pressure

1. Pressure at a given depth inside a stationary liquid is the same at all points in the horizontal plane. As the pressure at a point is given by $P = hdg$ the pressure of a given liquid of density (d) varies with the depth of the liquid. For a stationary liquid, all the points in a horizontal plane have the same depth (h). Hence, the pressure is the same at all points in the horizontal plane.
2. Pressure of a given liquid varies with the depth and is directly proportional to it. Hence, as the depth increases the pressure also increases.
3. A liquid seeks its own level. Take five tubes of various shapes as shown in the Fig. 4.4 connected to each other by a horizontal pipe at the bottom. Fix the apparatus in a vertical position. Pour water through any one of the vertical tubes. It is observed that the level of water is the same in all tubes.

Konnect

The **Hydrostatic Paradox** states the fact that in different shaped containers (having the same base area) which are liquid with liquid of the same height, the applied force by the liquid on the base of each container is exactly the same.

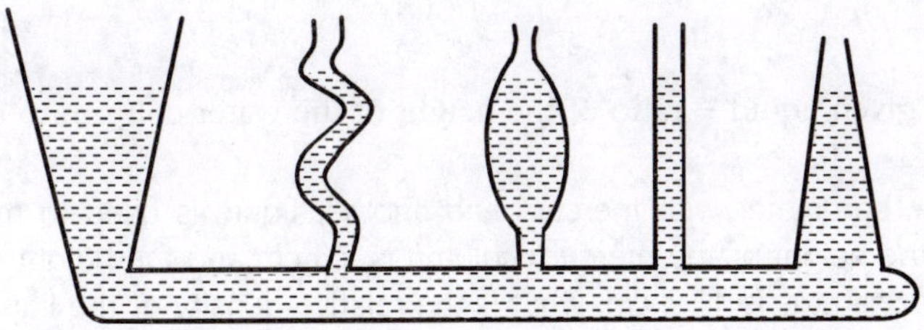

Figure 4.4 Beaker containing liquid to show that liquid seeks its own level

4. The upper surface of a stationary liquid is always horizontal.
5. The lateral pressure exerted by a liquid increases with the increase in the depth of the liquid. Due to this reason, the walls of dams are constructed in such a way that they are tapered upwards, i.e., their thickness gradually decreases from the bottom to the top.

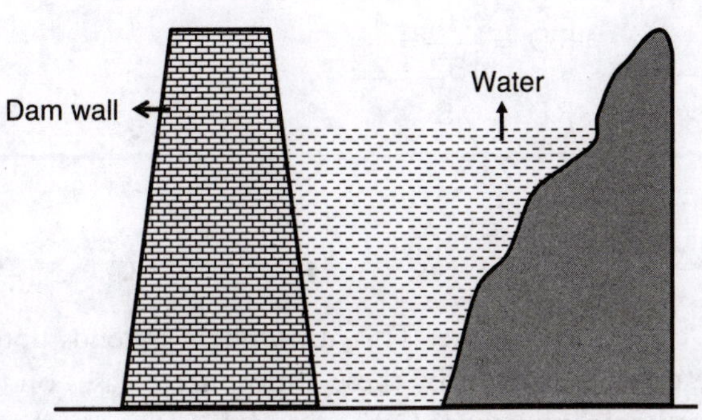

Figure 4.5 Pressure exerted by liquids increases with depth

Info Bytes!

The reason behind the body of a deep water sea fish often bursts when brought to the surface suddenly is pressure difference. The deep water fish is adaptive to the high pressure deep sea and when it comes on surface, it suddenly experiences very low pressure that makes its body to burst.

Hare's Apparatus

Hare's apparatus is used to measure the relative density of liquids. The liquids may or may not be miscible in water as they do not come in contact with each other. It consists of an inverted U-tube mounted on a vertical stand. It has an opening at the top end which is connected to a rubber tube with a pinch cock.

The two arms of the tube are immersed inside two beakers, one containing water and the other containing the liquid whose specific gravity is to be measured. Initially, the levels of water and the liquid inside the beakers is equal. The pinch cock is opened and air is sucked out. As the pressure in the U-tube decreases the liquids rise in the tubes. The pinch cock is closed and the heights of the water and the liquid column in the tubes are measured.

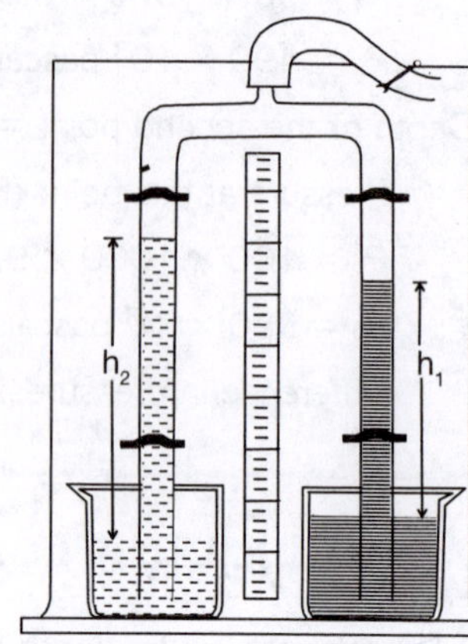

Figure 4.6 Hare's apparatus

Let them be h_1 and h_2, respectively. The top surface of both liquids inside the U tube experience the same pressure 'p'. The pressure acting on the surfaces of liquids in the beakers is atmospheric pressure, p_o. Let d_1 and d_2 be the density of water and liquid, respectively.

$$\therefore p_o - h_1 d_1 g = p \Rightarrow h_1 d_1 g = p_o - p \quad (4.1)$$

$$p_o - h_2 d_2 g = p \Rightarrow h_2 d_2 g = p_o - p \quad (4.2)$$

$$\therefore h_1 d_1 g = h_2 d_2 g$$

$$\frac{h_1}{h_2} = \frac{d_2}{d_1}$$

$$\therefore \text{R.D.} = \frac{h_1}{h_2}$$

Thus, the relative density of the given liquid = ratio of the height of the water column to the height of the liquid column.

EXAMPLE 4.4 A barometer with mercury and another liquid is used to measure atmospheric pressure. If the height of the mercury column is 76 cm and the height of the liquid column in the same apparatus is 152 cm, what is the relative density of the liquid with respect to mercury?

SOLUTION

Relative Density (R.D.) using the formula is given by: $R.D. = \frac{h_{mercury}}{h_{liquid}}$

Given:

$$h_{mercury} = 76\text{cm}$$

$$h_{liquid} = 152\text{cm}$$

Plugging in the values, we have,

$$\text{R.D.} = \frac{76}{152} = \frac{1}{2}$$

$$\text{R.D.} = 0.5$$

Atmospheric Pressure

The Earth is surrounded by an envelope of air called atmosphere. This atmosphere extends upto a height of about 300 km and is composed of a mixture of gases. The pressure exerted by these atmospheric gases on the surroundings and on the surface of the Earth is known as the **atmospheric pressure**. Other examples of atmospheric pressure such as nose bleeding at high altitudes , astronauts wear space suits etc.

Activity 1

Take a wide mouthed bottle with an outlet at the bottom. Place a rubber balloon as shown in the Fig. 4.7.

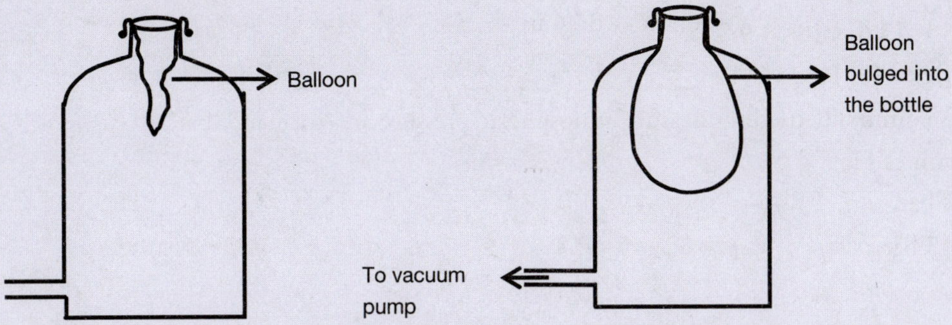

Figure 4.7 Experimental arrangement to show that atmosphere exerts pressure

Now, evacuate the bottle through the outlet. The balloon bulges due to the exertion of atmospheric pressure by the air inside the balloon. This shows that the atmosphere exerts pressure.

Activity 2

Take an empty can and pour water into it. Place the can on a tripod stand and heat it with a burner. After some time, the steam starts coming out, expelling air from the can. Continue heating till the steam is observed to come freely from the mouth of the can. Stop heating and immediately close the mouth of the can tightly. Remove the can from the tripod stand and pour cold water over it. It is observed that the can gets crushed, because of the pressure exerted by the atmosphere.

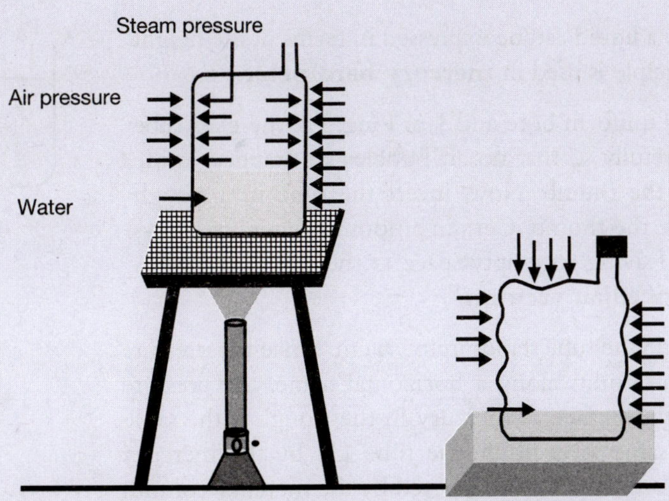

Figure 4.8 Experimental arrangement to show that atmospheric pressure can crush a bottle

As cold water is poured over the can, steam inside it condenses to water, creating a very low pressure. Outside the can, large atmospheric pressure acts on it, crushing it.

The atmospheric pressure is usually expressed in the units 'atmosphere' (atm). The atmospheric pressure at sea level is 1 atm. Experimentally it has been observed that at sea level, approximately 76 cm of mercury column exerts the same pressure as the atmospheric air.

$$P = hdg$$

Where h = height of mercury column = 76 cm of Hg (or) 0.76 m of Hg

d = density of mercury = 13.6 g cm^{-3} (or) 13.6×10^3 kg m^{-3}

$g = 9{\cdot}8$ m s^{-2}

$\therefore$ 1 atm = $0.76 \times 13.6 \times 10^3 \times 9.8$ Pa

$= 1.013 \times 10^5$ Pa $\cong 10^5$ Pa

The other units commonly used to measure atmospheric pressure are 'torr' and 'bar'.

1 torr = 1 mm of Hg

1 bar = 10^5 Pa

$\therefore$ 1 atm $\cong$ 1·013 bar.

Measurement of Atmospheric Pressure

The instruments used for the measurement of atmospheric pressure are called barometers. The types of barometers generally in use are:

1. Mercury or Torricellian barometer
2. Fortin's barometer
3. Aneroid barometer

Mercury Barometer

The pressure at a point inside a liquid is given by $p = hdg$. For a given liquid at a given place, d and g are constant.

$\therefore\ p \propto h$

Thus, the pressure exerted by a liquid can be expressed in terms of the height of the liquid column. This principle is used in **mercury barometer**.

Take a glass tube of a narrow uniform bore and 1 m long. Fill the glass tube with pure and dry mercury carefully so that no air bubbles are trapped inside and cover the open end with the thumb. Now, invert the tube in a trough containing mercury and remove the thumb. Certain amount of mercury flows from the tube into the trough leaving an empty space at the top of the tube. This empty space is called **Torricellian vacuum**.

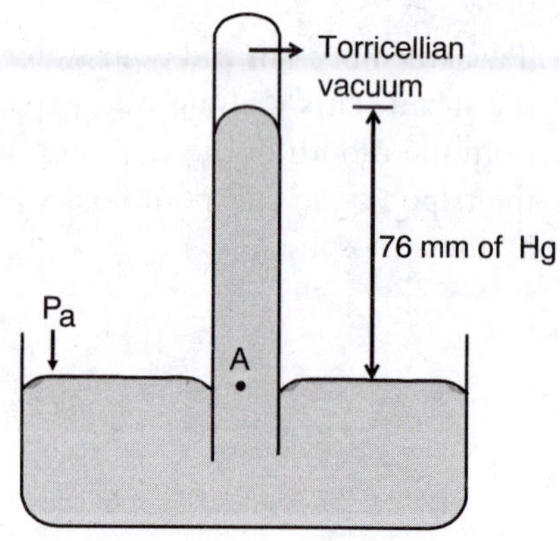

Figure 4.9 Torricellian vacuum

At sea level, the mercury inside the tube stands upto 76 cm. Since the pressure inside a liquid is the same at all points along a horizontal plane, the pressure exerted by the atmosphere on the surface of mercury in the trough is the same as the pressure exerted at the same level inside the tube (A) by the mercury column above that level. Therefore, the pressure exerted by the mercury column of height 76 cm is equal to the atmospheric pressure at the sea level. This pressure is taken as 1 atmosphere.

Due to seasonal changes in the climate, changes in the atmospheric pressure are indicated by changes in the height of the mercury column. Hence, it is very common to express atmospheric pressure in terms of the height of the mercury column.

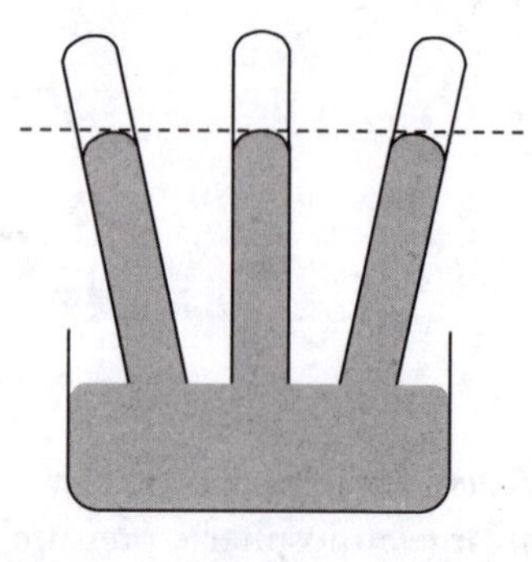

Figure 4.10 Barometer showing that the pressure inside a liquid is the same at all points along a horizontal plane

As we have learnt earlier that the vertical height of the liquid column is independent of the shape and size of the tube, it can be observed that the height of the mercury column in the tube, above the surface in the trough, remains the same even when the tube is tilted.

The height of the mercury is affected by the presence of moisture in mercury. Impurities present in mercury also affect the height of the mercury column. If water is used as barometric liquid in place of mercury, the height of the water column would be 10.34 m, the calculation of which is shown below.

Pressure exerted by the water column = atmospheric pressure

$$h_1 d_1 g = p_o \tag{4.3}$$

Pressure exerted by the mercury column = atmospheric pressure

$$h_2 d_2 g = p_o \tag{4.4}$$

From (4.3) and (4.4)

$$h_1 d_1 g = h_2 d_2 g$$

$$\therefore h_1 = h_2 \frac{d_2}{d_1} = 76 \text{ cm} \times 13.6$$

$$= 1033.6 \text{ cm}$$

$$h_1 = 10.34 \text{ m}$$

The height of the water tube required would be equivalent to the height of a three storeyed building! Further, the vapour pressure of the water formed in the vacuum would adversely affect the height of the liquid column. Hence, water is generally not used as a barometric liquid. Also, water sticks to the walls of the container.

EXAMPLE 4.5 The height of the mercury column in a barometer at a specific location is 72 cm. When a different liquid of unknown density is used, the height of the liquid column becomes 180 cm. Determine the density of this liquid.

SOLUTION

Given the atmospheric pressure remains constant in both situations, the relation is:

$h_1 \times d_1 = h_2 \times d_2$

Where:

h_1 is the height of the mercury column,

d_1 is the density of mercury (13.6 g cm^{-3}),

h_2 is the height of the liquid column, and

d_2 is the density of the liquid.

Given:

$$h_1 = 72 \text{ cm}$$

$$h_2 = 180 \text{ cm}$$

From the relationship above, $72 \times 13.6 = 180 \times d_2$

Solving for d_2, we get:

$$d_2 = \frac{72 \times 13.6}{180} = 5.44 \text{ gcm}^{-3}.$$

Hence, the density of the liquid is 5.44 g cm^{-3}

Disadvantages of Simple Mercury Barometer Constructed by Torricelli

The simple mercury barometer as constructed by Torricelli has certain disadvantages. Some of them are listed below:

1. Mercury in the barometer is exposed to the air due to which certain impurities may dissolve in mercury.
2. It is difficult and inconvenient to carry the barometer from one place to another, as the mercury in the trough could spill over.
3. As the level of mercury in the trough is not constant, the zero of the scale does not necessarily coincide with this surface.

Fortin's Barometer

Fortin's barometer is an improved form of mercury barometer which is used for the accurate measurement of atmospheric pressure. The barometer consists of a thick walled glass tube of one metre length. The glass tube contains a cistern of mercury. The bottom of the vessel is made of leather which can be raised or lowered by means of a screw provided below. The whole barometer is enclosed in a brass tube and glass windows are provided to take the readings. A brass or ivory index is fixed vertically to the lid of the vessel containing mercury. The tip of this index coincides with the zero of the vertical scale on the glass tube. At the upper end of the glass tube a vernier scale is fixed which slides up and down with the help of a screw called vernier screw (not shown in the figure).

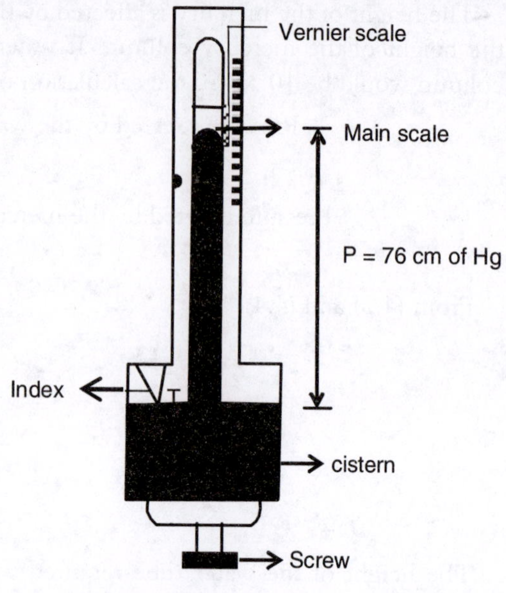

Figure 4.11 Fortin's Barometer

The height of the mercury column in the barometer is found using the vernier scale. This is done by making the zero of vernier coincide with the convex meniscus of mercury column in the tube by adjusting the screw provided near the vernier scale. Then main scale and vernier scale readings are noted. The least count of the vernier is also noted. Thus, the atmospheric pressure is given by barometric reading.

Barometric Reading = [M.S.R. + (V.C.D. × L.C.)] cm

Aneroid Barometer

The use of mercury in barometers makes the instrument quite heavy. Furthermore, the instrument has to be always held vertical. Due to these reasons, a mercury barometer is not portable. **Aneroid barometer**, which does not use any liquid, is light and can be fixed in any orientation. The aneroid barometer consists of a sealed metal box made of a corrugated iron sheet which is partially evacuated. The corrugated sheet acts as a diaphragm. From the middle of the diaphragm a thin rod is connected to the upper end such that the teeth of this rod fit into the teeth of a wheel, connected with a pointer. The pointer moves over a circular scale which is calibrated using a standard barometer.

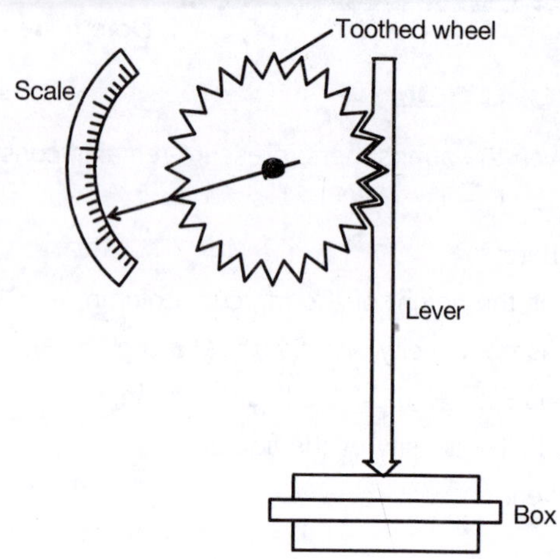

Figure 4.12 Aneroid barometer

When the atmospheric pressure increases, the surrounding air presses the diaphragm. Due to this, the diaphragm gets depressed. The pointer moves due to the rotation of the wheel in clockwise direction. When the atmospheric pressure decreases, the bulging of the diaphragm leads to the movement of the pointer in an opposite direction.

Advantages of an Aneroid Barometer Over a Simple Barometer

1. The aneroid barometer does not use any liquid, hence, no spillage of liquid can take place.
2. Errors due to differential expansion of the liquid and the glass container are avoided in an aneroid barometer.
3. The aneroid barometer is free from defects caused by impure or moist mercury.
4. The aneroid barometer is compact, light in weight and portable, and hence can be carried anywhere easily.
5. It can be fixed in any plane unlike the mercury barometer which has to be fixed only in an upright position.

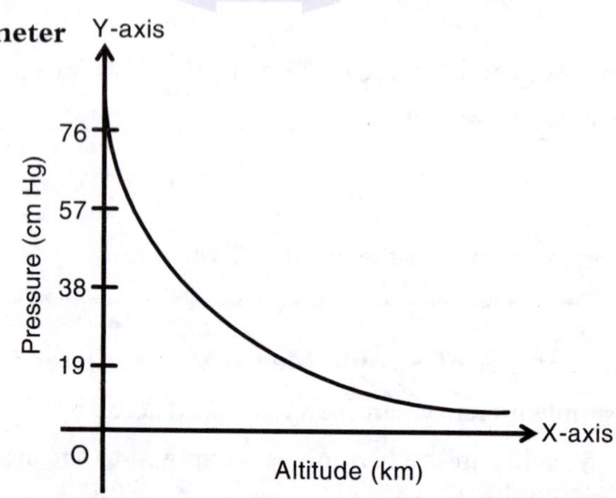

Figure 4.13 Pressure Vs altitude graph showing that atmospheric pressure decreases with increase in height

Disadvantage of the Aneroid Barometer

The measurement of the atmospheric pressure made by this barometer is not accurate.

Effect of Altitude on Atmospheric Pressure

The atmospheric pressure decreases as we go up from the sea-level due to a decrease in the density of air, as well as the decrease in the height of the air column. The atmospheric pressure increases as we go below the sea-level, for example deep inside a mine atmospheric pressure increases.

Taking the density of air 1.29 kg m^{-3}, we find that for every 105 m above the sea-level the pressure would decrease by 1 cm of Hg. However, the atmospheric pressure does not vary linearly (directly) with altitude, as the density of air changes with the height above sea-level. The graph given (in fig. 4.13) indicates the decrease in atmospheric pressure with increase in altitude from the sea level.

Info Bytes!

An aneroid barometer with a scale calibrated to read the altitude in metres can be used as an altimeter.

Altimeter

The instrument used to measure altitudes in aircrafts is called an **altimeter**. Closer to the surface of the Earth a fall in the atmospheric pressure by 1 cm of Hg in pressure corresponds approximately to an increase in altitude by 105 m.

Weather Forecast

The atmospheric pressure at a given place depends on the weather conditions such as temperature and moisture, since these affect the density of air. A fall in atmospheric pressure is called depression. A fall in pressure due to rise in temperature when there is no increase in humidity portends a dust storm. On the other hand a fall in pressure due to a rise in humidity indicates rainfall. If the fall in atmospheric pressure is sudden, we may forecast a storm or a cyclone.

Gas Manometer

Gas manometer is a device used for the measurement of the pressure of gas present in a closed vessel. This pressure is referred to as **gauge pressure**.

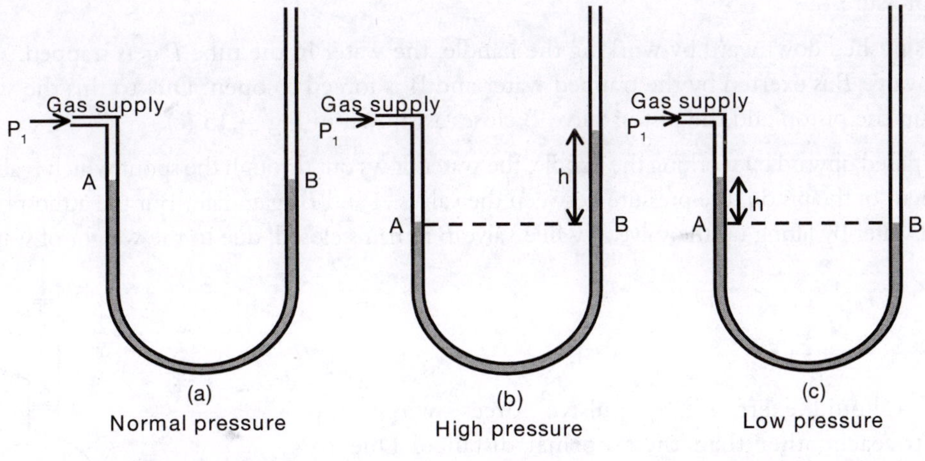

Figure 4.14 Liquid levels in manometer at various pressures

Lift Pump

Water can be lifted out of a well or can be forced to a great height by means of pumps. A pump uses the principle that atmospheric air exerts pressure and can support 10.34 m vertical column of water in a closed tube.

Construction: Two cylindrical iron tubes *P* and *Q*, are present in a lift pump. The tube *Q* is sunk in the ground, such that its lower end is well within the underground water table. Tube *P* has a larger diameter than tube *Q*. A foot valve (A) is fixed at the junction of tubes *P* and *Q*, which opens in the upward direction. Another piston valve (airtight valve *B*) is fitted at nearly the middle part of the tube P, which opens in the upward direction. This piston *B* is fitted with a straight rod to the handle of the pump. With the help of the handle, the piston may be raised, and any water above the piston valve flows out through a spout.

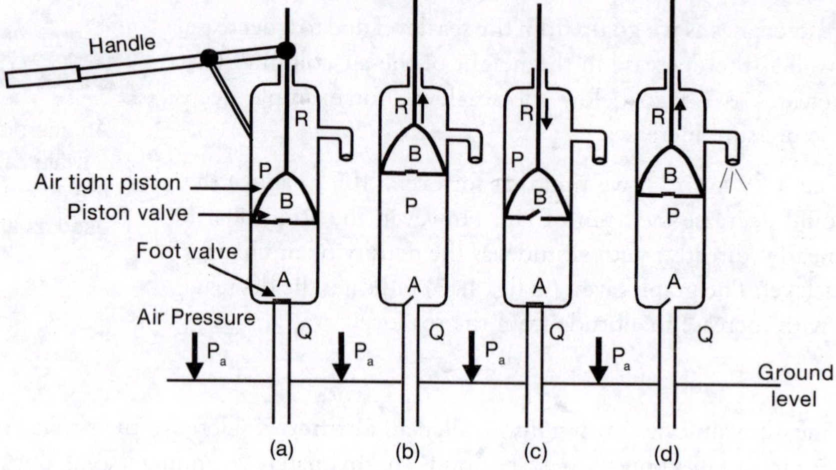

Figure 4.15 Various stages of lifting up ground water using lift pump

Working:

1. When the piston of the lift pump in tube *P* is at its lowest position, valves *A* and *B* are closed and water is at the junction of tubes *P* and *Q* as shown in Fig. 4.15 (a).
2. If the piston is raised upwards, the pressure inside the tube *P* decreases. The decrease in pressure is made up due to exertion of pressure on the ground by atmosphere which in turn forces the underground water upward by opening the valve *A*. The water flows into the tube *P* till it is filled with water upto the base of the piston as shown in Fig. 4.15 (b). Due to the weight of water above valve *A*, it closes while valve *B* remains closed on account of atmospheric pressure.
3. If the piston is pushed downward by working the handle, the water in the tube *P* gets trapped. An upward pressure on the piston valve *B* is exerted by the trapped water and B is forced to open. Due to this the water trapped in the tube *P* flows up the piston and the piston valve *B* closes as shown in Fig. 4.15 (c).
4. If the piston is raised upward by working the handle, the water flows out through the spout which is above the piston. Due to this movement of the piston, the pressure between the valves *A* and *B* again falls. But the atmospheric pressure pushes up the ground water by lifting up the valve *A* while valve *B* remains closed, due to the weight of water above it.

Pascal's Law

The molecules of a liquid exert great repulsive forces when they are pushed closer to each other than their normal distance. Due to this property, liquids cannot be easily compressed by application of thrust on the surface. Thus, any force applied on a liquid surface is immediately transmitted to every part of the liquid and the applied pressure at the surface is felt equally at every part of the liquid. This may be demonstrated by filling a long necked bulb, having a number of holes, with water. When pressure is applied on the water by pushing the piston fitted in the neck of the bulb, water rushes out with equal pressure from all the holes.

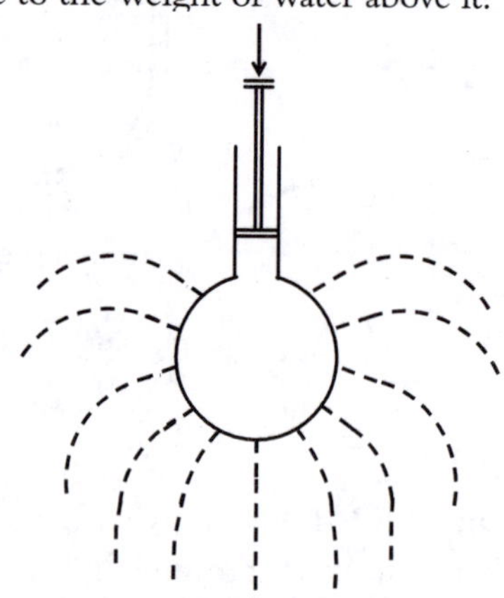

Figure 4.16 Figure showing that pressure applied on a liquid at rest is transmitted equally in all directions

This is summarized in **Pascal's law** as 'the pressure exerted by a liquid at rest is transmitted unchanged and equally in all directions, and acts at right angles to the surface of the container'.

Application of Pascal's Law

Bramah Press

Consider two cylinders A_1 and A_2. Let the area of cross-section of A_1 be 'x' sq.units and that of A_2 be 'y' sq.units such that 'y' is n times 'x'. The two cylinders are connected at the bottom by a horizontal connecting tube (T). The apparatus is filled with a liquid. The cylinders A_1 and A_2 are fitted with air tight pistons P_1 and P_2. Place a weight of $W_1\, g$ on the piston P_1. The pressure exerted on P_1 is W_1/x.

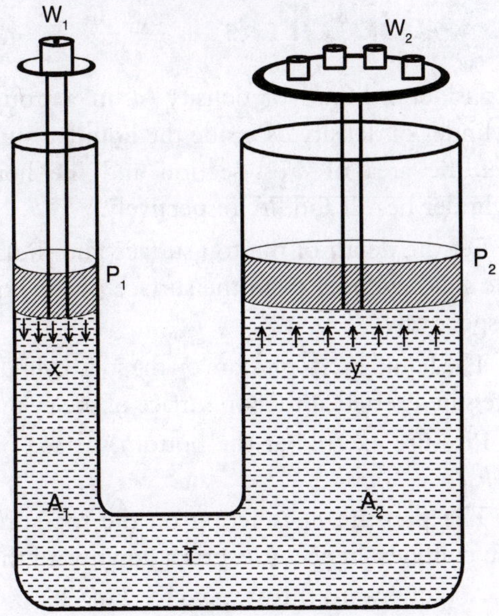

Figure 4.17 Bramah press

According to Pascal's law the pressure exerted on P_1 is transmitted unchanged equally by the liquid to piston P_2.

The downward pressure exerted on $P_1 = \dfrac{W_1}{x}$

The upward force exerted on P_2 = Pressure on P_2 × Area of cross-section of A_2.

For the piston P_2 to be in equilibrium, a weight W_2 is placed on it.

Then, W_2 = (Pressure on P_2)y.

According to Pascal's law pressure on P_2 = pressure on $P_1 = \dfrac{W_1}{x}$

$$\therefore\ W_2 = \left(\frac{W_1}{x}\right)y$$

But $\quad y = nx$

$$\Rightarrow W_2 = \frac{W_1}{x} \times nx$$

$$W_2 = W_1 n$$

Info Bytes!

Pascal's Law is the principle behind hydraulic lifts that can lift cars or even aeroplanes.

This shows $W_2 > W_1$. Therefore, a small force applied at a point can be used to exert a much larger force at another point. This formulates the principle of **'Bramah press'**.

One of the other applications of Pascal's law is a hydraulic press, which is used

1. to press the bales of cotton,
2. to extract oil from oil seeds, and
3. in hydraulic brakes that are used in brake systems of vehicles.

Mechanical Advantage

Mechanical advantage is defined as the ratio of load to effort. In the above case, the upward force applied on piston P_2 is load. The downward force applied on piston P_1 is effort.

$$\text{Hence, Mechanical advantage (M.A.)} = \frac{\text{Load}}{\text{Effort}} = \frac{P_2 \times y}{P_1 \times x}$$

But $P_2 = P_1$ (Pascal's law)

$$\therefore\ \text{M.A.} = \frac{y}{x}$$

Upthrust

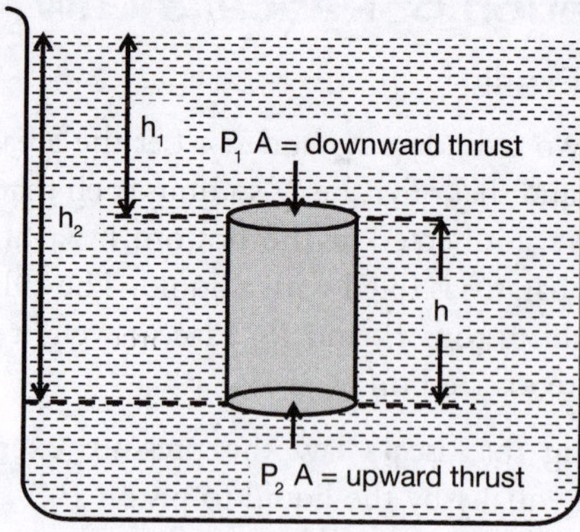

Figure 4.18 Upthrust acting on a cylinder placed in a liquid

Consider a liquid of density 'd' in a trough. Place a solid cylinder of density ds inside the liquid as shown in the figure. Let the area of cross-section and the height of the solid cylinder be 'A' and 'h', respectively.

Let the depth of the top surface and the bottom surface of the solid cylinder from the surface of the liquid be h_1 and h_2, respectively.

The liquid exerts pressure on the solid cylinder in all directions. Pressure exerted at the top surface of the cylinder, $p_1 = h_1dg$.

Pressure exerted at the bottom surface of the cylinder, $p_2 = h_2dg$.

The pressure p_1 is acting on the top surface of area A of the cylinder, hence, it exerts a downward thrust on the solid.

$\therefore$ Downward thrust $= p_1A = h_1dgA$.

The liquid also exerts lateral pressure on the sides of the cylinder. Total lateral pressure acting on one side is equal and opposite to the total lateral pressure acting on the other side. Hence, the net lateral pressure on the cylinder is zero.

Due to pressure p_2 acting on the bottom surface A of the cylinder, an upward thrust acts on the solid.

$\therefore$ upward thrust $= p_2A = h_2\,dgA$

Since $h_2 > h_1$, $h_2d_gA > h_1d_gA \Rightarrow p_2A > p_1A$

$\therefore$ Resultant thrust = upward thrust − downward thrust

$= p_2A - p_1A$

$= h_2dgA - h_1dgA$

$= (h_2 - h_1)\,dgA$

$= hdgA \; (\because h_2 - h_1 = h)$

$= Vdg \; (\because hA = V$, Volume of the solid)

This resultant thrust is in the upward direction, and hence called **upthrust** or **buoyant force**.

$\therefore$ Upthrust = weight of the liquid displaced.

Volume of the solid cylinder (V) $= Ah$

Mass of the cylinder (m) = Volume × Density

$\Rightarrow m = V \cdot d_s$

$\Rightarrow m = Ahd_s$

Weight of the cylinder $W_s = mg$

$\Rightarrow W = Ahd_sg$

Thus, the upthrust or buoyant force is directly proportional to

- the volume of the fluid displaced by a solid.
- the density of the liquid in which the solid is immersed.

Archimedes' Principle

Archimedes' principle states that, 'When a body is partially or wholly immersed in a fluid, it suffers an apparent loss of weight which is equal to the weight of the liquid displaced by it.'

Activity:

Take a spring balance, an overflow jar, a small beaker, a stone and a piece of string or thread.

1. Suspend the stone from the hook of the spring balance by means of a string.
2. Note the reading on the scale of the spring balance. Let the weight of the stone measured in air be W_1.
3. Now immerse the stone completely in the water taken in an overflow jar with a beaker kept under its spout, taking care that the stone does not touch the walls or the bottom of the jar.

4. The stone displaces some water which overflows through the spout into the beaker.
5. The reading on the scale of the spring balance is noted after the water stops dripping into the beaker. Let the weight of the stone measured in water be W_2.
6. It is observed that W_2 is less than W_1. Hence, the loss in the weight of the stone is given by $(W_1 - W_2)$, which is the buoyant force exerted on the stone by the water.
7. Find the weight of the displaced water (W_3) in the beaker. It is observed that the weight of water displaced is exactly equal to the buoyant force $(W_1 - W_2)$.
∴ **Apparent loss of weight = weight of liquid displaced = upthrust.**

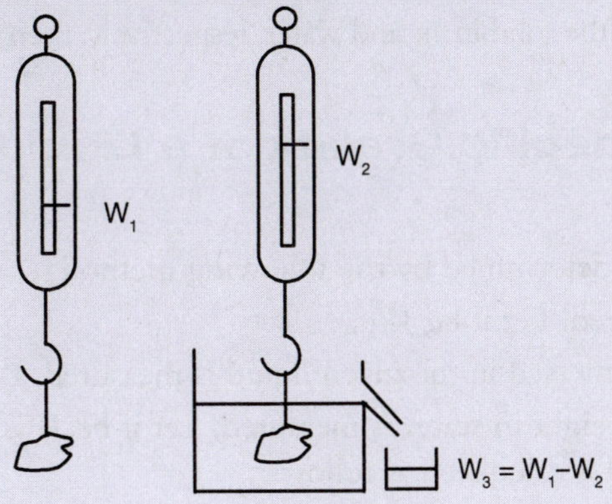

Figure 4.19 Experimental arrangement to show that weight of the liquid displaced is equal to the upthrust

Relative Density

Relative density is defined as the ratio of the density of a substance to the density of water at 4°C.

$$\therefore \text{R.D.} = \frac{\text{density of the substance}}{\text{density of equal volume of water at } 4^\circ \text{ C}}$$

$$\text{R.D.} = \frac{d}{d_w}$$

Relative density has no units.

Info Bytes!

Relative density is also called **specific gravity.**

Determination of Relative Density or Specific Gravity of a Solid

Archimedes' principle states that 'when a body is immersed in a liquid, it experiences an apparent loss in its weight which is equal to the weight of the displaced liquid or weight of liquid whose volume is equal to the volume of the solid'. Based on this, relative density of a solid can be calculated as follows.

$$\text{Relative density (R.D.)} = \frac{d}{d_w},$$

where d and d_w are the densities of the solid and water, respectively.

$$\therefore \text{R.D.} = \frac{\frac{m}{v}}{\frac{m_w}{v_w}};$$

Here m is the mass of solid, m_w is the mass of water, v is the volume of solid and v_w is the volume of water.

If $v = v_w$, then R.D. of the solid $= \frac{m}{m_w} = \frac{m}{m_w} \times \frac{g}{g} = \frac{W}{W_w}$ where W and W_W are the weight of the solid in air and the weight of water whose volume is equal to the volume of the solid, respectively.

i.e., W_w = weight of water displaced.

∴ By Archimedes Principle w_w = apparent loss of weight of the solid in water.

$$\therefore \text{R.D.} = \frac{\text{weight of the solid in air}}{\text{apparent loss of weight of the solid in water}}$$

If W_1 and W_2 represent the weight of the solid in air and water, respectively, then the relative density of the solid $= \frac{W_1}{W_1 - W_2}$

Determination of the Specific Gravity of a Liquid Using Archimedes' Principle

The relative density of a liquid can be determined by the following method:

1. Weight of a solid in air is measured. Let it be W_1.
2. Then the weight of the solid immersed in the given liquid is measured. Let it be W_3.
3. The body is wiped dry and its weight in water is measured. Let it be W_2.

The relative density of the given liquid is calculated as follows:

$$\text{Relative density of the liquid} = \frac{\text{mass of certain volume (v) of liquid}}{\text{mass of equal volume (v)of water}}$$

$$= \frac{\text{weight of the liquid dislplaced by the body}}{\text{weight of the water displaced by the same body}}$$

$$= \frac{\text{loss of weight of the body in the liquid}}{\text{loss of weight of the same body in water}} = \frac{W_1 - W_3}{W_1 - W_2}$$

EXAMPLE 4.6 A metal object has a weight of 60 N in the air. When submerged in a certain liquid, its weight is measured to be 45 N, while in water, its weight is 50 N. Determine the specific gravity of the liquid.

SOLUTION

Weight of the body in air W_1 = 60 N

Weight of the body in liquid W_3 = 45 N

Weight of the body in water W_2 = 50 N

∴ Specific gravity of the liquid

$$= \frac{W_1 - W_3}{W_1 - W_2}$$

$$= \frac{(60-45)}{(60-50)}$$

$$= \frac{15}{10} = 1.5$$

Hence, the specific gravity of the liquid is 1.5.

EXAMPLE 4.7 A body weighs 16 N in a liquid whose specific gravity is 6. Find the weight of the body in water if it weighs 40 N in air.

SOLUTION

Let W_1, W_2 and W_3 be the weight of the body in air, water and liquid, respectively.
$W_3 = 16$ N; $W_2 = x$ (to be determined)
$W_1 = 40$ N
Specific gravity of the liquid = 6

$$\Rightarrow \frac{W_1 - W_3}{W_1 - W_2} = 6 \Rightarrow \frac{40 - 16}{40 - x} = 6$$

$\Rightarrow x = 36$ N. Thus, weight of the body in water is 36 N.

EXAMPLE 4.8 A body weighs 20 N in water and 30 N in air. Find the density of the body. Take the density of water as 1.0 g cm^{-3}.

SOLUTION

Let W_1 and W_2 be the weights of the body in air and in water, respectively. Then $W_1 = 30$ N and $W_2 = 20$ N.

$$\text{Relative density of the body} = \frac{W_1}{W_1 - W_2} = 3$$

$\therefore$ Density of the body = 3 × density of the water = 3 g cm^{-3}

EXAMPLE 4.9 A body weighs 20 N in water and its relative density is 3. Find the weight of the body in air.

SOLUTION

Let W_1 be the weight of the body in air; and W_2 be its weight in water.
$\therefore W_2 = 20$ N
R.D. of the body = 3

$$\therefore \frac{W_1}{W_1 - W_2} = 3$$

$$\frac{W_1}{W_1 - 20} = 3 \Rightarrow W_1 = 30 \text{ N}$$

Floatation

You must have observed that some bodies like an iron nail sink in water while some others like cork, a log of wood, etc., float on water such that some part is immersed inside the water and the remaining part of it is outside. If a cork that floats on water is forcibly pushed into water and the force is removed, it again comes up. This means that the upthrust acting on the cork due to water is greater than the weight of the cork.

Obviously, this also means that when it is floating on the water surface, its weight acting downwards is equal to the upthrust. This leads to the law of a floatation, which can be stated as under.

If a body is floating in a liquid, then its weight acting vertically downward is equal to the upthrust or the buoyant force acting vertically up on the body. Thus, a floating body is under equilibrium condition.

The question which arises is why few bodies sink while others float in a liquid. This is determined by the following conditions.

Let d_s = density of the substance.

d_ℓ = density of the liquid.

1. If $d_s > d_\ell$, the body sinks in the given liquid.
2. If $d_s < d_\ell$, the body floats in the liquid.
3. If $d_s = d_\ell$, the body stays completely immersed in the liquid and remains at rest wherever placed.

EXAMPLE 4.10 A cylindrical body of area of cross section 100 cm^2 and length 20 cm is immersed in a liquid whose density is 1.5 g cm^{-3}. If the density of the solid is 2 g cm^{-3}, calculate the upthrust acting on the body.

SOLUTION

Upthrust $(F) = Vdg$

Where V = volume of the liquid displaced by the cylinder = the volume of the cylinder itself.

$\therefore V = A\ell$

$= 100\ cm^2 \times 20\ cm$

$= 2000\ cm^3$

$F = 2000\ cm^3 \times 1.5\ g\ cm^{-3} \times 980\ cm\ s^{-2}$

$= 2940000$ dyne

$\therefore F = 29.4$ N

Hydrometers

Hydrometer is a device used to measure the relative density of liquids. It works on the principle that, 'When a body floats in any liquid, its weight is equal to the weight of the liquid displaced by the immersed part of the body.'

Simple hydrometer consists of a uniform test tube. A graduated scale in the form of a strip of paper is pasted to the inside wall of the tube. In order that the tube remains totally vertical while floating in water or a given liquid its base is made heavier by taking few lead shots in it.

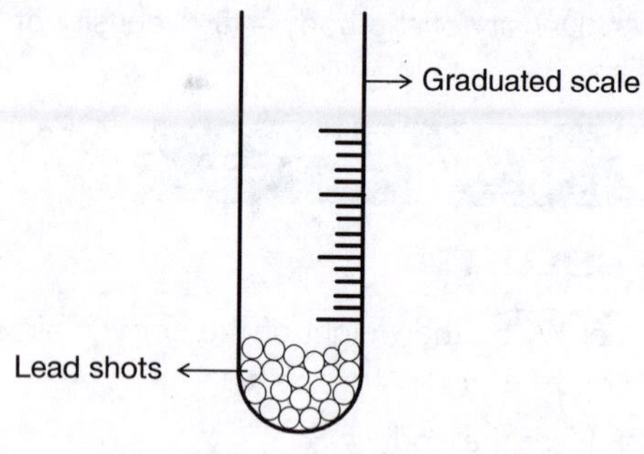

Figure 4.20 Simple hydrometer

Types of Hydrometer

The two types of hydrometers commonly used are:

1. **Constant Immersion Hydrometer:** The hydrometer is made to float at the same depth in water and the liquid whose relative density is to be found.

Let W_1 is the weight of the test tube along with lead shots. Let it float at depth h in water.

By law of floatation,

$$W_1 = Ahd_1g\ (d_1 = \text{density of water})$$

Now the tube is immersed in a given liquid and made to float at the same depth 'h' by adding or removing some lead shots. Let W_2 be the total weight of the tube with lead shots.

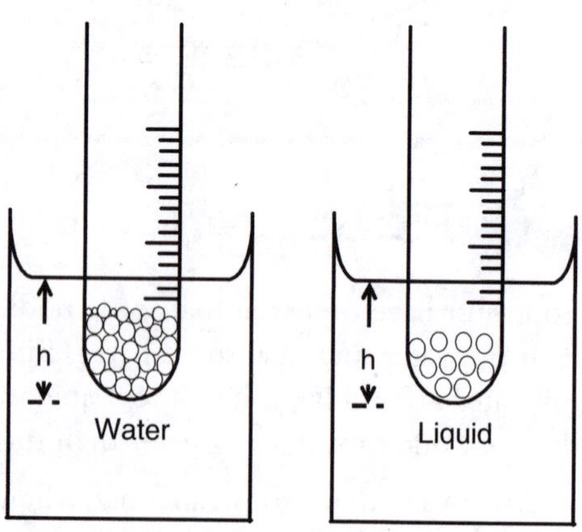

Figure 4.21 Constant immersion hydrometer

$$\therefore W_2 = Ahd_2g\ (d_2 = \text{density of liquid})$$

$$\frac{W_2}{W_1} = \frac{Ahd_2g}{Ahd_1g}$$

$$\frac{W_2}{W_1} = \frac{d_2}{d_1}$$

$$\therefore \text{ R.D. of liquid} = \frac{W_2}{W_1} = \frac{d_2}{d_1}$$

$$= \frac{\text{Weight of the tube for certain immersion in liquid}}{\text{Weight of the tube for the same immersion in water}}$$

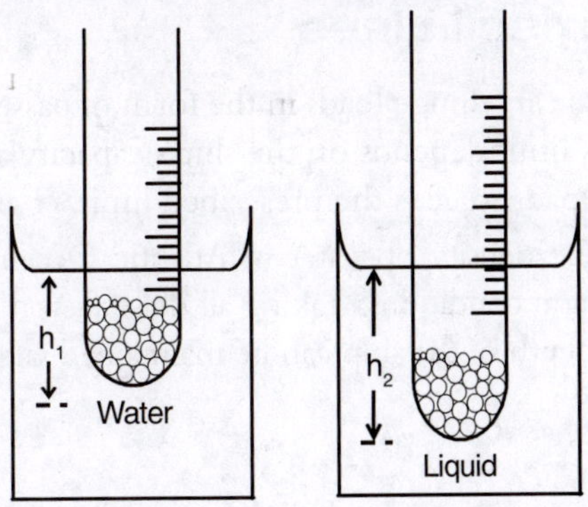

Figure 4.22 Variable immersion hydrometer

2. **Variable Immersion Hydrometer:** The weight of the hydrometer is kept constant so that it floats at different depths in various liquids depending on their relative densities.

Let W = Weight of tube with lead shots. This weight is kept constant as no lead shots are added or removed.

The tube is immersed in water and the depth h_1 at which it floats is noted. Now the tube is floated in liquid and the depth h_2 is noted.

For floatation in water

$$W = Ah_1d_1g \tag{4.5}$$

For floatation in liquid

$$W = Ah_2d_2g \tag{4.6}$$

Since the weight of the hydrometer is the same in both cases, weight of liquid displaced is also equal.

Thus, we have, $Ah_1d_1g = Ah_2d_2g$

$$\frac{h_1}{h_2} = \frac{d_2}{d_1}$$

$$\therefore \text{ R.D.} = \frac{h_1}{h_2}$$

Relative density of a liquid = ratio of the depth of immersion in water to that in the given liquid.

EXAMPLE 4.11

The weight of a constant immersion hydrometer is 15 gwt. When it is immersed in a liquid, few more lead shots were added to it so that it floats at the same depth as in water. If the weight of the hydrometer now is 20 gwt, find its relative density.

SOLUTION

$$\text{R.D.} = \frac{\text{Weight of the tube for certain immersion in liquid}}{\text{Weight of the tube for hte same immersion in water}} = \frac{20\text{gwt}}{15\text{gwt}}$$

$\therefore$ R.D. = 1.33

EXAMPLE 4.12

The depth of immersion of hydrometer in water is 10 cm. What will be the depth of immersion in a liquid whose density is 2 g cm^{-3}?

SOLUTION

Relative density is equal in magnitude to the density of substance in c.g.s. system.

$\therefore$ R.D. of a given liquid = density of liquid in c.g.s. system.

R.D. = 2

$$\text{R.D.} = \frac{h_w}{h_\ell}$$

$$2 = \frac{10\,\text{cm}}{h_\ell}$$

$\therefore$ h_ℓ = 5 cm.

Plimsoll Lines

Ships carry huge loads in the form of passengers and cargo. Care has to be taken that the ship is loaded upto a certain limit. This limit depends on the ship's capacity as well as the density of sea water through which it travels. The ship may sink if the load exceeds the prescribed limit.

The density of water in Atlantic Ocean is different from that in the Indian Ocean. It also changes with changes in the climatic conditions. Taking all these factors into account, several lines are marked on the sides of the ship which indicate that the depth of the ship can be maintained safely without the danger of it sinking due to the load. These lines are called **Plimsoll lines**.

Boyle's Law

The relation between pressure and volume of a fixed amount of gas at constant temperature was given by Robert Boyle, a British scientist in what is known as Boyle's law.

Boyle's law states that at a constant temperature, the pressure of the given mass of a gas is inversely proportional to its volume.

At constant temperature, $p \propto \frac{h_1}{h_2} = \frac{d_2}{d_1} \Rightarrow pV = \text{constant}$

i.e., let p_1 is the pressure due to gas when its volume is V_1.

Let the volume change to V_2 so that the pressure becomes p_2.

According to Boyle's law, $p_1V_1 = p_2V_2$ (at constant temperature)

Consider a cylinder with a cross-sectional area (A) containing a fixed mass of gas, which is enclosed by a movable air tight piston (P). Let the volume occupied by the gas be 'V'. Initially a weight W_1 is placed on the piston. Then the total pressure (p_1) of the gas is

$$p_1 = \text{atmospheric pressure} + \text{pressure due to weight}$$

$$p_1 = P_a + \frac{W_1}{A}$$

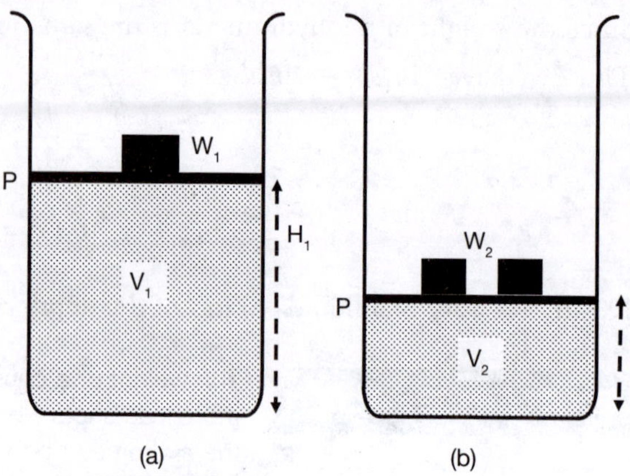

Figure 4.23 Boyle's law verification

If the height of the piston is H_1, then the initial volume V_1 of the gas is $(H_1 \times A)$

$$\therefore \quad \text{Product of } p_1V_1 = p_1V_1 = \left(p_a + \frac{W_1}{A}\right)(H_1 \times A) \tag{4.7}$$

Similarly if a second weight W_2 ($W_2 > W_1$) is placed on the piston, the piston moves downward, hence, the volume of the gas decreases. Let the pressure on the gas when W_2 is placed on the piston be $p_2 = \left(\frac{W_2}{A} + P_a\right)$.

If the height of the cylinder now is H_2, then the corresponding volume (V_2) of the gas is $(H_2 \times A)$

$$\therefore \quad \text{Product of } p_2V_2 = \left(\frac{W_2}{A} + p_a\right)(H_2 \times A) \tag{4.8}$$

By considering the values of the products of p_1V_1 and p_2V_2 it can be proved experimentally that both the values are equal, i.e., $p_1V_1 = p_2V_2$.

EXAMPLE 4.13 The pressure of a gas of volume 22.4 ℓ is 3 atm at certain temperature. Then find the pressure of the gas of volume 44.8 ℓ at the same temperature.

SOLUTION

According to Boyle's law,

$p_1V_1 = p_2V_2$

$3 \times 22.4 = x \times 44.8$, where x is the new pressure of the gas (to be determined)

$x = \frac{3}{2} = 1.5$ atm. Thus, the new pressure of the gas is 1.5 atm.

EXAMPLE 4.14 The pressure of a gas is doubled keeping its temperature constant. Find the ratio of the final volume of the gas to its initial volume.

SOLUTION

According to Boyle's law, at constant temperature $p_1V_1 = p_2V_2$

Given $p_2 = 2\ p_1$

$\therefore\ p_1V_1 = 2\ p_1V_2 \Rightarrow \frac{V_2}{V_1} = \frac{1}{2} \Rightarrow 1 : 2$

Bernoulli's Principle

We observe a calendar on the wall of a room fluttering when the ceiling fan in the room blows tair. During cyclones when wind blows at high speeds, the thatched roofs are blown away. An aeroplane is able to fly in air against its own weight. What phenomenon is responsible for these to happen?

When air blows over the top surface of any body with high speed, a pressure difference between the top and the bottom surfaces of the body is created. A low pressure region is created above the top surface of the body. Hence, the pressure of air above the top surface of the body is lesser than the pressure of air at the bottom surface. The relation between the two was discovered and developed by a scientist named Bernoulli and the principle is known as **Bernoulli's principle**.

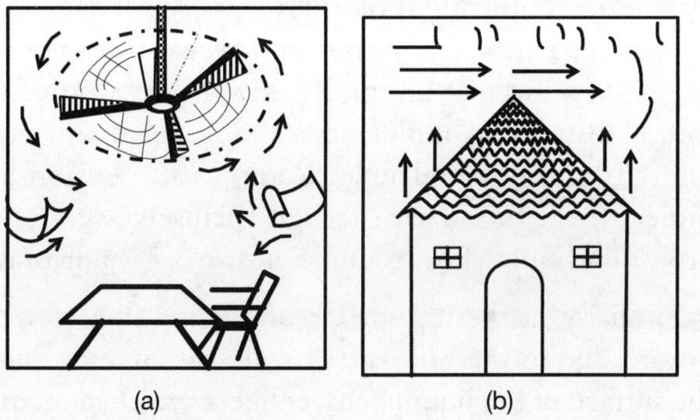

Figure 4.24 (a) Papers fluttering away from the table. (b) Thatched roof blowing away in cyclone

Explanation of Bernoulli's Principle

1. When wind blows at a very high speed over the roof of a hut a low pressure region is created above the roof. This creates a pressure difference between the top and the bottom surfaces of the roof. The pressure difference causes an upthrust on the roof, and hence, it is blown away.
2. If the wind is blowing horizontally over a paper placed on a table, a low pressure is created above the paper. The high pressure below the paper makes it fly away.
3. The flying of aeroplanes in air against their own weight is based on Bernoulli's principle.

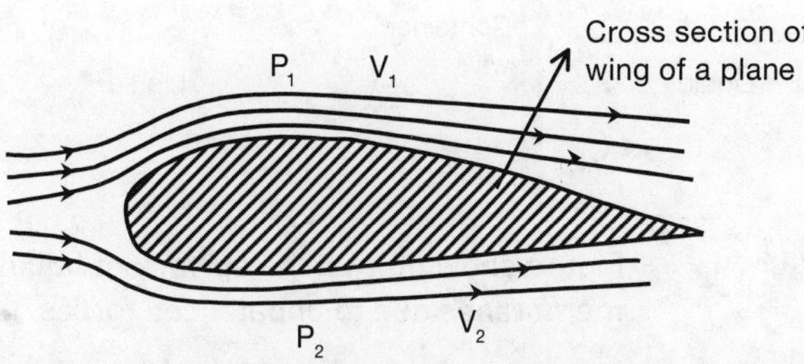

Figure 4.25 The shape of an aeroplane wing designed in way that the pressure on the top of it is greater than that at the bottom

The propeller present in front of an aeroplane helps in blowing the air backwards with high speed. The shape of the wings is such that the speed of air blown from the propeller creates a pressure difference between the top and the bottom surfaces of the wings. This is due to the speed of air above the wings being greater than that in the region below the wings. The difference of pressure (p) thus created is multiplied with the area of wings (A), giving an upward thrust (T) to the aeroplane, i.e., $T = p \times A$. If the plane has wings of a very large area, an upward thrust greater than the weight of the aeroplane acts on the wings, lifting the plane into the air.

$V_1 \longrightarrow$ velocity of air at the top surface of the wing

$V_2 \longrightarrow$ velocity of air at the bottom surfacae of the wing

$V_1 > V_2,\ P_1 < P_2$

Surface Tension

Surface tension is the property of a liquid at rest, due to which the top surface of a liquid contained in a vessel behaves like a stretched membrane occupying minimum surface area.

Explanation for Surface Tension

Consider a liquid in a jar. The molecules of the liquid experience a pull by the neighbouring molecules equally. Hence, the molecule is acted upon by balanced attractive **cohesive forces**. But the molecules present near the edges (top surface) are pulled inward because of the unbalanced cohesive forces. But these molecules cannot move inward due to the opposition offered by inner molecules leading to a tension at the surface. Thus, the molecules at the surface realign themselves giving a spherical shape to the drop of a liquid. For example, a drop of water is always spherical.

Similarly, at the top surface of a liquid in a vessel the molecules are pulled inward due to the unbalanced cohesive forces acting downward. Due to this, the surface of the liquid behaves like a stretched membrane. This phenomenon is called **'surface tension'**.

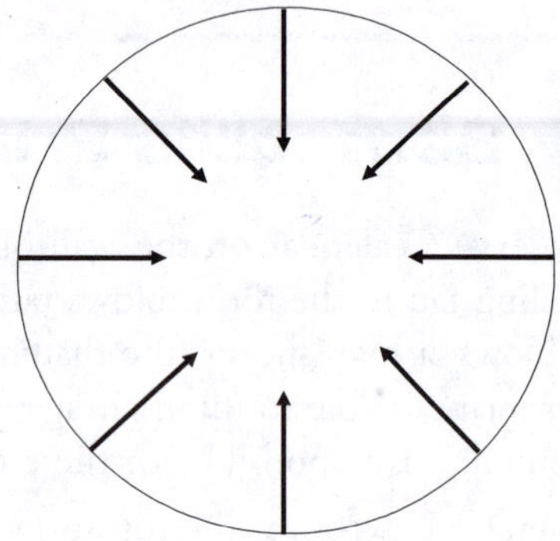

Figure 4.26 Spherical shape acquired by liquid drops due to surface tension

However, near the walls of the container, there exists adhesive force between the liquid molecules and the molecules of the material of the container. This adhesive force being different from the cohesive force, the surface near the container walls is either 'pulled' upward or downward as shown in the figure.

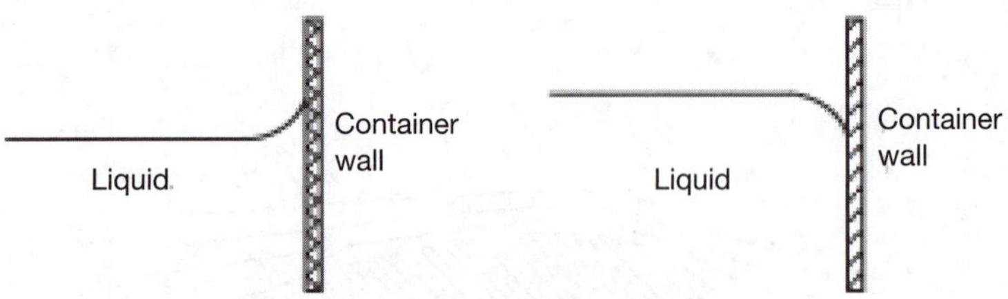

Figure 4.27 Figure showing that the surface of liquids acting like membranes due to unbalanced forces

Info Bytes!

Water striders use surface tension to essentially 'walk on water.'

This is seen clearly in a narrow tube such a burette or pipette, in which a curved surface is formed at the liquid surface. Such a curved surface formed is known as a **meniscus**.

There are two types of menisci. They are

1. convex meniscus
2. concave meniscus

A convex meniscus is formed due to more cohesive force between the molecules of liquid than the adhesive force between the molecules of liquid and the vessel (or container) taken as shown in the diagram below.

In a test tube containing mercury, the top surface of mercury takes convex shape. This is due to the presence of strong cohesive forces between the molecules of mercury at the exposed surface, as compared to less adhesive force of molecules of mercury with glass. Hence, mercury forms a convex meniscus.

If water is taken in a test tube, the molecules of water have a strong adhesive force with glass surface and a weak cohesive force. Hence, water forms a concave meniscus on account of high adhesive forces.

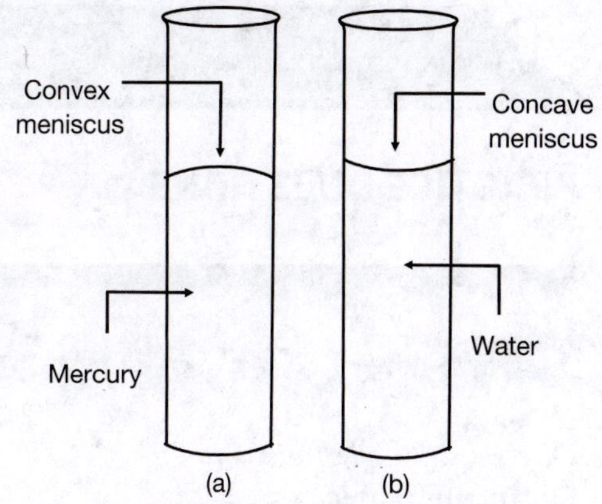

Figure 4.28 Types of minisci

POINTS TO REMEMBER

- ✔ Anything which has a mass and occupies space is called matter.
- ✔ The force of attraction between like molecules is called cohesive force.
- ✔ The same force between unlike molecules is called adhesive force.
- ✔ Pressure is defined as the ratio of the thrust (T) to the area of contact (A) on which the thrust is acting normally.
- ✔ The pressure exerted by the fluids on the sides of the vessel containing the fluid is called lateral pressure.
- ✔ The pressure exerted by these atmospheric gases on the surroundings and on the surface of the Earth is known as the atmospheric pressure. the pressure exerted by a liquid can be expressed in terms of the height of the liquid column. This principle is used in mercury barometer.
- ✔ The instrument used to measure altitudes in air crafts is called an altimeter.
- ✔ Gas manometer is a device used for the measurement of the pressure of gas present in a closed vessel. This pressure is referred to as gauge pressure.
- ✔ Relative density is defined as the ratio of the density of a substance to the density of water at 4°C.
- ✔ Hydrometer is a device used to measure the relative density of liquids.
- ✔ Surface tension is the property of a liquid at rest, due to which the top surface of a liquid contained in a vessel behaves like a stretched membrane occupying minimum surface area.

CLASSROOM WING

PRACTICE QUESTIONS

Very Short Answer Type Questions

Directions for questions 1 to 7:
Fill in the blanks.

1. The force of attraction between like molecules is called ________.
2. Molecules in liquids and gases have more freedom of movement, giving them a unique ability to ________.
3. A test tube floats to a depth 4 cm in water and to a depth 8 cm in a liquid. The relative density of the liquid is ________.
4. The pressure exerted by the fluids on the sides of the vessel containing the fluid is called ________.
5. Pressure at a point in a fluid is directly proportional to the depth of the point from the surface, the ________ of the fluid, and the acceleration due to gravity.
6. A pair of physical quantities having the same unit is ________.
7. The fall in pressure due to rise in humidity indicates ________.

Directions for questions 8 to 25:
Answer the following questions briefly.

8. What is surface tension?
9. Give the expression for the pressure at a point inside a liquid.
10. State the three factors on which the pressure at a point inside a liquid depends.
11. What is the use of Hare's apparatus?
12. What is the principle behind a mercury barometer?
13. State the law of transmission of pressure (Pascal's Law) in fluids.
14. Give the uses of a hydraulic press.
15. What is a barometer? Mention the types of barometers.
16. Why do dams have walls that are tapered upwards?
17. If the length of the mercury column in a mercury barometer is 76 cm, what is the equivalent height of the water column?
18. Name any two factors on which the height of the mercury column in a Torricelli barometer depends.
19. Name two factors on which the height of the mercury column in a Torricelli barometer depends.
20. If the height of the mercury column is to decrease by 1 cm, what should be the corresponding change in the altitude?
21. Define upthrust and how is the upthrust experienced by a body affected if its volume is doubled keeping its mass constant?
22. What is the difference between cohesive and adhesive forces?
23. Why do liquids and gases have the property of fluidity?
24. Write an expression for the relative density of a solid floating in a liquid in terms of the volume of the solid in the liquid and the total volume of the solid.
25. How does pressure vary inside a stationary liquid with depth?

Short Answer Type Questions

26. Explain how fluids differ from solids.
27. A liquid of mass 200 g exerts a pressure of 0.1 Pa at the bottom of container. What pressure would it exert if the area of cross section of the container is doubled?
28. What is the significance of the statement 'liquid seeks its own level'?
29. Two identical tanks contain water and a liquid of density 0.8 g cm^{-3}. Pressure exerted by the liquid is equal to the

pressure due to water column of 50 cm. Find the height of the liquid column in the tank?

30. Why do astronauts wear spacesuits in relation to atmospheric pressure?

31. Due to the presence of certain impurities in mercury, its effective density is 12 g cm^{-3}. What is the barometer reading at sea level?

32. How does the design of Fortin's barometer address the disadvantages of the simple mercury barometer?

33. A body weighs 20 N in a liquid whose relative density is 5. In water it weighs 40 N. Find its weight in air?

34. What are the advantages of an aneroid barometer over a mercury barometer?

35. A solid of mass 100 g and density 2 g cm^{-3} is immersed in water. Calculate the upthrust acting on it.

36. Explain the working of a lift pump briefly.

37. Explain the construction and working of Hare's apparatus.

38. Explain Plimsoll lines.

39. Why do few bodies float while other bodies sink in water?

40. What would you conclude if the heights of both liquids in a Hare's apparatus are equal?

41. What is hydrostatics?

42. Define thrust. What are the units of thrust?

Essay Answer Type Questions

43. Enlist some of the important postulates of kinetic theory of matter.

44. Derive an expression for the buoyant force acting on a body completely submerged in a liquid of density ℓ.

45. Elaborate on the importance of understanding the kinetic theory of matter in relation to the states of matter and their behaviour.

46. Discuss the significance of thrust and pressure in daily life and engineering applications.

47. Explain flying of aeroplanes as an application of Bernoulli's principle

COMPETITION WING

PRACTICE QUESTIONS

Level 1: Apply your Concepts

Directions for questions 1 to 10:
State whether the following statements are true or false.

1. Study of fluids under rest is called kinematics.
2. Force acting normally on a surface is called thrust.
3. Pressure is a scalar quantity.
4. Barometer can be used to measure the pressure of a gas filled inside a container.
5. In a hydraulic press the mechanical advantage is always equal to one.
6. A liquid drop takes spherical shape due to surface tension.
7. Wind blowing horizontally over a paper makes it fly away. This can be explained on the basis of Bernoullis principle.
8. When water is used as barometer liquid the height of the water column at sea level is 76 cm.
9. Force acting on a unit area is called pressure.
10. In the expression 'buoyant force or upthrust $= V \times \rho \times g$,' ρ is the density of the liquid displaced.

Directions for questions 13 to 19:
Fill in the blanks.

11. The walls of dams are constructed tapered upwards because the lateral pressure exerted by a liquid ________ with the increase in the depth of the liquid.
12. The _____ apparatus helps in measuring the relative density of liquids without allowing them to come in contact.
13. In a mercury barometer, the empty space at the top of the tube is called a _____ vacuum.
14. Mercury in the barometer reacts differently when exposed to the _____, which can cause certain impurities to dissolve in it.
15. Fortin's barometer provides a more accurate measure of atmospheric pressure due to its use of a vernier _____.
16. If X is the weight of an object in air and Y is its weight when completely immersed in water, then $\frac{X}{X-Y}$ _____.
17. A variable immersion hydrometer is immersed upto $\frac{1}{2}$ and $\frac{1}{3}$ of its volume in two given liquids, respectively. Then the ratio of the densities of the two liquids is ________.
18. One of the limbs of a mercury manometer is connected to a gas cylinder. The mercury level in the limb connected to the gas cylinder is 10 cm higher than that in the other limb. Then the gauge pressure of the gas is ________ cm of Hg.
19. A cuboid of dimensions 3 m × 2 m × 1 m is placed on a surface such that the face with maximum surface area is in contact. If the weight of the cuboid is 1kgwt, the pressure exerted by it on the surface is ________. (take $g = 10\ m\ s^{-2}$).

Direction for question 20:
Match the entries in Column A with the appropriate ones in Column B.

20.

Column A	Column B
A. Liquidless barometer	(a) Newton
B. Guage Pressure	(b) Hydraulic jack
C. Pascal's law	(c) Forms concave meniscus
D. Pressure	(d) Dust storm
E. Thrust	(e) Specific gravity of liquids
F. Water	(f) Aneroid barometer
G. Fall in pressure due to a rise in temperature	(g) Pascal
H. Hydrometer	(h) Pressure of gas present in a closed vessel

Directions for questions 21 to 45:
For each of the questions, four choices have been provided. Select the correct alternative.

21. What does the kinetic theory of matter suggest about the kinetic energy of molecules?
(a) It is inversely proportional to the absolute temperature.
(b) It has no relation to the absolute temperature.
(c) It is directly proportional to the absolute temperature.
(d) It remains constant irrespective of the temperature.

22. In which state of matter is the cohesive force negligible?
(a) Solid (b) Liquid
(c) Gas (d) Plasma

23. Which of the following best describes the term 'Thrust'?
(a) Force acting along the surface
(b) Force acting normal to a surface
(c) Force acting in the opposite direction to the surface
(d) Force acting tangentially to the surface

24. The Hydrostatic Paradox states that
(a) Pressure inside a liquid increases with the shape of the container.
(b) Pressure inside a liquid decreases with the shape of the container.
(c) The applied force by the liquid on the base of different shaped containers (having the same base area) filled with liquid of the same height is different.
(d) The applied force by the liquid on the base of different shaped containers (having the same base area) filled with liquid of the same height is the same.

25. As air bubble rises from bottom to the top of a water tank, the size of the bubble increases. It happens, because
(a) the pressure exerted by water on the bubble decreases as the height of the water column above it decrease.
(b) the density of water increases as we move downwards.
(c) at constant temperature, pressure inside the air bubble are volume of the bubble inversely proportional to each other.
(d) Both (a) and (c)

26. Which one of the following statements is true?
(a) The weight of a substance in air is always less than its weight in water.
(b) The mass of a substance is equal to the mass of an equal volume of water.
(c) The weight of a substance in water is always greater than its weight in some other liquid.
(d) The weight of a substance in water is always less than its weight in air.

27. No-liquid barometer is
(a) a mercury barometer
(b) an aneroid barometer
(c) a Fortin's barometer
(d) Torricelli's barometer

28. A cylindrical object floats in water such that (3/4) th of its volume is immersed in water. Its density is _____ kg m^{-3}.
(a) 250 (b) 0.75
(c) 0.25 (d) 750

29. A piece of nail sinks in water but a boat floats in it because
(a) there is no upthrust acting on the nail.
(b) a nail is heavier than a boat.
(c) a nail has a pointed end.
(d) upthrust acting on the nail is less than its weight.

30. An object of mass 100 kg is to be lifted by a 10 kg effort. The possible values of the area of cross sections of the pump piston and press piston are ______ and ______, respectively, both in the same unit.
(a) 100, 1 (b) 10, 1
(c) 1, 100 (d) 2, 20

31. The weight of the liquid displaced by a body when the body is immersed in it is called
(a) apparent weight
(b) upthrust
(c) lateral pressure
(d) relative density of the body

32. Which one of the following statements is true?
(a) Water forms concave meniscus on account of high cohesive forces.
(b) Mercury forms concave meniscus on account of more adhesive force than the cohesive forces.
(c) Water forms convex meniscus on account of high adhesive forces than the cohesive forces.
(d) Mercury forms convex meniscus on account of more cohesive force than adhesive force.

33. Which one of the following physical quantities increases as we go deep into the sea?
(a) temperature (b) gravity
(c) pressure (d) upthrust

34. The apparent weight of an object on the suface of the moon, if the mass of the object and liquid displaced are X and Y, respectively, is ______.
(a) $\frac{X-Y}{g}$ (b) $\frac{g}{6}(X-Y)$
(c) $6g(X-Y)$ (d) $\frac{6}{g}(X-Y)$

35. The roof of a house blows out during a storm because:
(a) the wind blows with high velocity under the roof.
(b) the weight of the roof is less than the weight of an equal volume of air.
(c) the wind blows with high velocity over the roof, causing an upthrust on the bottom side.
(d) the wind blows with high velocity over the roof, causing low pressure under the roof.

36. Pressure at a point inside a liquid does not depend on the
(a) density of the liquid.
(b) height of the liquid column above the point.
(c) acceleration due to gravity.
(d) base area of the container.

37. In a Bramah press, a small force is used to spend a much larger force. This is accomplished by
(a) increasing the area of cross-section of the pump piston.
(b) decreasing the area of cross-section of the press piston.
(c) increasing the area of cross-section of the press piston.
(d) increasing the load (weight) on the press piston.

38. The pair of physical quantities having the same units are
(a) stress and pressure.
(b) thrust and pressure.
(c) weight and stress.
(d) weight and pressure.

39. Arrange the following steps in proper sequence to determine the pressure exerted by a gas enclosed in a container using a manometer.
(A) Connect one end of the manometer to the container filled with gas.
(B) Both the limbs of the manometer are exposed to air, mercury level in both the limbs are equal due to atmospheric pressure.
(C) Determine the difference in level of the mercury in both the limbs of the manometer (ℓ).
(D) If the level of the mercury in the limb connected to the container is above the mercury level in the limb exposed to air, the pressure of the gas in the container is determined as atmospheric pressure $-\ell$.
(E) If the level of the mercury in the limb connected to the container is below the mercury level in the limb exposed to air, the pressure of the gas in the container is determined as atmospheric pressure $+\ell$.

(F) Note the level of the mercury in the limbs of the manometer.

(a) A B C E F E
(b) E B A D C F
(c) B A C F D E
(d) B C D A F E

40. An air bubble rises up in water because,

(a) there is no gravity in water.
(b) pressure inside the bubble is less than the pressure outside it.
(c) the upthrust acting on the bubble is more than the weight of the bubble.
(d) air cannot dissolve in water.

41. If the relative density of a solid is less than one, then

(a) it sinks in water.
(b) it floats in water.
(c) it sinks in all the liquids.
(d) it floats in all the liquids.

42. Two test tubes A and B of same mass with equal areas of cross-section are used as variable immersion hydrometer. If the length of test tube 'A' is double that of 'B', then the range of densities that can be measured by 'A' is

(a) more than the range of densities that can be measured using 'B'.
(b) less than the range of densities that can be measured using 'B'.
(c) equal to the range of densities that can be measured using 'B'.
(d) Both (b) and (c).

43. A constant immersion hydrometer weighing 20 g sinks upto mark 'x' in water and this hydrometer has to weigh 25 g to sink upto the mark 'x' in a given liquid. Then the relative density of the liquid is ______.

(a) 0.25
(b) 1.25
(c) 0.75
(d) 2.00

44. Arrange the following steps in proper sequence to determine the relative density of a liquid by using a constant immersion hydrometer.

(A) The test tube is made to float in the given liquid.
(B) The weight of the test tube with lead shots in air is determined (W_1).
(C) The depth of the test tube immersed in water (h) is determined.
(D) The test tube is made to float in water.
(E) Lead shots are added or removed from the test tube such that the test tube is immersed to the same depth (h) in the given liquid.
(F) The relative density of the liquid is measured as $\frac{W_1}{W_1}$.
(G) The test tube is taken out from the given liquid and its weight (W_2) is measured.

(a) B D C A E G F
(b) B D C A E F G
(c) B G F E A C D
(d) B A D C E F G

45. Assertion (A): When wind blows at a very high speed over the roof of a hut, the roof is blown away.

Reason (R): The pressure exerted by a fluid at rest is transmitted unchanged equally in all directions.

(a) A and R are correct and R is the correct explanation for A.
(b) A and R are correct but R is not the correct explanation for A.
(c) A is correct but R is wrong.
(d) Both A and R are wrong.

Level 2: Review your Concepts

46. When a Fortin's barometer is used to measure the pressure on the surface of the Earth and on the top of a building the main scale reading is found to be the same and the vernier scale reading is found to be 9 and zero, respectively. If one M.S.D. is 1 mm and number of vernier scale divisions is 10, calculate the height of the building. Take the average density of air as 1.3 kg m^{-3}, and that of mercury as 13.6 g cm^{-3}

47. In a Hare's apparatus when the air inside the tube is sucked the difference in the level of water and liquid in the container is found to be 3 cm and the difference in the tubes is found to be 4 cm. If the level of water in tube is 16 cm, calculate the relative density of the liquid. The density of liquid is more than the density of water and the level of liquid in the container is more than that of water.

48. In the following figures, state which of the cases is possible; discuss giving reasons in each case.

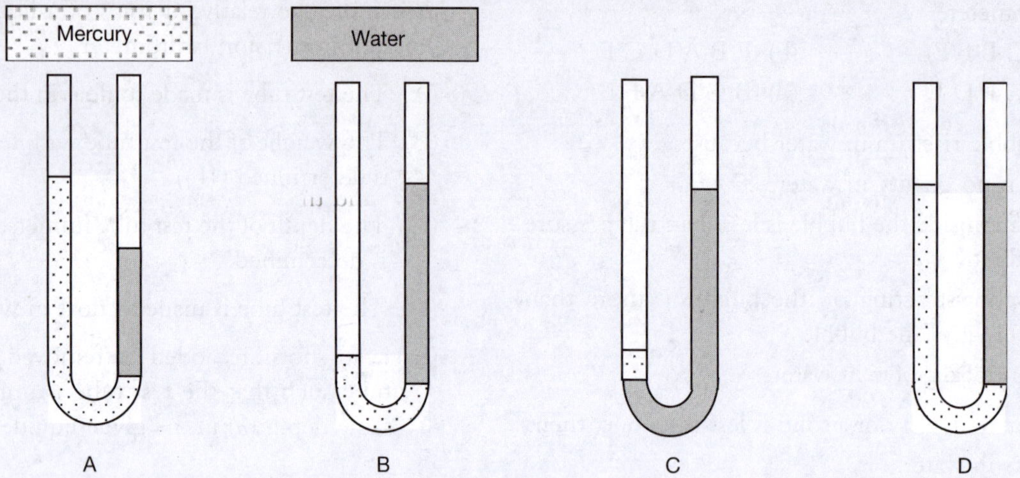

49. The 10% of total volume of the barometer liquid (mercury) contains impurities having an average density 5 g cm^{-3}. When this faulty barometer is used to measure the atmospheric pressure it reads 80 cm of the liquid column. Determine the correct atmospheric pressure.

50. The density of ice is 901 kg m^{-3}. What percentage of ice lies below water? The density of sea water is 1011 kg m^{-3}. What fraction of an iceberg can be seen by us if the ice berg has the same density as that of ice?

51. A car is lifted by a hydraulic jack that consists of two pistons. The diameter of the larger piston is 2 m and that of the smaller piston is 50 cm. If the force applied on the smaller piston is 240 N, find the weight of the car.

52. An object of weight 500 kgwt is lifted by using a hydraulic press. The radii of the cross sections of the pump piston and press piston are 10 cm and 20 cm, respectively. Calculate the effort required to lift the object. Calculate the displacement of the load if the effort is moved through a distance of 20 cm.

53. How does the Bramah Press illustrate the application of Pascal's Law?

54. A constant immersion hydrometer floats vertically in water when the weight of its float is 30 g. When it is made to float in a liquid (miscible in water), the weight of its float is increased by 10 g. Find the weight of the hydrometer when it is floated in a mixture containing equal masses of water and the liquid.

55. When a metallic sphere is released from the surface of water filled in a container of uniform area of cross section it is found to reach the bottom of the container in 2 s. If the density of the material of the sphere is 5 g cm^{-3}, calculate the pressure exerted by the liquid at the bottom of the container. Assume that only gravitational force and upthrust act on the body. ($g = 10$ m s^{-1})

56. When a metallic sphere is released from the surface of water filled in a container of uniform area of cross-section it is found to reach the bottom of the container in 2 s. If the density of the material of the sphere is 4.9 g cm^{-3}, calculate the pressure exerted by the liquid at the bottom of the container. Assume that only gravitational force and upthrust act on the body.

57. The relative density of pure gold is 19.3. When an ornament made of gold is immersed completely in water, the volume of the water displaced is 5 mL. If the mass of the ornament in air is 100 g, determine whether the ornament is made of pure gold.

58. What is the significance of upthrust or buoyant force?

59. How is Bernoulli's principle responsible for the flight of aeroplanes?

60. A man can lift a maximum weight of 30 kgwt. In order to lift an object of weight 50 kg placed in a container, he pours a certain liquid into the container so that the object is completely immersed in it. What is the density of the liquid if he can just lift the object? The volume of the liquid displaced is 10^{-2} m^3.

61. An effort applied on the small piston of a hydraulic jack lifts the load through a distance of 50 cm and the

effort is displaced through 2 m. If the diameter of the larger piston is 28 cm, calculate the area of the cross section of the smaller piston.

62. Suggest a method to fill water in a tank constructed at a height of 10 m from the ground by using a vacuum pump instead of an electric pump.

63. A pressure exerted by mercury at the bottom of a container of area of cross section 2 cm^2 is 10 Pa. Determine the weight of the mercury in the container.

64. A cuboid of dimensions 3 m × 2 m × 1 m is placed on a surface such that the face with maximum surface area is in contact. If the weight of the cuboid is 1 kgwt, determine the pressure exerted by it on the surface. (Take $g = 10$ m s^{-2}).

65. A body is immersed in a liquid of relative density 2.6. It is found that the weight of the body in the liquid is two-thirds of its weight in air. Calculate the density of the body.

Level 3: Assess Your Concepts

66. A test tube of uniform cross-section is floated vertically in a liquid '*A*' (density ρ_A) upto a mark on it when it is filled with '*x*' ml of a liquid '*B*' (density ρ_B). To make the test tube float in liquid '*B*' upto the same mark it is filled with '*y*' ml of the liquid '*A*'. Find the mass of the test tube.

67. An alloy of copper and zinc weighs 320 g in water and 302 g in a liquid of density 1·4 g cm^{-3}. If the density of copper is 8·9 g cm^{-3} and that of the zinc is 7·4 g cm^{-3}, find the measure of the masses of copper and zinc in the alloy.

68. A person carries an air-tight box and a bird sits in it. If the bird flies inside, what happens to the weight of the box?

69. An object suspended from a sensitive spring balance is placed inside a closed container. The other end of the container is closed by means of an air tight piston. Will there be any change in the spring balance reading when the piston is moved the inward and outward direction? Why?

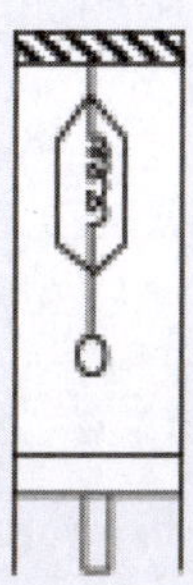

70. How is the hair set well when oil is applied to it?

71. Explain how the Hare's apparatus works and how it helps in determining the relative density of a given liquid.

72. A cylindrical object floats in water such that ¾th of its volume is immersed in water. Determine its density.

73. The density of a given mass of a gas when 10 Pa pressure acts on it is 2 kg m^{-3}. Calculate the density of the gas if the pressure is increased by 5 Pa at constant temperature.

74. A boy tied two metal spheres '*P*' and '*Q*' weighing 200 gwt and 150 gwt respectively to two ends of a stick with the help of a string. When he immersed them in water, they balanced each other as shown in the figure. If the R.D of the sphere *P* is 2, then the boy could successfully measure the R.D of the sphere Q. Find out the boy's answer.

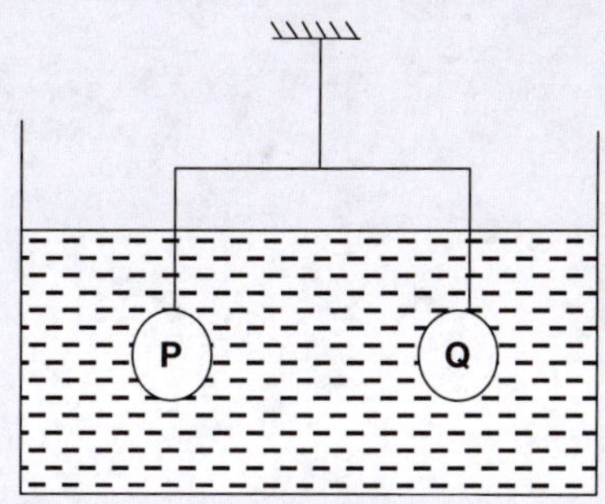

75. A hydrometer stem has a length 30 cm. If the hydrometer is immersed in water, its floatation bulb just sinks. If the same hydrometer is immersed in a liquid having density of 500 kg m^{-3}, two-third of the stem is immersed. Find the least specific gravity of a liquid that can be measured using the hydrometer.

76. A test tube of uniform cross-section is floated vertically in a liquid 'P' (density ρ_P) up to a mark on it when it is filled with 'x' mL of a liquid 'Q' (density ρ_Q). To make the test tube float in liquid 'Q' up to the same mark it is filled with 'y' mL of the liquid 'P'. Find the mass of the test tube.

77. Two metal spheres 'A' and 'B' weighing 400 gwt and 300 gwt respectively are hung at two ends of a stick with the help of strings. When the spheres are immersed in water, they balance each other. If the R.D. of the sphere A is 4, then find the R.D. of the sphere B.

78. A hydrometer stem has a length 40 cm. If the hydrometer is immersed in water, its floatation bulb just sinks. If the same hydrometer is immersed in a liquid having density of 500 kg m^{-3}, half of the stem is immersed. Find the least specific gravity of a liquid that can be measured using the hydrometer.

79. An effort applied on the small piston of a hydraulic jack lifts the load through 40 cm and the effort is displaced through 2 m. If the diameter of the larger piston is 30 cm, calculate the area of the cross-section of the smaller piston.

AT

JEE-NEET SPECIAL WING

PRACTICE QUESTIONS

Multiple-Answer Type Questions

Directions for questions 1 to 5:
Select one or more correct alternative(s) from the given choices.

1. Thrust is expressed in

   (a) newton (b) kg wt

   (c) N m (d) kg wt cm

2. Pressure is expressed in

   (a) kg wt

   (b) N m^{-2}

   (c) kg f

   (d) bar

3. Fluid pressure depends on

   (a) height of fluid column

   (b) density of fluid

   (c) acceleration due to gravity

   (d) area of cross–section

4. A student found the relative density of a liquid using Hare's apparatus. If h_1 is the height of water column and h_2 is the height of liquid column then,

   (a) $R.D = \frac{h_2}{h_1}$

   (b) $R.D = \frac{h_1}{h_2}$

   (c) $h_1 = R.D \times h_2$

   (d) $h_1 = \frac{R.D}{h_2}$

5. Identify the correct statement related to floatation.

   (a) If $d_s < d_\ell$, the body sinks.

   (b) If $d_s > d_\ell$, the body floats.

   (c) If $d_s > d_\ell$, the body sinks.

   (d) If $d_s < d_\ell$, the body floats.

Comprehension-Based Questions

Directions for questions 6 to 10:
These questions are based on the following information.

Pascal's Law

Pascal's law is a basic principle applicable for fluids given by Blaise Pascal. The law states that "When there is an increase in pressure at any point in a fluid at rest, the pressure gets distributed equally in all directions and acts at right angles to the surface of the container". Pascal's law helps us to understand how the air and fluid flow is affected with changes in air pressure. This law can be used to calculate the pressure, velocity, area and volume of a fluid.

6. The ratio of load to effort is

   (a) Bramah press

   (b) load arm

   (c) effort arm

   (d) mechanical advantage

7. Which of the following works on the principal Pascal's law?

   (a) Lever

   (b) Pulleys

   (c) Hydraulic lift

   (d) Motor

8. A hydraulic lift has two pistons with area 1.5 m^2 and 0.5 m^2. When 60 N is placed on the larger piston, the force exerted by the smaller piston is

   (a) 20 N (b) 40 N

   (c) 60 N (d) 80 N

9. Hydraulic press is not used

   (a) to extract oil from oil seeds

   (b) in submarines

   (c) to press the bales of cotton.

   (d) in hydraulic brakes.

10. "A small force applied at a point can exerts a larger force at another point." This formulates the principle of
    (a) Archimedes principle
    (b) Principle of moments
    (c) Bramah press
    (d) Surface tension

Directions for questions 11 to 15:
These questions are based on the following information.

Surface Tension

Surface tension is a property of liquid at rest. It is the tendency of liquid surfaces at rest to shrink into minimum surface area possible. The surface tension determines the behaviour of liquids in many phenomena. Whether a solid gets wet by a liquid, will an object float or sink in a fluid etc, are determined with the help of surface tension.

11. If the cohesive force is greater than adhesive force, then the meniscus is
    (a) Convex (b) Concave
    (c) Plane (d) Cylindrical

12. Water forms a concave meniscus in account of
    (a) low adhesive force
    (b) high adhesive force
    (c) high cohesive force.
    (d) None of these

13. The raindrops are spherical due to
    (a) Pascal's Law
    (b) Upthrust
    (c) Archimedes principle
    (d) Surface tension

14. The S. I. unit of surface tension is
    (a) J m^{-1}
    (b) J m
    (c) N m^{-1}
    (d) N m

15. The paints and lubricating oils have
    (a) high surface tension.
    (b) low surface tension
    (c) high pressure
    (d) low pressure

Match the Column

Directions for question 16:
The question is based on the following information.

Atmospheric Pressure

The Earth's atmosphere is a blanket of gases that surrounds the Earth. The pressure exerted by gases in the atmosphere on the surroundings and on the surface of Earth is called atmospheric pressure. It is an indicator of weather. Low pressure leads to cloudiness where in high pressure leads to calm weather. The atmospheric pressure varies with altitude. At sea level the pressure is high and with altitude pressure decreases.

16. Match the values in List - I with those in List - II:

List - I	List - II
A. 1 torr	a. 10^5 Pa
B. 1 bar	b. P ∝ h
C. 1 atm	c. 1.013 bar
D. Mercury barometer	d. MSR + (VCD×LC)
E. Fortin's barometer	e. 1 mm of Hg

    (a) A - c, B - a, C - e, D - d, E - b
    (b) A - a, B - c, C - e, D - d, E - b
    (c) A - e, B - a, C - c, D - b, E - d
    (d) A - a, B - b, C - d, D - c, E - e

ANSWER KEYS

Crossword

Across

4. Thrust
5. Plimsoll Line
7. Gauge Pressure
11. Specific Gravity
12. Surface Tension
13. Torricellian Vacuum
14. Altimeter

Down

1. Pressure
2. Atmospheric Pressure
3. Upthrust
6. Gas Manometer
8. Lateral Pressure
9. Pascal
10. Hydrometer

Classroom Wing

Very Short Answer Type Questions

1. Cohesive force
2. Flow
3. 0.5
4. Lateral pressure
5. Density
6. Thrust and weight
7. Rainfall

Competition Wing

Level 1: Apply your Concepts

1. False
2. True
3. True
4. False
5. False
6. True
7. True
8. False
9. False
10. True
11. Increases
12. Hare's
13. Torricellian
14. Air
15. Scale
16. Relative density
17. 2 : 3
18. –10
19. $\frac{5}{3}$ pa
20. A : f, B : h, C : b, D : g, E : a, F : c, G : d, H : e
21. (c)
22. (c)
23. (b)
24. (d)
25. (d)
26. (d)
27. (b)
28. (d)
29. (d)
30. (d)
31. (b)
32. (d)
33. (c)
34. (b)
35. (c)
36. (d)
37. (c)
38. (a)
39. (c)
40. (c)
41. (b)
42. (a)
43. (b)
44. (a)
45. (b)

Level 2: Review your Concepts

46. 941.5 cm (or) 9.4 m
47. 16/9
49. 75 cm
50. 0.11
51. 3840 N
52. 5 cm
55. 1,60,000 Pa
56. 15,2880 Pa
60. 2g cm^{-3}, (or) 2000 kg m^{-3}
61. 0.0154
63. 2×10^{-3} N
64. $\frac{5}{3}$ Nm^{-2}
65. 7.8×10^3 kg m^{-3}

Level 3: Assess Your Concepts

66. 51680 Pa
71. 4.24 m
72. 750 kg m^{-3}
73. $d = 3$ kg m^{-3}
74. 3
75. 0.4
77. 3
78. 0.33
79. 141.3 cm^2

JEE-NEET Special Wing

Multiple-Answer Type Questions

1. (a) and (b) **2.** (b) and (d) **3.** (a), (b) and (c) **4.** (b) and (c) **5.** (c) and (d)

Comprehension-Based Questions

6. (d) **7.** (c) **8.** (a) **9.** (b) **10.** (c)
11. (a) **12.** (b) **13.** (d) **14.** (c) **15.** (b)

Match the Column

16. (c)

For answer key of Classroom wing and Competition wing, refer to Hints and Solutions

Hints and Explanations

Classroom Wing

Very Short Answer Type Questions

1. Cohesive force
2. Flow
3. 0.5
4. Lateral pressure
5. Density
6. Thrust and weight
7. Rainfall
8. Property of a liquid at rest, due to which the top surface of a liquid contained in a vessel behaves like a stretched membrane occupying minimum surface area.
9. $P = \rho gh$
10. Depth, density and acceleration due to gravity.
11. It is used to measure the relative density of two liquids.
12. Pressure exerted by a liquid can be expressed in terms of height of the liquid column.
13. The pressure exerted by a liquid at rest is transmitted unchanged and equally in all directions and acts at right angles to the surface of the containers.
14. (i) To press the bales of cotton.
    (ii) To extract oil from oil seeds
    (iii) In hydraulic brakes
15. Instrument used for measurement of atmospheric pressure. Mercury, Fortin's and Aneroid are the three general types of barometer used.
16. The lateral pressure exerted by a liquid increases with depth. Therefore, to counteract this pressure and ensure stability, dam walls are tapered upwards, where their thickness decreases from the bottom to the top.
17. 10.3 m
18. External pressure, purity of mercury.
19. (i) Pressure at that point.
    (ii) Density of the liquid.
20. Increase
21. Weight of liquid displaced. Upthrust increases.
22. Cohesive forces are the forces of attraction between like molecules, while adhesive forces are the forces of attraction between unlike molecules.
23. Liquids and gases have more freedom of movement, allowing their molecules to change relative positions continuously. This gives them the unique ability to 'flow' from one point to another without any external force, leading to the property of fluidity.
24. R. D. $= \dfrac{W_2}{W_1 - W_2}$
25. Inside a stationary liquid, the pressure increases with depth. It is directly proportional to the depth, the density of the liquid, and the acceleration due to gravity.

Short Answer Type Questions

Note: This is how you should frame your answer covering.

26. (i) Intermolecular space
    (ii) Volume
    (iii) Cohesive force
    (iv) Mobility of molecules
    (v) Compressibility
27. Fluid pressure is independent of the area of cross-section.
28. This statement means that when a liquid is poured into interconnected tubes or vessels of different shapes, the level of the liquid will be the same in all of them, irrespective of their shapes.
29. Pressure exerted by 50 cm water =
    $= 1000 \times 10 \text{ m/s}^2 \times 0.5 \text{ m}$
    $= 5000 \text{ Pa}$
    Now, $= 5000 \text{ Pa}$
    $(800 \times 10 \times h) = 5000$
    height of liquid $= 0.625$ m
30. Astronauts wear spacesuits because of the lack of atmospheric pressure in space. Without spacesuits, they would be exposed to the vacuum of space which could be fatal.

31. Barometer height at sea level when density of mercury is taken as

$$P = 12\text{g/cm}^3 = \frac{12 \times 1000000}{10 \times 10 \times 10} = 12000\,\text{kg/m}^3$$

$$\text{Now, } h = \frac{13600 \times 0.76 \times 9.8}{12000 \times 9.8}$$

$$h = 0.861\text{m}$$

32. Fortin's barometer has a design that prevents exposure of mercury to the air, eliminates spillage during transport, and uses a vernier scale for more accurate readings. Its design addresses the issues of a shifting zero point and the inconvenience of transport.

33. $W_l = 20$ N

$W_b = w - 20$

Now, $W_w = 40$ N

$W_b = W - W_w = W - 40$

$$\text{R.D.} = \frac{\text{P of liquid of vol. V}}{\text{P of water of vol. V}}$$

$$= \frac{W - 20}{W - 40} = 5$$

$W - 20 = 5W - 200$

$4W = 180$

$W = 45$ N

34. (i) No liquid

(ii) Compact, light in weight and portable

(iii) Fixed in any plane

36. (i) Lift pump at its lowest position—valves *A* and *B* are closed.

(ii) Piston raised upwards—pressure decreases—water flows upward.

(iii) Piston pushed downwards—upward pressure—valve *B*.

37. Construction

Hare's apparatus is made up of an inverted U tube that is mounted on a vertical scale. At the top, this apparatus is open, while being connected to a rubber tube with help of pincock.

Working: The two arms of the tube are immersed in the beakers. The apparatus is used to compare the densities of two liquid and is based on Archimedes Principle.

38. Plimsoll lines is placed on the hull of a floating ship. It is a reference mark that indicates the maximum depth to which the ship may be safely immersed in the sea when loaded with cargo.

39. (i) Capacity of the ship

(ii) Limit to which ship is loaded

(iii) Density of sea water through which it travels

(iv) Lines marked on the sides of the ship

40. Liquids with same density.

41. Study of fluids under rest.

42. Force acting normally. Newton and dyne are the units of thrust.

Essay Answer Type Questions

Note: This is how you should frame your answer covering.

43. (i) Where is it used

(ii) Intramolecular space

(iii) Intermolecular attraction

(iv) Solids

(v) Liquids

(vi) Gases

44. (i) Cylindrical body its dimensions and density.

(ii) Liquid in beaker its density and depth.

(iii) Depth of the top and the bottom of a cylinder

(iv) Thrust due to liquid.

(v) Pressure due to liquid.

(vi) Net thrust due to liquid.

(vii) Upward thrust or upthrust – buoyant force (f)

$f = v\rho g$

$= mg = w$

45. The kinetic theory of matter provides a fundamental understanding of how molecules behave in various states of matter. It states that the kinetic energy of molecules is directly proportional to absolute temperature, implying that as temperature rises, so does molecular motion. This relationship is critical in comprehending phase transitions, such as why solids melt into liquids and liquids evaporate into gases when heated. The theory also delves into the nature of molecular forces. Because of the small inter-molecular spaces in solids, strong cohesive forces dominate, providing rigidity. As we progress to liquids and gases, this space expands, reducing cohesive forces and increasing fluidity. Understanding the kinetic theory gives us a better understanding of the micro-level interactions that determine the macro-level physical properties of substances.

46. Thrust and pressure are fundamental concepts that affect our daily lives and have important engineering applications. The footprint in the sand, which is caused by the thrust exerted by our weight on the sand, is an everyday example, as is the feeling of increased pressure when lying on a pointed object versus a flat surface. Understanding thrust and pressure is critical in engineering for designing structures such as bridges, dams, and buildings. Dam walls, for example, are tapered upwards to compensate for the increasing lateral pressure with depth. Similarly, understanding pressure is critical in pneumatic and hydraulic systems for power transmission. Understanding pressure distribution and its effects is essential for the design of tyres, footwear, and even the selection of materials in certain engineering applications.

47. (i) Bernoulli's principle

(ii) Propellers aeroplane

(iii) Wings of aeroplane

(iv) Size of wings

Competition Wing

Level 1: Apply your Concepts

21. As per the postulates mentioned in the text, the kinetic energy of molecules is directly proportional to the absolute temperature.

    Hence, the correct answer is (c).

22. The text mentions that for gases, the cohesive force is extremely negligible, resulting in them not having a definite shape or volume.

    Hence, the correct answer is (c).

23. Thrust is defined as the net force acting normal to a surface.

    Hence, the correct answer is (b).

24. The Hydrostatic Paradox is mentioned in the text stating that different shaped containers with the same base area and the same height of liquid exert the same force on their base.

    Hence, the correct answer is (d).

36 Pressure at a point inside a liquid does not depend on the base area of the container.

Hence, the correct answer is (d).

37. By increasing the area of cross section of the press piston, we can make a Bramah press exert a much larger force.

    Hence, the correct answer is (c).

38. The force acting on a unit area is called stress. Therefore, the unit of stress and pressure are same.

    Hence, the correct answer is (a).

39. (a) Initially both the limbs of manometer are exposed to air, level of mercury in both the limbs are equal due to atmospheric pressure.

    (b) Connect one end of the manometer to the cylinder filled with gas.

    (c) Determine the difference in the level of the mercury in both the limbs of the manometer.

    (d) Note the level of the mercury in the limbs of the manometer.

    (e) If the level of the mercury in the limb connected to the container is above the mercury level in the limb exposed to air, the pressure of the gas in the container is determined as atmospheric pressure – ℓ.

    (f) If the level of the mercury in the limb connected to the container is below the mercury level in the limb exposed to air, the pressure is determined as atmospheric Pressure + ℓ.

    Hence, the correct answer is (c).

40. An air bubble rises up in water because the upthrust acting on the bubble is more than the weight of the bubble.

    Hence, the correct answer is (c).

41. If relative density of a solid is less than one, it floats in water.

    Hence, the correct answer is (b).

42. As the volume of the test tube A is greater than the volume of test tube B, the minimum density that can be measured by A is greater than that of B.

    Hence, the correct answer is (a).

43. $$\text{R.D.} = \frac{\text{weight of hydrometer in liquid}}{\text{weight of hydrometer in water}}$$

    $$= \frac{25}{20} = 1.25$$

    Hence, the correct answer is (b).

44. (a) The weight of the test tube with lead shots in air (W_1) is measured.

    (b) The test tube is made to float in water.

    (c) The depth of the test tube immersed in water (h) is determined.

    (d) The test tube is made to float in the given liquid.

    (e) Lead shots are added or removed from the test tube so that the test tube is immersed to the same depth (h) in the given liquid.

    (f) The test tube is taken out from the liquid and its weight (W_2) is measured.

    (g) The relative density of the liquid is measured as $\frac{W_2}{W_1}$.

    Hence, the correct answer is (a).

45. When wind blows with high speed over the roof of a hut, the roof is blown away due to the pressure difference created between top and bottom surfaces of the roof. Hence, R is not the correct explanation of A.

    Hence, the correct answer is (b).

Level 2: Review your Concepts

Note: This is how you should frame your answer covering.

46. (i) Pressure at the bottom of the building,

P_1 = M.S.D.$_1$ + V.S.D.$_1$ × L.C.

Pressure at the top of the building,

P_2 = M.S.D.$_2$ + V.S.D.$_2$ × L.C.

Pressure exerted by the air at the bottom and top of the building are h_1dg and h_2dg.

Now, $P_1 - P_2$ = (M.S.D.$_1$ + V.S.D.$_1$ × L.C.) − M.S.D.$_2$ + V.S.D.$_2$ × L.C.) = $(h_1 - h_2)dg$

The height of the building $(h_2 - h_1)$ can be determined from the above equation

(ii) 941.5 cm (or) 9.4 m

47. 16/9

48. (i) Pressures at two different points in a horizontal surface are equal.

(ii) Lower density liquids will float on heavier denser liquids.

Here, dissimilar non-soluble liquids can seek their own level.

Is the pressure at different points inside liquid lying on the same horizontal plane equal?

Find the ratio of the densities of mercury and water.

Also find the ratio of the heights.

49. (i) Volume of impurity = 0.1 V

Volume of $H_{mercury}$ = 0.9 V

Density of the liquid in barometer

$$= \frac{\text{total mass}}{\text{total volume}}$$

$$\text{i.e., } d_1 = \frac{d_{Hg} \times 0.9V + d_{impurity} \times 0.1V}{V}$$

Now the pressure recorded by a standard barometer

$P_1 = h_{Hg}\, d_y\, g$ (1)

Pressure recorded by faulty barometer

$P_2 = h_2 \times dl \times g$ (2)

Equate (1) and (2) and determine value at h_{Hg}.

(ii) 75 cm

50. (i) Apply the law of floatation.

Weight of the floating body = weight of the displaced liquid.

This implies, V.D. = vd

The percentage of the ice lying below the water is

$$= \frac{v}{V} \times 100$$

Apply the same concept for the iceberg floating in sea water.

The percentage of the iceberg lying above the sea water is $= \left(100 - \frac{v}{V} \times 100\right)$

(ii) 0.11

51. (i) Give principle of Bramah's press.

What is Pascal's law?

Give the area of cross-section of the two pistons.

Substitute the values in the formula, $\frac{F_1}{A_1} = \frac{F_2}{A_2}$.

Find the value of 'F_2'.

(ii) 3840 N

52. (i) $\frac{\text{Load}}{\text{effort}} = \frac{(\text{radius of the lift pistion})^2}{(\text{radius of the press piston})^2}$

Work done on the load = Work done by the effort.

(ii) 5 cm

53. The Bramah Press consists of two cylinders connected with a liquid-filled tube. When force is applied to one piston, the pressure exerted is transmitted unchanged to the other piston due to Pascal's Law, illustrating that a small force can be transformed into a much larger force in another area.

54. (i) In constant immersion Hydrometer, will the level of the immersion of the hydrometer remain same (constant)?

Find the weight of the displaced water using law of floatation.

Is the volume of the displaced water = Volume of the immersed part of hydrometer = 30 cm^3?

What is the weight of the hydrometer when it floats in the liquid?

By using law of floatation, find the density of the liquid.

Since, density of the mixture contains equal masses of liquid and water,

$$\text{so, } \rho_{mixture} = \frac{M_w + M_L}{V_w + V_L} = ?$$

$$\text{But, } V_L = \frac{M_L}{D_L} \text{ and } V_w = \frac{Mw}{D_w}.$$

By applying, find the value of $\rho_{mixture}$.

Substitute the values in,

$W = U = V\rho_{mixture}\, g$

This gives the weight of the hydrometer.

(ii) 34.28 g

55. We know that the pressure exerted by the liquid at the bottom of the container, P = hdg

Where, h – height of the liquid in the container

d – Density of the liquid

g – acceleration due to gravity

It is given that a metallic sphere is released from the surface of water, and it reaches the bottom of the container in 2 s.

According to Newton's law,

$$F_g - F_B = ma$$

$$\Rightarrow m_s g - m_l g = m_s a$$

$$\Rightarrow V \times d_s \times g - V \times d_l \times g = V \times d_s \times a$$

$$\Rightarrow a = \frac{d_s - d_l}{d_s} \times g$$

$$\Rightarrow a = \frac{5-1}{5} \times 10 = 8 \text{m s}^{-2}$$

Now, distance travelled by the sphere,

$$h = ut + \frac{1}{2}at^2$$

$$\Rightarrow h = \frac{1}{2}at^2 = \frac{1}{2} \times 8 \times 2^2 = 16 \text{m}$$

Now, pressure at the bottom of the container,

$$P = hdg = 16 \times 1000 \times 10 = 1{,}60{,}000 \text{ Pa}$$

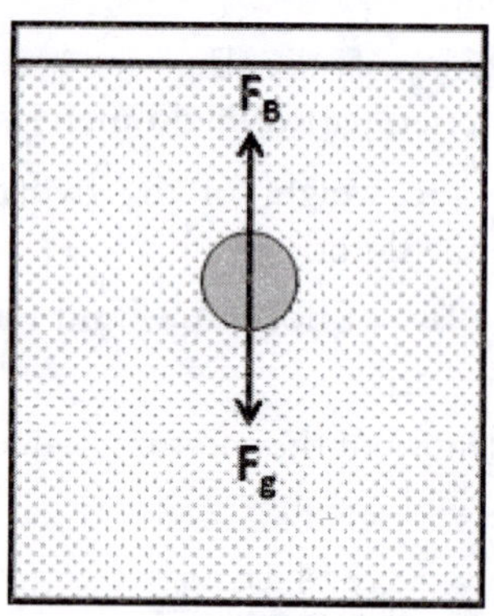

56. (i) $V_o \times d_o \times a = V_{lo} \times d_l \times g - V_o \times d_l \times g$

$$A = \frac{g(d_0 - d_1)}{d_0}$$

$$S = ut + \frac{1}{2}at^2$$

$$P = hdg$$

(ii) 15,2880 Pa

57. (i) Density $= \frac{m}{v}$

$$\text{Density} = \frac{\text{mass}}{\text{Volume of liquid displaced}}$$

If the ornament is made of pure gold, the density of the ornament must be equal to the density of gold.

(ii) 20 g cm^{-3}

58. Upthrust or buoyant force is the upward force that acts on a body immersed in a fluid, counteracting its weight. It determines if an object will float or sink, and its magnitude is equal to the weight of the fluid displaced by the body.

59. According to Bernoulli's principle, the shape of aeroplane wings and the speed of air blown from the propeller create a pressure difference between the top and bottom surfaces of the wings. This pressure difference, multiplied by the wing area, provides an upward thrust that can exceed the aeroplane's weight, allowing it to fly.

60. (i) Apparent weight = Actual Weight – Upthrust

Upthrust = $V_1 \times d_1 \times g$

(ii) 2g cm^{-3}, (or) 2000 kg m^{-3}.

61. d_l = 50 cm

$$\therefore \text{M.A.} = \frac{L}{E} = \frac{d_E}{d_L} = \frac{2}{0.5} = 4$$

$$4 = \frac{\pi_2^{\ 2}}{\pi r_1^{\ 2}}$$

$$4 = \frac{\frac{22}{7} \times 0.14 \times 0.14}{A_1}$$

$$A_1 = 0.0154$$

62. Construct a tank at a height of 10 m and create vacuum inside it by using a vaccum pump. Water raises to a height of 10.34 cm due to the atmospheric pressure. One end of a pipe is placed in the water at the ground. When the other end is connected to vacuum pump water raises up due to atmospheric pressure. The water can be filled in the tank.

63. Pressure, $P = \frac{\text{Thrust (weight)}}{\text{Area}}$

Thrust = Area × pressure = $2 \times 10^{-4} \times 10 = 2 \times 10^{-3}$ N

Weight of mercury = 2×10^{-3} N.

64. Pressure $= \frac{F}{A} = \frac{1 \times 10}{3 \times 2} = \frac{10}{6} = \frac{5}{3} \text{Nm}^{-2}$

65. Let 'ρ' be the density of the body and V_1 its volume, then according to Archimedes' principle

$$V_1\rho g - V_1\rho_1 g = \frac{2}{3}V_1\rho g$$

(ρ_1 = density of the liquid)

$$\therefore V_1\rho g - V_1\rho g = \frac{2}{3}V_1\rho g$$

$\Rightarrow \rho = 3\rho_1 = 3 \times 2.6 \times 10^3 \text{ kg m}^{-3}$
$= 7.8 \times 10^3 \text{ kg m}^{-3}$

Density of the body is $7.8 \times 10^3 \text{ kg m}^{-3}$

Level 3: Assess Your Concepts

Note: This is how you should frame your answer covering.

66. (i) What is law of floatation?

Is mass of the test tube (float) changed, when it is immersed in different liquids?

Then, can we say that it is a constant immersion hydrometer?

Assume the mass of the test tube = M.

When immersed in liquid 'A', the float is filled with 'x' ml of liquid B.

Then find the weight of the float.

Is the volume of liquid 'B' in the float = x mL

Then, weight of the liquid = vdg.

Now, the weight of the float = $mg + x\,\rho_B g$

Similarly, find the weight of the float when immersed in liquid 'B'.

Is the weight of the float = $mg + y\,\rho_A g$

But, weight of the float = weight of the displaced liquid.

The volume of the displaced liquids (both A and B) are equal.

Then get the volume of displaced liquids from above two cases in form of equations and equate them.

From this, obtain the mass of the test tube.

(ii) 51680 Pa

67. (i) Give the mass of alloy in water and liquid as W_2 and W_3.

Let the mass of the alloy in air be W_1.

According to Archimedes' principle,

$$\text{The density of water} = \frac{W_1}{W_1 - W_2} \quad (1)$$

$$\text{The density of liquid} = \frac{W_1 \times W_3}{W_1 - W_2} \quad (2)$$

From the above equations, find the weight of the alloy in air.

Find the volume of the alloy from the weight of the displaced water.

Then, the total volume of copper and zinc is the volume of the alloy.

Volume of copper be expressed by

$$= \frac{\text{mass of copper}}{\text{density of copper}}$$

Similarly, volume of zinc can be replaced by

$$= \frac{\text{mass of zinc}}{\text{density of copper}}$$

$$\Rightarrow \frac{M_{cu}}{8.9} = \frac{M_{zn}}{7.4} \quad (3)$$

Volume of the alloy.

Now, replace M_{Zn} with (mass of Alloy in air – M_{cu})

From the above equation, find the masses of copper and zinc present in the alloy.

(ii) Maximum density = 5 g cm^{-3}

68. (i) Action and reaction

(ii) 20 g cm^{-3}

69. Apparent weight = Actual weight – Upthrust

70. (i) Surface tension

(ii) 0.6 g cm^{-3}

71. An inverted U-tube serves as the Hare's apparatus. One arm is submerged in water, while the other is submerged in the test liquid. Both liquids rise as air is sucked out. After reaching equilibrium, the heights of the water and liquid columns (h1 and h2) are measured. Because both columns are under the same pressure, the ratio of the heights of the two columns gives the relative density of the liquid. This apparatus allows for the measurement of relative density without the liquids mixing or coming into direct contact.

72. $\frac{d_0}{d_w} = \frac{3}{4}$

$d_w = \frac{3}{4} \times 1000$

750 kg m^{-3}

73. $p \propto d$ at constant temperature

$\frac{P_1}{d_1} = \frac{P_2}{d_2}; \frac{10}{2} = \frac{15}{d}$

$5 = \frac{15}{d}$

$d = 3$ kg m^{-3}

74. Weight of P in air, $W_{1p} = 200$ gwt

Let weight of P in water be W_{2p}

∴ the apparent loss of weight of 'P' in water

$= W_{1p} - W_{2p}$

∴the relative density of 'P' $\frac{W_{1p}}{W_{1p} - W_{2p}} = 2$(given)

$\therefore \frac{200}{200 - W_{2p}} = 2 \Rightarrow W_{2p}$

$= 200\left(1 - \frac{1}{2}\right) = 100$gwt

Weight of 'Q' in air, $W_{1q} = 150$ gwt

Let weight of 'Q' in water be W_{2q}

∴ the apparent loss of weight of 'Q' in water

$= W_{1q} - W_{2q} = 150 - W_{2q}$

But $W_{2p} = W_{2q}$

∴ apparent loss of weight of 'Q' in water

= 150 – 100 = 50 gwt

∴the specific gravity of Q' $= \frac{W_{1q}}{W_{1q} - W_{2q}} = \frac{150}{50} = 3$

75. Let 'V' be volume of the hydrometer upto the beginning of its stem (i.e., volume of gravity bulb + floatation bulb)

Let 'a' be the area of cross section of the stem. When the hydrometer is immersed in water,

$V \times 1$ = mass of hydrometer.

Density of the given liquid = 500 kg m^{-3} = 0.5 g cm^{-3}

Length of the stem immersed in the liquid

$= \frac{2}{3}$(total length) $= \frac{2}{3} \times 30 = 20$ cm

∴ volume of the hydrometer in the liquid = $V + 20a$

∴ mass of liquid displaced = $(V + 20a)0.5$ = mass of hydrometer

∴ $(V + 20a)\ 0.5 = 20\ a = V \Rightarrow V + 20a = 2V$

or $a = \frac{V}{20}$

let 'ρ' be the density of the liquid on which the hydrometer floats upto its full length of stem.

Then mass of hydrometer = $(V + 30a)\rho = V$

$\Rightarrow \rho = \frac{V}{(V + 30a)} = \frac{V}{V + 30\left(\frac{V}{20}\right)}$

$\rho = 0.4$

∴ least specific gravity of the liquid that can be measured using the hydrometer is 0.4.

76. Let V_T be the volume of the test tube in liquids A and B. Given that the densities of liquids A and B are ρ_A and ρ_B respectively.

From the figure,

For liquid – A:

$Mg + x\rho_B g = VT\rho_A g$

$\Rightarrow M + x\rho_B = VT\rho_A$ (1)

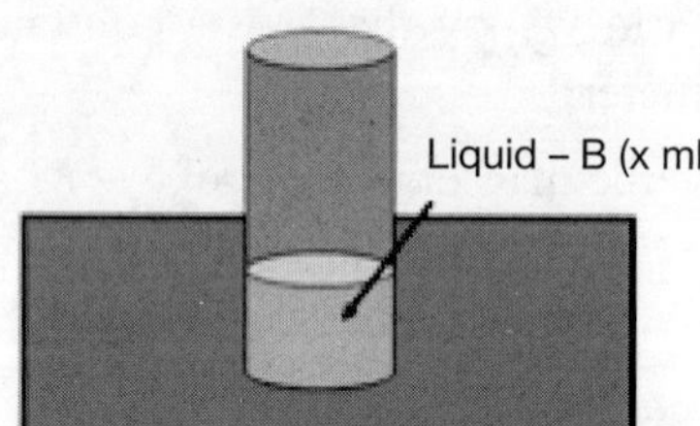

For liquid – B:

$Mg + x\rho_A g = VT\rho_B g$

$\Rightarrow M + x\rho_A = VT_{\rho}B$ (2)

As the volume of the test tubes inside the liquids A and B is same, equate the expressions of V_T from both the equations.

Frome quation (1), $VT = \frac{M + x\rho_B}{\rho_A}$

Frome quation (2), $VT = \frac{M + x\rho_A}{\rho_B}$

Then $\frac{M + x\rho_B}{\rho_A} = \frac{M + x\rho_A}{\rho_B}$

$\Rightarrow M = \frac{x\rho_B^2 - y\rho_A^2}{\rho_A - \rho_B}$

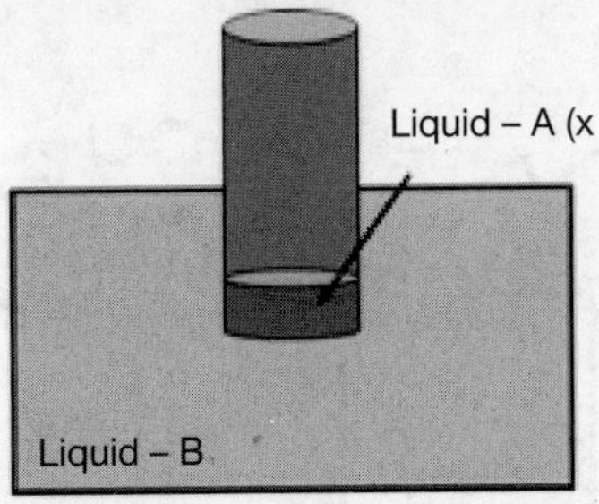

77. Weight of sphere A in air, $W_{1A} = 400$ gwt

Let weight of sphere A in water be W_{2A}

∴ The apparent loss of weight of sphere 'A' in water = $W_{1A} - W_{2A}$

∴ The relative density of sphere A = $\frac{W_{1A}}{W_{1A} - W_{2A}} = 4$

$$\Rightarrow \frac{400}{400 - W_{2A}} = 4 \quad \Rightarrow 400 = 4(400 - W_{2A})$$

$$\Rightarrow 4W_{2A} = 1600 - 400 \quad \Rightarrow W_{2A} = \frac{1200}{4} = 300 \text{ gwt}$$

$$\Rightarrow W_{2A} = 300 \text{ gwt}$$

Weight of sphere B in air, $W_{1B} = 300$ gwt

Let weight of sphere B in water be W_{2B}

∴ The apparent loss of weight of sphere 'B' in water = $W_{1B} - W_{2B}$

Given that when the spheres are immersed in water, they balance each other.

i.e., the apparent loss of weight of sphere 'A' in water is equal to the apparent loss of weight of sphere 'B' in water.

$$W_{1A} - W_{2A} = W_{1B} - W_{2B}$$

$$\Rightarrow 400 - 300 = 300 - W_{2B}$$

$$\Rightarrow W_{2B} = 300 - 100 = 200 \qquad \Rightarrow W_{2B} = 200$$

$$\text{Now, R.D. of sphere 'B'} = \frac{W_{1B}}{W_{1B} - W_{2B}} = \frac{300}{300 - 200} = 3$$

78. Given, Length of the stem of hydrometer, $l = 40$ cm

Let 'V' be volume of the hydrometer (volume of gravity bulb + floatationbulb)

If the hydrometer is immersed in water, its floatation bulbjust sinks.

i.e., V × Density of water × g = Mass of hydrometer × g

$\Rightarrow$ V × 1 × g = Mass of hydrometer × g (∵ Density of water = 1 g cm^{-3})

$\Rightarrow$ V = Mass of hydrometer

Let 'a' be the area of cross section of the stem.

Density of the given liquid = 500 kg m^{-3} = 0.5 g cm^{-3}

Length of the stem immersed in the liquid = $\frac{1}{2} \times 40$ cm = 20 cm

∴ Volume of the hydrometer in the liquid = V + 20a

∴ Mass of liquid displaced = (V + 20a) 0.5 = mass of hydrometer

$$\Rightarrow (V + 20a) \times \frac{1}{2} = V \qquad \Rightarrow V + 20a = 2V$$

$$\Rightarrow 20a = V$$

$$\Rightarrow a = \frac{V}{20}$$

Consider a liquid of low density (d) such that if the hydrometer is immersed, thehydrometer floats upto its full length of stem. The measurement of R.D. or specific gravity given by the hydrometer is the least specific gravity of the liquid.

Then (V + 40a) d = mass ofhydrometer

$$\Rightarrow d = \frac{V}{V + 40a}$$

$$\Rightarrow d = \frac{V}{V + 40\left(\frac{V}{20}\right)} = \frac{V}{V + 2V} = \frac{1}{3} = 0.33$$

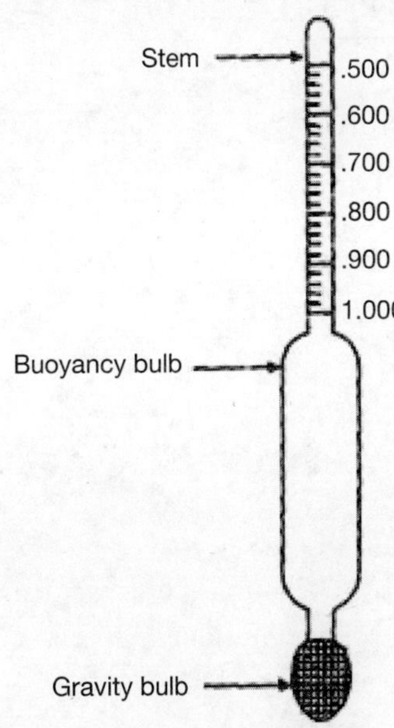

79. Given, distance moved by load, $d_l = 40\ cm = 0.4\ m$

distance moved by effort, $d_e = 2\ m$

diameter of thelarger piston, $D_2 = 30\ cm$

Then radius of larger piston, $r_2 = \frac{30}{2} = 15\ cm$

We have, Mechanical Advantage,

$$M.A. = \frac{L}{E} = \frac{\text{distance moved by effort}(d_e)}{\text{distance moved by load}(d_l)}$$

Therefore, $M.A. = \frac{2}{0.4} = 5$

From figure, Load, $L = W_2$

Effort, $E = W_1$

P_1 and P_2 are the pressures on smaller and bigger pistons respectively.

A_1 and A_2 are the areas on smaller and bigger pistons respectively.

From Pascal's law, $P_1 = P_2$

i.e., $\frac{W_1}{A_1} = \frac{W_2}{A_1}$

$$M.A. = \frac{L}{E} = \frac{W_2}{W_1} = \frac{A_2}{A_2}$$

Therefore, $M.A. = \frac{(\pi r_2^2)}{A_1}$

$\Rightarrow 5 = \frac{(\pi \times 15^2)}{A_1}$

$\Rightarrow A_1 = 141.3\, cm^2$

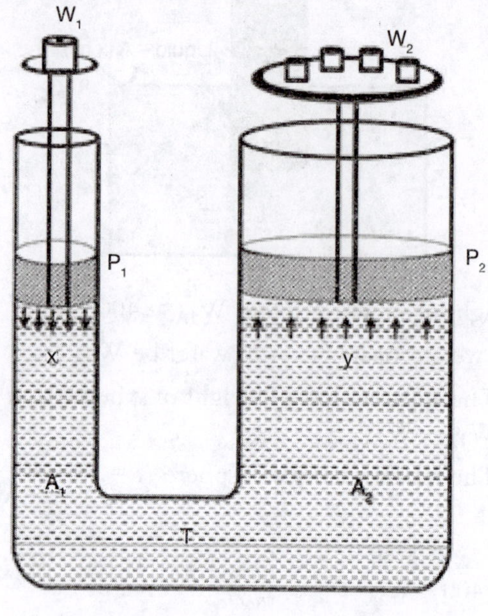

JEE-NEET Special Wing

Multiple-Answer Type Questions

1. 1 kg wt = 9.8 N
Hence, the correct option is (a) and (b).

2. S. I. unit of pressure is N m^{-2} or Pa
The meteorological unit of pressure is bar
1 bar ≈ 10^5 Pa
Hence, the correct option is (b) and (d).

3. $P = h\rho g$
Hence, the correct option is (a), (b) and (c).

4. Relative density (RD) $= \frac{d_l}{d_w}$

We have $P_l = P_w$, where P_l is pressure of liquid column and P_w is pressure of water column.

$\Rightarrow h_l \times d_l \times g = h_w \times d_w \times g$

$\Rightarrow h_l \times d_l = h_w \times d_w$

$\Rightarrow \frac{d_l}{d_w} = \frac{h_w}{h_l} \Rightarrow \frac{d_l}{d_w} = \frac{h_1}{h_2}$

$\Rightarrow RD = \frac{h_1}{h_2} \Rightarrow h_1 = RD \times h_2$

Hence, the correct option is (b) and (c).

5. (c) If $d_s > d_\ell$, the body sinks **-True.**
(d) If $d_s < d_\ell$, the body floats **-True.**
Hence, the correct option is (c) and (d).

Comprehension-Based Questions

6. Mechanical advantage (MA) $= \frac{\text{Load}}{\text{Effort}}$.

Hence, the correct option is (d).

7. Hydraulic lift works on the principal Pascal's law.
Hence, the correct option is (c).

8. According to Pascals' law
$P_1 = P_2$

$P = \frac{F}{A}$

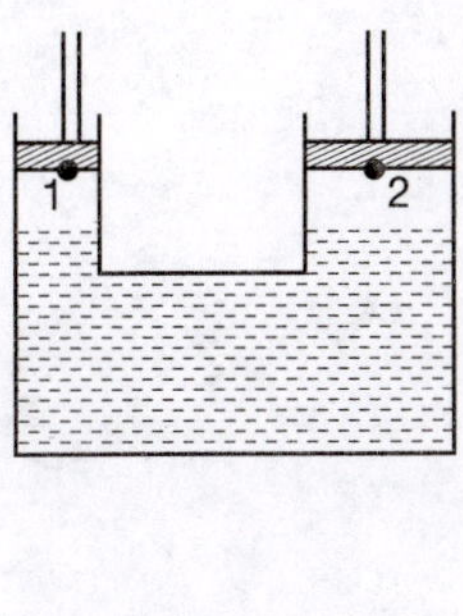

$\frac{F_1}{A_1} = \frac{F_2}{A_2}$

$\frac{F_1}{0.5} = \frac{60}{1.5}$

$F_1 = \frac{60 \times 0.5}{1.5} = \frac{30}{1.5}$

$F_1 = 20$ N

Hence, the correct option is (a).

9. Submarines are based on Archimedes' principle.
Hence, the correct option is (b).

10. Concept based.
Hence, the correct option is (c).

11. **Adhesive force:** Forces between the different kinds of molecules.
Cohesive force: Forces between the same kind of molecules.
A convex meniscus occurs when the molecules have stronger attraction with its molecules than to the container. For example, mercury filled in glass takes convex meniscus.
Hence, the correct option is (a).

12. When adhesive force is greater than cohesive force the meniscus formed is concave.
Hence, the correct option is (b).

13. Water tries to occupy smaller area due to surface tension. The smallest area possible is in spherical shape.
Hence, the correct option is (d).

14. Surface tension $= \frac{\text{force}}{\text{length}} = \frac{\text{N}}{m} = Nm^{-1}$

Hence, the correct option is (c).

15. Due to low surface tension, it can spread over a large surface area.
Hence, the correct option is (b).

Match the Column

15. **Choice (c) follows.**
1 torr = 1 mm of Hg
1 bar = 10^5 Pa
1 atm = 1.013 bar
The principle of mercury barometer is $P \propto h$.
In Fortin's barometer, barometric reading = MSR + (VCD×LC)

CHAPTER

5

Wave Motion and Sound

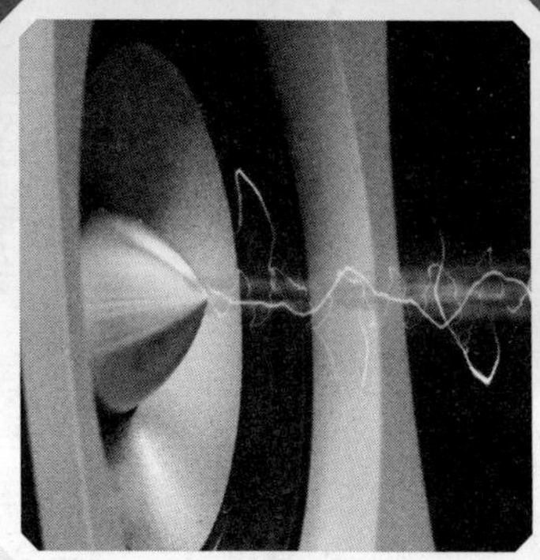

Key Ideas

After completing this chapter, you should be able to:

- understand the oscillatory motion.
- study the laws of simple pendulum.
- discuss the different types of waves and changes happening in the medium during the propagation of a wave.
- recognize sound as a mechanical wave and to discuss the different terms associated with the study of sound wave.

Remember

Before beginning this chapter, you should be able to:

- define motion and types of motion such as translatory motion, vibratory motion, etc.
- recognize sound as a form of energy.

Scientific Crypt

A Tribute to Heinrich Rudolf Hertz (1857—1894)

Heinrich Herty was born on 22nd February 1857, in Hamburg, Germany. His father Gustav Hertz, was head of the judiciary in the city of Hamburg and his mother's name was Elisabeth Pfefferkorn Hertz. From his childhood days itself, he started showing unusual talent in science, mathematics, manual skills and languages. As a teenager, he constructed a spectrometer and a Galvanometer which he used during his university studies also. Hertz did his graduation from the gymnasium in Hamburg in 1875 and completed his regular engineering studies from the University of Munich in 1877. During this time, he developed a preference for physics to engineering. This lead to the remarkable combination of theoretical and experimental work, and he received the degree of Magna Cum Laude for 'Induction in Rotating Spheres'.

This German physicist also discovered the photoelectric effect and gave the first experimental proof of the existence of radio waves. With his acumenship, he experimentally produced and studied electromagnetic waves (also known as Hertzian waves). He studied electric charge in rarefied gases and also produced the great works 'Electric Waves' and 'Principles of Mechanics'. In his honour, the unit of frequency is named 'hertz'. This great physicist left the world on January 1st, 1894 but not before leaving a huge impact in the field of science.

Crossword

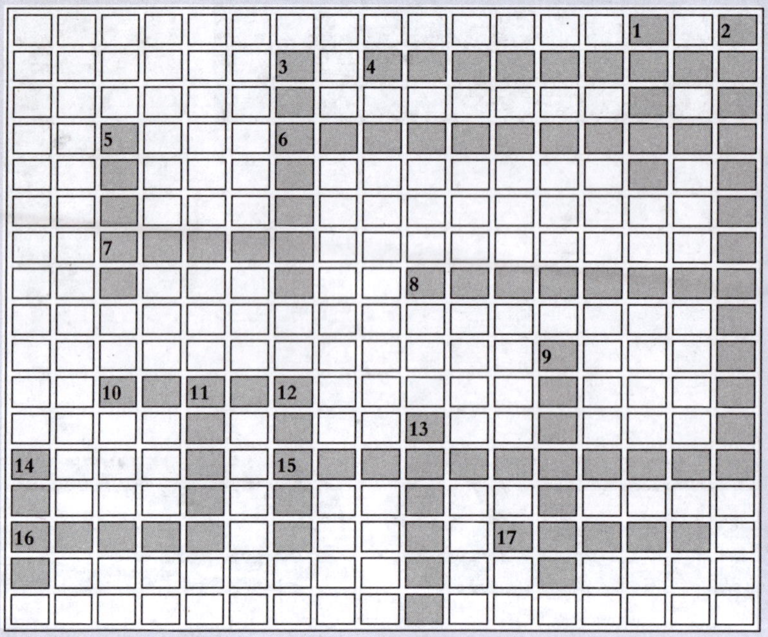

Across

4. Time period of a simple pendulum is independent of this.
6. The pressure is maximum at these point in a medium through which the sound is propagated.
7. This sound is unpleasant to hear.
8. This characteristic of sound depends upon amplitude.
10. This characteristic of sound depends upon the frequency.
15. At this point in a medium through which a longitudinal wave is travelling the pressure is minimum.
16. An example for stringed instrument.
17. An example for wind instrument.

Down

1. This sound is pleasant to hear
2. The kinetic energy of the bob of a oscillating simple pendulum is maximum at this point.
3. The loudness of sound is measured in this unit.
5. This is produced by vibrating bodies.
9. An example for wind instrument.
11. An example for drum instrument.
12. This is the unit of frequency.
13. Time period of a simple pendulum increases with this.
14. Disturbance created in a medium.

INTRODUCTION

Motion of particles and bodies plays an important role in physics. We have studied in detail the translatory motion of bodies and the cause of such motion in the chapters 'kinematics' and 'dynamics'. However, the vibrating string of a sitar, the motion of a child on a swing, the oscillations of the atoms, etc., are not the examples of translatory motion. In such cases, at regular intervals the motion is repeated over and over. Motion which is periodic and repetitive in nature is called periodic motion.

Some examples of periodic motion are the revolution of the Earth around the sun and the motion of the minute hand of a clock.

However, there is a difference between the motion of a pendulum bob or the motion of the minute hand of the clock and motion of the Earth and the motion of a vibrating string, though they are all periodic in nature. In the latter cases, the motion is to-and-fro, unlike the periodic motion of the bodies in which the bodies never reverse the direction of motion, the motion is vibratory or oscillatory in nature. When the string of a guitar is plucked the string vibrates. Similarly a mass suspended from a spring oscillates when pulled and released. Here the bodies move to and fro and this motion is referred to as vibratory or oscillatory motion.

There are some physical quantities/terms which characterize the vibratory motion. For example, when the bob of a pendulum is pushed gently to one side it performs oscillations or vibrations, and when it completes one full to and fro motion it is said to have completed one cycle. The rest position of the bob before it was made to oscillate is called mean position and the two positions where the bob changes its direction of motion are called extremes. The horizontal displacement from the mean position to either of the extremes is called amplitude of the vibration. The time taken for the bob to complete one cycle or oscillation is the period or the time period of oscillation, and the number of oscillations performed by the bob in one second is referred to as frequency.

Let us understand this with the help of an example, if a bob takes one minute (i.e., 60 s) to complete 20 oscillations, then the time period (T) and the frequency (n) are $T = \frac{60s}{20} = 3s$, and $n = \frac{20 \text{ oscillation}}{60s} \frac{1}{3} s^{-1}$

Thus, we see that n and T are related as $n = \frac{1}{T}$

Simple Pendulum

A **simple pendulum** consists of a particle of mass '*m*' usually called **bob,** suspended from a rigid support with the help of an unstretchable, mass less string. A practical simple pendulum has a small metallic bob suspended from an unstretchable thread and its length 'ℓ' is the distance between the point of suspension and the centre of gravity of the bob.

Figure 5.1 Simple pendulum

Credit line: *Feel good studio. Shutterstock*

Info Bytes!

The concept of a simple pendulum dates back to ancient times. However, it was Galileo Galilei who first studied the properties of a pendulum systematically.

When a simple pendulum is set to oscillate it moves to and fro about it's mean position between the two extremes A and B with constant amplitude as shown in the Figure 5.2.

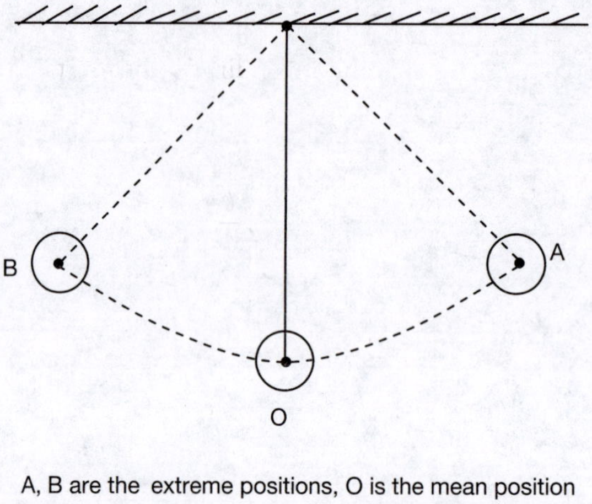

Figure 5.2 Figure showing the mean and extreme positions of a simple pendulum

When we plot the horizontal displacement and the time on a graph paper the curve obtained would be in the form of a wave.

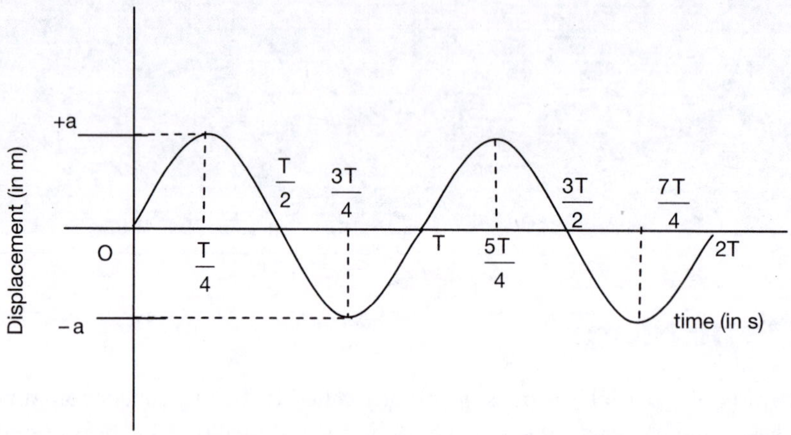

Figure 5.3 Displacement vs time graph of a simple pendulum

Each loop of the graph represents one complete oscillation of the pendulum. When the bob is at its mean position the displacement is zero and at its extremes the displacement is either '+*a*' or '–*a*' corresponding to the amplitude of the oscillation.

Laws of Simple Pendulum

A freely oscillating simple pendulum of a given length always possesses a constant time period and thus it can be used as a time measuring device.

Info Bytes!

Galileo discovered the laws of simple pendulum.

First Law of Simple Pendulum

For small values of amplitude, the time period of a simple pendulum of a given length is independent of the amplitude of oscillation.

Second Law of Simple Pendulum

For small values of amplitude, the period of a simple pendulum of a given length is independent of its mass, size, density and shape of the bob.

Third Law of Simple Pendulum

For small values of amplitude the time period of a pendulum is directly proportional to the square root of its length.

$$T \propto \sqrt{\ell}$$

$$\frac{T}{\sqrt{\ell}} = \text{constant} \quad \text{or} \quad \frac{\sqrt{\ell}}{T} = \text{constant}$$

Verification of Laws of Simple Pendulum

Verification of 1st Law

Suspend a simple pendulum of length 100 cm from the cork fixed to a retort stand as shown in the Figure 5.4. Set the simple pendulum to oscillate uniformly about its mean position with a small amplitude, say, 8 cm. Tabulate the time taken by the bob for 20 oscillations in two trials by using a stop watch. Repeat the same procedure by changing the amplitude in two steps say 6 cm and 4 cm. Determine the time period in each case. Determine the average time period of pendulum in each case.

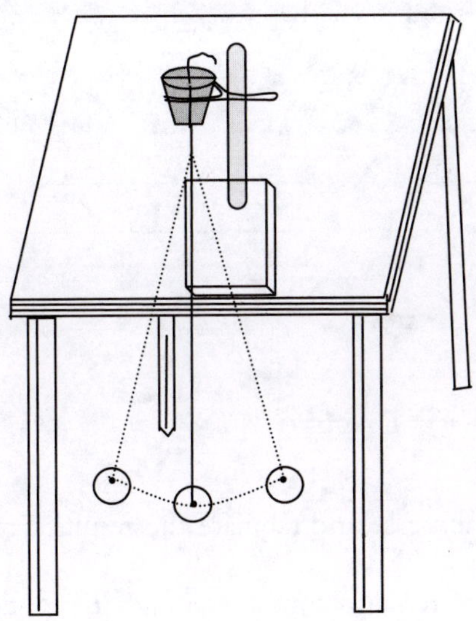

Figure 5.4 Experimental arrangement to show that time period of a simple pendulum is independent of its amplitude

From the observations tabulated we find that the time period of oscillation remains the same, establishing the **first law**.

S. No.	Amplitude	Time for 20 oscillations		Average time period
		Trail (1) (t_1) (s)	Trail (2) (t_2) (s)	$T = (t_1+t_2)/ 40$
1	8 cm			
2	6 cm			
3	4 cm			

Verification of 2nd Law

Take three simple pendulums whose bobs are made up of different material or of different radii. Suspend each pendulum from a different retort stand with equal length (say 100 cm) and set them to oscillate freely with a small amplitude. Note the time taken by each pendulum for 20 oscillations in two trials with the help of a stop watch and determine their time periods.

S.No	Pendulum's order	Time taken for 20 oscillations		Average time period $T = (t_1+t_2)/40$
		trial 1 (t_1) (s)	trial 2 (t_2) (s)	
1	1st			
2	2nd			
3	3rd			

From the observations recorded we find that the time period of the pendulum is the same irrespective of the size, shape, mass or density of the bob. This establishes the **second law**.

Verification of 3rd Law

Suspend a simple pendulum of length 50 cm from a retort stand using a cork. Oscillate it freely with a small amplitude. Note the time taken to complete 20 oscillations, and determine the time period by taking the mean of the values obtained in two trials. Increase the length of the pendulum to 100 cm in steps of 10 cm and determine the time period of the pendulum in each case with the help of a stop watch.

S.No.	Length of the pendulum (ℓ) cm	Time taken for 20 oscillations		Time period $T = \frac{t + t_2}{40}$ (s)	$T/\sqrt{\ell}$ = constant
		trial 1 (t_1) (s)	trial 2 (t_2) (s)		
1	50				
2	60				
3	70				
4	80				
5	90				
6	100				

Calculate the value of $\frac{T}{\sqrt{\ell}}$ or $\frac{T^2}{\ell}$ in each case and tabulate the results. From the results obtained it can be observed that according the third law, the value of $\frac{T}{\sqrt{\ell}}$ remains constant though T is not constant when the length of the pendulum is changed.

Wave Motion

Consider the surface of still water in a pond. If a pebble is thrown into the water, a disturbance is created in water which travels outward in all directions from the point of disturbance in the form of ripples on the surface. The ripples created on the surface of water are circular in shape. When observed closely, we find that as a ripple is moving away from the point of disturbance, the water particles do not exhibit translatory motion but vibrate up and down, i.e., the water particles do not travel along with the ripples. This can be understood by observing a leaf that floats on the water surface. The floating leaf has up and down motion in the vertical direction, but it does not have lateral translatory motion along the surface of water.

The energy given to the surface of water by the pebble is transmitted to other parts of water surface through ripples without actual translatory motion of the water particles. This is the principle of wave motion.

Thus, a **wave** is defined as 'a disturbance created in a medium which propagates in all directions, from the point of generation, without actual translatory motion of particles of the medium', and the propagation of the wave is called '**wave motion**'.

Transverse Waves

The circular ripples produced on the surface of water expand and propagate through water. As the ripples move horizontally across the surface of water, the water particles vibrate up and down. Thus, as the water waves (ripples) propagate horizontally, the particles of the medium (here water) vibrate in a transverse (perpendicular) direction to the direction of wave propagation. Such waves are known as **'transverse waves'**. Thus, transverse waves are defined as, 'the waves in which the particles of the medium vibrate in a direction perpendicular to the direction of wave propagation'. Ripples are the waves formed on surface of water and so these are also called **surface waves**.

Consider a string of a certain length, with one end attached to a fixed support. Hold the other free end of the string in hand, stretch and vibrate it in a perpendicular direction to the length of the string. A wave pattern is observed in the string as shown in the Figure 5.5.

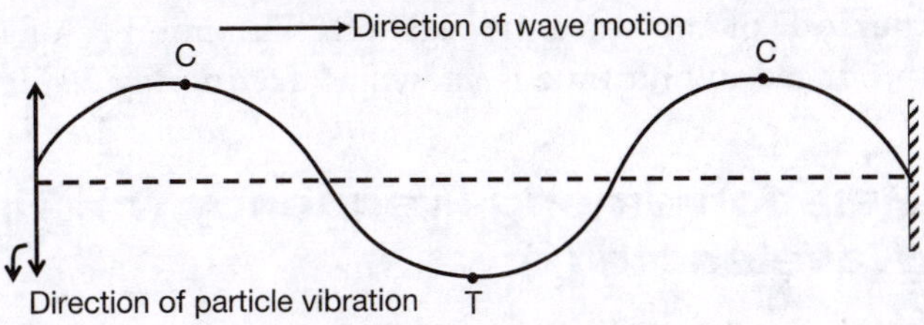

Figure 5.5 Transverse wave in string

The rest position or mean position of the string is shown by a dotted line in the figure. As the wave propagates from left to right, the particles of the string vibrate up and down, thus forming a transverse wave in the string. At a given moment there are some positions in the wave where the vibrating particles have maximum displacement in the upward direction from the mean position.

These positions are known as '**crests**' and are shown by 'C' in the Figure 5.5. At the same moment, there are some positions in the wave, where the vibrating particles have maximum displacement in the downward direction from the mean position. These positions are known as '**troughs**' and are shown by 'T' in the Figure 5.5. This maximum displacement of the vibrating particle from the mean position, either upward or downward, is known as '**amplitude**'. The wave pattern between two successive crests or troughs is fixed for a given wave form and the whole wave can be obtained by repetition of this pattern. So, the distance between two successive 'crests' or between two successive 'troughs' is constant for a given wave and is known as 'wavelength', a physical quantity with which a wave is characterized. It is denoted by the Greek letter 'λ' (lambda). The time taken to produce one complete wave is known as '**time period**', denoted by 'T' and the number of complete waves produced in one second of time is known as '**frequency**', denoted by '*n*' and measured in 'hertz' (Hz).

Longitudinal Waves

Consider a long spring placed on a table and fixed at one end as shown in Figure 5.6, with the other end remaining free. If we give a gentle pull to the free end and leave it, the spring executes oscillations along its length. The rings of the spring will oscillate to and fro about their mean positions or rest positions and the pull given at the free end of the spring travels to the other end.

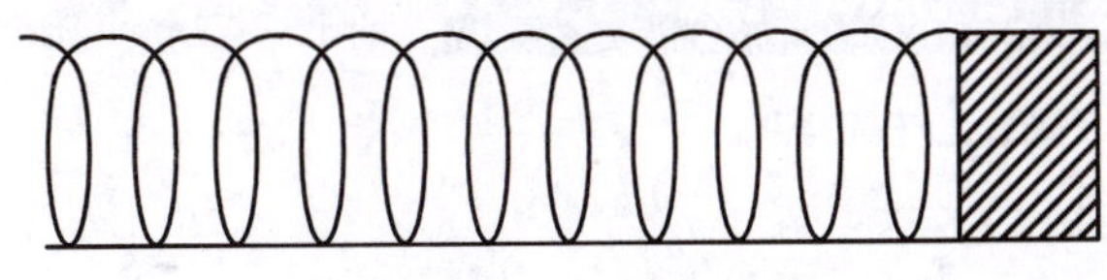

Figure 5.6 A long spring

As the rings of the spring vibrate to and fro, we find that at any given moment, in some regions in the spring the distance between two adjacent rings is less than the distance between them before the disturbance was started. Such regions are known as **'compressions'** and are denoted by 'C' in Fig. 5.7.

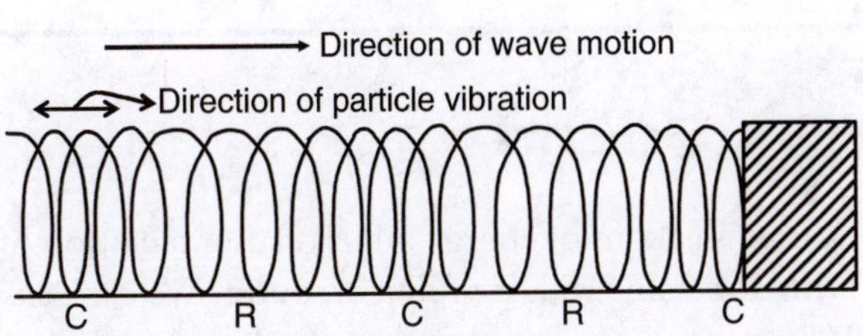

Figure 5.7 Formation of longitudinal waves in a spring

Similarly, at the same moment there are some regions in the spring, where the distance between two adjacent rings is larger than the distance between them when they were at the mean position. Such regions in the spring are known as **'rarefactions'** and are denoted by 'R' in Fig. 5.7. As the spring vibrates, a series of compressions and rarefactions propagate from one end to the other end of the spring; and so energy is propagated from one end to another without translatory motion of the particles. Thus, a wave is formed. In this wave, the particles of the medium (here the rings) vibrate in a direction parallel to the direction of the wave propagation. Such a wave is known as a 'longitudinal wave'. Thus, a **longitudinal wave** is defined as 'a wave in which the particles of the medium vibrate in a direction parallel to the direction of wave propagation'. So, longitudinal waves propagate in a medium in the form of compressions and rarefactions.

In the case of longitudinal waves, the distance between two successive compressions or the distance between two successive rarefactions is known as '**wavelength**' and the time interval between two successive compressions or the time interval between two successive rarefactions at a given point is known as '**time period**' of the wave propagation. The number of compressions or rarefactions produced in unit time is known as '**frequency**'.

Konnect

Sound wave travelling in air or in any gas is an example of longitudinal wave propagation.

Relation among Frequency (n), Time Period (T) and Wavelength (λ)

Time period (T) of a wave is defined as the time taken to produce one complete wave; and **frequency (n)** of a wave is defined as the number of complete waves produced in unit time.
Thus, they are related as

$$n = \frac{1}{T} \text{ or } T = \frac{1}{n}.$$

In one time period (T), a wave advances by a distance equal to one wavelength. Thus, if 'V' is the velocity of the given wave, it is given by,

$$V = \frac{\lambda}{T}.$$

As $n = 1/T$ we may write $V = n\lambda$

Thus, velocity of wave propagation = frequency × wavelength.

Info Bytes!

- Transverse waves are commonly observed in surface water waves, light waves, and seismic S-waves.
- Longitudinal waves are responsible for the movement and sensations you feel in earthquakes as P-waves (Primary waves).

EXAMPLE 5.1 A tuning fork produces a sound wave with a frequency of 440 Hz. If the speed of sound in air is 342ms^{-1}, determine the wavelength of the sound wave produced.

SOLUTION

$V = n\lambda$

$$\Rightarrow \lambda = \frac{V}{n} = \frac{342}{440} = 0.7773 \text{ m} \approx 0.78 \text{m}$$

Thus, the wavelength of the sound wave produced by the tuning fork is approximately 0.78 meters.

Sound

Sound is a form of energy which causes sensation of hearing. Sound is produced by vibrating bodies. When a bell is struck with a metallic rod, it produces sound. We can sense the vibrations of the bell while it is producing sound by touching it. We can even observe that the sound ceases when the bell stops vibrating.

Experiment to Verify that Vibrating Bodies Produce Sound

Consider a tuning fork fixed to a rigid support as shown in Figure 5.8. A pithball suspended from a support is held close to one of the prongs of the tuning fork.

When the fork is excited with a rubber hammer and if the pithball is in contact with the fork, we observe that the ball is flicked away by the fork, indicating that the tuning fork which is producing sound is vibrating and the pithball is flicked away by the vibrations of the fork. From this we may conclude that sound is produced by vibrating bodies. When we speak, the vocal chords present in a cavity of our throat, called **larynx**, vibrate and produce sound. The vibrating strings of a guitar, veena, etc., cause the production of sound in the '**sounding boxes**' of these instruments.

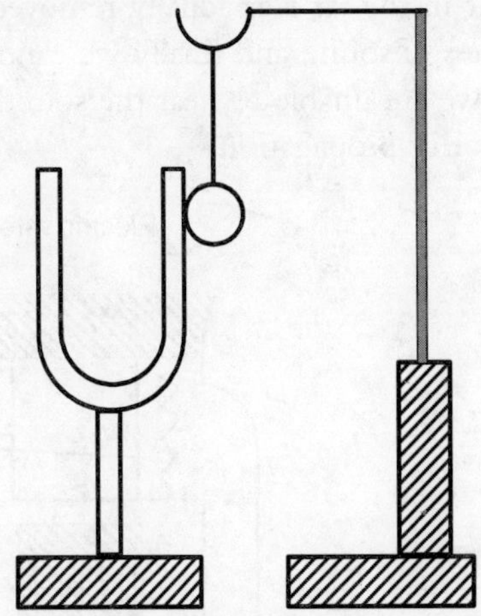

Figure 5.8 Experimental arrangement to show that vibrating bodies produce sound

Transmission of Sound

Sound propagates in the form of mechanical waves. So, it requires a material medium to propagate from one place to another. Sound can propagate through solids, liquids and also through gases. When an earthquake occurs, the shock waves produced at the point where the earthquake occurred travel in all possible directions. They travel through layers of the Earth which consist of solid rock materials as well as liquid water bodies. On reaching the surface of the Earth, these sound waves travel through air and reach our ears and produce the sensation of hearing. Thus, sound waves travel through solids, liquids and gases too.

If a person scratches one end of a long rail, the sound produced would almost instantaneously be heard by another person holding his ear to the rail at the other end. The same sound traveling through air would take longer (nearly 14 times more time!) to be heard over the same distance. Furthermore, its intensity would also be much lower. Thus, we find that sound travels faster in solids than in gases or air.

Consider two divers under water, separated by a considerable distance. If one of them produces a sound, the other can hear it after a certain time. Separated by the same distance, if these two persons are above water, and if one produces a sound, the other would take a little more time to hear it than the time taken under water. This indicates that sound travels faster in liquids than in gases or air.

If the two divers under water are stationed at two ends of a sufficiently long metal rod, and one of them taps the rod at his end, the other diver would find that he is able to hear the sound earlier if he holds his ear to the rod. This shows that sound travels faster in solids than in liquids. Thus, velocity of sound is the highest in solids, less in liquids and the least in gases or air.

Longitudinal Nature of Sound Waves in Air

Consider sound emitted by a loudspeaker with high intensity. When a piece of paper is held in front of the speaker, we observe that the paper is set into vibration by the sound emitted by the speaker. Thus, the sound produced by a vibrating body sets the surrounding layers of air (just as the piece of paper considered above) to vibrate. These layers of air vibrate in a direction parallel to the direction of wave motion; thus forming longitudinal waves. Thus, sound travels in air in the form of longitudinal waves.

Sound Requires a Medium for Propagation

As discussed earlier, sound requires a material medium for its propagation and does not travel through vacuum. Consider a glass jar with an outlet at the bottom and an electric bell suspended from its lid, made of cork, by means of strings as shown in the Fig. 5.9. The electrical connections (not shown in the figure) are made to the bell and it is switched on.

As the bell rings we can hear the sound produced by the bell. Now the outlet of the jar is connected to a vacuum pump, and the air in the jar is gradually removed. As the air in the jar is gradually removed, we observe a gradual decrease in the loudness of sound and finally we cannot hear the sound. As the air is removed, vacuum is created in the jar, because of which we are unable to hear the sound. This shows that sound cannot travel through vacuum and requires a material medium for its propagation.

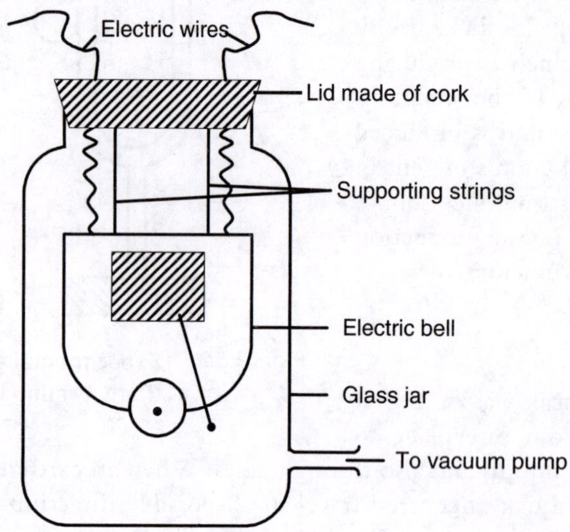

Figure 5.9 Experimental arrangement of a bell jar experiment

Konnect

Sound can travel through solids, liquids, and gases, but it travels fastest through solids because the molecules are closely packed.

Music and Noise

The sound that produces a pleasing effect on our ears is called **music**, whereas sound that produces an unpleasant or irritating effect on our ears is called **noise**.

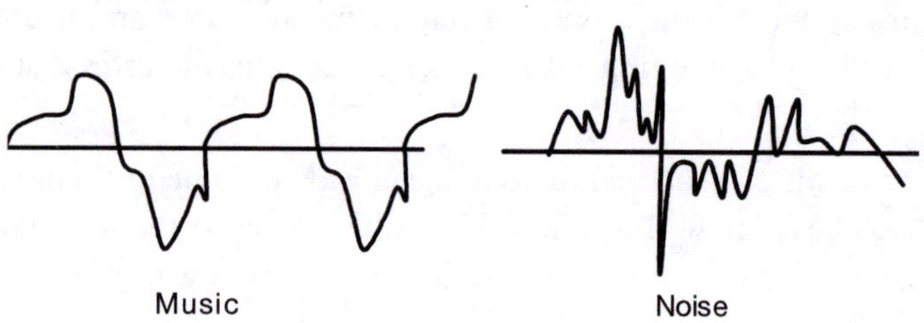

Figure 5.10 Note of a music and a noise

Konnect

Each type of musical instrument—wind, string, percussion—creates sound through different forms of vibration.

A sound that produces a pleasant effect on one person may have an unpleasant effect on another person. So, it is difficult to classify a given sound as music or noise.

Info Bytes!

Loudness is the property of sound which is used for differentiating between the faint and loud sound.

Pitch is the characteristic of sound which is used for differentiating between the flat and shrill sound

Musical Instruments

Instruments that produce musical notes are called musical instruments. Depending on the mode of production of music, these instruments are classified into three kinds. They are:

(a) Instruments that produce music by vibrating strings,

(b) Instruments that produce music by vibrating membranes

(c) Instruments that produce music by vibrating air columns.

Stringed Instruments

These instruments have stretched strings and vibration of these stretched strings produce musical notes. Increasing or decreasing the thickness and tension of the strings and also their length, can produce musical notes of different pitch. Veena, sitar, guitar, violin, etc., fall under this category of musical instruments. These instruments have a sounding box, which vibrates at the same frequency as the stretched string and increases the intensity of the sound produced.

Percussion Instruments (Drum Instruments)

These instruments have stretched membranes that are usually made of leather, and vibration of these membranes produce musical notes. Exciting these membranes at different locations produce musical notes with different pitches. Drums, mridangam, tabla, etc., fall under this category of musical instruments.

Wind Instruments (Blow Type Instruments)

These are generally made of long and hollow pipes with a certain number of holes on the lateral side. Musical notes are produced by blowing through a nozzle at one end and changing the length of the air column by selectively closing or opening some of the holes. Wind instruments are of three types:

1. Flute type organ-pipes
2. reed type organ pipes
3. brass instruments

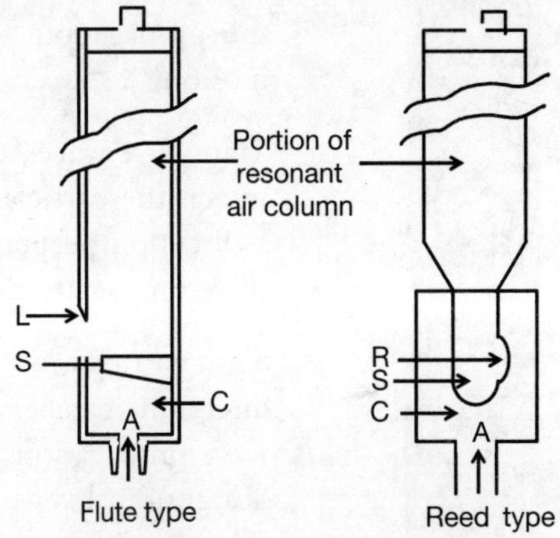

Figure 5.11 Organ pipes

In flute type instruments the compressed air entering the instrument is forced through a slit and strikes a lip. Different notes can be produced by opening/closing holes along the length of the instrument. Flute, piccolo, etc., are examples of flute type organ-pipes.

In reed type wind instruments, the note is determined by the reed. Saxophone, clarinet, bassoon and oboe belong to the reed type organ-pipes. In brass instruments, the lips of the performer act as a double reed and different notes are produced by changing the length of the air column with valves or an adjustable slide.

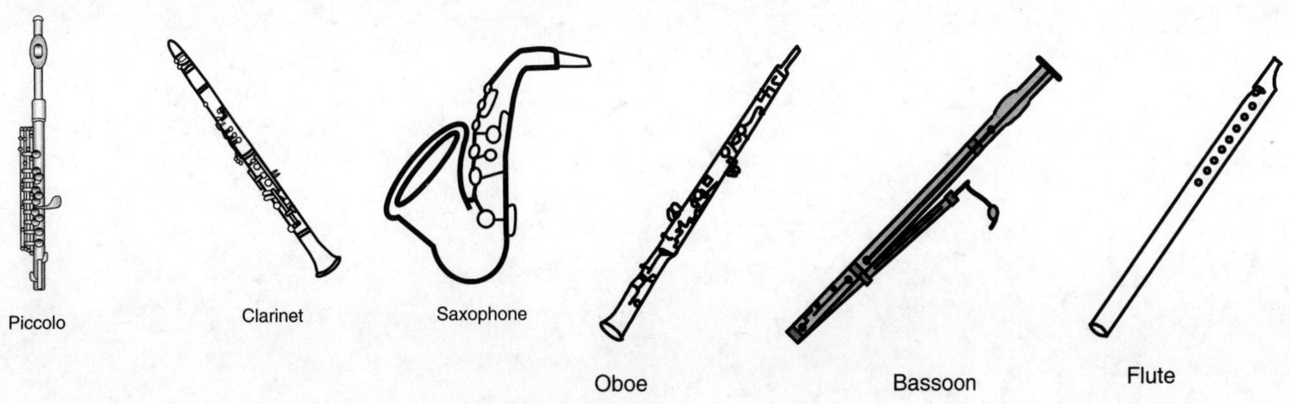

Figure 5.12 Musical instruments

POINTS TO REMEMBER

- ✔ A simple pendulum consists of a particle of mass '*m*' usually called bob, suspended from a rigid support with the help of an unstretchable, mass less string.
- ✔ A disturbance created in a medium which propagates in all directions, from the point of generation, without actual translatory motion of particles of the medium', and the propagation of the wave is called 'wave motion'.
- ✔ Transverse waves are defined as, 'the waves in which the particles of the medium vibrate in a direction perpendicular to the direction of wave propagation'.
- ✔ The particles of the medium vibrate in a direction parallel to the direction of the wave propagation. Such a wave is known as a 'longitudinal wave'.
- ✔ Sound propagates in the form of mechanical waves. So, it requires a material medium to propagate from one place to another.
- ✔ The sound that produces a pleasing effect on our ears is called music, whereas sound that produces an unpleasant or irritating effect on our ears is called noise.
- ✔ Instruments that produce musical notes are called musical instruments
- ✔ Stringed instruments have stretched strings and vibration of these stretched strings produce musical notes.
- ✔ Percussion instruments have stretched membranes that are usually made of leather, and vibration of these membranes produce musical notes.
- ✔ Wind instruments are generally made of long and hollow pipes with a certain number of holes on the lateral side.

DW

CLASSROOM WING

PRACTICE QUESTIONS

Very Short Answer Type Questions

Directions for questions 1 to 12:
Fill in the blanks.

1. As the sound propagates through a medium, its _________ changes.
2. If a pendulum makes 2 oscillations per second, its time period is _________ s.
3. In transverse waves, the particles of the medium vibrate _______ to the direction of propagation of the wave.
4. Sound cannot travel in ______.
5. The speed of the bob of an oscillating simple pendulum is maximum at its _______ position.
6. The time period of a pendulum is directly proportional to ______.
7. The instrument that produces sound by a vibrating membrane is called _______.
8. The positions of maximum displacement of a particle from the mean position of a transverse wave is called _______.
9. If the time period in second for 20 oscillations noted down in an experiment are 38.6, 40.0, 41.5, 42.8, and 39.4, the average time period of a given simple pendulum is ________s.
10. A liquid contained in a 'U'-tube, when disturbed, executes _______ motion.
11. A loaded spring produces _____ waves.
12. The amplitude of the pendulum is measured from ______ position to ______ position.

Directions for questions 13 to 25:
Answer the following questions briefly.

13. Among solids, liquids and gases, in which medium is the velocity of sound the maximum and in which medium is the velocity of sound the minimum?
14. Name some musical instruments that produce sound by vibration of stretched strings, by vibration of stretched membranes and vibration of air columns.
15. When a simple pendulum oscillates with a small amplitude 'a', its time period is T. What is its time period, when it oscillates with a small amplitude $2a$?
16. Define time period.
17. Define a transverse wave and a longitudinal wave.
18. Sound of thunder is heard 't' s after the flash of lightning is seen. Determine the distance of the cloud from the ground if the velocity of sound is v m s^{-1}. [Neglect the time taken for the light to travel]
19. The frequencies of two tuning forks A and B are 200 Hz and 100 Hz, respectively. What is the ratio of the velocity of sound, when the sound is propagated through a given medium?
20. To increase the frequency of oscillation of a pendulum, how should the length, time period and amplitude be changed?
21. Identify the propagation of a disturbance due to vibratory motion of the particles of a medium.
22. Define the wavelength of a longitudinal wave.
23. Define a compression and a rarefaction.
24. If V_1 and V_2 are the velocities of sound in solid and liquid, respectively, then $\frac{V_1}{V_2}$.
25. Sound produced by a tuning fork travel from air to glass. Does the frequency remain the same?

Short Answer Type Questions

26. Distinguish between transverse and longitudinal waves.

27. If 5 waves are produced in half a second of time, what is the frequency of the wave?

28. The frequency of a wave is 200 Hz and its wavelength is 60 m. Find its velocity.

29. Explain the formation of transverse waves in a string.

30. Describe briefly an experiment to prove the first law of simple pendulum.

31. The distance between a crest and an immediate trough in a transverse wave is 20 m. Find its wavelength.

32. Find the ratio of time periods of two pendula whose lengths are in the ratio 1 : 4.

33. Explain longitudinal nature of sound waves in air.

34. Describe briefly an experiment to prove the second law of simple pendulum.

35. The adjacent figure shows a displacement vs distance graph of a wave. If the velocity of the wave is 14 m s^{-1} calculate its

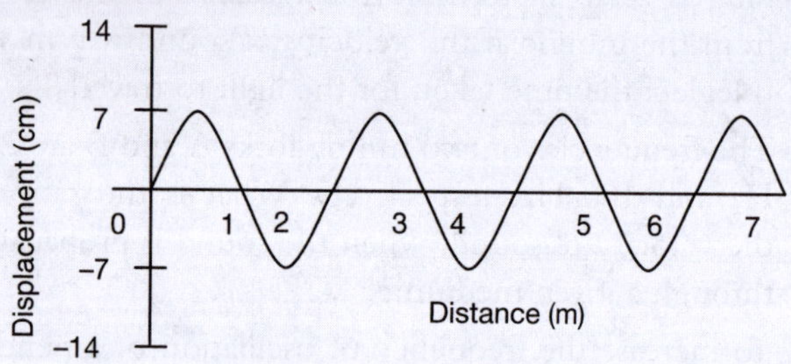

(i) wavelength,

(ii) frequency and

(iii) amplitude of the wave.

36. Explain why the loudness of a sound note varies with the distance from the source of sound.

37. Describe briefly an experiment to prove the third law of simple pendulum.

38. The distance between the 2nd compression and the 3rd compression in a longitudinal wave is 200 cm. Find the wavelength of the wave.

39. A sound wave travels from kerosene to glass. What changes occur in the velocity, frequency and wavelength of the sound wave? Explain.

40. If the velocity of a wave is 200 m s^{-1} and the time period of its source is 0.001 s, then calculate its wavelength.

41. The frequency of vibration of a pendulum is '*n*'. What is its time period if the length of the pendulum is doubled?

42. The displacement time graph of a simple pendulum is shown below. Calculate its frequency in Hz.

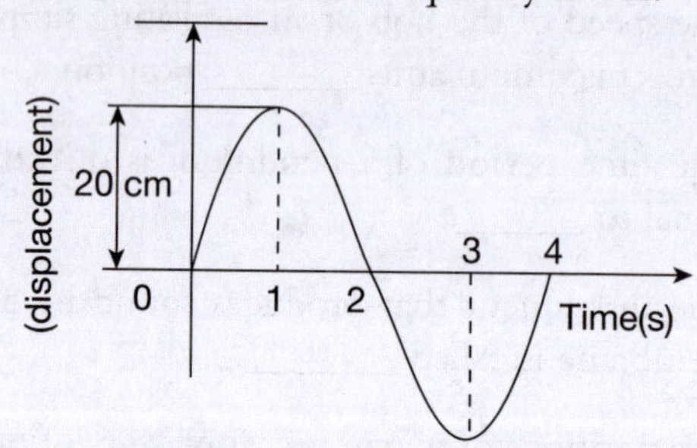

43. How are different musical notes produced in stringed instruments, in musical instruments having stretched membranes and in musical instruments of blow type?

44. Frequency of oscillation of a pendulum change with which factors?

Essay Answer Type Questions

45. Explain the formation of longitudinal waves in a long spring.

46. Show through an experiment that sound cannot travel through vacuum.

47. Describe an experiment to show that vibrating bodies produce sound.

48. Describe string instruments in detail.

49. Explain through an example that velocity of sound is more in solids as compared to that in air.

COMPETITION WING

PRACTICE QUESTIONS

Level 1: Apply your Concepts

Directions for questions 1 to 12:
State whether the following statements are true or false.

1. Sound waves have the maximum velocity among all the waves.
2. Sound cannot travel through vacuum.
3. Mathematically, time period is reciprocal of frequency.
4. In stringed instruments, vibrations are caused by the string.
5. Sound is form of energy which causes sensation of hearing.
6. If the period of a simple pendulum is 2 s, then its frequency is 0.5 Hz.
7. The velocity of sound is the highest in gases.
8. If a pendulum clock loses time, then the length of the pendulum should be appropriately decreased.
9. In a transverse wave, the distance between two successive troughs is $\lambda/2$.
10. The distance between the point of suspension of the pendulum and the bottom of the bob is the length of a simple pendulum.
11. The ripples in water waves are created due to the translatory motion of particles.
12. Velocity of wave propagation is the product of its wavelength and time period.

Directions for questions 13 to 19:
Fill in the blanks.

13. The time period of a pendulum of length 'ℓ' and mass of the bob 'm' is T. The time period of a pendulum with a mass of the bob $2m$ and length ℓ is ________.
14. The value of acceleration due to gravity increases as we move from equator to poles. For a given simple pendulum, a constant time period can be achieved by _______ its length correspondingly.
15. If the time periods of two pendulums are 2 s and 4 s, then the ratio of their lengths is ___.
16. The instruments that produce sound by vibrating strings are called ______.
17. A sound wave travels with a speed of 330 m s^{-1} in air. If the wavelength of the wave is 330 cm, then the frequency of the wave is ______.
18. If 4 waves are produced in 2 s, then the time period of the wave is _______.
19. If the wavelength of the wave is 24 cm, then the distance between the first compression and the third subsequent rarefaction in a longitudinal wave is ________ cm.

Directions for question 20:
Match the entries in Column A with the appropriate entries in Column B.

20. Match the statements of Column A with those of Column B

Column A	Column B
(A) Velocity of a wave	(p) Velocity × Time period
(B) Frequency of a wave	(q) $\frac{\text{Number of waves}}{\text{time taken}}$
(C) Wavelength	(r) Depends on the source
(D) Frequency	(s) Depends on medium

Directions for questions 21 to 46:
For each of the questions, four choices have been provided. Select the correct alternative.

21. Time period of a pendulum changes when which of the following happens?
    (a) When the work done to oscillate the pendulum is changed.
    (b) When the bob is immersed in water.

(c) When the mass of the bob is increased.
(d) When the weight of the pendulum is increased without changing its mass.

22. Which of the following statements is true?
(a) Sound travels faster in iron than in water.
(b) Sound can travel through inert gases.
(c) Sound travels in the form of compressions and rarefactions in air.
(d) All the above

23. Which of the following are mechanical waves?
(a) Sound (b) Light
(c) Radio (d) All the above

24. Both sound and light waves can be propagated through
(a) vacuum (b) air
(c) Both (a) and (b) (d) None of the above

25. When a disturbance is created in a medium, the particles in the medium perform ______.
(a) non-periodic motion
(b) circular motion
(c) translatory motion
(d) periodic motion

26. If the time between two successive compressions of a wave is 5 seconds, then the time taken to complete 4 successive compressions is ______.
(a) 5 seconds (b) 10 seconds
(c) 2.5 seconds (d) 15 seconds

27. In a transverse wave, the time interval between 1st crest and 11th crest is 50 s, then the time period of the wave is ______.
(a) 5 s (b) 10 s
(c) 20 s (d) 2 s

28. In a tsunami, the shock waves originating in the ocean bed propagate
(a) as transverse waves only.
(b) as longitudinal waves only.
(c) as both transverse and longitudinal waves.
(d) Neither as transverse nor as longitudinal waves.

29. If the distance between two successive crests of a wave is 12 cm, then the distance between two successive troughs is ______.
(a) 24 cm (b) 6 cm
(c) 12 cm (d) 4 cm

30. The loudness of sound of the bell in the bell jar experiment gradually decreases with ___.
(a) decrease in the quantity of air
(b) increase in the quantity of air
(c) increase in the atmospheric pressure
(d) None of the above

31. The bob of an oscillating simple pendulum arrives at one of the extreme positions 100 times in 200 s. Then, the time period of the pendulum is ______ s.
(a) 2.5 (b) 2.0
(c) 1.5 (d) 1.0

32. Instruments capable of producing musical notes is/are:
(a) viola (b) oboe
(c) cello (d) All the above

33. Which of the following statements is incorrect?
(a) Sound travels faster in summer than in winter.
(b) Sound travels in a straight line.
(c) Sound travels faster in vacuum than in air.
(d) Sound travels in the form of longitudinal mechanical waves.

34. Among the following statements,
A: A simple pendulum of a given length and at a given place has a constant time period.
B: A simple pendulum with constant time period can be used as a time measuring device.
(a) Only A is true
(b) Only B is true
(c) Both A and B are true
(d) Both A and B are false

35. If the distance between two successive compressions of a sound wave is 16 cm, then the distance between a compression and the next rarefaction is ______.
(a) 16 cm (b) 32 cm
(c) 4 cm (d) 8 cm

36. In a simple pendulum experiment, the time in seconds taken for 20 oscillations is noted in 5 trials as 39.2, 38.4, 40.8, 41.4, 40.2, then the average frequency is ______.
(a) 0.5 s (b) 2 s^{-1}
(c) 2 s (d) 0.5 s^{-1}

37. As the acceleration due to gravity increases, the time period of the simple pendulum ______

(a) increases
(b) decreases
(c) remains same
(d) first increases and then decreases.

38. Time taken for 20 oscillations noted down in an simple pendulum experiment are 38.6 s, 40.0 s, 41.5 s, 42.8 s, and 39.4 s. Calculate the time period of the given simple pendulum.

(a) 2.5 (b) 2.2
(c) 2.0 (d) 10.1

39. Write down the steps to verify the third law of simple pendulum in a proper sequence.

(A) Set the pendulum into ostillation and determine the time taken for 20 oscillations.
(B) Determine the square of the time period (T^2).
(C) Change the length of the simple pendulum and repeat the experiment.
(D) Determine the time period of oscillation (T).
(E) Determine the l ength of the pendulum.
(F) Note the value of $V = \frac{\lambda}{T}$ in each case.

(a) A D B C E F (b) E A D B C F
(c) E A B C F D (d) E F A B D C

40. The time taken by a vibrating body to move from one extreme position to the other extreme position is 0.1 s. If the distance between adjacent crests is 2 m, write the steps to determine the wave velocity in proper sequence.

(A) Determine the frequency of the wave (f).
(B) Note down the wavelength (λ).
(C) Note down the time period (T).
(D) Determine the velocity of the wave as $v = f\lambda$.

(a) A B C D (b) B C A D
(c) D A B C (d) D C B A

41. The bell jar experiment shows that

(a) sound cannot travel through vacuum.
(b) sound can travel through gas.
(c) sound can travel through vacuum.
(d) velocity of sound is least in gases.

42. Following are down the steps of an experiment to prove that medium is required for the propagation of sound waves. Arrange these steps in proper sequence.

(A) Consider a glass jar with an outlet connected to a vacuum pump and a closed lid.
(B) Suspend an electric bell.
(C) Evacuate the jar by using a vaccum pump.
(D) Switch on the electric bell.
(E) Observe that the intensity of the sound is less when the jar is evacuated.
(F) This proves that medium is required for the propagation of sound.

(a) F E D A B C (b) A B D E C F
(c) A B D C E F (d) A B C D E F

43. **Assertion (A):** A child produces a higher pitched sound compared to that of an adult.

Reason (R): Pitch depends on the frequency of sound.

(a) A and R are correct and R is the correct explanation of A.
(b) A and R are correct but R is not the correct explanation of A.
(c) A is correct but R is not correct.
(d) Both A and R are not correct.

44. **Assertion (A):** Sound cannot be propagated on the moon.

Reason (R): Sound requires a medium to propagate.

(a) A and R are correct and R is the correct explanation of A.
(b) A and R are correct but R is not the correct explanation of A.
(c) A is correct but R is not correct.
(d) Both A and R are not correct.

45. Two tuning forks A and B of frequencies 200 Hz and 400 Hz are vibrated simultaneously. Then, the ratio of time taken by the sound produced by A and B to travel 660 m and 990 m, respectively in air is ______ (velocity of the sound in air = 330 m s^{-1})

(a) 1 : 2 (b) 1 : 3
(c) 2 : 3 (d) 1 : 1

46. Two pendulums A and B of length 9 m and 16 m, respectively are made to oscillate on the Earth's surface then the ratio of their frequency is ______.

(a) 3 : 4 (b) 9 : 16
(c) 16 : 9 (d) 4 : 3

Level 2: Review your Concepts

47. If the length of a pendulum of time period T is doubled, calculate its frequency.

48. A disc siren with certain number of holes rotates uniformly 270 times in one and half minute. The frequency of the note emitted is 48 Hz. If the velocity of sound in air is 336 m s^{-1}, find its wavelength and number of holes on the disc.

49. Two astronauts go to the surface of the moon and would speak to each other. Explain how they could achieve this.

50. A wave of time period 10 ms travels with a velocity of 1.5 m s^{-1}. If the time period of another wave is 6 ms, find its velocity and also find the ratio of their velocities. (Assume that the wavelength of the two waves is same).

51. A sound wave of frequency 660 Hz incidents normally on a perfectly reflecting object. If the speed of sound in air is 330 m s^{-1}, what is the shortest distance from the wall at which the wave particles have (a) the maximum and (b) the minimum displacement?

52. If 500 sound waves are produced in one minute, then find the time taken by a vibrating particle to move from its mean position to the immediate rarefaction.

53. For the range of frequencies of sound 11 kHz to 11 MHz, find the range of wavelengths of sound at 0°C, given the velocity of sound in air as 330 m s^{-1} at 0°C.

54. A tuning fork is excited first in air and then in water. In which case is the amplitude more? Explain.

55. A sound wave travelling in air is made to propagate through a liquid such that the velocity of sound is quadrupled. If the frequency of the sound wave is constant, find the change in the wavelength of the sound wave.

56. A sound wave travels 60 m in the time taken to produce 50 waves. Find the wavelength of the sound wave in centimetres.

57. What would be the time period of a seconds pendulum constructed on the Earth if it is taken to the surface of the moon. The acceleration due to gravity on the surface of the moon is 1/6 g_{earth}.

58. If the percentage decrease in the length of a simple pendulum is 10%, then find the percentage decrease in its time period.

59. The frequency of a sound wave is 200 Hz and its wavelength is 150 cm. What is the distance travelled by a sound wave in the time taken to produce 150 waves?

60. The time period of a simple pendulum is given by

$$T = 2\pi\sqrt{\frac{\ell}{g}},$$

where 'l' is the length of the pendulum and 'g' is the acceleration due to gravity at that place.

(a) Express 'g' in terms of T.

(b) What is the length of the seconds pendulum? (Take g = 10 m s^{-2}).

61. The wavelength of a sound wave travelling in a solid becomes one third when it propagates through air. If the frequency of the wave remains constant, then find the decrease in the velocity of the wave.

62. The oscillation of a simple pendulum is graphically represented as follows. Determine the

(a) time period

(b) frequency

(c) amplitude

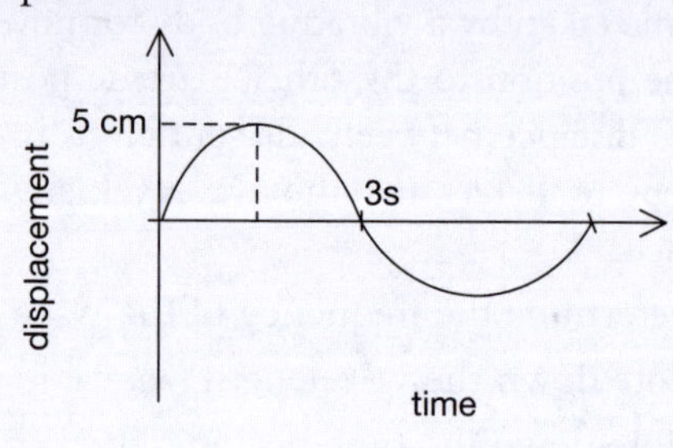

63. The range of the frequency of audible sound is 20 Hz to 20 kHz. What is the range of wavelength for the audible sound at 0°C? (Take velocity of sound as 330 m s^{-1} at 0°C.)

64. Sound produced by a tuning fork travel through solid and liquid media. If f_1 and f_2 are the frequencies of sound in solid and liquid, then find the value of $\frac{f_1}{f_2}$.

65. What is the new time period of a pendulum, if the length of a pendulum of time period T is doubled?

66. If the velocity of the sound wave is 330 m s^{-1} and the frequency of oscillations is 10 Hz, then calculate the distance between an adjacent compression and rarefaction.

Level 3: Assess Your Concepts

67. If the length of a second pendulum is first decreased by 10 cm and its time period is measured and then increased by 15 cm and the time period is measured, then calculate the ratio of the time periods in two cases. (Take $g = 9.8$ m s^{-2})

68. 'Sound travels in rocks in the form of both longitudinal and transverse waves, but in air, sound travels only in the form of longitudinal waves'. Explain.

69. How does the time period T of a simple pendulum vary with altitude? Discuss.

70. The length of the seconds pendulum is first increased by 10 cm and then decreased by 5 cm. If the time period is determined in each case, find their ratio. (Take $g = 10$ m s^{-2}, $\pi^2 \simeq 10$)

71. Two iron rods of length of 2.2 m and 0.8 m of uniform densities are suspended from their ends and made to oscillate. Find the time periods of the two rods. Which rod gains time as compared to the time period of seconds pendulum?

72. The time period of a pendulum on the surface of the moon is 5 s. If it is a seconds pendulum on earth and the acceleration due to gravity on the Earth is 9.8 m s^{-2}, find the acceleration due to gravity on the surface of the moon.

73. Two pendula of the same length oscillate with amplitudes of 3 cm and 5 cm, respectively. The average time period noted for 3 trials for the first pendulum is found to be 2 s; what will be the average time period for the second pendulum?

74. If the length of a seconds pendulum is first decreased by 10 cm and its time period is determined and then increased by 20 cm and the time period is once again determined, find the ratio of the time periods in two cases. (Take $g = 9.8$ m s^{-2})

75. When a string fixed between two ends is plucked, a wave propagates along the string and reflects at the other end. Find the distance of maximum and minimum displacement of the particle in a wave from its first end, given that the velocity of wave propagation is 330 m s^{-1} and the frequency of vibration is 1320 Hz.

76. The velocity of sound increases by 75% when it enters a liquid from air. Find the percentage increase in its wavelength.

77. The ratio of loudness of sound produced by two sources is 2 : 3. What is the ratio of amplitude of their vibrations?

78. Sound waves travel from air to water. The velocity of the sound waves in air is 332 m s^{-1} and wavelength is 2 m. If the wavelength of the sound waves in water is 850 cm, find its velocity in water.

79. A sound wave of frequency 660 Hz incidents normally on a perfectly reflecting surface. If the speed of sound in air is 330 m s^{-1}, what is the time taken by a particle in the medium to complete one vibration? Determine the wave length of the wave.

80. The velocity of sound waves in a metal is found to be 1400 m s^{-1}. When they travel from metal to air its velocity changes to 340 m s^{-1}. If the wavelength of sound waves in air is 200 m, find its wavelength in the metal.

81. A wave of time period of 20 ms travels with a velocity of 2 m s^{-1}. If the time period of another wave is 5 ms, then find velocity of second wave and the ratio of their velocity. (Wavelength of the two waves is the same)

82. The velocity of sound increases by 50% when it enters a liquid from air, and when it enters another liquid from air, the increase in velocity is 150%. Then find the ratio of % increase in the wavelength in two cases.

83. When a string fixed between two ends is plucked, a wave propagates along the string and reflects at the other end. If the velocity and frequency of the wave is 330 m s^{-1} and 1200 Hz respectively, then find the distance of the first node and the first antinode from the fixed end of the string.

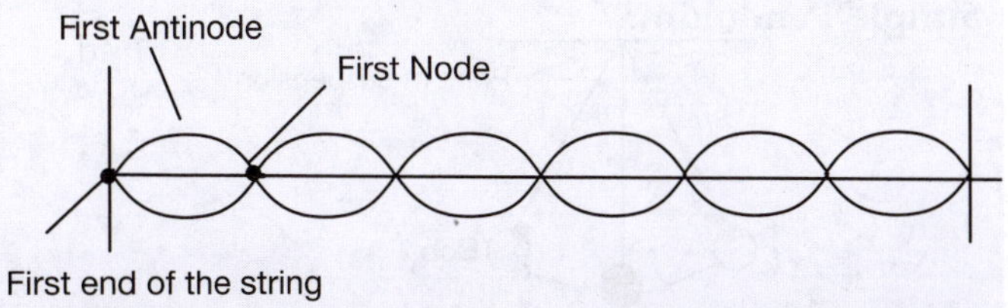

84. A boy plays with two tuning forks A and B. When strikes them with a rubber hammer, he observes that 256 and 512 waves are generated per second from A and B with amplitude 1 mm and 2 mm respectively. Find the percentage of difference in the loudness of the sound waves produced by one fork with the other.

JEE-NEET SPECIAL WING

PRACTICE QUESTIONS

Multiple-Answer Type Questions

Directions for questions 1 to 5: **Select one or more correct alternative(s) from the given choices.**

1. The unit of frequency is
   (a) m s^{-1} (b) s^{-1}
   (c) Hz (d) s

2. Longitudinal waves comprise of
   (a) Crests
   (b) Trough
   (c) Compressions
   (d) Rarefactions

3. Identify the correct relation.
   (a) $v = \frac{\lambda}{T}$
   (b) $v = T\lambda$
   (c) $v = n\lambda$
   (d) $v = \frac{n}{\lambda}$

4. The frequency of a sound wave propagating in air with a velocity 330 m s^{-1} is 47 Hz. The wavelength of the sound wave produced is
   (a) 7 m
   (b) 8 m
   (c) 8×10^2 m
   (d) 7×10^2 cm

5. Instruments that produce music by vibrating strings are
   (a) Mridangam
   (b) Veena
   (c) Sitar
   (d) Tabla

Comprehension-Based Questions

Directions for questions 6 to 10: **These questions are based on the following information.**

Simple Pendulum:

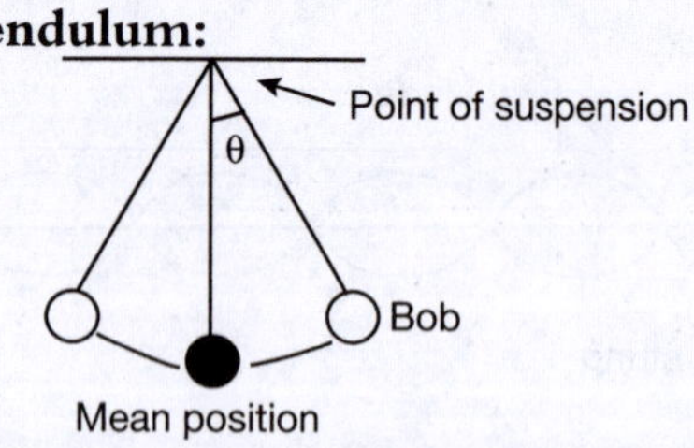

Simple pendulum is a mechanical system that executes an oscillatory motion. It has a heavy point mass (bob) suspended from a rigid support by a massless string. When bob is pulled and released from one side, it is subjected to a restoring force due to gravity which will accelerate it back towards the mean position and thus will swing back and forth periodically.

6. If a simple pendulum oscillates with a frequency of 0.25 Hz, its time period will be
   (a) 2 s
   (b) 4 s
   (c) 6 s
   (d) 8 s

7. If a pendulum clock gains time, the length of the pendulum would be
   (a) Increased
   (b) Decreased
   (c) Constant
   (d) No effect on length

8. If the lengths of two pendulums are given by 9 cm and 16 cm respectively then the ratio of their time periods is
(a) 1: 2 (b) 3: 1
(c) 3: 4 (d) $2\sqrt{2}$: 1

9. In a simple pendulum experiment, the time period was found to be T. If the same experiment is conducted in the polar region, the value of time period will
(a) Increase
(b) Decrease
(c) Remains unchanged
(d) First increase then decrease

10. According to third law of simple pendulum, for small values of amplitude
(a) $T\sqrt{\ell}$ = constant
(b) $\frac{\sqrt{\ell}}{T}$ = constant
(c) $\frac{\ell}{\sqrt{T}}$ = constant
(d) $\frac{T}{\sqrt{\ell}}$ = constant

Match the Column

Directions for question 11: **The question is based on the following information.**

Wave Motion: A wave is a disturbance that transfer energy from one place to another through a medium or vacuum. All waves have their own characteristic features which define the wave motion. Waves are of two types ie., transverse wave and longitudinal wave based on the vibration of particles with respect to the direction of propagation. In transverse wave, particles vibrate perpendicular to the direction of motion of wave whereas in longitudinal wave, the particle vibrates along the direction of propagation of wave motion.

11. Match the values in List - I with those in List - II:

List - I	List - II
A. Time period	a. Faint and loud sound
B. Frequency	b. Unpleasant effect on ears
C. Loudness	c. Flat and shrill sound
D. Pitch	d. Time to produce one complete wave.
E. Noise	e. No. of complete waves produced in unit time

(a) A - e, B - d, C - b, D - c, E - a
(b) A - a, B - d, C - e, D - b, E - c
(c) A - d, B - e, C - a, D - c, E - b
(d) A - e, B - d, C - c, D - a, E - b

ANSWER KEYS

Crossword

Across

4. Amplitude 6. Compression 7. Noise 8. Loudness 10. Pitch
15. Rarefaction 16. Veena 17. Flute

Down

1. Music 2. Mean position 3. Decibel 5. Sound 9. Piccolo
11. Tabla 12. Hertz 13. Length 14. Wave

Classroom Wing

Very Short Answer Type Questions

1. Amplitude 2. 0.5 s 3. Perpendicular 4. Vacuum 5. Mean
6. $(\text{length})^{1/2}$ 7. Percussion instrument 8. Crests and troughs 9. 2.2
10. oscillatory 11. Longitudinal 12. Mean, extreme 18. Distance = v.t
24. frequency remains same 25. $\frac{V_1}{V_2} > 1$

Short Answer Type Questions

31. 40 m 32. $\frac{1}{2}$ 40. 20 cm 41. $\sqrt{2}/n$ 42. 0.25 Hz

Competition Wing

Level 1: Apply your Concepts

1. False 2. True 3. True 4. True 5. True
6. True 7. False 8. True 9. False 10. False
11. False 12. False 13. T 14. Increasing 15. 1 : 4
16. String instruments 17. 100 Hz 18. 0.5 s 19. 60 cm
20. A : s, B : r, C : p, D : q 21. (b) and (d) 22. (d) 23. (a)
24. (b) 25. (d) 26. (d) 27. (a) 28. (c)
29. (c) 30. (a) 31. (b) 32. (d) 33. (c)
34. (b) 35. (d) 36. (d) 37. (b) 38. (c)
39. (b) 40. (b) 41. (a) 42. (c) 43. (b)
44. (a) 45. (c) 46. (d)

Level 2: Review your Concepts

47. $\frac{1}{\sqrt{2T}}$ 48. 16 50. 3 : 5 51. (a) 12.5 cm, (b) zero
52. 60 ms 53. 30 mm to 30 μm 56. 120 cm 57. 4.9 s 58. 5%
59. 225 m 61. 2/3 63. 16.5 mm to 16.5 m 65. $\sqrt{2}T$
66. 16.5 m

Level 3 : Assess Your Concepts

67. $\sqrt{\frac{6}{7}}$ 70. 42 : 41 71. 2.1 s, 1.3 s, first rod 74. $\sqrt{3}:2$ 76. 75%
77. $\sqrt{2}:\sqrt{3}$ 78. 1411 m s^{-1} 79. $\frac{1}{2}$, $\frac{1}{600}s$ 80. 823.5 cm 81. 8 m s^{-1}, $\frac{1}{4}$
82. $\frac{1}{3}$ 83. 0.06875 m 84. 300%

JEE-NEET Special Wing

Multiple-Answer Type Questions

1. (b) and (c) **2.** (c) and (d) **3.** (a) and (c) **4.** (a) and (d) **5.** (b) and (c)

Comprehension-Based Questions

6. (b) **7.** (b) **8.** (c) **9.** (b) **10.** (d)

Match the Column

11. (c)

For answer key of Classroom wing and Competition wing, refer to Hints and Solutions

Hints and Explanations

Classroom Wing

Very Short Answer Type Questions

1. When sound propagates through a medium, its amplitude changes.

2. Frequency = 2 Hz

   Time period = $\frac{1}{2}$ = 0.5 s

3. Perpendicular

4. Vacuum

5. Mean

6. $(\text{length})^{1/2}$

7. Percussion instrument

8. Crests and troughs

9. 2.2

10. oscillatory

11. Longitudinal

12. Mean, extreme

13. Maximum—solids
    Minimum—gases.

14. (i) Veena, sitar
    (ii) Drum, table
    (iii) Flute, piccolo

15. The time period of a pendulum is independent of amplitude provided amplitude is small.

16. Time taken to produce one complete wave.

17. (i) Particles of the medium vibrate perpendicularly to the direction of wave propagation.
    (ii) Particles of the medium vibrate parallel to the direction of wave propagation.

18. Distance travelled = velocity × time = $v \times t$

19. Velocity of a wave is independent of the source.

20. To increase the frequency, the time period should be reduced and to reduce the time period, the length should be reduced.

21. Wave motion

22. Distance between two successive compressions or between two successive rarefactions.

23. (i) Regions in a wave, where the distance between two particles is larger than the distance between them when they were at mean position.
    (ii) Regions in a wave, where the distance between two particles is smaller than the distance between them when they were at mean position

24. Velocity of sound in solid (V_1) > velocity in liquid

    $$\therefore \frac{V_1}{V_2} > 1$$

25. When the sound travels from one medium to another its frequency remains the same.

Short Answer Type Questions

Note: This is how you should frame your answer covering.

26. (i) Definition of transverse wave.
    (ii) Definition of longitudinal wave
    (iii) Characteristics of transverse waves.
    (iv) Characteristics of longitudinal waves.

27. $f = 10$ cps

28. $n = 200$ Hz, $\lambda = 60$ m

    $V = n\lambda \Rightarrow v = 200 \times 60 = 12000 \text{ m s}^{-1}$

29. (1) Tie a string to a peg.
    (2) Hold the other end in the hand.
    (3) Vibrate the free end of the string in the perpendicular direction to its length.

30. (i) Suspension of a pendulum from a retort stand placed on a table.
    (ii) Time for 20 oscillations for different amplitudes.
    (iii) Tabulation of data.
    (iv) Constant time period.

31. $\frac{\lambda}{2} = 20 \text{ m} \Rightarrow \lambda = 40 \text{ m}$

32. $T \propto \sqrt{\ell}$

    $$\frac{T_1}{T_2} = \sqrt{\frac{\ell_1}{\ell_2}} = \sqrt{\frac{1}{4}} = \frac{1}{2}$$

33. (i) Sound emitted by loud speaker
(ii) Piece of paper held in front of a speaker
(iii) Paper set into vibration
(iv) Sound transmitted to surrounding layers of air.

34. (i) Suspension of three pendulums from a retort stand placed on a table.
(ii) Bobs with different material and radii, but equal length.
(iii) Time for 20 oscillations in 2 trials.
(iv) Average time period
(v) Tabulation of data.
(vi) Constant time period.

35. Definition of wavelength and amplitude, $n = \frac{V}{\lambda}$

(i) 2m (ii) 7Hz (iii) 7cm

36. As the wavelength varies, amplitude also vary. So, the loudness of a sound note varies with the distance from the source of sound.

37. (i) Suspension of a simple pendulum from a retort stand
(ii) Time for 20 oscillations for a given length.
(iii) Change length and again time for 20 oscillations.
(iv) Tabulate the data
(v) $T \propto \sqrt{\ell}$

38. λ = 200 cm

39. The change in velocity when sound passes from liquid to a solid.

40. Velocity $= f\lambda = \frac{\lambda}{T}$

$$200 = \frac{\lambda}{0.001} \Rightarrow \lambda = 0.2 \text{ m} = 20 \text{ cm}$$

41. $f_1 = n$

$l_2 = 2l_1$

$$\frac{T_1}{T_2} = \sqrt{\frac{\ell_1}{\ell_2}}$$

$$\frac{f_1}{f_2} = \sqrt{\frac{\ell_2}{\ell_1}} = \sqrt{\frac{2\ell_1}{\ell_1}} = \sqrt{2}$$

$$f_2 = \frac{f_1}{\sqrt{2}}$$

$$f_2 = \frac{n}{\sqrt{2}}$$

$$\frac{1}{T_2} = \frac{n}{\sqrt{2}} \Rightarrow T_2 = \frac{\sqrt{2}}{n}$$

42. Frequency $= \frac{1}{T}$

Time period = 4 s

$\therefore$ frequency = 1/4

= 0.25 Hz

43. (i) Vibrating stretched strings
(ii) Vibrating stretched membranes
(iii) Changing the length of air column

44. The frequency, $f = \frac{1}{\text{Time Period}}$

The time period depends on the length. Hence, the frequency depends on both the time period and length of the pendulum.

Essay Answer Type Questions

Note: This is how you should frame your answer covering.

45. (i) Long spring on a table in a straight position.
(ii) Hold one end of the spring in the hand.
(iii) To and fro motion of the end in hand in a direction parallel to its length.

46. (i) Suspension of an electric bell in a jar.
(ii) Give electric connections to the bell.
(iii) Pump out air in the jar by vacuum pump.
(iv) Loudness of sound decreases gradually.

47. (i) Suspend a pendulum from a retort stand.
(ii) Fix a tuning fork to a stand.
(iii) Vibrate with rubber hammer.
(iv) Make the bob of pendulum in contact with the fork.

48. (i) Have stretched strings
(ii) Varying thickness, tension, length of string produce musical notes of different pitch.
(iii) Have sounding box, vibrates at the same frequency as the stretched string.

49. (i) Sound travelling through a metal rail
(ii) Sound through air
(iii) Comparison of times taken to hear

Competition Wing

Level 1: Apply your Concepts

1. False, Among the waves, light has the highest velocity.
2. Sound cannot travel through vacuum.

13. The time period of a pendulum is independent of the mass of the bob. Thus, time period = T

20. Velocity of a wave depends on medium; A → s

Frequency of a wave depends on the source; B → r

$$\text{Wavelength} = \frac{\text{Velocity}}{\text{Frequency}} = \text{Velocity} \times \text{time period};\ C \to p$$

$$\text{Frequency} = \frac{\text{number of waves}}{\text{time taken}};\ D \to q$$

21. Time period of a pendulum depends upon both length and acceleration due to gravity. When the weight of a body is changed without changing its mass, the value of 'g' also changes.

Hence, the correct answer are (b) and (d).

36. Time taken for 20 oscillations

$$\frac{39.2+38.4+40.8+41.4+40.2}{5} = \frac{200}{5} = 40\,\text{s}$$

$$\text{Time taken for one oscillation} = \frac{40}{20} = 2\,\text{s}$$

i.e., Time period 2 s

$$\text{Frequency} = \frac{1}{\text{Time period}} = \frac{1}{2} = 0.5\,\text{s}^{-1}$$

Hence, the correct answer is (d).

37. Time period of a simple pendulum is inversely proportional to the acceleration due to gravity.

$$T \propto \frac{1}{\sqrt{g}}$$

Hence, the correct answer is (b).

38. $$T = \frac{\dfrac{38.6+40+41.5+42.8+39.4}{5}}{20}$$

$$= 2.023\,\text{s} \approx 2\,\text{s}$$

Hence, the correct answer is (c).

39. Initially the length of the pendulum (ℓ) is determined (E).

The pendulum is set into oscillation and the time taken for 20 oscillation is determined (A).

The time period (T) of the pendulum is determined (d).

The value of (T^2) is determined (B).

The length of the pendulum is changed and the experiment is repeated (C)

In each case the value of $\frac{\ell}{T^2}$ is determined (F).

Hence, the correct answer is (b).

40. Initially the wavelength (λ) is noted (B). From the time period of oscillation the frequency (F) is determined (C, A).

The velocity of the wave v is determined as velocity $v = f\lambda$ (D).

Hence, the correct answer is (b).

41. Bell jar experiment shows that sound requires a medium for its propagation and cannot travel through vacuum.

Hence, the correct answer is (a).

42. Take a glass jar with closed lid and an outlet connected to a vaccum pump (A).

Suspend an electric bell (B) and switch it on (D).

Now evacuate the jar (C) and observe that the intensity of sound is decreased when the jar is evacuated (E).

This proves that a medium is required for the propagation of sound (F).

Hence, the correct answer is (c).

43. A child produces a higher pitched sound compared to that of an adult. Because pitch depends on the length and thickness of a vibrating body, i.e., vocal cord in this case. So, A is correct.

The pitch depends on the frequency of sound. R is also correct but not the correct explanation of A.

Hence, the correct answer is (b).

44. As there is no atmosphere on the moon, sound cannot propagate on the moon. Because, sound requires a medium to propagate.

Hence, the correct answer is (a).

45. Velocity of sound 'v'

$$= \frac{\text{distance travelled by sound } (d)}{\text{time taken } (t)}$$

Then, the ratio of time taken by A and B to cover a distance of 660 m and 990 m, respectively is

$$\frac{t_A}{t_B} = \frac{\frac{d_A}{v}}{\frac{d_B}{v}} \Rightarrow \frac{d_A}{d_B} = \frac{660}{990} = \frac{2}{3} = 2:3$$

Hence, the correct answer is (c).

46. $T \propto \sqrt{\ell}, \frac{T_A}{\sqrt{\ell_A}} = \frac{T_B}{\sqrt{\ell_b}}; \frac{T_A}{T_B} = \sqrt{\frac{\ell_A}{\ell_B}} = \sqrt{\frac{9}{16}} = \frac{3}{4}$

$$T_A : T_B = 3:4 \text{ But } \frac{T_A}{T_B} = \frac{1/n_A}{1/n_B} \Rightarrow \frac{n_B}{n_A} = 3/4$$

Hence, the correct answer is (d).

Level 2: Review your Concepts

Note: This is how you should frame your answer covering.

47. $\frac{T_1}{T_2} = \sqrt{\frac{\ell_1}{\ell_2}}$

$$\frac{T_1}{T_2} = \sqrt{\frac{\ell_1}{2\ell_1}} \Rightarrow \frac{T_1}{T_2} = \frac{1}{\sqrt{2}}, T_2 = \sqrt{2}T_1$$

$$\text{Frequency} = \frac{1}{T}$$

$$f_2 = \frac{1}{T_2} \Rightarrow f_1 = \frac{1}{T_1}$$

$$T_2 = \frac{1}{f_2}$$

$$\therefore \frac{1}{f_2} = \sqrt{2}\frac{1}{f_1}, f_2 = \frac{f_1}{\sqrt{2}} = \frac{1}{\sqrt{2T}}$$

48. (i) $\lambda = \frac{v}{n}$,

$$\text{No. of holes} = \frac{\text{frequency}}{\text{No. of ratation in one sec}}$$

(ii) 16

49. Absence of atmosphere on the surface of moon

50. (i) $\frac{V_1}{V_2} = \frac{T_2}{T_1}$

(ii) 3 : 5

51. (i) To build your answer, find the frequency and speed of sound in air from the given data.

Do the sound waves after reflection from a wall form stationary or standing waves?

Find the wavelength of this sound wave.

Find when the nodes and antinodes are formed in a stationery wave.

Here, the shortest distance from the wall to Antinode and Node is $\lambda/4$ and $\lambda/2$, respectively,

(ii) (a) 12.5 cm, (b) zero

52. (i) Half the time period.

(ii) 60 ms

53. (i) $V = n\lambda$

(ii) 30 mm to 30 μm

54. Among air and water find which exerts more frictional force.

Find out how is the amplitude affected by the frictional force?

55. (i) When sound moves through different media, will its frequency (n) change?

Find how many times the velocity of sound in air (V1) increases when made to pass through liquid (V2).

Then, take velocity, wavelength of sound in air and liquid as V_1, λ_1, V_2, λ_2, respectively.

Here, $V_1 = n\lambda_1$ and $V_2 = \lambda_2$ (1)

is $V_2 = 4V_1$ (2)

Substitute (2) in (1) and find the relation between λ_1 and λ_2.

Now, find the change in 'λ', i.e., $(\lambda_2 - \lambda_1)$.

(ii) Increase in wave length is thrice the initial wave length

56. (i) One wave is equal to one wavelength.

(ii) 120 cm

57. (i) To build your answer, find the the length and time period of a seconds pendulum on the surface of the Earth.

Then, the formula for time period (T) is given by,

$$T = 2\pi\sqrt{\frac{\ell}{g}}.$$

Take the time of seconds pendulum as 'T_E' and 'T_M' on the surface of the Earth and the moon, respectively.

Take the values of acceleration due to gravity on the surface of the Earth and the moon as 'g_E' and 'g_M', respectively.

Given that $g_E = \frac{1}{6} g_M$

Now, $T_E = 2\pi\sqrt{\dfrac{\ell}{g_E}}$ and T_M

$T_M = 2\pi\sqrt{\dfrac{\ell}{g_M}}$

Take, $T_E = 2$ s.
Substitute the value of (1) in (2) and find the value of T_M.

(ii) 4.9 s

58. (i) $\ell_2 = \ell_1 - 10\%$ of ℓ_1, $\dfrac{T_1}{T_2} = \sqrt{\dfrac{\ell_1}{\ell_2}}, \dfrac{T_1 - T_2}{T_1} \times 100$

(ii) 5%

59. (i) Find the wavelength of the given sound wave. Then, distance traveled by 150 waves is 150(λ).

(ii) 225 m

60. (i) $T = 2\pi\sqrt{\dfrac{\ell}{g}}$ (1)

Square equation (1) on both the sides write g in term of 'ℓ' and "T".

(ii) 101 cm

61. (i) $\dfrac{V_1}{V_2} = \dfrac{\lambda_1}{\lambda_2}, V_1 - V_2$

(ii) 2/3

62. (a) Time period = 6 s

(b) Frequency $\dfrac{1}{T} = \dfrac{1}{6}$ Hz

(c) Amplitude = 5 cm

63. The range of audible sound is 20 Hz to 20 kHz.

Velocity of sound at 0°C = 330 m s^{-1}.

Then wavelength (l_1) of sound at a frequency of 20Hz

$\lambda_1 = \dfrac{330}{20} = 16.5$ m

Wavelength (l_2) of sound at a frequency of 20 kHz

$\lambda_2 = \dfrac{330}{20 \times 10^3}$

$= 16.5 \cdot 10^3$ m or 16.5 mm

∴ Range of wavelength for audible sound is 16.5 mm to 16.5 m

64. Frequency is independent of medium ∴ $\dfrac{f_1}{f_2} = 1$ m s^{-2}

65. $T \propto \sqrt{\ell}$

$\dfrac{T_1}{T_2} = \sqrt{\dfrac{\ell_1}{\ell_2}}; l_2 = 2l_1$

$\dfrac{T_1}{T_2} = \sqrt{\dfrac{\ell_1}{2\ell_1}} \Rightarrow \dfrac{T_1}{T_2} = \dfrac{1}{\sqrt{2}} \Rightarrow T_2 = \sqrt{2}T_1$

$T_2 = \sqrt{2}T$

66. Velocity $= n\lambda$

$330 = 10 \times \lambda;\ \lambda = 33$

Distance between compression and rarefaction $= \lambda/2$

$= \dfrac{33\,\text{m}}{2} = 16.5\,\text{m}$

Level 3: Assess Your Concepts

Note: This is how you should frame your answer covering.

67. $l_0 = 100$ cm $T_0 = 2$ s

$l_1 = 90$ cm $T_1 = ?$

$l_3 = 105$ cm $T_2 = ?$

$T_1 = 2\pi\sqrt{\dfrac{l_1}{g_1}}$

$= 2\pi\sqrt{\dfrac{90}{980}}$

$= 2\pi\sqrt{\dfrac{9}{98}}$

$T_2 = 2\pi\sqrt{\dfrac{l_2}{g_2}}$

$= 2\pi\sqrt{\dfrac{105}{980}}$

$\dfrac{T_1}{T_2} = \dfrac{2\pi\sqrt{\dfrac{9}{98}}}{2\pi\sqrt{\dfrac{105}{980}}}$

$\Rightarrow \dfrac{T_1}{T_2} = \sqrt{\dfrac{9}{98}} \times \sqrt{\dfrac{980}{105}}$

$\Rightarrow \dfrac{T_1}{T_2} = \sqrt{\dfrac{90}{105}} = \sqrt{\dfrac{18}{21}} = \sqrt{\dfrac{6}{7}}$

68. Longitudinal waves are possible in those media which resist change in volume.

Transverse waves are possible in those media which resist change in shape.

69. If altitude increases, find how the value of 'g' varies.

From the formula, $T = 2\pi\sqrt{\frac{\ell}{g}}$

Find how the value of 'T' varies with the value of 'g'.

70. (i) $T_1 = 2\pi\sqrt{\frac{\ell + \ell^1}{g}}$, $T_2 = 2\pi\sqrt{\frac{\ell^1 - \ell^{11}}{g}}$

(ii) 42 : 41

71. (i) The rod which has more time period loses time

(ii) 2.1 s, 1.3 s, first rod

72. $T \propto \sqrt{\frac{1}{g}}$

$$\frac{T_E}{T_M} = \sqrt{\frac{g_M}{g_E}}$$

$$\frac{2}{5} = \sqrt{\frac{g_M}{g}}$$

$$\frac{4}{25} = \frac{g_M}{g}$$

$$g_M = \frac{4}{25} \times 9.8 \left(\because g = 9.8\, ms^{-2}\right)$$

$$= 1.6\, s^{-2}$$

73. The average time period for the second pendulum is also 2 s. Because for a given length, the time period is independent of amplitude of oscillation.

74. The time period of given simple pendulum is = 2 s

We know that $T\, 2\pi\sqrt{\frac{\ell}{g}} \Rightarrow 2 = 2\pi\sqrt{\frac{\ell}{9.8}}$

$$\Rightarrow \ell = \frac{9.8}{(3.14)^2} = 0.99\text{m} \Rightarrow \ell = 100\text{cm (nearly)}$$

Then, $\frac{T_1}{T_2} = \sqrt{\frac{L-10}{L+20}} = \sqrt{\frac{100-10}{100+20}}$

(Since, $T \propto \sqrt{\ell}$)

$$\Rightarrow \frac{T_1}{T_2} = \sqrt{\frac{90}{120}} = \sqrt{\frac{9}{12}} = \sqrt{\frac{3}{4}} = \frac{\sqrt{3}}{2}$$

$\therefore T_1 : T_2 = \sqrt{3} : 2$

75. $V = 330$ m s^{-1}, $n = 1320$ Hz, $V = n\lambda$

$330 = 1320\ \lambda$

$$\lambda = \frac{330}{1320}; \lambda = \frac{1}{4} = 0.25\text{m}$$

Distance of maximum diisplacement from one end

$$= \frac{\lambda}{4} = \frac{0.25}{4} = 0.0625\text{m} = 6.25\text{ cm}$$

Distance of minimum displacement from one end = 0

76. $V_1 = V$

$$V_2 = V + \frac{75}{100}V = 1.75\text{V}$$

$$= \frac{V_1}{V_2} = \frac{\lambda_1}{\lambda_2}$$

$$\frac{V}{1.75V} = \frac{\lambda_1}{\lambda_2}$$

$$\Rightarrow \lambda_1 = 1.75\,\lambda_1$$

Increase in wavelength = $\lambda_2 - \lambda_1$

$= 1.75\ \lambda_1 - \lambda_1 = 0.75\ \lambda_1$

Percentage increase in wavelength

$$= \frac{\lambda_2 - \lambda_1}{\lambda_1} \times 100$$

$$= \frac{0.75\lambda_1}{\lambda_1} \times 100 = 75\%$$

77. Loudness $\propto$ Amplitude^2

Given $\frac{L_1}{L_2} = \frac{2}{3} = \frac{A_1}{A_2} = ?$

$$\frac{L_1}{L_2} = \left(\frac{A_1}{A_2}\right)^2 \Rightarrow \frac{2}{3} = \frac{A_1^2}{A_2}$$

$$\Rightarrow \frac{A_1}{A_2} = \frac{\sqrt{2}}{\sqrt{3}} = \sqrt{2} : \sqrt{3}$$

78. Let us first calculate the frequency of the sound waves.

$$v = n\lambda \qquad (1)$$

Substituting the values of $V = 332$ m s^{-1} and $\lambda = 2$ m,

we get $\frac{v}{\lambda} = \frac{332}{2}$

$n = 166$ Hz.

The frequency of the sound waves remains constant, as it travels from air to water. Hence, using the formula $v = n\lambda$ and substituting $n = 166$ Hz and $\lambda = 850$ cm $= 8.5$ m, we get

$v = 166 \times 8.5 = 1411$ m s^{-1}.

79. Frequency of the wave (n) = 660 Hz

Speed of the sound wave (V) = 330 m s^{-1}

$\therefore$ Wavelength (λ) = $\frac{V}{n} = \frac{330}{660} = \frac{1}{2}$

Time period, $T = \frac{1}{f} = \frac{1}{660}$ s

80. $V_{met} = 1400$ m s^{-1} $\lambda_{met} = ?$

$V_{air} = 340$ m s^{-1} $\lambda_{air} = 200$ cm

$V = n\lambda$

$$\frac{V_{met}}{V_{air}} = \frac{\lambda_{met}}{\lambda_{air}} = \frac{1400}{340} = \frac{\lambda_{met}}{200}$$

$\Rightarrow \lambda_{met} = 823.5\,\text{cm}$

81. $T_1 = 2\times10^{-3}$s; $T_2 = 5\times10^{-3}$s

$\lambda_1 = \lambda, \lambda_2 = \lambda$

$V_1 = 2$ m s^{-1} $V_2 = ?$

$$V = \frac{\lambda}{T} \quad \Rightarrow \frac{v_1}{v_2} = \frac{\lambda_1 \times T_2}{\lambda_2 \times T_1}$$

$$\frac{2}{v_2} = \frac{\lambda\times5\times10^{-3}}{\lambda\times20\times10^{-3}}$$

$V_2 = 8$ m s^{-1}

The ratio $\frac{v_1}{v_2} = \frac{2}{8} = \frac{1}{4}$

82. $v_1 = v$ $v_2 = 1.5$ v, $V_3 = 2.5$ v

$$\frac{v_1}{v_2} = \frac{\lambda_1}{\lambda_2}$$

$$\lambda_2 = \frac{v_2}{v_1}\lambda_1$$

$$= \frac{1.5\,v}{v}\times\lambda_1$$

$= 1.5\lambda_1$

II Method

As ratio of % increase in velocities in two cases is 1 : 3, the % increase in wavelength also 1 : 3.

$\therefore \lambda_2 = 1.5\lambda_1$

$$\frac{v_1}{v_3} = \frac{\lambda_1}{\lambda_3}$$

$$\lambda_3 = \frac{v_3}{v_1}\lambda_1$$

$$= \frac{2.5v}{v}\lambda_1$$

$= 2.5\lambda_1$

$\therefore \lambda_3 = 2.5\lambda_1$

% increasing I case = 50%

% increasing II case = 150%

Ratio $= \frac{50}{150} = \frac{1}{3}$.

83. $\lambda = \frac{v}{f} = \frac{330}{1200} = 0.275$ m

$\lambda = 0.275$ m

Distance of first node from first end of string

$$= \frac{\lambda}{2} = \frac{0.275}{2} = 0.1375 \text{ m}$$

Distance of first Anti node is

$$= \frac{\lambda}{4} = \frac{0.275}{4} = 0.06875 \text{ m.}$$

84. Amplitudes,

$A_A = 1$ mm, $A_B = 2$ mm

$N_A = 256$Hz, $N_B = 512$Hz

Loudness $\propto (\text{Amplitude})^2$

$$\frac{L_A}{L_B} = \frac{A_A^2}{A_B^2} = \left(\frac{10}{20}\right)^2 = \frac{1}{4}$$

$L_B = 4L_A$

$L_B > L_A$

$$\left(\frac{(L_B - L_A)}{L_A}\times100\right) = \left(\frac{L_B}{L_A} - 1\right)\times100$$

$= (4-1)\times100 = 300\%$

JEE-NEET Special Wing

Multiple-Answer Type Questions

1. $f = \frac{1}{T}$

   Unit $\rightarrow$ s^{-1} or Hz

   Hence, the correct option is (b) and (c).

2. Longitudinal waves comprise of compressions and rarefactions.

   Hence, the correct option is (c) and (d).

3. $v = \frac{\lambda}{T}$

   $= \lambda \frac{1}{T}$

   $v = \lambda n \left[\because \frac{1}{T} = n\right]$

   Hence, the correct option is (a) and (c).

4. $v = n\lambda$

   $\lambda = \frac{v}{n} = \frac{330}{47} = 7$ m

   $= 700$ cm

   Hence, the correct option is (a) and (d).

5. Mridangam and Tabla are drum instruments.

   Hence, the correct option is (b) and (c).

Comprehension-Based Questions

6. $f = \frac{1}{T}$

   $T = \frac{1}{f}$

   $= \frac{1}{0.25}$

   $= 4$ s

   Hence, the correct option is (b).

7. If a pendulum gains time, it implies it makes more vibrations than required. Thus, its period of oscillation has decreased which is made by decreasing the length of the pendulum.

   Hence, the correct option is (b).

8. $T = 2\pi\sqrt{\frac{\ell}{g}}$

   $T \propto \sqrt{\ell}$

   $\frac{T_1}{T_2} = \sqrt{\frac{\ell_1}{\ell_2}} = \sqrt{\frac{9}{16}} = \frac{3}{4}$

   Hence, the correct option is (c).

9. As we move towards the pole, the value of g increases. Since,

   $T = 2\pi\sqrt{\frac{\ell}{g}}$

   ie., $T \propto \frac{1}{\sqrt{g}}$

   The time period of the pendulum decreases.

   Hence, the correct option is (b).

10. $T \propto \sqrt{\ell}$

    $\therefore \frac{T}{\sqrt{\ell}} = \text{constant}$

    Hence, the correct option is (d).

Match the Column

6. Choice (c) follows.

   A - d, B - e, C - a, D - c, E - b

Heat

CHAPTER

6

Key Ideas

After completing this chapter, you should be able to:

- ✦ understand the difference between heat and temperature.
- ✦ obtain temperature with the help of different thermometers and to do conversions.
- ✦ study the factors affecting the absorption of heat energy.
- ✦ discuss the factors affecting the expansion of substances and to study in detail the change of state of matter.

Remember

Before beginning this chapter, you should be able to:

- ☛ define heat and temperature.
- ☛ find measurement of temperature with the help of thermometers.

Scientific Crypt

A Tribute to James Watt (1736–1819)

James Watt, was a mechanical engineer by profession and a famous Scottish inventor.

He is well known for making improvement to the Newcomen steam engine. His improvements not only made the steam engines highly cost-effective but also enhanced the power and efficiency of the steam engines manifold. The modified steam engine eventually became the foremost energy source which led to the industrial revolution across the world. The cost-effective and efficient steam engines developed by Watt helped transforming the world from an agricultural society into an industrial one.

Because of his ill health, his initial part of schooling was done at home and it was only when he was fourteen that he started his formal schooling. His experience with the tools from his father's carpenter bench provided him the basics of engineering and tooling. His experience with his mother's tea kettle provided him an insight into the fundamental nature of steam, which ultimately led to his greatest contribution to mankind. The concept of horsepower was developed by Watt and the SI unit of power, the watt, was named in his honor.

Crossword

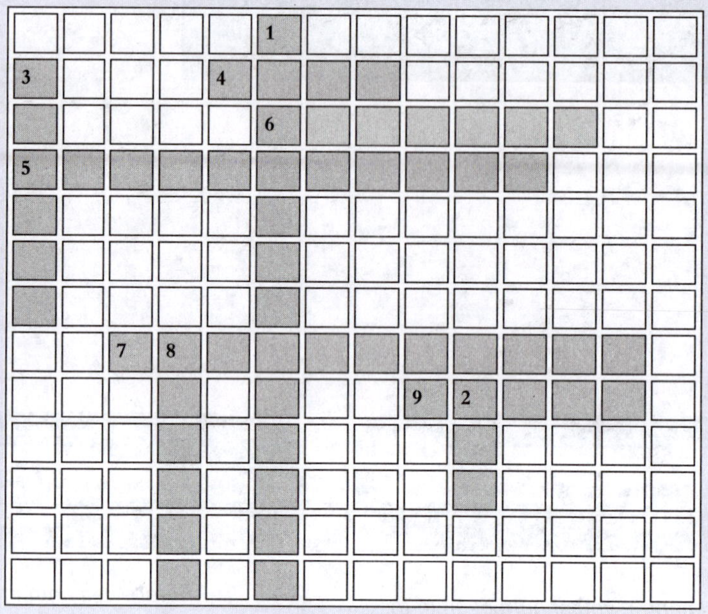

Across

4. Change in temperature when 1 g of ice is melted.
5. Heat energy required to change the state.
6. Thermometric liquid used in cold countries.
7. Direction of flow of heat.
9. SI unit of heat energy.

Down

1. Depends on the mass of the substance.
2. Specific heat capacity of 1666 g of water in calories.
3. Absolute scale of temperature.
8. Heat energy required to melt 1 g of ice in calories.

INTRODUCTION

Heat is an invisible form of energy that can produce the sensation of heat or cold. The property that tells us how hot or cold a particular body is called its temperature, i.e., the degree of hotness or coldness of a body is denoted by its temperature. When heat is supplied to a body its temperature increases and when heat is taken away from a body, its temperature decreases. The heat energy can be transformed into other forms of energy like electrical, mechanical, light, etc., by suitable methods. Heat energy can bring about changes in the physical dimensions, state and the chemical properties of a substance. Heat energy can also be defined as the sum total of potential and kinetic energy of molecules. Temperature can also be defined as the average kinetic energy of all molecules.

Flow of Heat Energy and Thermal Equilibrium

We know that water always flows from a higher level to a lower level, similarly heat energy is always transferred from a body at higher temperature to a body at lower temperature till a thermal equilibrium is attained. Hence, heat lost by a body at higher temperature is equal to heat gained by a body at lower temperature. Hence, temperature is a physical quantity which determines the direction of the flow of heat between two bodies.

The flow of heat continues till both the bodies attain the same temperature. This temperature is called **equilibrium temperature.** The state of two bodies at the same temperature in which there is no net flow of heat energy between them is called state of **thermal equilibrium**.

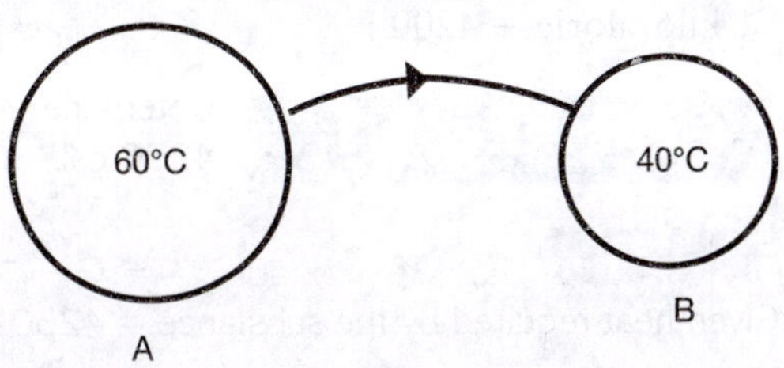

Figure 6.1 Direction of flow of heat energy

Table 6.1 Difference between Heat energy and Temperature

Heat energy	Temperature
Heat energy is the cause	Temperature is the effect
A calorimeter is used to measure heat energy.	A thermometer is used to measure temperature.
The S.I. unit of heat is joule.	The S.I. unit of temperature is kelvin.
It is the sum of the potential and the kinetic energy of the molecules of the substance.	It is the average kinetic energy of the molecules.
Heat energy lost by a hot body is equal to the heat energy gained by a cold body.	The increase in temperature of a cold body need not be equal to the decrease in temperature of the hot body.

Measurement of Temperature

A device used to measure temperature is called **thermometer**. Generally thermometers are based on the principle that matter expands on heating. For example, the volume of a liquid increases with increase in temperature. Depending on the type of matter used, we have solid thermometers, liquid thermometers and gaseous thermometers.

In general, a liquid at higher temperature will have more volume than what it has at lower temperature. This property of increase in volume with increase in temperature is the principle on which a liquid thermometer is constructed.

Similarly, gases and solids expand on heating. This property is the principle on which the gas thermometers and the solid thermometers are constructed. As gases expand the most on heating, gas thermometers are most sensitive. For general purposes we use liquid thermometers.

Some other properties of matter which change linearly with an increase in temperature can also be used to construct thermometers. You will be studying about these in higher classes.

Heat

Heat energy is measured in calories. One calorie of heat energy is defined as the amount of heat energy required to raise the temperature of 1 gram of water through 1°C. However, one calorie of heat energy is a very small quantity. So, a bigger unit, kilocalorie is used. One kilocalorie of heat energy is defined as the amount of heat energy required to raise the temperature of 1 kilogram of water through 1°C.

Konnect

Heat is also measured in joules, as it is a form of energy. (joule is the S.I. unit of heat).

Units of Heat: The experimental results show that 4.2 joules of mechanical work produces 1 calorie of heat energy. Thus,

1 calorie = 4.2 J

1 kilocalorie = 4200 J

EXAMPLE 6.1 Determine the heat required in joules to raise the temperature of a certain substance by 4250 cal.

SOLUTION

Given heat required by the substance = 4250 cal

We know,

1 cal = 4.2 J

Heat required in joules = 4250 × 4.2 = 17850 J or 17.850 kJ

Thus, the heat required to raise the temperature of the substance is 17.850 kJ.

Specific Heat Capacity

Unit mass of different substances absorb different amounts of heat energy, for unit rise in the temperature. For example, to raise the temperature of 1 kg of water through 1°C, 4186 J energy is absorbed by it whereas 1 kg of copper absorbs 385 J of heat energy for a rise of 1°C. Thus, the amount of heat energy needed to raise the temperature of unit mass of different substances is not equal as it depends on their nature. This energy is called specific heat capacity of a substance. Thus, **specific heat capacity** of a substance is defined as the quantity of heat required to raise the temperature of unit mass of a substance through one degree celsius or one kelvin.

Info Bytes!

Water has a high specific heat capacity, which is why it takes a longer time to boil compared to other liquids.

The S.I. unit of specific heat capacity is J kg^{-1} K^{-1}. If heat energy is measured in cal or kcal, then the unit of specific heat capacity is given by cal g^{-1} °C^{-1} or kcal kg^{-1} °C^{-1}. The heat energy absorbed by a given body increases in direct proportion to its mass (m) and rise in temperature ($\Delta\theta$), thus, the heat energy absorbed by a given body is given as

$$Q = m \times s \times \Delta\theta$$

where m is the mass, s is the specific heat capacity and $\Delta\theta$ is rise in temperature.

Heat Capacity

When a given body is heated, it absorbs certain amount of heat energy for 1°C rise in its temperature. The heat energy thus absorbed by it is known as its **heat capacity**. Heat capacity is denoted by 'c'.

Let a body absorb Q calories of heat energy and as a result, let its temperature rise by $\Delta\theta$ °C. Then, for a rise of 1°C, the heat energy absorbed by the body is $(Q/\Delta Q)$, which by definition is the heat capacity.

The S.I. unit of heat capacity is joule per kelvin ($J\ K^{-1}$) and general unit is cal°C^{-1} or kcal°C^{-1}. The heat energy absorbed by a body is given by $Q = m \times s \times \Delta\theta$. Dividing both sides of the above equation by $\Delta\theta$, we get $\left(\frac{Q}{\Delta\theta}\right) = m \times s$. But $(Q/\Delta Q)$ by definition is the heat capacity. Therefore, the heat capacity is given by heat capacity $= m \times s$.

Heat capacity and specific heat capacity are different. Heat capacity depends upon the mass of a substance whereas specific heat capacity does not depend on mass. Heat capacity is not a fixed quantity. It increases with increase in mass for the same material. Specific heat capacity is a fixed quantity for a given material. The specific heat capacity of some common materials are given below.

Table 6.2 Specific heat capacity of some common materials:

Substance	Specific heat capacity cal g^{-1}°C^{-1}	Specific heat capacity J g^{-1} °C^{-1}	Substance	Specific heat capacity cal g^{-1}°C^{-1}	Specific heat capacity J g^{-1}°C^{-1}
Water	1.000	4186	Iron	0.110	460
Alcohol	0.548	2294	Copper	0.092	385
Ice	0.500	2130	Silver	0.056	236
Steam	0.500	2093	Mercury	0.033	138
Aluminium	0.214	900	Lead	0.031	130

Info Bytes!

Water is one of the liquids having high specific heat capacity.

EXAMPLE 6.2 The heat capacity of 50 kg aluminium is found to be 4.5 kJ K^{-1}. Determine its specific heat capacity.

SOLUTION

The heat capacity (C) is given by the relation, $C = m \times s$, where m is the mass of the substance, and s is its specific heat capacity.

We are given that, $m = 50$ kg, and heat capacity = 4.5 kJ K^{-1}.

Substituting these values in the equation for heat capacity, we get $4.5 = 50 \times s$

$s = 4.5/50 = .09$ kJ $kg^{-1}\ K^{-1}$ or 90 J $kg^{-1}\ K^{-1}$.

∴ The specific heat capacity of lead = 90 J $kg^{-1}\ K^{-1}$.

EXAMPLE 6.3 Find the specific heat capacity of ice if 1.2 kg of ice absorbs 50.4 kJ of heat to raise its temperature from −20°C to 0°C.

SOLUTION

Here we use the relation, $Q = m \times s \times \Delta\theta$

Substituting, $Q = 50.4$ kJ $= 50400$ J

$m = 1.2$ kg

$\Delta\theta = 20$°C

$Q = m \times s \times \Delta\theta$

$$s = \frac{Q}{m \times \Delta\theta} = \frac{50400}{1.2 \times 20} = 2100 \text{ J kg}^{-1}\text{ K}^{-1}$$

EXAMPLE 6.4 Two bodies A and B of equal masses are supplied with equal amount of heat energy. If rise in temperature of A is more than that in B, what is the relation between their specific heats?

SOLUTION

For body A, $Q = m \times s_A \times \Delta\theta_A$ (1)

and for body B, $Q = m \times s_B \times \Delta\theta_B$ (2)

Dividing (1) by (2), $\frac{l_A}{C_B} = \frac{\Delta\theta_B}{\Delta\theta_A}$.

This shows that specific heat is inversely proportional to rise in temperature. Thus, specific heat of A is less than that of B.

Advantages of High Specific Heat Capacity of Water

The following are some of the advantages of the high specific heat capacity of water.

1. **Formation of Sea and Land Breezes:** During day time, land is heated to higher temperature than sea water as its specific heat capacity is much less than that of water. The hot air above land rises up and causes decrease in pressure. But the pressure of air above sea water is comparatively high as it is cooler. Due to this difference in pressure over land and sea, air starts blowing from sea to land, which is called **sea breeze.**

   During night time, land cools faster than sea as it loses heat energy rapidly, in comparison to sea water. The pressure over land increases and is more than pressure of air over the sea. The air, thus, starts blowing from land to sea, which is called **land breeze**.

2. **Use of Water for Fomentation:** Fomentation is the process in which swollen body parts of patients are maintained at moderate temperature, around 50°C. By fomentation a patient suffering from pain gets a lot of relief. For fomentation, hot water is used in bottles since water can store a large amount of heat energy at relatively low temperature due to high specific heat capacity.

3. **Water as Coolant:** Owing to its high specific heat capacity, water can absorb a large amount of heat energy, without its temperature becoming too high. This property of water makes it a good coolant. Water is used as coolant in automobile engines such as cars and buses, in factories, etc.

4. **Use of Water in the Internal Heating of Buildings:** In cold countries, the rooms in a building are kept warm by circulating hot water through pipes. The water is preferred as it can carry a large amount of heat energy from the furnace, at moderate temperatures.

Conductors and Insulators of Heat Energy

Heat energy passes easily and rapidly through some materials and slowly through some other materials. The materials through which it passes rapidly are called **good conductors of heat** and the materials through which it passes slowly are called **bad conductors of heat**. All metals are good conductors of heat. The specific heat capacity of good conductors is low. The examples of bad conductors of heat are wood, cork, paper, mica, etc.

Thermal Expansions in Solid

Generally, the materials expand on heating and contract on cooling. This is called **thermal expansion** and **contraction,** respectively. Thermal expansion and contraction are sometimes advantageous and, at other times, disadvantageous. This can be explained below with the help of examples:

Due to thermal expansion, a railway truck would bend, if no gaps are left between two successive rails. A pendulum clock loses or gains time due to thermal expansion or contraction of its length.

However, the thermal expansion and contraction can be used advantageously as discussed below.

1. **Fixing a Flat Iron Ring to a Wooden Cart Wheel:** The iron ring is made such that its diameter is just less than the diameter of the wooden cart wheel. The flat iron ring is heated to red hot and then carefully slipped on to the cart wheel. On pouring water, it contracts and grips the wooden wheel tightly.

2. **Riveting:** A rivet is nail or bolt used for holding metal plates together firmly. In the construction of ships and boilers, there is a need to fix steel plates firmly. The heated rivet is passed through the holes which are made in the steel plates. The hot rivet is then hammered to fix it firmly. When it is cooled, it contracts and holds the metal plates together more firmly.
3. **Bimetallic Strip:** A bimetallic strip is made up of strips of two different metals joined together by riveting. When it is heated, it bends due to unequal expansions of two metallic strips. On cooling, the bimetallic strip bends in the opposite direction to that when heated. The bimetallic strips are used in fire alarms, thermal switches such as those used in refrigerators, bimetallic thermometer, etc.

Thermometer

By touching, we can compare the temperatures of two given bodies but we can not say their exact temperatures. The instrument used to measure temperature accurately is called **thermometer**.

To measure temperature, some property of a substance that changes linearly with it is used. For example, a substance expands on heating. This property of expansion with rise in temperature can be used to measure the temperature. Of the three states of matter, gases expand maximum followed by liquids and solids. When expansion of mercury is used to measure the temperature, the thermometer is called mercury thermometer and the mercury is called thermometric liquid.

A mercury thermometer consists of a small cylindrical bulb made of glass and a long, narrow glass tube of uniform area of cross section attached to it as shown in the Figure 6.2.

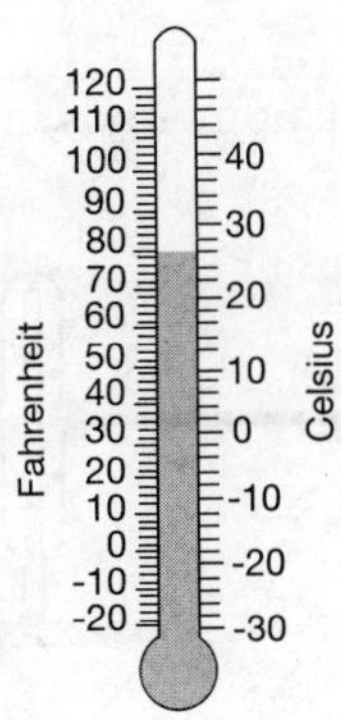

Figure 6.2 Calibration of a mercury thermometer in Celsius and Fahrenheit

The bulb and certain length of the glass tube is the filled with mercury and the remaining part of the tube is evacuated and closed at the other end. The glass tube (also called stem) is calibrated according to suitable temperature scale. When the mercury in the bulb expands, the level of mercury in the glass tube rises.

Types of Temperature Scales

The temperatures of certain substances are arbitrarily chosen as standard temperatures and a temperature scale is made. For example, in Celsius scale of temperature, the standard temperatures taken are melting point of ice as the lower fixed point (LFP) and boiling point of pure water as the upper fixed point (UFP). The temperature on Celsius scale is called **degree celsius (°C)**. The temperature at lower fixed point is assigned the value 0°C and the temperature at upper fixed point is assigned 100°C. The distance between 0°C and 100°C on the thermometer is divided into 100 equal parts. Each equal part corresponds to 1°C.

In Fahrenheit scale of temperature, the lower fixed point is taken as melting point of ice and it is assigned the value 32°F and upper fixed point (UFP) is taken as boiling point of water which is assigned the value 212°F. The distance between lower and upper fixed points on the thermometer is divided into 180 equal parts. Each equal part correspond to 1°F.

Construction of Celsius Thermometer

A thermometer tube is a thick walled glass capillary with a thin walled glass bulb at one end. Through its other end mercury is filled with the help of a funnel. While filling the tube with mercury, the glass bulb is placed in a hot oil bath so that air escapes in the form of bubbles.

The bulb, and the tube are completely filled with mercury and some mercury also stands in the tube. Now the funnel is removed and the open end is closed after that the bulb is cooled.

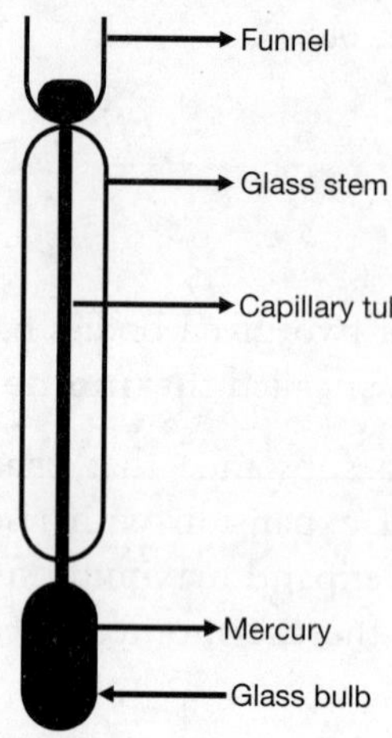

Figure 6.3 Celsius thermometer construction

Marking of Fixed Points

To mark lower fixed point (LFP), the bulb of the thermometer is immersed in melting ice, taken in a funnel as shown in the figure 6.4.

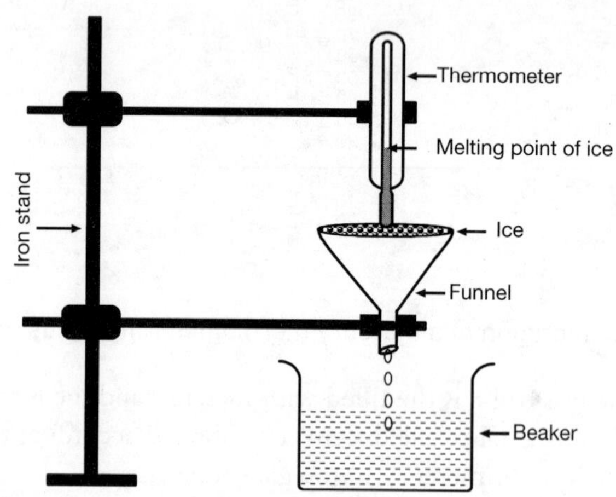

Figure 6.4 Experimental arrangement to mark the fixed points of a thermometer

Due to low temperature of ice, mercury in the bulb contracts and its level falls. The level of mercury is monitored for a few minutes and when it remains steady, a mark of 0°C is made on the stem against the mercury level, which is the lower fixed point. To mark the upper fixed point (UFP), the thermometer bulb is held in a special instrument called **hypsometer** such that the bulb is maintained at the boiling point of water, and does not touch water as shown in the figure 6.5.

In the hypsometer, pure water is boiled at standard pressure and the steam formed by the boiling water is used to raise the temperature of the bulb. The mercury in the bulb expands and its level in the glass capillary rises. When the level remains steady for a few minutes, a mark of 100°C is made against the mercury level, which is the upper fixed point (UFP).

The distance between 0°C and 100°C on the thermometer is divided into 100 equal parts. The thermometer now is ready for use.

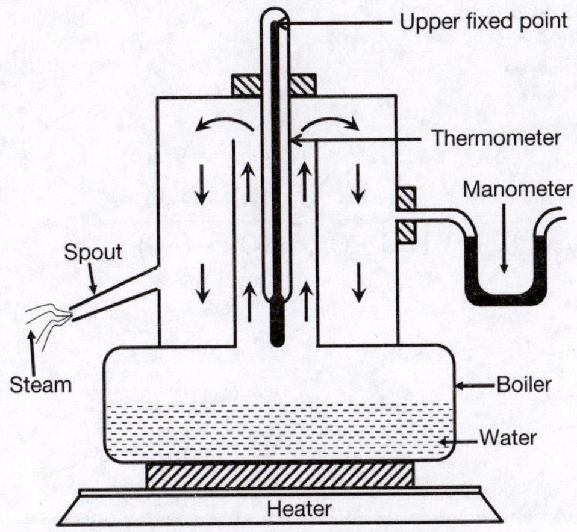

Figure 6.5 Hypsometer

To measure the temperature of a solid, the bulb of the thermometer is brought in contact with the solid. The temperature of a liquid is measured by immersing the bulb in the liquid. Depending on the temperature of a substance, the level of mercury in the thermometer may rise or fall. When the mercury level remains steady, the marking on the stem against the mercury level gives the temperature of the substance.

Relation between Different Scales

For any temperature scale, the ratio $\frac{\text{Reading - LFP}}{\text{UFP - LFP}}$ remains constant. This fact can be used to convert the temperature in one scale to another scale. The above equation can be used to convert Celsius to Fahrenheit scale.

$$\frac{C-0}{100-0} = \frac{F-32}{212-32}$$

In case the temperature is measured with a faulty scale the following relation can be used to find the correct temperature.

$$\left(\frac{S-LFP}{UFP-LFP}\right)_{\text{faulty scale}} = \left(\frac{S-LFP}{UFP-LFP}\right)_{\text{correct scale}}$$

Konnect

–40° *F* is equal to –40° *C*. This is the point where both temperature scales match.

EXAMPLE 6.5 At what temperature on the Fahrenheit scale is the reading five times the reading on the Celsius scale?

SOLUTION

Use the relation

$\frac{C}{5} = \frac{F-32}{9}$ and substitute C = x °C. F = 5x °F

$$\frac{x}{5} = \frac{5x-32}{9}$$

$9x = 25x - 160$

$16x = 160 \Rightarrow x = \frac{160}{16} = 10°C$

The temperature in Fahrenheit scale is $5x = 5 \times 10 = 50°F$

EXAMPLE 6.6 The lower and upper fixed points of a faulty thermometer are –2°C and 102°C, respectively. If the thermometer reads 50°C on this thermometer, find the correct temperature on the celsius scale.

SOLUTION

The relation to be used is

$$\left(\frac{S-LFP}{UFP-LFP}\right)_{\text{correct scale}} = \left(\frac{S-LFP}{UFP-LFP}\right)_{\text{faulty scale}} \Rightarrow \left(\frac{S-0}{100-0}\right) = \frac{50-(-2)}{102-(-2)}$$

$$\frac{S}{100} = \frac{52}{104}$$

$$S = \frac{52}{104} \times 100 = 50°C$$

Clinical Thermometer

To measure human body temperature, doctors use a special thermometer, called **clinical thermometer**. The scale in clinical thermometer is marked from 95°F to 110°F. The normal human body temperature which is 98.4°F is marked with a red arrow. There is a constriction near the bulb.

This prevents the mercury thread to flow back into the bulb so that the doctor can read the temperature accurately at his convenience .To take the next reading the thermometer is given a jerk so that the mercury in the tube falls back into the bulb.

For sterilizing, the thermometer is not placed in boiling water because the bulb may break as it is made of thin glass. Instead, formaldehyde, which is a liquid, is used for sterilization.

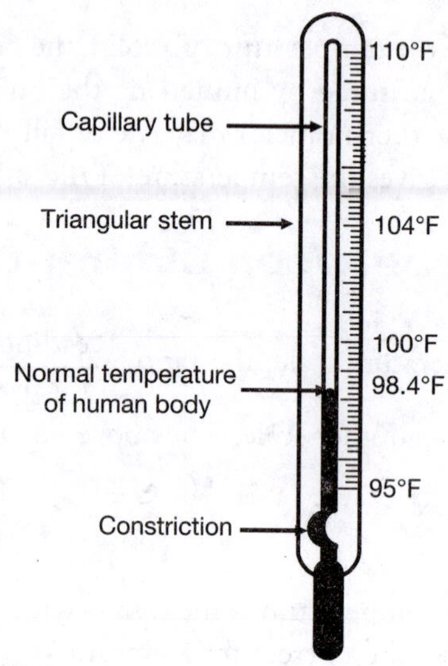

Figure 6.6 Clinical thermometer with its constriction

Six's Maximum and Minimum Thermometer

This thermometer automatically records the maximum and minimum temperature of the day. It consists of a cylindrical and a spherical glass bulbs *A* and *B* connected by *U* tube. Bulb *A* is filled with alcohol completely and *B* partially. The U tube is filled with mercury, as shown in the figure. The day's maximum and minimum temperature is shown by two light weight dumbbell-shaped iron indices, I_{max} and I_{min}.

Both the indices touch the mercury surface and are held in position by means of small springs. As the day's temperature rises, the alcohol in A expands, pushing the mercury downward. This pushes the index I_{max} up but I_{min} remain unaffected.

Later in the day when temperature falls, the alcohol in *A* contracts and the index I_{min} is pushed up. The index I_{max} remains in its place. Next day, the previous day's maximum and minimum temperature can be noted. To record maximum and minimum temperatures of the next day, the two indices are brought down to the level of mercury with the help of a magnet.

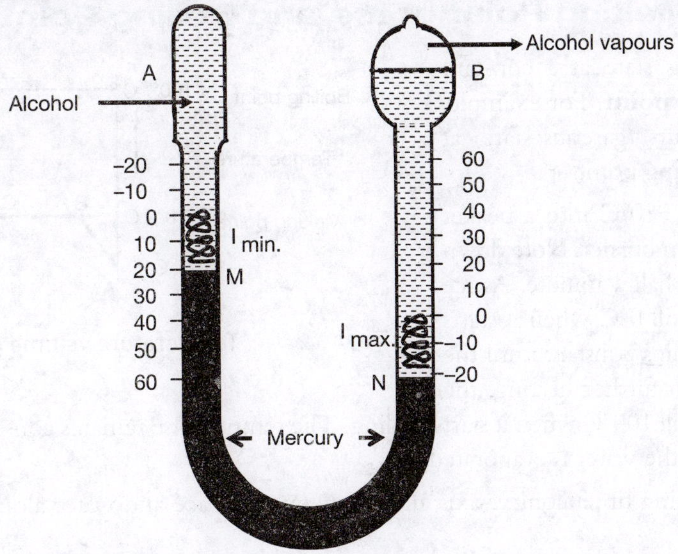

Figure 6.7 Six's Maximum and Minimum Thermometer

Galileo's Thermometer

Galileo was the first scientist to construct a thermometer based on the thermal expansion. He called his thermometer the **thermoscope**. In thermoscope, Galileo used the expansion of gas to measure the temperature.

The liquid level in the thermoscope rises or falls corresponding to the rise or the fall in temperature of the surrounding. A scale is attached to the tube and is caliberated to read the temperature directly.

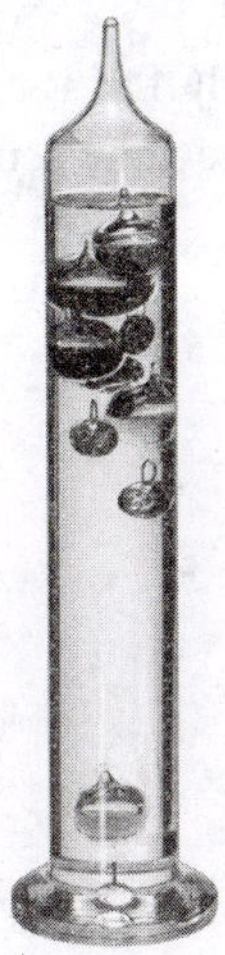

Figure 6.8 Galileo's Thermometer

Credit line: *Achim Prill / 123RF*

Change of State

We know that matter exists in solid, liquid or gaseous state. Iron, stone, glass, wood, etc., are present in solid state whereas kerosene, water, mercury, etc., are present in liquid state. The few examples of substances present in gaseous state are oxygen, carbon dioxide, sulphur dioxide, etc. The state in which a given substance is present is not permanent. For example, water vapourizes at boiling point and gets converted from liquid to gaseous state. When it is cooled in a refrigerator, it forms ice, which is in a solid state. Thus, every substance can be converted from one state to another state by either heating or cooling.

Determination of Melting Point of Wax

When a substance changes state, its temperature remains constant. If the substance is solid, the constant temperature at which the substance changes from solid state to liquid state at normal atmospheric pressure is called **melting point** of the given solid. For example, melting point of wax is 60°C which means that the wax is converted from its solid state to liquid state at the temperature of 60°C.

> **Konnect**
>
> Different types of wax have different melting points. For example, beeswax melts at a higher temperature than paraffin wax.

To determine the melting point of wax, take a small quantity of wax in a beaker and slowly heat the beaker by a candle or a bunsen burner.

Note down the temperature of wax, say after every ½ minute. The temperature of wax increases initially but once it starts melting, its temperature remains constant which is called its melting point. On further supplying heat the temperature remains constant at melting point until the whole of the wax is converted into liquid.

Determination of Melting Point of Ice and Boiling Point of Water

A liquid changes into gaseous state at a constant temperature called its **boiling point**. For example, water is converted into vapours (gaseous state) at 100°C and so 100°C is its boiling point.

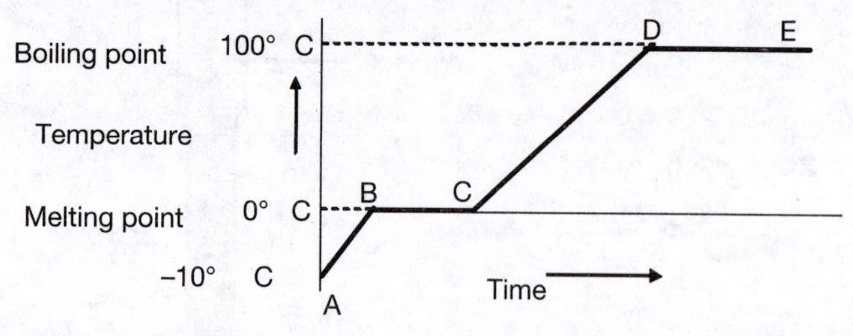

Figure 6.9 Temperature vs time graph of heat energy supplied

Take a few pieces of ice at −10°C into a beaker and heat the beaker with Bunsen burner. Note down its temperature, say after every half a minute. As ice is heated, its temperature rises till 0°C when it starts melting. The temperature remains constant until the whole ice melts into water. On further heating, the temperature of water increases till 100°C when it starts boiling. The temperature remains constant at 100°C. The temperature of water increases only after all the water is evaporated.

We can draw a graph by taking time along x-axis and temperature of ice and water along y-axis. A curve as shown in the figure 6.9 is obtained.

Experiment to Determine the Melting Point of Ice and Boiling Point of Water

The curve ABCDE is called heating curve. BC and DE portions of the heating curve represent constant temperature at the change of state. The temperature corresponding to BC is melting point and the one corresponding to DE is boiling point.

Table 6.3 The table given below gives the melting point (M.P.) and the boiling point (B.P.) of some substances.

S. no	Substance	M.P.	B.P.
1	Water	0°C	100°C
2	Wax	60°C	–
3	Mercury	–39°C	357°C
4	Ether	–120°C	35°C
5	Glass	1127°C	–
6	Iron	1537°C	–

Latent Heat of Fusion

The amount of heat energy absorbed by a solid substance to change it into the liquid without any rise in temperature is called **latent heat of fusion**. The value of latent heat of fusion of a given solid will be different for different mass of the solid taken. If the mass of the solid is more, the latent heat of fusion is also more. To find latent heat of fusion of a solid, the latent heat required by unit mass of a substance is considered and this energy is called specific latent heat of fusion.

Specific Latent Heat of Fusion

Specific latent heat of fusion is defined as amount of heat energy required to melt one kilogram of solid at its melting point, without any rise in temperature.

Units of specific latent heat of fusion:

In C.G.S. System cal g^{-1}

In S.I. System – J kg^{-1}

Specific latent heat of ice is 3.36×10^5 J kg^{-1} (or) 336 J g^{-1} or 80 cal g^{-1}

Latent Heat of Vapourization

The amount of heat energy absorbed by a liquid to change into its gaseous state, without any rise in temperature. The latent heat of vapourization of a given liquid is determined by the amount of liquid, hence, more the mass of a liquid, more is its **latent heat of vapourization**. Thus, latent heat of vapourization of same liquid is different depending upon its mass and is determined for a definite mass of the liquid known as specific latent heat of vapourization. Thus, **specific latent heat of vapourization** is the amount of heat energy required to change unit mass of a liquid at its boiling point, without nay rise in temperature.

Units of specific latent heat of vapourization:

In C.G.S. system – cal g^{-1}

In S.I. system – J kg^{-1}

Info Bytes!

Specific latent heat of vapourization of steam is 2260 J g^{-1} or 226 × 10^4 J kg^{-1} or 540 cal g^{-1}

EXAMPLE 6.7 Calculate the mass of steam that should be passed though 60 g of water at 20°C, such that the final temperature is 40°C. (Take specific latent heat of steam is 2250 J g^{-1}).

SOLUTION

The relation to be used is

Let mass of steam be *m* gm

Heat given out by steam to form water at 100°C = $m \times 2250$ J g^{-1}

Heat given out by water at 100°C

$= m\, s_w \Delta\theta = m \times 4.2 \times (100 - 40)$

$= 252$ m J g^{-1}

Total heat given out = 2250 m + 252 m

$= 2502$ m J g^{-1}

Heat gained by water at 20°C = $60 \times 4.2 \times (40 - 20)$

= 5040 J

∴ Heat lost by a body = Heat gained by a body

2502 m = 5040

$$m = \frac{5040}{2502} = 2 \text{ g}$$

EXAMPLE 6.8 Calculate the amount of ice, which is sufficient to cool 45 g of water, contained at 30°C, such that the final temperature of the mixture is 10°C. (Take specific latent heat of fusion of ice is 336 J g^{-1}.)

SOLUTION

Let mass of ice be *m* g

Heat gained by ice to form water at 0°C = $m \times 336$ J

Heat gained by water formed from ice

$= ms\,\Delta\theta$

$= m \times 4.2 \times (10 - 0)$

= 42 m J

Total heat gained = 336 m + 42 m = 378 m J

Heat lost by water at 30°C = $ms\theta_f$

$= 45 \times 4.2 \times (30 - 10) = 3780$ J

Heat gained = Heat lost

378 m = 3780

$$m = \frac{3780}{378} = 10 \text{ g}$$

Effect of Pressure and Soluble Impurities

The melting and boiling points of a given substance change in accordance with the external pressure and presence of soluble impurities.

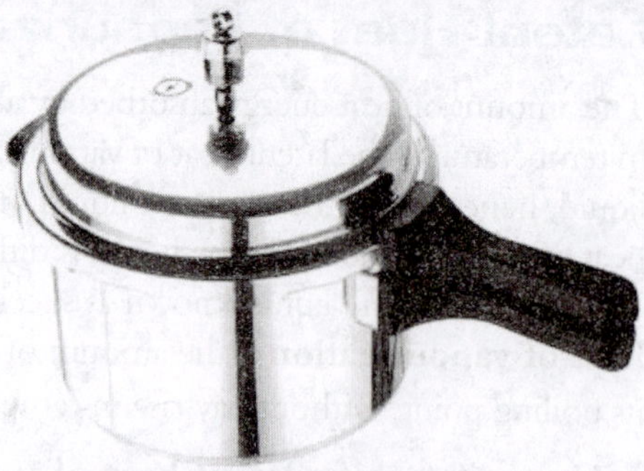

Figure 6.10 Pressure Cooker

Pressure Cooker

The time required to cook the food is greatly reduced, if the water is made to boil at a higher temperature than its boiling point, which is 100°C. The pressure cooker is used to cook food faster as it raises the boiling point of water, upto 120°C.

In a pressure cooker, the steam formed from the boiling water is not allowed to escape. The steam so formed increases the pressure inside the pressure cooker and so the water boils at a higher temperature.

A pressure cooker consists of a container and a lid, which fits firmly over the container. The container is made strong by using a thick stainless steel or aluminum. The lid is provided with a rubber gasket, weight-valve and a safety valve.

The rubber gasket does not allow the steam to go out of the container. If the steam pressure is excess, then the steam escapes through the weight-valve. If the steam pressure reaches dangerous level due to any reason, then the steam escapes through the safety valve.

At high altitude regions such as mountains, the cooking of food becomes difficult as water boils at lower temperature due to lower atmospheric pressure. The problem can be solved by using a pressure cooker.

Figure 6.11 A kid skating

MediaGroup_BestForYou. Shutterstock

Skating

Skating is a sport popular in regions covered with snow such as cold countries, Himalayan mountains, etc. In this sport, a person uses shoes with wedge shaped soles and can move over ice rapidly, with high speed. When he stands on ice, the melting point of ice lowers due to increase in pressure and it starts melting at lower temperature, thus forming water under the wedges. This way, the person moves forward rapidly and attains high speed. Once he moves forward, the ice left behind him solidifies again due to decrease in pressure.

Info Bytes!

The boiling and melting points can change if pressure is applied or if impurities are present in the substance.

POINTS TO REMEMBER

- One kilocalorie of heat energy is defined as the amount of heat energy required to raise the temperature of 1 kilogram of water through 1°C.
- The state of two bodies at the same temperature in which there is no net flow of heat energy between them is called state of thermal equilibrium.
- The amount of heat energy needed to raise the temperature of unit mass of different substances is not equal as it depends on their nature. This energy is called specific heat capacity of a substance.
- To measure human body temperature, doctors use a special thermometer, called clinical thermometer.
- If the substance is solid, the constant temperature at which the substance changes from solid state to liquid state at normal atmospheric pressure is called melting point of the given solid.
- A liquid changes into gaseous state at a constant temperature called its **boiling point**.
- The amount of heat energy absorbed by a solid substance to change it into the liquid without any rise in temperature is called latent heat of fusion.
- Specific latent heat of fusion is defined as amount of heat energy required to melt one kilogram of solid at its melting point, without any rise in temperature.
- The latent heat of vapourization of a given liquid is determined by the amount of liquid, hence, more the mass of a liquid, more is its latent heat of vapourization.
- Specific latent heat of vapourization is the amount of heat energy required to change unit mass of a liquid at its boiling point, without nay rise in temperature.

DW

CLASSROOM WING

PRACTICE QUESTIONS

Very Short Answer Type Questions

Directions for questions from 1 to 6:
Fill in the blanks.

1. The boiling point of pure water is ______°C, at normal atmospheric pressure.
2. In Galileo's thermometer, the expansion of _____ is used to measure the temperature.
3. The physical quantity which determines the direction of the flow of heat energy when two bodies are brought into contact is _____.
4. The ratio of heat capacity and specific heat capacity of a body gives its _____.
5. Specific heat capacity of water is _______J $kg^{-1}K^{-1}$.
6. 8400 J = _________ calories.

Directions for questions from 7 to 25:
Answer the following questions briefly.

7. What all may or may not happen when heat energy flows from one body to another?
8. Give three examples of each good and bad conductors of heat.
9. A piece of ice is floating in water. The temperature of both water and ice is 0° C. What will happen when the surrounding temperature is –5° C?
10. Which of the following: boling point, melting point, density; plays an important role when water is used as a coolant?
11. State the use of Six's maximum and minimum thermometer.
12. What is the specific heat capacity of water?
13. Into how many equal parts is a Fahrenheit scale divided?
14. Define melting and boiling points.
15. What is the normal human body temperature?
16. Why is the handle of a pressure cooker made of ebonite?
17. What relation is used to convert temperature in one scale to other scale?
18. If the pressure is changed, what happens to melting and boiling points of a substance?
19. Express 102°F in celsius scale of temperature.
20. The temperature of a body increases by 1°C. How much is the corresponding rise in Fahrenheit temperature?
21. What is the use of safety valve in a pressure cooker?
22. When does the temperature of a body change?
23. What is the standard temperature taken on the upper fixed point(UFP) in Celsius scale of temperature?
24. For the same rise in temperature, which expands more, alcohol or mercury?
25. Temperatures of three bodies A, B and C are 20° C, 20 K and 20° F, respectively. Which among them has the highest temperature?

Short Answer Type Questions

26. The temperature of three bodies A, B and C are increased by 1°C, 1°F and 1 K, respectively. What will be the relation between these temperatures, if these changes in temperature are represented by ΔC, ΔF and ΔK, respectively?
27. At what temperature will the centigrade (Celsius) and Fahrenheit scales have the same numerical value?
28. A body at 110°C is dropped into water at 100°C. What happens to the quantity of water in the container?

29. Find the heat energy required to boil 5 kg of water if its initial temperature is 30°C (specific heat of water is 4200 J kg^{-1} K^{-1} and boiling point is 100°C).

30. The thermal capacity of 11 kg of water is same as 120 kg of copper. If specific heat capacity of water is 4200 J kg^{-1} K^{-1}, find the specific heat capacity of copper.

31. Distinguish between heat and temperature.

32. At what temperature the reading on the Celsius scale, is half the reading on the Fahrenheit scale?

33. What will happen to a body in its solid state, when it is dropped into its liquid form (neglect the flow of heat to the surroundings)?

34. Why the difference between the day and the night temperatures high in Pokran desert?

35. How are LFP and UFP marked in a Celsius scale? Explain.

36. A faulty thermometer who's LFP is –5°C and UFP is 105°C measures a temperature as 80°C. What is the correct temperature?

37. Describe, with a neat diagram, the working of a clinical thermometer.

38. The temperature of a body 'A' is 60°C and the temperature of a body 'B' is 122°F. What will happen when they are in contact with each other?

39. 1000 cal of heat energy is supplied to 100 g of ice at 0° C. What is the final temperature of the content?

40. At what temperature is the reading on a Fahrenheit thermometer twice that on the Celsius scale?

41. Which of the following: melting point, boiling point, density; plays an important role when water is used for fermentation?

42. Why is a constriction provided in a clinical thermometer?

43. Define calorie and kilocalorie.

44. Define specific heat capacity and heat capacity.

45. What is the specific heat capacity of water?

Essay Answer Type Questions

46. Describe an experiment to determine melting point of ice and boiling point of water.

47. Explain why a constriction is provided in a clinical thermometer, considering the fact that during expansion mercury level while increasing passes through the same constriction.

48. Describe an experiment to determine melting point of wax.

49. Describe, with a neat diagram, the working of Six's maximum and minimum thermometer.

COMPETITION WING

PRACTICE QUESTIONS

Level 1: Apply your Concepts

Directions for questions 1 to 12:
State whether the following statements are true or false.

1. Heat is a form of energy.
2. Platinum is used in clinical thermometer.
3. Alcohol thermometers are preferred to a mercury thermometer in cold countries.
4. Amount of heat energy needed to raise the temperature of unit mass of a substance is called specific heat capacity.
5. 4186 J g^{-1}°C^{-1} is the specific heat capacity of water.
6. A body at 20°C is in thermal equilibrium with a body at 293K.
7. In six's maximum and minimum thermometer, the thermometric liquid is mercury.
8. Heat energy can be supplied to a substance without increasing its temperature.
9. Liquefaction is the process in which a solid changes into liquid on supply of heat.
10. When equal masses of water and iron are heated to the same change in temperature, the heat absorbed by iron is more than the heat absorbed by water.
11. A body can have a temperature −10 K.
12. If the heat energy absorbed by two identical bodies A and B is 1 calorie and 1 joule, respectively, the rise in temperature of A is greater than the rise in temperature of B.

Directions for questions 13 to 19:
Fill in the blanks.

13. If the melting point of ice at a given place is 0°C, the atmospheric pressure at that place is ______.
14. A good conductor of heat will have _____ specific heat capacity.
15. Increase in pressure _______ the melting point of ice.
16. In Six's maximum and minimum thermometer, the indices are brought down to the level of the mercury with the help of _____.
17. The iron rims are fitted to the wooden wheels of bullock carts and tongas by process of ________
18. The normal human body temperature on Fahrenheit scale is 98.4°F, then its corresponding temperature on Kelvin scale is nearly _________.
19. The average kinetic energy of the molecules of a substance _____ during the process of melting.

Directions for question 20:
Match the entries given in Column A with appropriate ones in Column B.

20. Match the statements of Column A with those of Column B

Column A	Column B
(A) Temperature	(a) form of energy
(B) Heat	(b) depends on mass
(C) Specific heat	(c) does not depend on mass
(D) Heat capacity	(d) degree of hotness

Directions for questions 21 to 47:
For each of the questions, four choices have been provided. Select the correct alternative.

21. Which of the following represents the smallest temperature change?
    (a) 1°C (b) 1°F
    (c) 1K (d) Both (a) and (c)

22. If C, F and K are the temperatures on Celsius, Fahrenheit and Kelvin scale, ΔC, ΔF and ΔK are the change in temperature in Celsius, Fahrenheit and Kelvin scale, respectively, the correct relation among the following is

(a) $\frac{C}{5}=\frac{F}{9}=\frac{K-273}{5}$

(b) $\frac{\Delta C}{5}=\frac{\Delta F}{9}=\frac{\Delta K}{5}$

(c) $\frac{\Delta C}{5}=\frac{\Delta F-32}{9}=\frac{\Delta K-273}{5}$

(d) $\frac{C}{5}=\frac{F}{9}=\frac{K}{5}$

23. The degree of hotness or coldness of a body is called its

(a) heat capacity

(b) temperature

(c) latent heat capacity

(d) None of these

24. When equal amount of heat is supplied to two different substances A and B, the rise in temperature with time is graphically represented as follows.

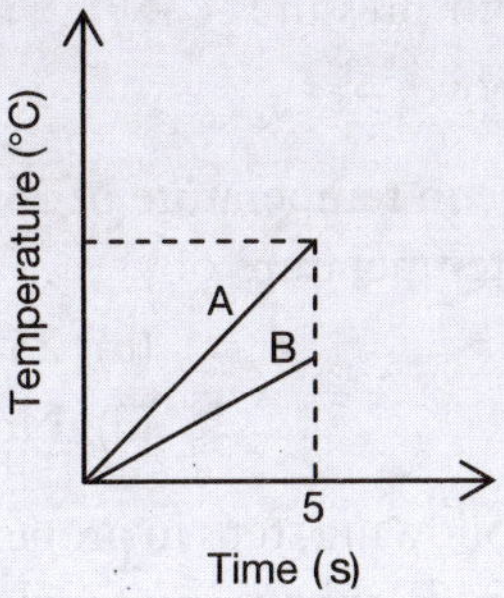

Choose the correct statement.

(a) If masses of A and B are equal, specific heat of A is equal to specific heat of B.

(b) If mass of A is greater than mass of B the specific heat capacity of A is greater than the specific heat capacity of B.

(c) Heat capacity of A is less than heat capacity of B.

(d) None of these

25. For a certain engineering application, it is required to rise the temperature of a given mass of a body as quickly as possible. The material should have

(a) high specific heat capacity.

(b) high density.

(c) low specific heat capacity.

(d) heat capacity.

26. The specific heat capacity of water is ______.

(a) 1 cal $g^{-1}°C^{-1}$

(b) 4186 J $g^{-1}°C^{-1}$

(c) 4186 kJ kg^{-1} K^{-1}

(d) All the above

27. Under normal conditions, naphthalene changes its state from ______.

(a) solid to liquid

(b) liquid to gas

(c) liquid to solid

(d) solid to gas

28. The distance between the LFP and UFP of a thermometer is 18 cm. The reading on the thermometer in Fahrenheit scale when the length of the mercury thread is 8 cm is ______.

(a) 212°F (b) 112°F

(c) 80°F (d) 180°F

29. A: At high altitude regions the cooking of food becomes difficult.

B: Water boils at lower temperature when the pressure is low.

(a) Both A and B are wrong.

(b) A and B are correct and B is not the correct explanation of A.

(c) A and B are correct and B is the correct explanation of A.

(d) A is correct but B is wrong.

30. The change in temperature of a body is 20°C, then the change in temperature on Kelvin scale is

(a) 293 K (b) 25 K

(c) 20 K (d) 253 K

31. In the process of boiling,

(a) kinetic and potential energy of water molecules increase.

(b) kinetic energy of molecules increases and potential energy of molecules decreases.

(c) potential energy of molecules increases and kinetic energy of molecules remains same.

(d) kinetic energy of molecules increases and potential energy of molecules remains the same.

32. When the pressure is increased,
(a) melting point of ice decreases and boiling point of water increases.
(b) melting point of ice and boiling point of water decreases.
(c) melting point of ice and boiling point of water increases.
(d) melting point of ice increases and boiling point of water decreases.

33. Food in the pressure cooker is cooked faster, as
(a) the boiling point increases due to an increase in pressure.
(b) the boiling point decreases due to an increase in pressure.
(c) more steam is available at 100°C.
(d) more pressure is available at 100°C.

34. Given that the ratio of specific heat capacity of alcohol to that of water is 13 : 25, which of the following statements is true?
A: When temperature is raised through 1°C the heat energy absorbed by 2 kg of alcohol is less than the heat energy absorbed by 1 kg of water.
B: Heat capacity of 2 kg alcohol is more than the heat capacity of 1 kg water.
(a) A is true and B is false.
(b) A and B are true.
(c) A is false and B is true.
(d) A and B are false.

35. –40°C is numerically equal to
(a) –40°F (b) 233 K
(c) −32°R (d) All the above

36. Which of the following properties are suitable for making cooking utensils?
(a) High specific heat and high conductivity.
(b) Low specific heat and low conductivity.
(c) High specific heat and low conductivity.
(d) Low specific heat and high conductivity.

37. The advantage of alcohol as thermometric liquid is due to its
(a) low-boiling point. (b) low-freezing point.
(c) high-vapour pressure. (d) All the above

38. The temperature at which molecular movement of matter ceases is called ________.
(a) normal temperature
(b) zero kelvin
(c) abnormal temperature
(d) None of these

39. Gas thermometers are more sensitive as compared to liquid thermometers, as their
(a) coefficient of expansion is very high.
(b) coefficient of expansion is very low.
(c) density is very high.
(d) None of these.

40. Which among the following is the hottest substance?
(a) Water at 100 °C.
(b) Steam at 100 °C.
(c) Mercury at 100 °C.
(d) All the above are equally hot.

41. Mercury is used as thermometer liquid. Which among the following properties of mercury is used in this?
(a) Low specific heat capacity
(b) High boiling point and low melting point
(c) Low vapour pressure
(d) All the above

42. The difference in temperature of 25 °F is equal to the difference in temperature of
(a) 25 °C (b) 25 K
(c) 25 °R (d) None of these

43. Arrange the following steps in proper sequence for the construction and calibration of Celsius thermometer.
(A) Lower fixing point is marked by immersing the bulb of the thermometer in melting ice taken in a funnel.
(B) The distance between the two fixed points is called fundamental interval. It is divided into 100 equal divisions in Celsius scale.
(C) Take a thick walled capillary tube with thin walled glass bulb and fill it with mercury with the help of a funnel.
(D) Mark the upper fixing point with the help of hypsometer.

(E) Place the glass bulb in a hot oil bath while filling the mercury to remove the air bubbles.

(a) C A D E B (b) C E A D B
(c) C E A B D (d) C D B E A

44. Arrange the following substances in the increasing order of their specific heat capacities.

(A) 100 cal heat is required to change the temperature of 10 g of a substance from 10°C to 20 °C.

(B) 200 cal heat is required to change the temperature of 5 g of a substance from 200 K to 230 K.

(C) 420 joule of heat is required to change the temperature of a substance of mass 50 g from 0°C to 5 °C.

(a) ABC (b) CBA
(c) BCA (d) CAB

45. **Assertion (A):** Cooking becomes difficult on the top of a mountain.

Reason (R): At higher altitude, the pressure is less, and hence, the boiling point of water decreases with altitude.

(a) A and R both are correct, and R is correct explanation of A.

(b) A and R both are correct, and R is incorrect explanation of A.

(c) A is correct but R is incorrect.

(d) A is incorrect but R is correct.

46. **Assertion (A):** The sea and land breezes are formed due to the convection current of air.

Reason: During the daytime, sea water gets heated faster than land.

(a) A and R both are correct, and R is correct explanation of A.

(b) A and R both are correct, and R is incorrect explanation of A.

(c) A is correct but R is incorrect.

(d) A is incorrect but R is correct.

47. **Assertion:** If the humidity is high, the chance of rainfall is high.

Reason: If humidity is high, water vapour will condense to form rain.

(a) A and R both are correct, and R is correct explanation of A.

(b) A and R both are correct, and R is incorrect explanation of A.

(c) A is correct but R is incorrect.

(d) A is incorrect but R is correct.

Level 2: Review your Concepts

48. The density of two spheres of equal radius are in the ratio 1 : 3 and their specific heat capacities in the ratio 2 : 1. What is the ratio of their heat capacities?

49. The total distance between the lower fixed point and the upper fixed point of a thermometer is 12 cm. When this thermometer is placed in a vessel containing 500 g water the reading on the scale was 3 cm. When 10 lead shots at 100°C were dropped into this container the mercury level in the thermometer rose to 31 mm. Find the average heat capacity of the lead shots. (you may leave the answer as a fraction). Specific heat capacity of water = 4.2 kJ kg^{-1} K^{-1}

50. When the mercury thread rises to 3/4th of the distance between the two fixed points, what is the temperature indicated by the Fahrenheit scale?

51. On a certain scale of temperature, the freezing and boiling points of water are marked as 20 and 180 degrees, respectively. What is the temperature of a patient suffering with a high fever of 104°F on that scale?

52. Two cylindrical bodies '*A*' and '*B*' have their radii in the ratio of 1 : 2 and their lengths are in the ratio of 3 : 2. When equal amount of heat energy is supplied to them, the rise in the temperature of *A* is found to be double the rise in temperature of *B*. Determine the ratio of their specific heat capacity. The ratio of density of *A* and *B* is 3 : 1.

53. The rate at which ice melts is more at the top when compared to the bottom of the glacier. Explain whether the statement is true or false.

54. The density of two identical spheres are in the ratio 2 : 3 and their specific heat capacities in the ratio 4 : 5. What is the ratio of their heat capacities?

55. In a new scale of temperature the lower fixed point is marked as 0 corresponding to the melting point of a substance which is equal to 25°C and the upper fixed point is marked corresponding to the boiling point of a substance which is equal to 175°C. The total length of the scale between the UFP and LFP is divided into

200 equal parts. Determine the temperature in the new scale when the temperature of a substance measured by a celsius scale thermometer is 50°C.

56. How is water useful in the protection of fruits and vegetables from damage during storage at sub zero temperature?

57. Two substances *P* and *Q* are heated by using similar heating devices. The mass of *P* and *Q* are 100 g and 75 g, respectively. The initial temperature of P is 35°C whereas the initial temperature of *Q* is 25°C. If the temperature of the substance '*P*' is increased to 75°C in 40 minutes, determine the time required to raise the temperature of *Q* to the same value. The specific heat capacity of *P* and *Q* are 0.9 cal g°C^{-1} and 0.6 cal g°C^{-1}, respectively.

58. Why is salt sprinkled under ice cube trays in a refrigerator?

59. The temperature of a body is measured in Kelvin scale, Fahrenheit scale and Celsius scale. Which among them is a more accurate reading? Explain.

60. Arrange the following substances in the increasing order of their heat capacity.

Substance	Mass	Initial temperature	Final temperature	Heat energy absorbed
a	10 g	5° C	10° C	100 cal
b	20 g	20° C	50° C	200 cal
c	30 g	40° C	50° C	400 cal

61. A new scale of temperature is introduced. One degree temperature difference on the new scale is found to be equal to $\frac{5}{8}$ °C. Determine the temperature in Celsius scale when the new scale and the Celsius scale shows the same reading. The lower fixed point on the new scale is 33° degrees.

62. Convert 55 °C into Fahrenheit and Kelvin scales.

63. Three metallic spheres *A*, *B* and *C* have their masses in the ratio 1 : 2 : 3, specific heat capacities in the ratio 6:3:4. When the initial temperatures of the spheres are measured in Celsius scale, the ratio of their temperature is found to be 1 : 2 : 3. Initially the two spheres *A* and *B* are brought into contact. When equilibrium temperature is attained, sphere *B* is brought into contact with '*C*'. Determine the ratio of the final temperatures of *A*, *B* and *C* as measured in Celsius scale.

64. If 3360 J of heat is required to melt 10 g of ice, how many kilocalories of heat should be supplied to melt 1 kg ice?

65. Find the amount of heat energy required to convert 100 g of ice at –10 °C into steam at 120 °C.

(Take S_{ice} = 0.5 cal g^{-1} °C^{-1}, S_w = 1 cal g^{-1} °C^{-1}, S_{steam} = 0.5 cal g^{-1} °C^{-1}, L_f = 80 cal g^{-1}, L_v = 540 cal g^{-1})

66. Which of the following statement/statements are correct?

(A) The melting point of all substances decreases with increase in pressure

(B) The boiling point of water increases with the addition of impurities

Level 3: Assess Your Concepts

67. 15 g of water at 100° C is mixed with 15 g of ice at 0° C. What is the temperature of the mixture?

68. Two containers *X* and *Y* are filled with water at different temperatures. When 10 g of water from container *X* is mixed with 20 g of water from container *Y*, the resultant temperature is found to be 20°C. When 20 g of water from container *X* is mixed with 10 g of water from container *Y*, the resultant temperature is found to be 30°C. Determine the initial temperature of water in containers *X* and *Y*.

69. A 200 W water heater is used to heat 1000 g of water. The heater is switched ON for 4.2 minutes and the initial temperature of water is 35°C, then the final temperature of water is ________.

70. When two heating devices are used to heat two different substances *A* and *B* the heat absorbed by *A* after 2 seconds is found to be equal to the heat absorbed by *B* after 3 seconds. The rise in temperature of *A* after 5 seconds is found to be equal to the rise in temperature of *B* after 6 seconds. If the ratio of masses of *A* and *B* is 1 : 2, determine the ratio of the specific heat capacities of two substances.

71. Ice cubes at 0° each of mass 200 g are dropped one after the other into 2 kg water at 30°C in such a away that after the first one melts completely, the second one is dropped. If the heat energy required to melt 1 g of ice is 80 cal, determine the maximum number of ice cubes that can be dropped into the water such that no ice is left in the water without melting.

72. If specific heat capacity of mercury is 0.033 cal g^{-1} $°C^{-1}$, how much heat is gained by 0.05 kg of mercury when its temperature rises from 68 ° F to 313 K?

73. The heat capacity of a vessel is 300 cal $°C^{-1}$ and the heat capacity of water contained in the vessel is also 300 cal $°C^{-1}$. How much heat (in joules) is required to raise the temperature of water in the vessel by 126 °F?

74. A new scale of temperature called TIME is introduced. The reading on the new scale is twice the reading on a Celsius scale when the temperature of a certain body is 373 K. The reading on a Fahrenheit scale is found to be (17/15) th the reading on TIME scale when the temperature of a body is 20 °C. Determine the upper fixed point and lower fixed point of the TIME scale.

75. Two thermometers *A* and *B* are calibrated in different scales. When both the thermometers are placed in a container filled with hot water the mercury thread in the thermometer *A* has moved through divisions whereas the mercury thread in thermometer B has moved though 15 divisions. The reading on thermometers *A* and *B* are 20° and 40°, respectively. If the lower fixed point of the thermometer *A* is 0°, determine the lower fixed point of the thermometer *B*.

76. Two bodies of different metals *A* and *B* having an equal mass are given equal quantities of heat. Given that the molecular weight of *A* is greater than that of *B*, compare the specific heat capacities of the two metals. (Note that the rise in temperature is a measure of the increase in the average kinetic energy of the molecules).

77. Two spheres made of iron and copper, having 1 kg mass each are at room temperature of 25 °C. Both the spheres are heated so that they attain a temperature of 100 °C each. Is the heat energy supplied to both the spheres, the same? If not, what is the difference in the heat energies supplied to them? Specific heat capacity value of iron and copper is 0.45 J g^{-1}° C^{-1} and 0.385 J g^{-1} $°C^{-1}$ respectively.

78. A liquid 'X' of mass 225 g at 80 °C is cooled to 20 °C, when it radiates out 10800 J of heat energy. Find the specific heat capacity of the liquid.

79. The lower and upper fixed points of a faulty thermometer are –4° and 102° respectively. If the reading is 50° on this thermometer, find the correct temperature on the Celsius scale and Fahrenheit scale.

80. A lady kept 10 g of ice at –5 °C in her hand. She observed that 2 g of ice is melted at the end of 3 minute. Find the heat lost by her hand. [Take L_{Ice} = 80 cal g^{-1}, s_{Ice} = 0.5 cal g^{-1} $°C^{-1}$]

81. The amount of heat energy gained by a body of mass 200 g while sliding on a surface varies as $Q = k\,f\,t^2$, where Q, f, t are heat in joule, frictional force opposing the motion of the body in newton and time in second respectively. Find the change in the temperature of the body from 3 s to 8 s, if frictional force is 2 newton and specific heat capacity of the body is 0.12 J g^{-1} $°C^{-1}$.
(Take the value of proportionality constant, $k = 6\ m/s^2$).

AT

JEE-NEET SPECIAL WING

PRACTICE QUESTIONS

Multiple-Answer Type Questions

***Directions for questions 1 to 5:* Select one or more correct alternative(s) from the given choices.**

1. The specific latent heat of vaporisation of steam is

(a) 2260 J g^{-1}

(b) 540 Cal g^{-1}

(c) 226×10^5 J kg^{-1}

(d) 2.26×10^6 J kg^{-1}

2. The normal human body temperature is

(a) 98.4° C (b) 98.4° F

(c) 37° C (d) 37° F

3. The portions of heating curve that represents constant temperature are

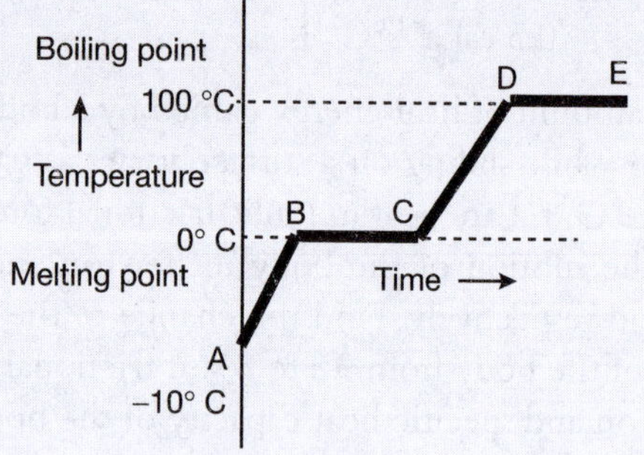

(a) AB

(b) BC

(c) CD

(d) DE

4. The scale in clinical thermometer is marked as

(a) 92° F to 100° F

(b) 95° F to 110° F

(c) 35° C to 43° C

(d) 33° C to 38° C

5. Identify the correct relation.

(a) $\dfrac{C-0}{100-0}=\dfrac{F-32}{212-32}$

(b) $\dfrac{C}{5}=\dfrac{F-32}{9}$

(c) $\dfrac{C-0}{212-32}=\dfrac{F-32}{100-0}$

(d) $\dfrac{C}{180}=\dfrac{F-32}{100}$

Comprehension-Based Questions

***Directions for questions 6 to 10:* These questions are based on the following information.**

Heat Capacity and Specific Heat Capacity

Thermal capacity or heat capacity is a property of matter which is defined as the amount of heat required to raise the temperature of a given mass by one degree Celsius. If E is the amount of heat energy supplied and T is the corresponding change in the temperature then,

Heat capacity (c) $=\dfrac{E}{T}$

Heat capacity and specific heat capacity convey different notion as the former depends on the mass of substance whereas the latter does not depend on it.

6. The liquid with the highest specific heat capacity is

(a) Alcohol

(b) Milk

(c) Kerosene

(d) Water

7. As the mass of the material increases, the heat capacity
   (a) increases
   (b) decreases
   (c) remains unaffected
   (d) cannot be determined.

8. If m is the mass and s is the specific heat capacity, then heat capacity (c) is given by
   (a) $c = m \times s \times \Delta\theta$
   (b) $c = m \times s$
   (c) $c = \dfrac{m \times s}{\Delta\theta}$
   (d) $c \times \Delta\theta = m \times s$

9. Water is used as coolant in automobile engines due to
   (a) its high melting point.
   (b) its high boiling point
   (c) its high specific heat capacity
   (d) its cohesive and adhesive properties

10. The specific heat capacity of lead is given as 130 J g^{-1} °C^{-1}. Its heat capacity for 70 kg lead is found to be (in k J k^{-1})
    (a) 7200
    (b) 8700
    (c) 9100
    (d) 9700

Directions for questions 11 to 15: **These questions are based on the following information.**

Change of State

A physical change in the state of matter is referred to as the change of state. These changes are reversible and does not alter the chemical composition of matter. Once energy is added or removed from a substance it will affect the way the particles interact with one another that results in the change in state.

11. The state of any substance can be changed by
    (a) Heating
    (b) Cooling
    (c) Either heating or cooling
    (d) Neither heating nor cooling

12. The constant temperature at which a substance changes from solid to liquid state at normal atmospheric pressure is
    (a) Melting point
    (b) Boiling point
    (c) Atmospheric temperature
    (d) at 60° C

13. The figure below shows the heating curve of water. The temperature corresponding to BC is

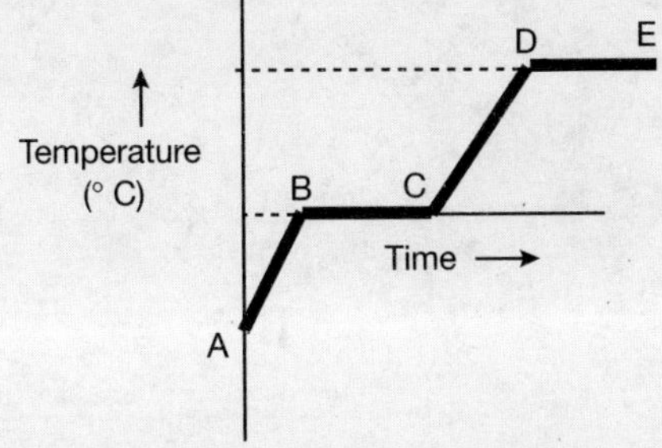

    (a) Melting point (b) Boiling point
    (c) Triple point (d) UPF

14. The amount of heat energy required to melt one kilogram of solid at its melting point, without any rise in temperature is
    (a) Latent heat of vaporisation.
    (b) Specific latent heat of vaporisation.
    (c) Latent heat if fusion.
    (d) Specific latent heat of fusion:

15. The S. I. unit of specific latent heat of vaporisation is
    (a) J kg^{-1}
    (b) cal g^{-1}
    (c) J g^{-1}
    (d) cal kg^{-1}

Match the Column

Directions for question 16: **The question is based on the following information.**

Thermometer

The device that measures temperature or temperature gradient of a given body accurately is a thermometer. The working of liquid thermometer is based on the principle that a liquid expands on heating and contracts on cooling. It has two important elements; a sensor that sense the change in temperature and some means to convert this change into magnitude. A thermometer can measure the temperature of solid (like food), a liquid (like water) or a gas (like air).

16. Match the values in List - I with those in List - II:

List - I	List - II
A. UFP	a. 95° F to 110° F
B. LFP	b. Thermoscope
C. Clinical thermometer	c. Boiling point of pure water
D. Galileo's' thermometer	d. U tube filled with mercury
E. Six's maximum and minimum thermometer	e. Melting point of ice

(a) A - e, B - d, C - b, D - c, E - a

(b) A - b, B - c, C - e, D - a, E - d

(c) A - c, B - e, C - a, D - b, E - d

(d) A - a, B - c, C - b, D - d, E – e

ANSWER KEYS

Crossword

Across

4. Zero
5. Latent heat
6. Alcohol
7. Temperature
9. Joule

Down

1. Heat Capacity
2. One
3. Kelvin
8. Eighty

Classroom Wing

Very Short Answer Type Questions

1. 100
2. Gas
3. Temperature
4. Mass
5. 4200
6. 2000
12. 1 cal $g^{-1}°C^{-1}$
19. 38.9°C
20. 1.8

Short Answer Type Questions

30. 385 J Kg^{-1} K^{-1}
32. 320°F
36. 77.27°C
39. 0°C

Competition Wing

Level 1: Apply your Concepts

1. True
2. False
3. True
4. True
5. True
6. True
7. False
8. True
9. False
10. False
11. False
12. True
13. 76 cm of Hg
14. Low
15. Decreases
16. Magnet
17. Thermal expansion
18. 310 K
19. Remains same
20. A : d, B : a, C : c, D : b
22. (b)
23. (b)
24. (c)
25. (c)
26. (a)
27. (d)
28. (b)
29. (c)
30. (c)
31. (c)
32. (a)
33. (a)
34. (c)
35. (a)
36. (d)
37. (b)
38. (b)
39. (a)
40. (d)
41. (d)
42. (d)
43. (b)
44. (b)
45. (a)
46. (c)
47. (a)

Level 2: Review your Concepts

60. BAC
62. $F = 131°F$, 328K
63. 3 : 5 : 5
64. 80 kcal
65. 73,500 cal
66. (b)

Level 3: Assess Your Concepts

67. 10°C
69. 47°C
71. 3.75 ice cubes
72. 33 cal
73. 176.4 kJ
75. 10°
77. 4875 J
78. 0.8 J g^{-1} $°C^{-1}$
79. 123.8°F
80. 185 cal
81. 27.5 °C

JEE-NEET Special Wing

Multiple-Answer Type Questions

1. (a) and (b)
2. (b) and (c)
3. (b) and (d)
4. (b) and (c)
5. (a) and (b)

Comprehension-Based Questions

6. (d)
7. (a)
8. (b)
9. (c)
10. (c)
11. (c)
12. (b)
13. (a)
14. (d)
15. (a)

Match the Column

16. (c)

For answer key of Classroom wing and Competition wing, refer to Hints and Solutions

Hints and Explanations

Classroom Wing

Very Short Answer Type Questions

1. 100
2. Gas
3. Temperature
4. Mass
5. 4200
6. 2000
7. During the flow of heat energy, temperature may not always change and the substance may not always change its state. Physical contact is not required for the flow of contact by radiation.
8. Copper, silver and aluminium are good conductors of heat while wood, cork and paper are bad conductors.
9. As the surrounding temperature is less than 0°C water converts to ice.
10. The high specific heat capacity is an important property.
11. Automatically records the maximum and minimum temperature of the day.
12. Specific heat capacity of water is 1 cal $g^{-1}°C^{-1}$
13. 180
14. A constant temperature at which liquid changes into gaseous state—boiling point. A constant temperature at which solid changes into liquid state—melting point
15. 98.4°F
16. Ebonite is a bad conductor of heat.
17. $\dfrac{S - LFP}{UFP - LFP}$
18. Increase in pressure, decreases melting point. Increase in pressure, increases boiling point.
19. $\dfrac{C}{5} = \dfrac{F - 32}{9}$

    F = 102

    $\dfrac{C}{5} = \dfrac{102 - 32}{9} = \Rightarrow \dfrac{C}{5} = \dfrac{70}{9}$

    $c = \dfrac{5 \times 70}{9} = 38.9°C$
20. 1.8
21. If the stream pressure reaches very high level, then it escapes through safety-valve.
22. Temperature can also change when the heat flows in the form of radiation.
23. Boiling point of pure water
24. Alcohol
25. At the ice point, the Celsius scale has the lowest reading (0° C), hence, 20° C is the highest temperature.

Short Answer Type Questions

Note: This is how you should frame your answer covering.

26. The number of divisions in the Celsius and Kelvin scales are the same and are the highest in the Fahrenheit scale. Hence, the $\Delta C = \Delta K > \Delta F$
27. –40 degrees.
28. As the temperature of the substance is 110°C, some amount of water evaporates.
29. $Q = mc\Delta\theta$
30. $m_w \; s_w = m_c s_c$ Specific heat capacity of copper $= 385 \text{ J Kg}^{-1} \text{K}^{-1}$
31. Heat

    (i) A cause

    (ii) Measured using calorimeter

    (iii) Unit is joule or calorie

    (iv) Sum of P.E. and K.E. of molecules of a substance

    Temperature

    (i) The effect

    (ii) Measured using temperature

    (iii) S.I. unit – kelvin

    (iv) Average kinetic energy of the molecules.
32. 320°F
33. If their temperature is the same, heat flows from one to another. If the temperature of the solid form is greater than that of the liquid form, it may melt.

34. The main reasons for the temperature fluctuations between day and night are the lack of humidity and cloud cover. Because of water's relatively high specific heat, humid air takes longer to warm or cool, while drier air warms or cools more quickly. Because desert areas receive a large amount of sunlight, the temperatures can get very high, but when the sun is no longer providing heat, the dry air cools quickly. The lack of cloud cover overhead allows the warmer air to rise into the atmosphere while cooler air settles in its place.

35. (i) LFP–Melting point of ice
(ii) UFP–Boiling point of pure water
(iii) LFP–0°C
(iv) UFP–100°C
(v) Divided into 100 equal parts between 0 to 100.
(vi) Each equal part corresponds to 1°C.

36. $\left(\dfrac{S-LFP}{UFP-LFP}\right)_{\text{Correct scale}} = \left(\dfrac{S-LFP}{UFP-LFP}\right)_{\text{Incorrect scale}}$

$\dfrac{S-0}{100-0} = \dfrac{80-(-5)}{105-(-5)}$ or $\dfrac{S}{100} = \dfrac{85}{110}$ or $S = 77.27°C$

37. (i) Scale is marked from 95°F to 110°F
(ii) Normal human body temperature marked with red arrow.
(iii) A constriction near the bulb.
(iv) Prevents the mercury thread to flow back into the bulb.
(v) Records temperature accurately by the doctor.
(vi) For next reading given a jerk so that the mercury in the tube falls back into the bulb.

38. $\dfrac{122-32}{180} = \dfrac{C-0}{100}$

$C = 50°C$

Temperature of A = 60°C and that of B = 50°C

Hence, heat flows from A to B.

39. $Q = m\,L$

$Q = 100 \cdot 80 = 8000$

To melt the ice, 8000 cal of heat is required.

Therefore, the resultant temperature is 0°C

40. $\dfrac{C}{5} = \dfrac{F-32}{9}$

41. Water is used for fermentation as it has a high specific heat capacity.

42. To prevent the mercury thread to flow back into the bulb for accurate reading of the temperature.

43. Amount of heat energy required to raise the temperature of 1 gram of water though 1°C.

1 kcal = 1000 cal

44. Amount of heat energy needed to raise the temperature of unit mass of a substance. Amount of heat energy absorbed for 1°C rise in temperature of a substance.

45. 1 cal $g^{-1}°C^{-1}$ or 4186 J $g^{-1}°C^{-1}$

Essay Answer Type Questions

Note: This is how you should frame your answer covering.

46. (i) U-tube, with bulb on one side
(ii) Alcohol and mercury
(iii) Iron indices

47. The constriction prevents the mercury thread to flow back into the bulb so that the doctor can read the temperature accurately at his convenience .

48. (i) Ice cubes in water in a beaker
(ii) Tripod stand and burner
(iii) Thermometer

49. (i) Wax in beaker
(ii) Tripod stand and Bunsen burner
(iii) Thermometer

Competition Wing

Level 1: Apply your Concepts

20. Temperature is the measure of hotness or coldness

 A → d

 Heat is a form of energy

 B → a

 Specific heat capacity does not depend on mass.

 C → c

 Heat capacity depends on mass.

 D → b

36. Low specific heat and high conductivity are the properties which are suitable for making utensils.

 Hence, the correct answer is (d).

37. Because of its low freezing point (–130 °C), it can be used to record very low temperatures.

 Hence, the correct answer is (b).

38. The temperature at which molecular movement of matter ceases is called absolute zero or zero kelvin (0 K).

 Hence, the correct answer is (b).

39. Gas thermometers are more sensitive as compared to liquid thermometers, due to their large cubical expansion.

 Hence, the correct answer is (a).

40. The degree of hotness or coldness depends on the temperature.

 As all the substances have the same temperature all the three substances are equally hot.

 Hence, the correct answer is (d).

41. All the properties mentioned are favourable for the choice of a thermometer liquid.

 Hence, the correct answer is (d).

42. The number of divisions on Fahrenheit scale is not equal to the number of divisions on any one of the given scales.

 Hence, the correct answer is (d).

43. The construction and calibration of a Celsius thermometer involves the following steps. Take a thick walled capillary tube with thin walled glass bulb and fill the bulb with mercury using a funnel (C) from one end and while filling it with the mercury place the glass bulb in a hot oil bath to remove the air bubbles (E), now mark the lower fixing point by placing the bulb in melting ice taken in a funnel (A). Mark the upper fixing point with the help of hypsometer (D).

 The distance between the two fixed points is called fundamental interval. In Celsius scale, the fundamental interval is divided into 100 equal divisions and it is calibrated (B).

 Hence, the correct answer is (b).

44. (A) $100 = 10 \cdot s \cdot 10$

 $s = 1 \text{ cal g}^{-1}{}^\circ\text{C}^{-1}$

 (B) $200 = 5 \times s \cdot 30$

 $s = \frac{200}{150} = \frac{4}{3} = \text{ cal g}^{-1}{}^\circ\text{C}^{-1}$

 (C) $\frac{420}{4.2} = 50 \cdot s \cdot 5$

 $s = \frac{100}{250} = \frac{2}{5} \text{ cal g}^{-1}{}^\circ\text{C}^{-1}$

 The increasing order is CBA.

 Hence, the correct answer is (b).

45. At the top of a mountain, cooking is difficult as the pressure is less there.

 Hence, the correct answer is (a).

46. Sea and land breezes are due to the convection current of air. This is because during day time, land gets heated faster and during night land gets cooled faster.

 Hence, the correct answer is (c).

47. If humidity is high, water vapour condenses resulting into rainfall.

 Hence, the correct answer is (a).

Level 2: Review your Concepts

Note: This is how you should frame your answer covering.

48. (1) $c = ms$

 (2) Express mass in terms of density and volume of the sphere.

49. 12 cm = 100°C

 3 cm = x°C

 31 mm= y°C

 Find x and y.

 Rise in temperature of water = 1 mm = $(y - x)$ K

 Heat gained/lost, $Q = m \times s \times \Delta\theta$

 Heat capacity $H = m \times s$

 $\therefore$ Heat lost by the hot body $= H \times \Delta\theta_{\text{lead shots}}$

 $= H\,(100 - y)$

Calculate the heat gained by the cold water. Let this be Q

Find, $H = \dfrac{Q}{100 - y}$

If N is the number of lead shots,

Average heat capacity $= \dfrac{Q}{N\ (100 - y)}$

50. Consider the length of mercury thread between the two fixed points as 'ℓ'.

Then, $\ell = \Delta F = 180°F$ (1)

Find $\frac{3}{4}\ell$ by multiplying $\frac{3}{4}$ with 180°F. (2)

Here, LFP for Fahrenheit scale is 32°F. So, add 32°F to the answer obtained in the equation (2).

This becomes the temperature indicated by the Fahrenheit scale when the mercury thread rises to (3/4) th of the distance between its two fixed points.

51. What are the LFP and UFP for Fahrenheit scale?

Now for given scale of temperature, take LFP and UFP as 20° and 180°.

Then, take corresponding temperature of 104° F as 'T' in the given scale.

Find the value of 'T' from the formula,

$$\frac{\text{T} - \text{LFP}}{\text{UFP} - \text{LFP}} = \text{constant}$$

52. Compare the heat absorbed by A and B.

$Q = m\ s\ \Delta t$

But mass = density × volume

And volume = length × area of cross section.

53. Where does the weight of the glacier act?

Is the pressure at the bottom of the glacier more than at any other part of the glacier?

How does the pressure variation affect the melting point of the ice?

When pressure increases, does the M.P. of the ice come down below 0°C, or does it increase?

54. The ratio of heat capacities of two given spheres is

$$\frac{H_1}{H_2} = \frac{m_1 s_1}{m_2 s_2} \quad (1)$$

The ratio of their specific heat capacities and densities are given.

If given spheres are identical, then the ratio of their volumes is 1 : 1.

Here, mass of a sphere = (volume of the sphere) (density of the sphere)

Therefore, $\dfrac{m_1}{m_2} = \dfrac{V_1 d_1}{V_2 d_2}$ (2)

Substitute the values of $\dfrac{H_1}{H_2}$ and $\dfrac{H_1}{H_2}$ in (1), and obtain the value of $\dfrac{H_1}{H_2}$.

55. In the new scale of temperature,

The lower fixed Point (LFP) = Melting Point of a substance = 0 units = 25°C

The upper fixed Point (LFP) = Boiling Point of a substance = 175°C

The total length of the new scale = 200 units

Find out 50°C = how many units in new scale?

56. At subzero temperature, does water convert into ice by loosing heat energy equal to its latent heat of fusion? What role does the specific heat capacity of water play? Find the amount of (heat energy) latent heat of fusion. Can this energy be used to protect the fruits and vegetables from freezing temperatures?

57. $Q = ms\Delta t$

Determine the heat energy required to increase the temperature through the given value for both the substances.

Also determine the heat energy produced by the heating device per minute.

Determine the time taken to produce the required amount of heat energy in the case of the substance Q.

58. Ice forms when the temperature of water reaches 32°Fahrenheit (0 degrees Celsius). When you add salt, that temperature drops: A 10% salt solution freezes at 20°F (-6°C), and a 20% solution freezes at 2°F (-16°C). This means that if you sprinkle salt on the ice, you can melt it. The salt dissolves into the liquid water in the ice and lowers its freezing point and it melts quickly. So, if you freeze salt water it would remain cold for a longer time as its temperature is much lower than frozen normal water.

59. Construct your answer on the fact that number of divisions between LFP and UFP in Fahrenheit scale is 180 which is more than that on Kelvin or Celcius scale.

60. (A) $C = \frac{Q}{\Delta t} = \frac{100}{5} = 20 \text{ cal°C}^{-1}$

(B) $C = \frac{200}{30} = \frac{20}{3} \text{ cal°C}^{-1}$

(C) $C = \frac{400}{10} = 40 \text{ cal°C}^{-1}$

∴ The increasing order is BAC

61. We can begin to build one, assuming from the fact that that on new scale,

One degree temperature difference = 5/8°C

Lower Fixed Point (LFP) on new scale= 33 degrees

Find least count and then,

Find temperature in new scale = temperature on Celsius Scale

62. $\frac{55-0}{100} = \frac{F-32}{180}$

$F = 131$ °F

$\frac{55-0}{100} = \frac{K-273}{100}$

$K = 273 + 55 = 328\text{K}$

63. Let the masses of A, B and C be m, $2m$ and $3m$ the specifi c heat capacities be 6s, 3s and 4s, and the initial temperatures be t, $2t$ and $3t$.

Since the temperature of A is less than the temperature of B, heat flows from B to A when these two are brought into contact.

If θ_1 is the equilibrium temperature, $t < \theta_1 < 2t$

Heat lost by hot body = heat gained by cold body

$$\therefore (2m)(3s)(2t - \theta_1) = (m)(6s)(\theta_1 - t)$$

$$6(2t - \theta_1) = 6(\theta_1 - t)$$

$$2\theta_1 = 3t$$

$$\theta_1 = \frac{3t}{2}$$

(You may observe here that since $m_1s_1 = m_2s_2$, $\Delta t_1 = \Delta t_2$ and θ_1 is the average of t and $2t$)

Thus, $t_A = t_B = \frac{3t}{2}$

When B and C are brought into contact the equilibrium temperature θ_2 will be greater than that of B $\left(= \frac{3t}{2}\right)$ and less than that of C (= 3t)

Once again heat lost by hot body (C) = heat gained by cold body (B)

I,e., $(3m)(4s)(3t - \theta_2) = (2m)(3s)\left(\theta_2 - \frac{3t}{2}\right)$

$$2(3t - \theta_2) = \left(\theta_2 - \frac{3t}{2}\right)$$

$$3\theta_2 = 6t + \frac{3t}{2}$$

$$\theta_2 = \frac{5t}{2}$$

$$\text{i.e., } t_B = t_C = \frac{5t}{2}$$

$$\therefore t_A : t_B : t_C = \frac{3t}{2} : \frac{5t}{2} : \frac{5t}{2} = 3:5:5$$

64. Heat required to melt 10 g of ice

$= 3360 \text{ J} = \frac{3360}{4.2} \text{ cal} = 800 \text{ cal}$

Heat required to melt 1 g of ice = 80 cal

Heat required to melt 1000 g of ice = 80,000 cal

∴ 80 kcal of heat is required to melt 1 kg ice.

65. Mass of ice = 100 g. Temperature of ice, $t_1 = -100$ °C.

$S_{ice} = 0.5 \text{ cal g}^{-1}\text{°C}^{-1} : L_f = 80 \text{ cal g}^{-1}$

$S_w = 1 \text{ cal g}^{-1}\text{°C}^{-1} : L_v = 540 \text{ cal g}^{-1}$

$S_{steam} = 0.5 \text{ cal g}^{-1}\text{°C}^{-1}$: Amount of heat supplied to increase the temperature of ice from -10 °C to 0 °C is $Q = M\,S_{ice}(\Delta t)$.

$Q_1 = 100 \times 0.5 \times [0-(-10)] = 100 \times 0.5 \times 10 = 500$ cal

The amount of heat supplied to convert ice into water at 0 °C is, $Q_2 = ML_F = 100 \times 80 = 8000$ cal

The amount of heat supplied to increase the temperature of water from 0 °C to 100 °C is

$Q_3 = MS_w\,\Delta t = 100 \times 1 \times (100 - 0)$

$= 100 \times 100 = 10{,}000$ cal

The amount of heat supplied to convert water into steam at 100 °C is,

$Q_4 = ML_v = 100 \times 540 = 54{,}000$ cal

The Amount of heat supplied to increase the temperature of steam from 100 °C to 120 °C is,

$Q_5 = MS_{steam}(\Delta t)$

$100 \times 0.5 \times (120 - 100) = 100 \times 0.5 \times 20$

$= 1000$ cal

Total heat energy supplied; $Q = Q_1 + Q_2 + Q_3$

$+ Q_4 + Q_5 = 500 + 8000 + 10,000 + 54,000 + 1000$
$= 73,500$ cal

66. The melting point of certain substances, like water, decreases with pressure. In the case of certain other substances, it increases with pressure. Boiling point water increases with the addition of impurities.

Hence, B is the only correct statement.

Level 3: Assess Your Concepts

Note: This is how you should frame your answer covering.

67. $M_w = 15$ g; $T_w = 100°$ C (hot)
$M_{ice} = 15$ g; $T_{ice} = 0°C$
Temperature of mixture (T) = ?
Specific heat capacity of water = 1 cal $g^{-1}°C^{-1}$
Specific heat capacity of ice = 0.5 cal $g^{-1}°C^{-1}$
Heat lost by hot body =
Heat gained by cold body =
$m_w s_w(t_w - x) = M_i L_i + m_w s_w(x - 0)$
$15 \times 1(100 - x) = 15 \times 80 + 15 \times 1(x - 0)$
$1500 - 15x = 1200 + 15x$
$300 = 30x$
$x = 10°C$

68. Heat lost by the body at higher temperature = Heat gained by the body at lower temperature. $Q = ms\Delta t$

69. $P = 200$ W
$M = 1000$ g = 1 kg
$T_1 = 35°$ C, $S_w = 1$ cal $g^{-1}°C^{-1}$ = 4200 J $kg^{-1}°C^{-1}$
$T_2 = ?$
$P \cdot t = m(T_2 - T_1)S_w$
$200 \times 4.2 \times 60 = 1 \cdot 4200 \times (T_2 - 35)$

$$\therefore T_2 = \frac{200 \times 4.2 \times 60}{4200}$$
$$= 12 + 35 = 47°C$$

70. Equate the heat absorbed by A in 2 s to that of B in 3 s. Find the ratio of heat supplied to A and B in unit time.

Find the ratio of heat supplied in 5 s to A to heat supplied to B in 6 s to determine the ratio of specific heat.

71. Heat lost by water = Heat gained by Ice
m s_w $(t_2 - t_1)$ = nml
$(2 \times 103) \times 1 \times (30 - 0) = n \times 200 \times 80$
$\Rightarrow n = 3.75$ ice cubes.

72. The initial temperature = 68°F

$$= \left[\frac{5}{9}(68 - 32\right]°C = 20\ C°$$

Final temperature = 313 K = (313 – 273) °C = 40 °C
Mass of mercury given = 0.05 kg = 50 g
Specifi c heat capacity of mercury = 0.033 cal g^{-1} $°C^{-1}$
i.e., heat gained by 1 g of mercury for 1 °C rise = 0.033 cal
Hence, heat gained by 50g mercury for 1 °C rise
= 0.033 × 50 = 1.65 cal
∴ Heat gained by 50 g mercury for 20 °C rise = 33 cal.

73. A rise in temperature of 9 °F is equal to a rise in temperature of 5 °C.
∴ A rise in temperature of 126 °F is on the Celsius scale equivalent to

$$126 \times \frac{5}{9} = 14 \times 5 = 70\ °C$$

Quantity of heat required to raise the temperature of the vessel by 1 °C = 300 cal
∴ Heat required to raise its temperature by 70 °C = 70 × 300 =21000 cal.
Similarly heat required to raise the temperature of water by 70 °C = 70 x 300 = 21000 cal
∴ the total heat required = (21000 + 21000) cal = 42000 cal
= 42000 × 4.2 = 176.4 kJ

74. Let °T represent the temperature in TIME scale.
373 K = 100 °C
$U = 200$ °T

$$\frac{20 - 0}{100} = \frac{F - 32}{180}$$

$$\frac{20}{100} = \frac{F - 32}{180}$$

$F - 32 = 18 \times 2$
$F = 36 + 32 = 68$ °F
Temperature on TIME scale corresponding to 20 °C

$$= \frac{68 \times 15}{17} = 60\ °T$$

$$\frac{68-32}{180} = \frac{60-L}{200-L}$$

$$(200 - L) = 300 - 5L$$

$$4L = 100$$

$$L = 25\ °T$$

∴ The lower fixed point and upper fixed point are 25 °T and 200 °T, respectively.

75. The difference of temperature readings on A and B are 10° and 15°, respectively.

But $\frac{\Delta A}{U_1 - L_1} = \frac{\Delta B}{U_2 - L_2}$

Where U_1, U_2 are the upper fixed points and L_1, L_2 are the lower fixed points of the thermometers A and B.

$$\frac{U_1 - L_1}{U_2 - L_2} = \frac{10}{15} = \frac{2}{3}$$

$$\frac{20 - L_1}{U_1 - L_1} = \frac{40 - L_2}{U_2 - L_2} \Rightarrow \frac{U_1 - L_1}{U_2 - L_2} = \frac{20 - L_1}{40 - L_2}$$

$$\frac{2}{3} = \frac{20 - L_1}{40 - L_2} \Rightarrow \frac{2}{3} = \frac{20 - 0}{40 - L_2}$$

$$80L - 2L_2 = 60$$

$$-2L_2 = -20$$

$$L_2 = 10$$

∴ Lower fixed point of B is 10°.

76. Specific heat capacity is the amount of heat energy absorbed by a unit mass of substance when its temperature is increased through 1K. Let A and B be two substances of unit masses. Let the molecular weight of A be greater than the molecular weight of B ($M_A > M_B$). As the mass of A and B are equal, the number of molecules of B is greater than the number of molecules of $A (n_B > n_A)$.

When equal amount of heat energy is supplied to A and B, the kinetic energy per molecule of A is greater than that of B as the number of molecules of A is less than that of 'B'.

That is the rise in temperature of A is greater than the rise in temperature of B. Therefore, B can absorb more amount of heat energy at less temperature. So, the specific heat capacity decreases as the molecular weight increases.

77 Mass of both the iron and copper spheres is the same, m = 1 kg.

Initial temperature of both the iron and the copper spheres is the same, $T_i = 25$ °C

Final temperature of both the iron and the copper spheres is the same, $T_f = 100$ °C

Given, specific heat capacity of iron, $s_i = 0.45$ J g^{-1} °C^{-1}

Specific heat capacity of copper, $s_c = 0.385$ J g^{-1} °C^{-1}

Heat absorbed by a solid is given by Q = msΔT, m is the mass, s is the specific heat capacity and ΔT is the-temperature difference of the solid.

Here, m and ΔT for both the sphere is the same, but the specific heat capacity of iron and copper is different. Hence, the heat absorbed by both the spheres is different.

The difference in heat absorbed by both the speres,

$\Delta Q = m\Delta T(s_i - s_c) = 1000$ g × (100 °C – 25 °C) × (0.45 J g^{-1} °C^{-1} – 0.385 J g^{-1} °C^{-1})

$= 10^3$g × 75 °C × 0.065 J g^{-1} °C^{-1} = 4875 J

78. Heat lost by a material is given by Q = msΔT, m is the mass of the material, s is the specific heat capacity and ΔT is the temperature difference.

Given, mass, m = 225 g

Initial temperature, $T_i = 80$ °C

Final temperature, $T_f = 20$ °C

$\Rightarrow \Delta T = T_f \sim T_i = 60$ °C

∴ Q = m s ΔT ⇒ s = Q/mΔT = 10800 J / (225 g × 60 °C) = 0.8 J g^{-1} °C^{-1}.

79. For the Faulty thermometer:

Lower fixed point, LFP = – 4°

Upper fixed point, UFP = 102°

Scale reading, S = 50 °C

Using:

$$\frac{S - LFP}{UFP - LFP} = \frac{C - LFP}{UFP - LFP}$$

(C = temperature on Celsius scale)

$$\frac{50-(-4)}{102-(-4)} = \frac{C-0}{100-0}$$

$$\frac{54}{106} = \frac{C}{100}$$

$$C = \frac{54 \times 100}{106} = 51\ °C$$

$$\frac{S-LFP}{UFP-LFP} = \frac{F-LFP}{UFP-LFP}$$

(F = temperature on Fahrenheit scale)

$$\frac{50-(-4)}{102-(-4)} = \frac{F-32}{212-32}$$

$$\frac{54}{106} = \frac{F-32}{180}$$

$$F-32 = \frac{54 \times 180}{106}$$

$$F-32 = 91.8$$

$$F = 91.8 + 32 = 123.8\ °F$$

80. Given: 2 g of Ice out of 10 g melted in the hand of Lady at the end of 3 minute.

Specific heat step:

First, 10 g of Ice at –5 °C gets converted to 10 g of Ice at 0 °C.

Using, $Q = m\ s\ \Delta t$,

Here, mass of Ice, m = 10 g

Specific heat capacity of Ice, $s = 0.5\ cal\ g^{-1}\ °C^{-1}$

Initial temperature, $t_1 = -5\ °C$

Final temperature, $t_2 = 0\ °C$

Change in temperature, $\Delta t = 5\ °C$

Hence, $Q_1 = 10\ g \times 0.5\ cal\ g^{-1}\ °C^{-1} \times 5\ °C$

$Q_1 = 25\ cal \rightarrow (1)$

Latent heat step:

The quantity of Ice melted is 2 g. Hence, out of 10 g, 2 g of Ice at 0 °C gets converted to 2 g of water at 0 °C.

Using: $Q = m\ L$,

Here, mass of Ice melted, m = 2 g

Latent heat of Ice, $L = 80\ cal\ g^{-1}$

Hence, $Q_2 = 2\ g \times 80\ cal\ g^{-1}$

$Q_2 = 160\ cal \rightarrow (2)$

Therefore, total heat lost by the hand of Lady will be given by (1) + (2)

Hence, $Q = Q_1 + Q_2$

$Q = 25\ cal + 160\ cal = 185\ cal.$

81. Given: The amount of heat energy gained by the body while sliding on a surface varies as, $Q = k\ f\ t^2$

Mass of body, m = 200 g

Frictional force, f = 2 N

Specific heat capacity of the body, $s = 0.12\ J\ g^{-1}\ °C^{-1}$

Proportionality constant, $k = 6\ m\ s^{-2}$

In 3 s, let the body move from 'A' to 'B'.

Hence, quantity of heat gained at the end of 3 s,

$Q_3 = 6\ m\ s^{-2} \times 2\ N \times (3\ s)^2$

$Q_3 = 108\ N\ m = 108\ J.$

In 8 s, let the body move from 'A' to 'C'.

Hence, quantity of heat gained at the end of 8 s,

$Q_8 = 6\ m\ s^{-2} \times 2\ N \times (8\ s)^2$

$Q_8 = 768\ N\ m = 768\ J.$

Now, the quantity of heat gained from 3 s to 8 s (i.e., from 'B' to 'C'),

$Q = Q_8 - Q_3$

$Q = 768\ J - 108\ J = 660\ J.$

Using, $Q = m\ s\ \Delta t$,

$660\ J = 200\ g \times 0.12\ J\ g^{-1}\ °C^{-1} \times \Delta t$

$$\Delta t = \frac{660}{200 \times 0.12}\ °C$$

$\Delta t = 27.5\ °C.$

Hence, the change (increase) in temperature of the body from 3 s to 8 s is 27.5 °C.

JEE-NEET Special Wing

Multiple-Answer Type Questions

1. The specific latent heat of vaporisation of steam is 2260 J g^{-1} (or) 540 Cal g^{-1}.
Hence, the correct option is (a) and (b).

2. The normal human body temperature is 98.4° F (or) 37° C.
Hence, the correct option is (b) and (c).

3. BC and DE represent constant temperature at the change of state.
Hence, the correct option is (b) and (d).

4. 95° F = 35° C
110° F = 43.33° C
Hence, the correct option is (b) and (c).

5. From the given options,
(a) $\frac{C-0}{100-0} = \frac{F-32}{212-32}$ - **True.**
(b) $\frac{C}{5} = \frac{F-32}{9}$ - **True.**
Hence, the correct option is (a) and (b).

Comprehension-Based Questions

6. The liquid with the highest specific heat capacity is water.
Hence, the correct option is (d).

7. Heat capacity is directly proportional to mass.
Hence, the correct option is (a).

8. $S = \frac{Q}{m\Delta T} = \frac{C}{m}$, where C is specific heat capacity.
$C = m \times S$
Hence, the correct option is (b).

9. Water is used as coolant in automobile engines due to its high specific heat capacity.
Hence, the correct option is (c).

10. S = 130 J / g / C°
= 130×10^3 J kg^{-1} $°C^{-1}$
c = m × S
= $70 \times 130 \times 10^3$
= 9100×10^3 J K^{-1}
= 9100 k J K^{-1}
Hence, the correct option is (c).

11. The state of any substance can be changed by either heating or cooling.
Hence, the correct option is (c).

12. At atmospheric pressure, the boiling point of water is 100° C.
Hence, the correct option is (b).

13. BC represents constant temperature at the change of state.
Hence, the correct option is (a).

14. The amount of heat energy required to melt one kilogram of solid at its melting point, without any rise in temperature is specific latent heat of fusion.
Hence, the correct option is (d).

15. The S. I. unit of specific latent heat of vaporisation is J kg^{-1}.
Hence, the correct option is (a).

Match the Column

15. **Choice (c) follows.**
(A) UFP: Boiling point of pure water
(B) LFP: Melting point of ice
(C) Clinical thermometer: 95° F to 110° F
(D) Galileo's' thermometer: Thermoscope
(E) Six's maximum and minimum thermometer: U tube filled with mercury
A - c, B - e, C - a, D - b, E - d

Light

CHAPTER

7

Key Ideas

After completing this chapter, you should be able to:

- discuss different terms related to the study of light.
- study reflection of light by plane mirror and spherical mirrors.
- understand the phenomenon of bending of light rays and their applications.
- observe spliting of white light into its constituent colours and its applications.

Remember

Before beginning this chapter, you should be able to:

- define light, sources of light, etc.
- learn about laws of reflection and images formed by plane mirror and their applications.

Scientific Crypt

A Tribute to Thomas Young (1773—1829)

Thomas young was born in 1773, the eldest of ten children, belonged to a Quaker family of Milverton. At the age of 14, Young learned Greek and Latin and was acquainted with 11 languages.

Young studied in London and received the degree 'Doctor of Physics' in 1796 from Gottingen, Germany. In 1797, he entered Emmanuel college, Cambridge and in 1799 he established himself as a physician. Young published many of his first academic articles anonymously to protect his reputation as a physician. In 1801, Young was appointed professor of natural philosophy at the Royal Institution. In two years, he delivered 91 lectures, and in 1802 he was appointed foreign secretary of the Royal society. In 1828, he was elected as a foreign member of the Royal Swedish Academy of Sciences.

One of his many achievements was to establish the wave theory of light with the help of a ripple tank. He demonstrated the interference phenomenon in the context of water waves. By the double slit experiment, he demonstrated interference phenomenon in the context of light as a wave. Young described the characteristics of elasticity, that came to be known as Young's modulus and is denoted as 'E'. Young is called founder of Physiological Optics. He was the first to describe astigmatism. In 1804, Young developed the theory of capillary phenomenon on the principle of surface tension. Young also devised a rule of thumb for determining a child's drug dosage. In his encyclopedia Britannica article 'languages', Young also compared the grammar and vocabulary of 400 languages. He also developed Young temperament, a method of tuning musical instruments.

Crossword

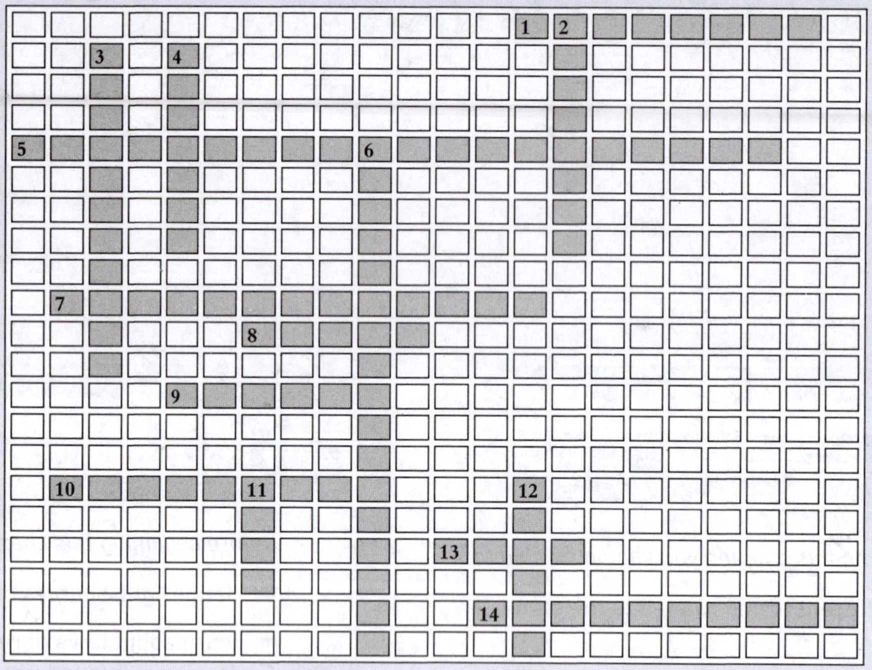

Across

1. The image formed of an object kept at a principal focus of concave mirror.
5. For a given pair of media the relation between sin i and sin r.
7. The angle between the reflecting surface and the reflected ray or incident ray.
8. Tube light which is longer is preferred to an incandescent bulb as a source of light as it forms smaller ______.
9. Example of a point source of light.
10. Device used in submarines to see objects above the water surface.
13. Pinhole camera does not require______.
14. The phenomenon by which sun appears slightly elliptical at sunrise.

Down

2. The sign of magnification for real image.
3. The radiations used to detect fake currency notes.
4. The mirror used in solar cooker.
6. Reflection of light from the surface of glycerine is an example of ______.
11. The colour obtained by mixing blue and green.
12. The mirrors provided in ATM centres.

INTRODUCTION

The branch of physics which deals with nature, source, properties and the effects of light is called optics. When rays of light coming from an illuminated object strike the eye, an object is seen. Thus, light is necessary to see an object. During the day time, we see objects due to light from the sun. Sun is the main and a natural source of light. At night we receive light from stars, moon, bulbs, candles, etc.

Nature of Light and its Sources

Moon does not emit light on its own but the moon is visible due to the light falling on it. Moon is a non-luminous body. Thus, bodies which emit light on their own are called **luminous bodies** and bodies which do not emit light on their own but are visible, when light falls on them are called **non-luminous bodies**.

Sun, stars, electric fish, some species of fish and insects are the examples of luminous bodies.

Moon, planets, etc are the examples of non-luminous bodies.

Artificial sources of light are fluorescent bulb, incandescent bulb, candles, etc. Incandescent bulb and candles emit light when they are heated whereas fluorescent bulb, neon bulb, sodium vapour lamp emit light without a rise in temperature. Thus, sources which emit light due to rise in temperature are called **hot sources** and sources which emit light without rise in temperature are called **cold sources**.

When a light emitted from a candle is viewed or seen through a pinhole made in a cardboard, the light emerges only through a pinhole. This pinhole acts like a point source of light.

When a candle is seen without a card board, light emerges from all points of the flame of the candle. Thus, the flame of candle is an extended source. Other examples of extended sources are bulb, tube light, etc. If a source of light is bigger than a point source, then the source is an extended source.

Propagation of Light

Light does not require a material medium to travel, it can travel through vacuum. This is the best illustrated by light travelling from the sun to the earth through vast spaces. Apart from vacuum and gases, light also travels through solids and liquids. The medium which allows most of the incident light to pass through is called **transparent** medium.

Example: Glass, bottle, transparency sheet, light bulb, thermometer, ice, spectacles, etc.

Info Bytes!

A small bundle of these rays is known as a pencil of rays and large bundles of these rays are known as beams of light.

When a bulb is seen through an oiled paper or a stained glass the intensity of the emerging light is reduced. The oiled paper or the stained glass allows only a part of the light to travel through it. Oiled paper, stained glass are examples of **translucent** bodies.

The bodies which allow only a part of the incident light to travel through them are called translucent bodies. Light does not travel through wood, stone, walls, etc., such bodies are known as opaque bodies. **Opaque** bodies are bodies which do not allow light to pass through them.

Light passing through an open window or a door can be easily made out due to the minute particles present in air which receive light. When we observe the path of these minute particles, we observe that they travel in a straight line. Thus, light travels from point A to point B in a given homogeneous medium along a straight line. This property of light is known as rectilinear propagation of light. The straight line from A to B is called **ray of light**.

A bundle of rays in which rays are parallel to one another is called **parallel beam of light.**

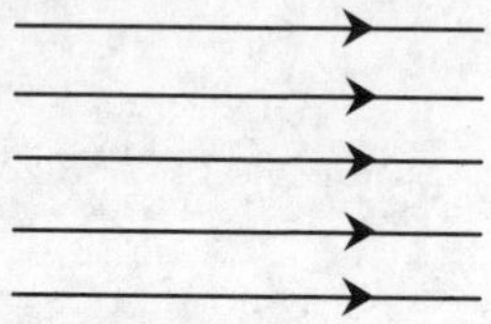

Figure 7.1 Parallel beam

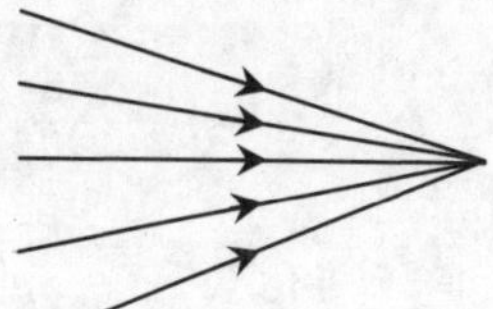

Figure 7.2 Convergent rays

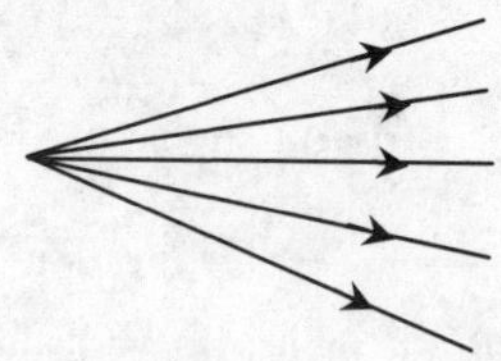

Figure 7.3 Divergent rays

The rays of light which are not parallel to each other and which proceed towards a point or meet at a point are known as **convergent rays**.

The rays of light which are not parallel to each other and which spread out from a point are called **divergent rays**.

Properties of Light

1. Light does not require any material medium to propagate. It can travel through vacuum.
2. It travels with a very high velocity of about 3×10^8 m s^{-1} in air or vacuum.
3. It always travels in a straight line. This property is known as the **rectilinear propagation of light.**
4. Light does not change the properties of the medium through which it passes.
5. The velocity of light decreases as it travels from a rarer medium to denser medium.

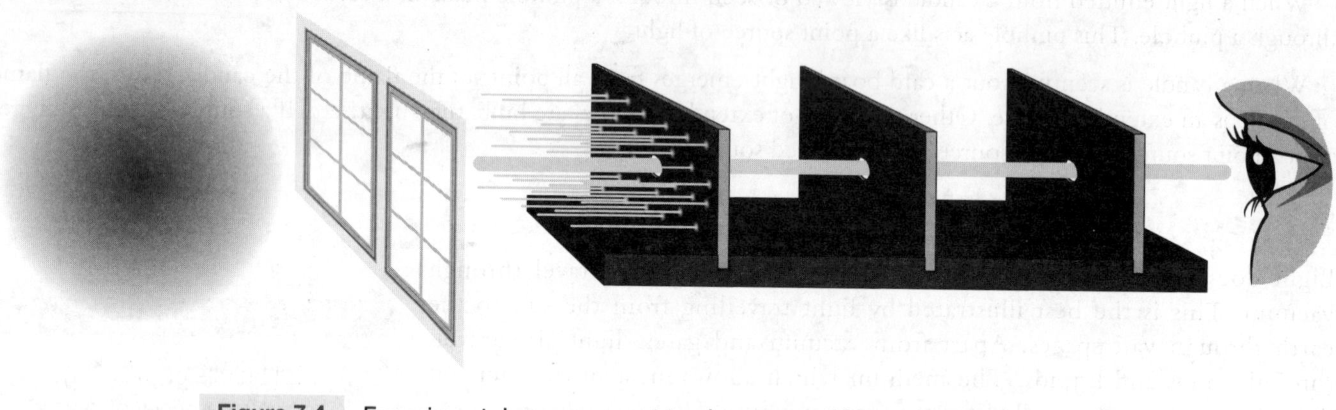

Figure 7.4 Experimental arrangement to observe rectilinear propagation of light

Credit line: *udaix / 123RF*

The path of the light in a straight line changes only when the medium changes or it is obstructed by an obstacle. The rectilinear propagation of light can be proved experimentally.

Activity

Consider a simple experiment. Take three wooden uprights *P*, *Q* and *R*. Make a small hole at the same height from the base on each of *P*, *Q* and *R* such that the holes are in a straight line. Place a lighted candle towards the upright *P* facing the hole. Look through the hole of upright *R*. The candle flame is clearly visible which would disappear if one of the upright is moved proving that light has rectilinear propagation. The casting of shadows and eclipses are due to the rectilinear propagation of light.

Shadows

When an opaque or translucent object is brought between a lighted candle and a wall, a dark patch is formed on the wall. This dark patch is known as the **shadow**. A shadow may consist entirely of a dark patch called **umbra** or it may be surrounded by a less darker patch called **penumbra**, depending on the nature of the source and the size of the object. Thus, a shadow is formed when rays of light are stopped by an opaque object.

Konnect

If a point source of light is used to cast the shadow of an opaque body, only umbra is formed, but if an extended source of light is used, both umbra and penumbra are formed.

Formation of Shadow by a Point Source

Consider a cardboard having a pinhole at its centre. Place the cardboard in front of a light source (candle). The pinhole on the card board acts as a point source. Place a screen on the other side of the cardboard. If an object *AB* is placed between the pinhole and the screen, a totally dark patch is formed on the screen. This region is known as an **umbra** (Figure 7.5). If the distance between the cardboard (point source) and the object is increased, the size of the dark patch decreases. By varying the distance between the point source and the opaque object, the size of the dark patch can be varied.

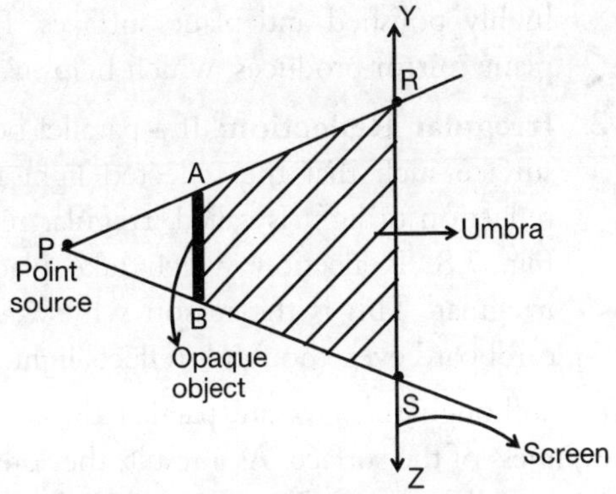

Figure 7.5 Shadow formed by point source

Formation of the Shadow by An Extended Source

An extended source PP^1, an object *EF* and a screen *XY* are arranged as shown in Figure 7.6.

The light rays starting from point *P* and point P^1 of an extended source along an opaque object meet the screen *XY* at points *B*, *D* and *A*, *C*, respectively. It is observed that the regions, *AB* and *CD* are partly illuminated by *P* and P^1, respectively. Hence, the regions *AB* and *CD* form **penumbra** while the region, *BC* forms **umbra**, where the light is not incident from any part of the source. Hence, an extended source of light forms both **umbra** and **penumbra** when an opaque object is placed in its path. To increase the regions of **umbra** and penumbra, either the screen is moved away from the opaque body or the source is moved towards the opaque body.

Konnect

In conducting the above experiment, the flame of the candle, the pinhole and the object should be in the same straight line.

If the extended source is bigger than the opaque body, the region of umbra is smaller than that of **penumbra**. The region of **umbra**, can be further decreased until it completely disappears by either moving the source of light towards the opaque body or by moving the screen away from the opaque body.

The above discussion explains why a tube light forms very faint shadow and also why shadows of flying objects like aeroplane are not formed on the earth.

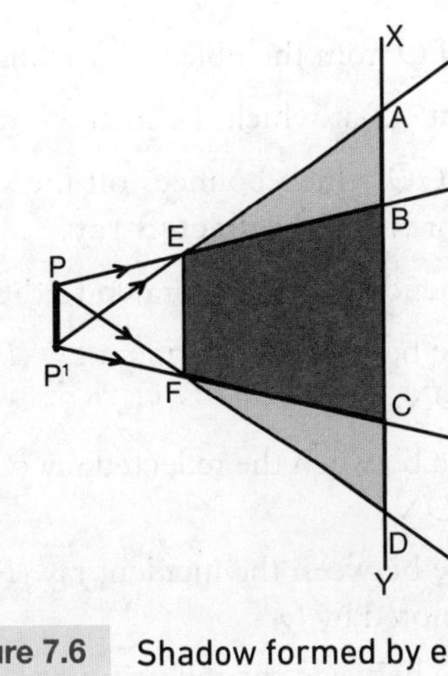

Figure 7.6 Shadow formed by extended source

Eclipses

The phenomenon in which the moon's shadow falls on the earth or the earth casts its shadow on the moon is known as an **eclipse**. When the moon comes in between the earth and the sun and if all the three are in the same straight line, some part of the earth does not receive light from the sun at all and some other regions of the earth receive partial light. This is known as **solar eclipse**.

When the earth comes between the sun and the moon and if all the three are in the same straight line, then the shadow of the earth falls on the moon. As a result some part of the moon is not visible. This is known as **lunar eclipse**.

Reflection of Light

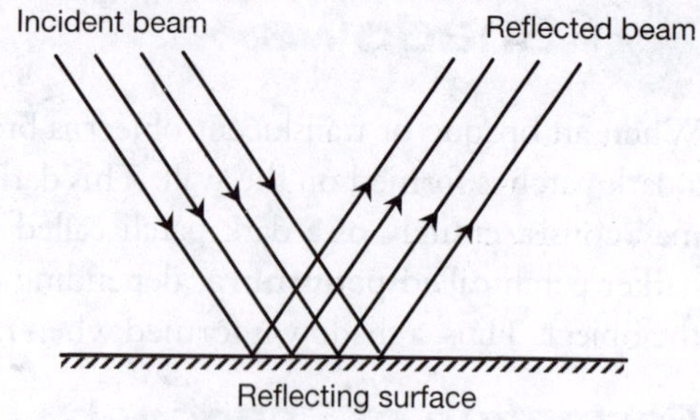

Figure 7.7 Regular reflection

When we enter a dark room, we cannot see objects in the room but when the room is illuminated with a candle, objects are visible. This is due to the turning or the bouncing of light by an object. This bouncing of light into the same medium, from which the light ray is incident, is called **reflection.**

Reflection can be classified as regular reflection and irregular reflection.

1. **Regular Reflection:** If a parallel beam of light is incident on a surface such that the reflected light rays also form a parallel beam of light, then such a reflection is known as regular reflection as shown in Fig. 7.7. Regular reflection takes place when light is incident on highly polished and plane surfaces. It is regular reflection that a plane mirror produces, which helps us see our image in the mirror.
2. **Irregular Reflection:** If a parallel beam of light is incident on a surface such that the reflected light rays are not parallel, such a reflection of light is called irregular reflection of light as shown in Fig. 7.8. Reflection which take place on an uneven surface is irregular. This is the reason why we cannot see our image on a cardboard even though it reflects light.

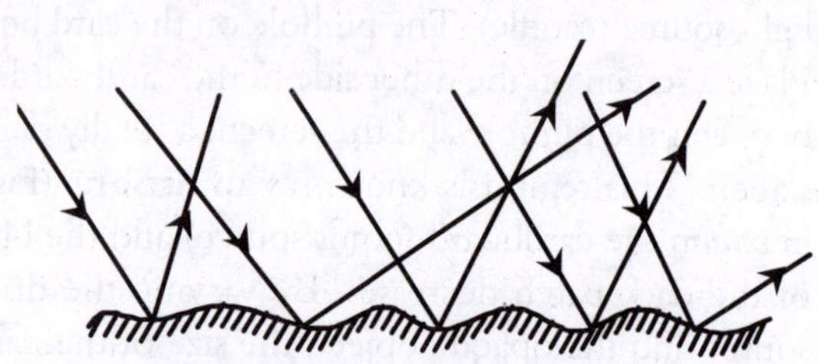

Figure 7.8 Irregular reflection

Even though the rays are parallel the angles of incidence are different due to the unevenness of the surface. As a result, they are reflected at different angles, and therefore, are not parallel to each other.

Konnect

Regular reflection produces a glare and gives crystal clear image. Irregular reflection is responsible for us to see objects from any corner of the room.

Definitions Related to Reflection

Consider an object at a point *P*. Let MM^1 be a highly polished plane surface which we refer to as a mirror as shown in Figure 7.9.

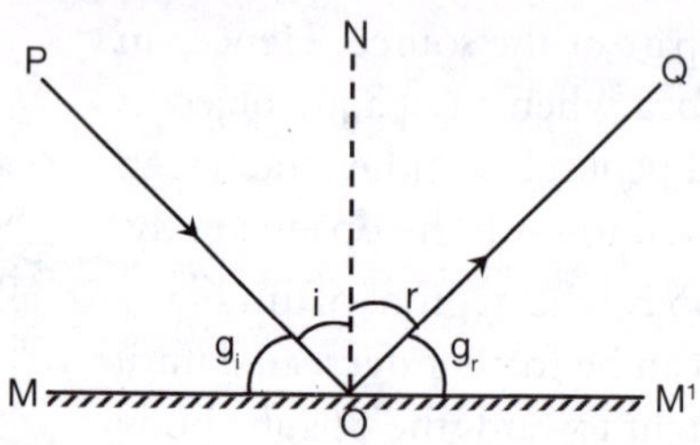

Figure 7.9 Reflection by a plane mirror

Info Bytes!

Moon is visible to us because the light which falls on it is reflected.

1. The ray *PO* from the object, travelling towards the mirror is called **incident ray**.
2. The point '*O*' at which the incident ray meets the mirror is called **point of incidence**.
3. The ray *OQ* which bounces off the surface of the mirror when the incident ray strikes the mirror is called **reflected ray**.
4. The perpendicular (*ON*) drawn to the surface of the mirror at the point of incidence is called **normal ray**.
5. The angle between the incident ray (*PO*) and the normal (*ON*) is called **angle of incidence** and is denoted by '*i*', i.e., $\angle PON$.
6. The angle between the reflected ray (*OQ*) and the normal (*ON*) is called **angle of reflection** and is denoted by '*r*', i.e., $\angle QON$.
7. The angle between the incident ray (*PO*) and the reflecting surface (MM^1) is called **glancing angle of incidence** and is denoted by 'g_i'.
8. The angle between the reflecting surface (MM^1) and the reflected ray (*OQ*) is called **glancing angle of reflection** and is denoted by 'g_r'.

Laws of Reflection

The reflection of light rays at a particular point always satisfies the following laws.

1. The incident ray, the reflected ray and the normal, all lie in the same plane.
2. The angle of incidence is equal to the angle of reflection. $\angle i = \angle r$

Experiment to Verify the Laws of Reflection

Apparatus Required:
Plane mirror, four pins, scale and protractor, white paper, drawing board.

Procedure:

1. Draw a straight line MM^1 on a white paper fixed to a drawing board.
2. Draw a perpendicular line ON to MM'.
3. Draw a line PO such that it makes suitable acute angle with the normal (Refer Figure 7.10).
4. Place a plane mirror on MM'.
5. Fix two pins P and Q on the line PO. PO is the incident ray.
6. Looking from the other side of the normal observe the image of the pins P and Q.
7. Fix two more pins P' and Q' in line with the images of the pins P and Q.
8. Remove the plane mirror.
9. Join P' and O, OP' gives the reflected ray.
10. Measure $\angle PON$ and $\angle P'ON$. $\angle PON$ gives the angle of incidence. $\angle P'ON$ gives the angle of reflection.
11. Repeat the experiment for different angles of incidence and tabulate the results.

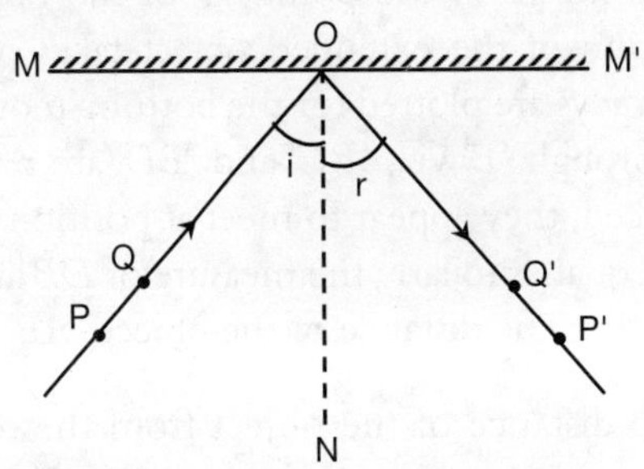

Figure 7.10 Reflection of light from a mirror

Observation:

Trial no.	$\angle PON = i$	$\angle P'ON = r$

Result:

1. The incident ray, the reflected ray and the normal all lie in the plane of the paper (same plane).
2. It is found that the angle of incidence is equal to the angle of reflection. $\angle i = \angle r$
   This proves the **laws of reflection**.

Reflection by Plane Mirrors

Plane mirror is a looking glass which is highly polished on one surface and is silvered on the other surface. When a light ray strikes the polished surface, it is reflected by the silvered surface.

An '**image**' is defined as the impression of an object carried over and formed by light reflected from it. An image is said to be a real image if it can be caught on a screen, and a virtual image if it cannot be caught on the screen. For example, the image on the screen in a theatre is a real image and the image observed in a plane mirror is a virtual image.

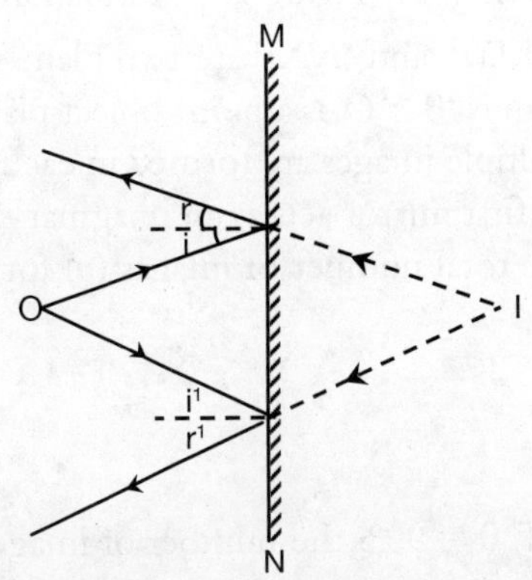

Figure 7.11 Reflection of a point object in a plane mirror

1. **Reflection of a Point Object in a Plane Mirror:** Consider a point object 'O' placed in front of a plane mirror, as shown in Figure 7.11. To

get the position of its image, we take two divergent rays from the object and consider the reflection of those two rays. The two reflected rays are divergent and do not meet each other. Hence, when we produce them back, they appear to meet at point '*I*'. The position where two divergent reflected rays that are produced appear to meet is the position where the image is formed.

2. **Reflection of an Extended Object in a Plane Mirror:** Consider an extended object '*AB*' placed in front of a plane mirror *MN* as shown in Figure 7.12. Consider the light ray '*AC*' from position '*A*' incident on the mirror at '*C*'. Since the angle of incidence is zero, the angle of reflection is also zero and the light ray retraces its path and travels along '*CA*'. Another light ray '*AD*' from position '*A*' of the object is incident on the mirror at '*D*' and gets reflected along '*DE*'. The two reflected rays, '*CA*' and '*DE*' when produced back, intersect at position 'A^1'.

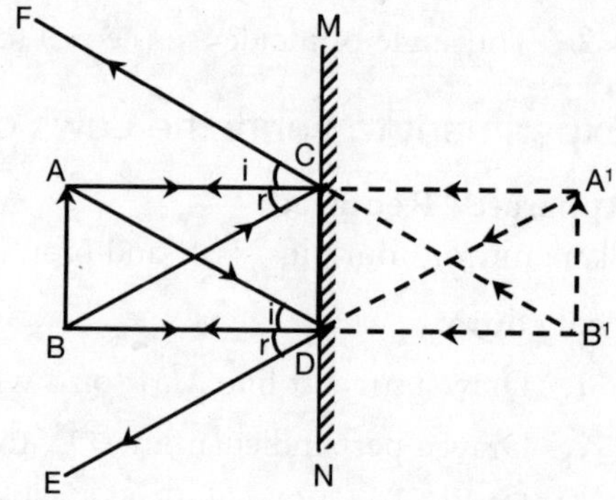

Figure 7.12 Reflection of an extended object in a plane mirror

The image of the point '*A*' of the object is formed at 'A^1'. Similarly, the reflection of the extended object takes place throughout the body '*AB*' and similar rays are plotted for the bottom-most position of the object '*B*'. The light rays through '*B*' viz, '*BC*' and '*BD*' are reflected along '*CF*' and '*DB*', respectively, and when these two reflected rays are produced, they appear to meet at position 'B^1'. If the lengths of the object *AB* and the image *A'B'* are measured, it is found to be equal. Similarly the measure of *DB* and *DB'* are found to be equal. Hence, the total image of the object '*AB*' is formed as 'A^1B^1'. The distance of the object '*AB*' from the plane mirror is equal to the distance of the image from the mirror.

The distance of the object from the mirror is known as '**object distance**', denoted by '*u*' and the distance of the image from the mirror is known as '**image distance**', denoted by '*v*'. The image formed is erect but is laterally inverted when compared to the object, i.e., if you face a plane mirror, your left side will appear as the right side of the image and vice versa. The image formed by a plane mirror cannot be obtained on a screen. Such images are called '**virtual images**' whereas the images which can be obtained on a screen are called '**real images**'.

Hence, the image formed by a plane mirror is

1. Of the same size as that of the object.
2. At the same distance behind the mirror as the object is in front.
3. Erect but laterally inverted.
4. Virtual.

Konnect

In a plane mirror, the image appears the same distance behind the mirror as you stand in front of it.

Image Formed by Two Mirrors

Consider two mirrors that are placed such that they make an angle 'θ' with each other and their reflecting surfaces face towards each other. If an object is placed between them as shown in the Figure 7.13, formation of more than one image takes place.

'MM^1' and 'NN^1' are two plane mirrors placed such that the angle between them is 'θ'. '*O*' is a point object placed between them as shown in Figure 7.13. Multiple images are formed in each of the mirrors, as the image of the object in the first mirror acts as an imaginary object for the second mirror and vice versa. The total number of images (*n*) formed is given by the expression,

$$n = \left[\frac{360^\circ}{\theta} - 1\right]$$

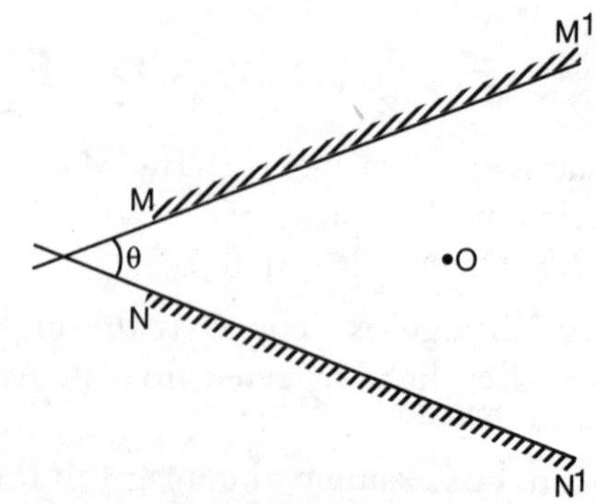

Figure 7.13 Reflection by two mirrors placed facing towards each other

If $\theta = 90^\circ$, the number of images formed is $n = \dfrac{360^\circ}{90^\circ} - 1 = 3$

If $\theta = 0^\circ$, i.e., the mirrors are parallel to each other, infinite images are formed but their brightness decreases.

EXAMPLE 7.1

Find the number of images formed by two mirrors whose reflecting surfaces intersect at an angle of 22½°.

SOLUTION

In the given problem the angle of intersection of the reflecting surfaces, $\theta = 22\frac{1}{2}°$

The number of images formed, $n = \frac{360}{\theta} - 1$

$$\therefore n = \left(\frac{360}{22\frac{1}{2}}\right) - 1 = \left(\frac{360}{\frac{45}{2}}\right) - 1 = 16 - 1 = 15$$

15 images are formed.

Uses of Plane Mirrors

1. Plane mirrors are primarily used as looking glasses.
2. Since a combination of mirrors can produce multiple images, they are used to provide false dimensions, in showrooms.
3. They are also used as reflectors in solar cookers.
4. Plane mirrors are used in the construction of periscopes.

Periscope

Plane mirrors are used in the construction of a reflecting periscope. A reflecting periscope works on the principle of the reflection of light. It consists of a cylindrical cardboard or wooden tube bent twice at right angles as shown in Figure 7.14. Two plane mirrors are fixed at the bends of the tube at an angle of 45° with the side of the tube. The inner side of the cylindrical tube is blackened to avoid any reflection of light.

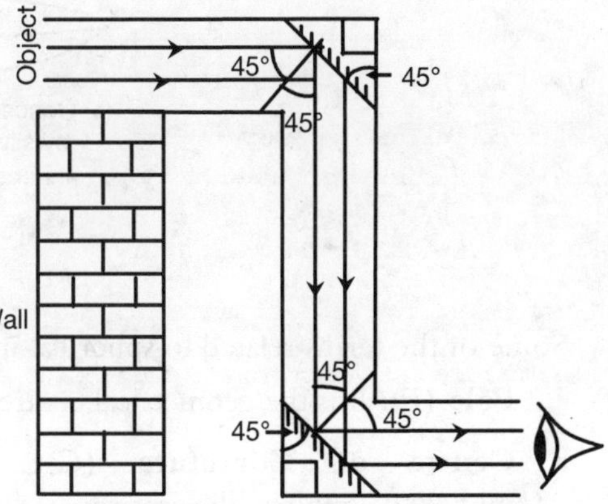

Figure 7.14 Reflecting periscope

The parallel rays entering the cylindrical tube from the upper end from an object strike the plane mirror at an angle of 45°, and hence are reflected through an angle of 45° (using principle of reflection). These reflected rays strike the second mirror at an angle of 45° and are further reflected through an angle of 45°. Finally the reflected rays reach the eye and the image of the object can be viewed from the other end.

Periscopes are used in submarines to see the objects on the surface of water and by soldiers present in a trench warfare to observe the movement of the enemy.

Kaleidoscope

Three rectangular plane mirrors of the same size are placed such that the reflecting surfaces face each other. The mirrors are bound together by a string. The system is placed in cylindrical tube of suitable size. One end of cylindrical tube is closed with plane mirror. Glass bangle pieces or paper bits of different, bright colours are placed in the tube. Looking through the open end of the tube, we find different, beautiful patterns that are obtained on rotating the tube. Intricacy of the design can be increased by using more beads.

Figure 7.15 Kaleidoscope

Credit line: *Keith Biros / 123RF*

Spherical Mirrors

Mirrors which are used by dentists, mirrors used as rear view mirrors in automobiles, and mirrors used for shaving are not plane mirrors. These are called **spherical mirrors**. Spherical mirrors form a part of a sphere. Consider a hollow glass sphere as shown in Figure 7.16, with its centre at '*O*'.

When the hollow glass sphere is cut along '*AB*' as shown in above given figure, the part that is cut off appears to be like a dish. If the cut off portion is silver coated at the bottom, i.e., on the convex side or the bulged out side or the outer side, the inner side or the concave side becomes the reflecting surface and the mirror thus obtained is called **'concave mirror'** or **'converging mirror'** given in Figure 7.17.

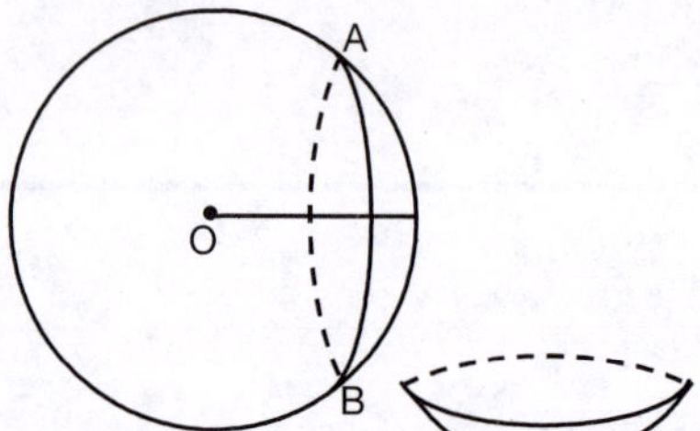

Figure 7.16 Hollow glass sphere and a section of it

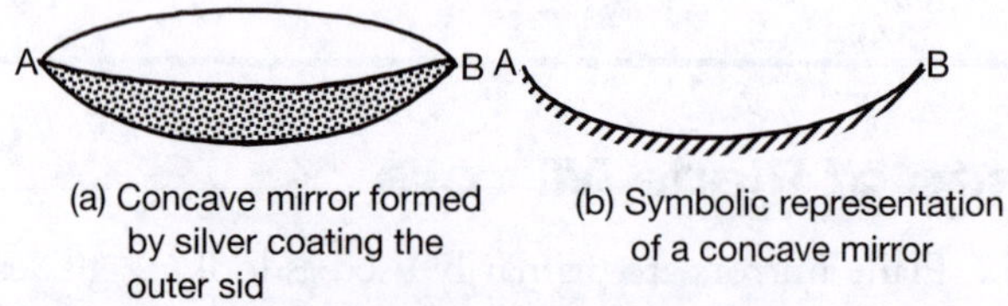

Figure 7.17 Concave mirror

If the cut-off part of the glass sphere is silver coated on the inside surface (concave side), the reflecting surface is the outer one and such a spherical mirror formed is called **'convex mirror'** or a **'diverging mirror'**. (Fig. 7.18)

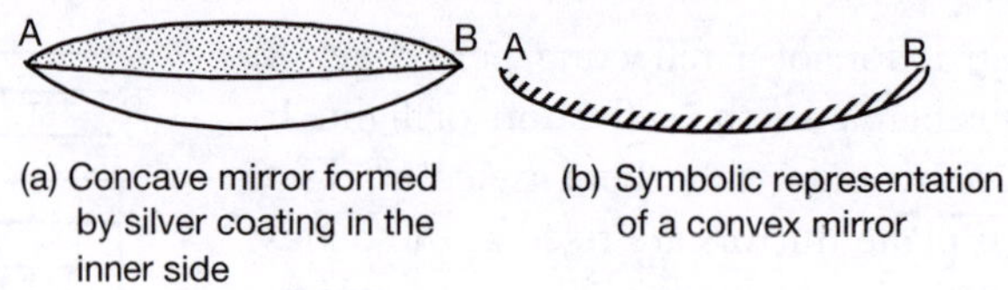

Figure 7.18 Convex mirror

Some of the terms related to spherical mirror are as follow:

1. **Pole (*P*):** It is the geometrical centre of the spherical mirror. *P* is the pole of the mirror.
2. **Centre of Curvature (*C*):** It is the centre of the sphere of which the mirror is a part. *C* is the centre of curvature.
3. **Radius of Curvature (*R*):** It is the radius of the sphere of which the spherical mirror is a part. *PC* is the radius of curvature.
4. **Principal Axis:** It is the line passing through the pole and the centre of curvature. *PM* is the principal axis.
5. **Principal Focus (*F*):** Incident rays close to and parallel to the principal axis, after reflection converge at a fixed point on the principal axis in the case of a concave mirror or appear to diverge from a fixed point on the principal axis in the case of convex mirror. This fixed point is known as the principal focus. *F* is the principal focus.

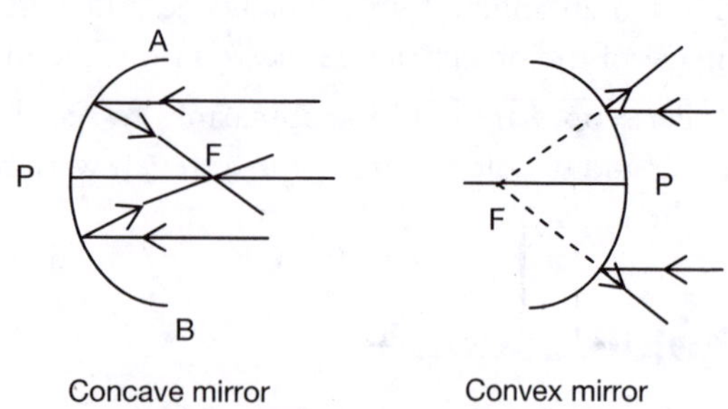

Figure 7.19 Images showing pole and focus of spherical mirrors

6. **Focal Length (*f*):** It is the distance between the pole and the principal focus. The distance between *P* and *F* is the focal length. Focal length is denoted by *f*.

Path of the Reflected Rays in Spherical Mirrors

Draw an arc of a circle of convenient radius with the centre at *C*. Draw the line *PC*. The line passing through *P* and *C* is the principal axis. *CB* and *CY* are the normal to the spherical surface at point *B* and *Y*, respectively. Draw two lines *AB* and *XY* parallel to the principal axis. Determine by geometrical construction the direction of the reflected rays, *BD* and *YG*, i.e., from the laws of reflection.

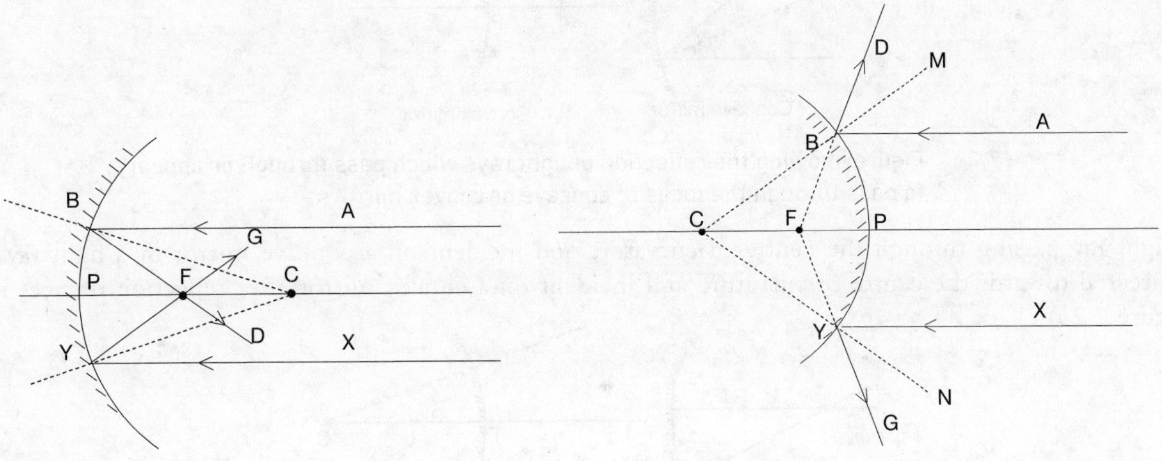

Figure 7.20 Figure showing the reflection of light rays which pass through or appear to pass through the focus of concave or convex mirrors

$\angle CBD = \angle ABC$ and $\angle CYG = \angle XYC$ in (Figure 7.20) and $\angle MBD = \angle ABM$ and $\angle GYN = \angle NYX$ in Figure 7.21 (The angle of incidence is equal to the angle of reflection).

By construction we can find that the two reflected rays meet at a fixed point *F* in the case of concave mirror and in convex mirror they appear to diverge from the fixed point *F* on the principal axis.

The incident rays parallel to the principal axis after reflection from the spherical mirror passes through principal focus in the case of concave mirror and appears to diverge from the principal focus in case of convex mirror. Conversely, an incident ray passing through the principal focus in the case of concave mirror or an incident ray that is directed towards the principal focus in the case of convex mirror is reflected parallel to the principal axis.

Rules for Construction of Ray Diagrams Formed in Spherical Mirrors

To know the position and the nature of the image of an object placed in front of a spherical mirror, any two of the following light rays coming from a point on the object are drawn.

1. A light ray parallel to the principal axis incident on a spherical mirror, after reflection, passes through the principal focus in the case of a concave mirror and appears to come from the principal focus in the case of a convex mirror (Figure 7.21).

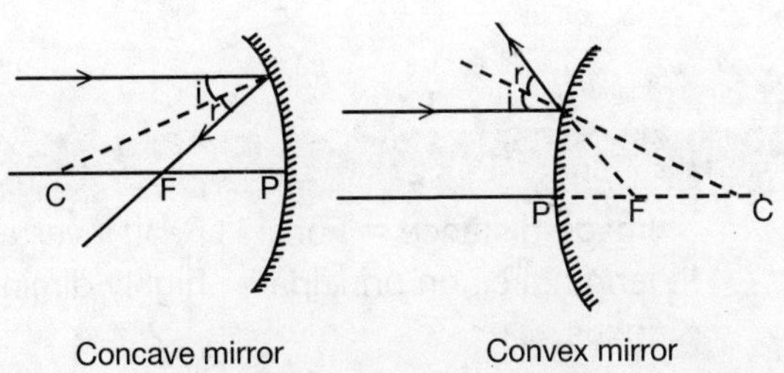

Figure 7.21 Figure showing the reflection of light rays which are parallel to the axial line of concave or convex mirrors

Info Bytes!

Parabolic mirrors, a type of spherical mirror, are used in telescopes to minimize distortion.

2. A light ray passing through the principal focus and incident on a concave mirror or a light ray which is directed towards principal focus and incident on a convex mirror is reflected parallel to its principal axis (Figure 7.22).

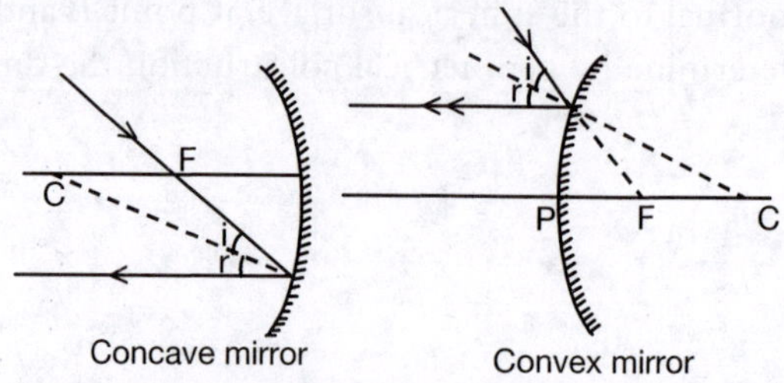

Figure 7.22 Figure showing the reflection of light rays which pass through or appear to pass through the focus of concave or convex mirrors

3. A light ray passing through the centre of curvature and incident on a concave mirror or a light ray which is directed towards the centre of curvature and incident on a convex mirror after reflection retraces its path (Figure 7.23).

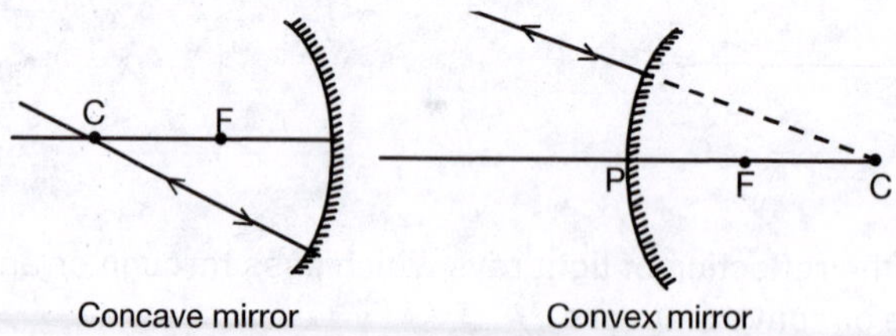

Figure 7.23 Figure showing the reflection of light rays which pass through or appear to pass through the center of curvature of concave or convex mirrors

4. A ray of light incident at the pole of the mirror gets reflected following angle i = angle r

Reflection Through Spherical Mirrors

Magnification

If the size of the image is larger than the size of the object such an image is called magnified image. The ratio of the size of an image to the size of its object is known as **magnification** and is denoted by 'm'. It is just a number and does not have any units. Magnification can be expressed in terms of the distances of the object and the image from the mirror.

$$\text{Magnification, } m = \frac{\text{size of the image } (h_i)}{\text{size of the object } (h_0)} = -\frac{v}{u} = \frac{\text{-images distance}}{\text{object distance}}$$

If the image size is smaller than the object, it is called '**diminished image**'.

Formation of Images by Concave Mirror

Table 7.1 Formation of images by concave mirror.

Diagram	Object distance	Image distance	Nature of the image
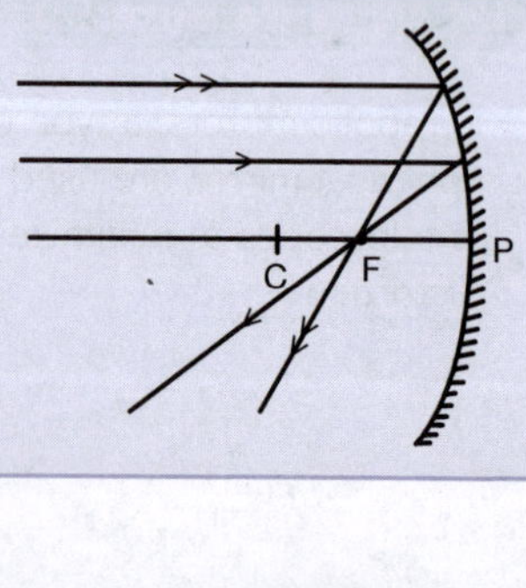	Infinity, i.e., $u = \infty$	Image distance = Focal length, i.e., on principal focus	Real, inverted and highly diminished

(*Continued*)

Table 7.1 (Continued)

Diagram	Object distance	Image distance	Nature of the image
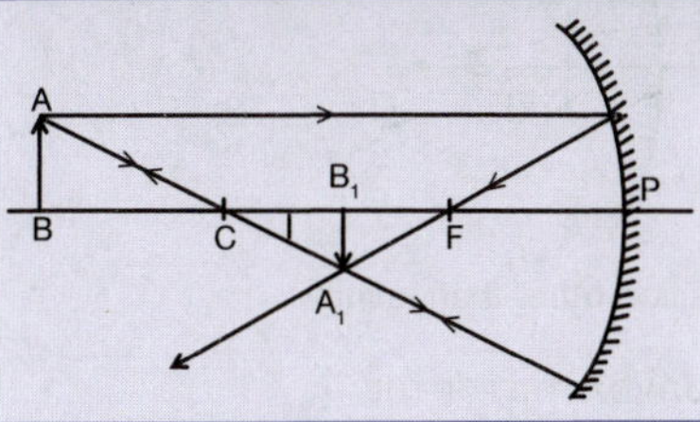	Beyond C but not at ∞ ($\infty > u > R$)	Image lies between *F* and *C*	Real, inverted and diminished
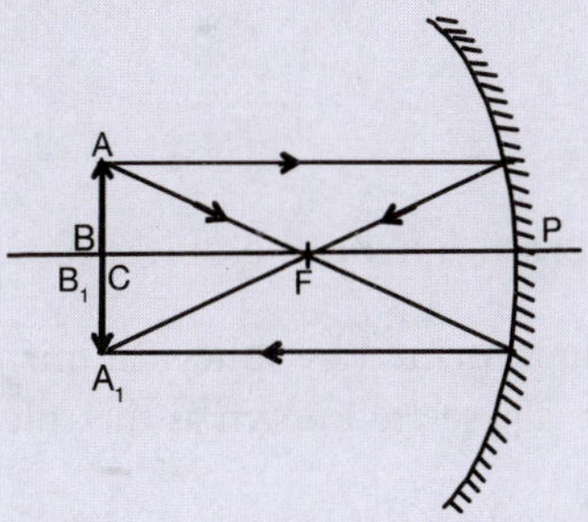	At *C*, i.e., $u = R$	at *C*, i.e., $v = R$	Real, inverted and of same size as that of the object.
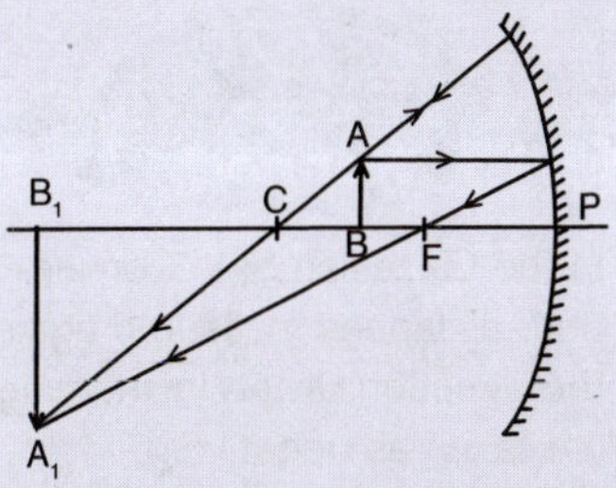	Between *C* and *F* ($R > u > f$)	Beyond *C* ($v > R$)	Real, inverted and magnified
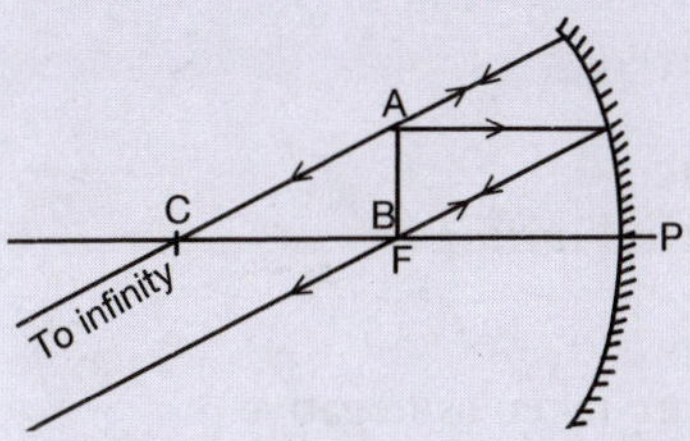	At *F*, $u = f$	At infinity ($v = \infty$)	Real, inverted and highly magnified
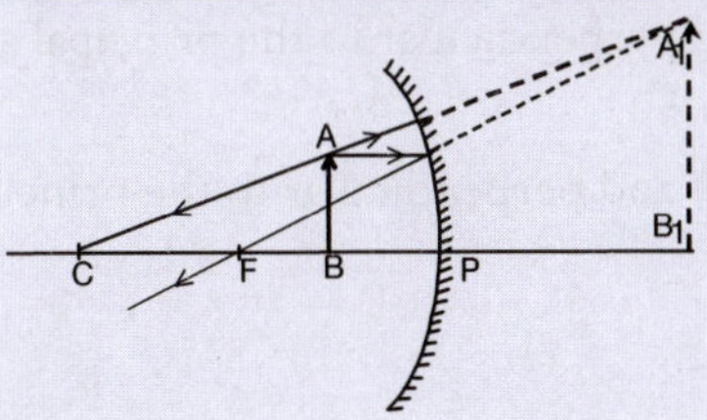	Between *F* and *P* ($u < f$)	Beyond the mirror	Virtual, erect and magnified and formed on the opposite side of the mirror as that of the object.

Formation of Images by Convex Mirror

When the object is at infinity, or it is nearer to the mirror, the nature of the image is almost similar. Wherever the object is placed, the image formed by a convex mirror is always, erect, virtual and diminished. The only difference is, when the object is at infinity, the image is highly diminished and formed at the principal focus. When the object is placed at any other position, the position of the image lies between the principal focus and the pole of the mirror as shown in the following figures.

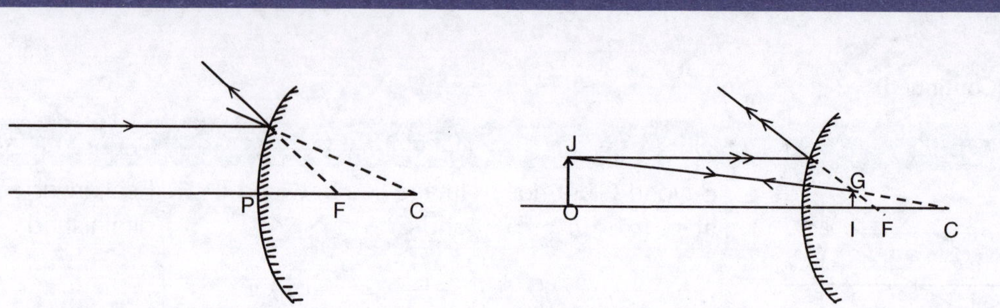

(a) When object is at infinity (b) When object is at any position other than infinity

Figure 7.24 Figure showing the position of images formed by convex mirror for various positions of object

Mirror Formula and Cartesian Sign Convention

The mirror formula is given by, $\frac{1}{f} = \frac{1}{u} + \frac{1}{v}$; where f, u and v are the focal length of spherical mirror, the object distance and the image distance, respectively. In order to solve numerical problems related to images formed by spherical mirrors, in an easy manner; positive and negative signs are adopted to the spherical mirror systems. These are known as the rules of sign convention to be followed to solve the problems (Figure 7.25).

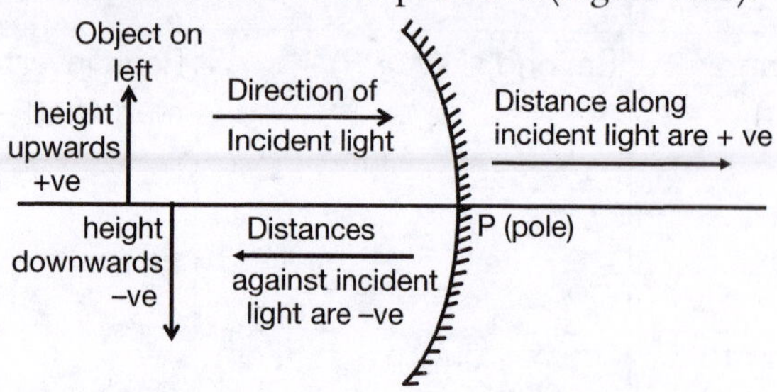

Figure 7.25 Cartesian sign convention

Konnect

In the Cartesian Sign Convention, distances measured against the direction of the incident light are taken as negative.

They are as follows:

1. All distances parallel to the principal axis are measured from the pole of the spherical mirror.
2. The distances measured in the direction of incident light are taken as positive.
3. The distances measured in a direction opposite to the direction of incident light are taken as negative.
4. The height of objects or images measured upwards (above the principal axis) and perpendicular to the principal axis are considered as positive.
5. The heights of objects or images measured downwards (below the principal axis) and perpendicular to the principal axis are considered as negative.

Experiment to Show Formation of Images by Concave Mirror

Apparatus Required: Mirror stand, screen, scale and concave mirror.

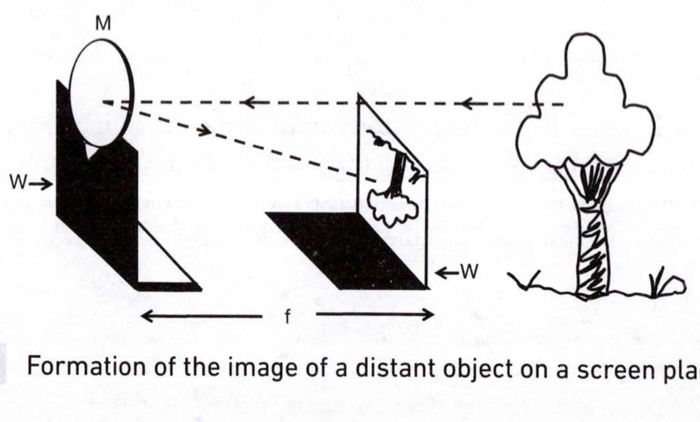

Figure 7.26 Formation of the image of a distant object on a screen placed at focus

Procedure

1. Mount a concave mirror on the mirror stand.
2. Focus the mirror to a distant object.
3. Introduce a screen and adjust the position of the screen such that a clear, sharp image of the distant object is formed on it.
4. Measure the distance between the screen and the concave mirror. This distance gives the focal length of the given mirror. Parallel beams from the distant object after reflection converges at the principal focus.

Observation

1. The image formed on the screen is smaller in size to that of the object.
2. The image obtained on the screen is inverted.
3. It is real image because it is caught on the screen.

Experiment to Obtain Image when the Object is at a Small Distance

Apparatus Required: Concave mirror, mirror stand, screen, scale and object (candle)

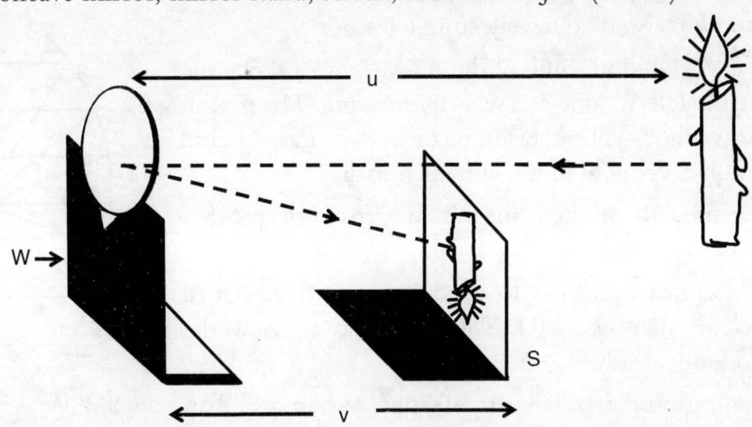

Figure 7.27 Formation of image due to a concave mirror-object at finite distance

Procedure

1. Mount a concave mirror on the mirror stand.
2. Place the mirror in front of an object (lighted candle) at a certain distance.
3. Place the screen between the object and mirror but not in line with them.
4. Adjust the position of the screen and the mirror until a bright and sharp image is obtained on the screen.
5. Measure the distance between the object and the mirror. This distance gives the object distance u.
6. Measure the distance between the concave mirror and the screen. This gives the image distance v.
7. Repeat the experiment for different values of object distance and tabulate the results.
8. The focal length of the given concave mirror can be found out using the mirror formula.

$$f = \frac{uv}{u+v}$$

Trial no	'u' (in m)	v (in m)	$f = \frac{uv}{u+v} (m)$

Observation

1. The image obtained on the screen is inverted.
2. It is a real image since it is caught on the screen.
3. The size of the image depends on the object distance.
4. If the object distance is greater than $2f$ of the concave mirror, the image will be smaller in size.
5. If the object distance is greater than the focal length but lesser than the radius of curvature of a given mirror, magnified image is obtained.

If a spherical mirror is given, we can easily identify whether the given mirror is concave or convex.

Concave mirror forms an enlarged and erect image of an object when it is much nearer to the object and if the object is moved further away from the mirror, the image becomes smaller. The convex mirror forms an erect and diminished image of the object.

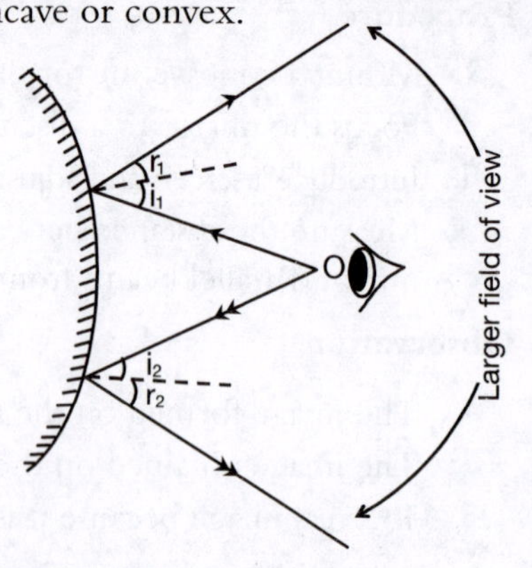

Figure 7.28 Increase in field view due to the presence of convex mirror

Uses of Spherical Mirrors

1. A convex mirror is a diverging mirror and it forms a diminished image. So, it is used as a side view mirror in vehicles so that the driver can observe a wide range of vehicles coming behind his vehicle (Figure 7.28).
2. Convex mirrors, at times, are placed at the traffic junctions where signals are not provided so that during the day time, drivers of the vehicles moving along one direction can be aware of any vehicles moving across their path. Spherical mirrors are also used in reflecting telescopes.
3. Convex mirrors are also placed in some of the ATM centres above the machine at some height. This is done as a security measure. The person operating the ATM machine will be aware of others who are behind him by being able to observe them in the convex mirror.
4. Concave mirrors are used to produce magnified virtual images. So, these can be used as shaving mirrors.
5. Due to the ability of concave mirrors to produce magnified, virtual images they are used by dentists and E.N.T. specialists to view the interior portions of a body clearly.
6. Concave mirrors can be used as reflectors of light. When a bulb is kept at the focus of the mirror, we obtain a parallel beam of light reflected from the mirror (Figure 7.29).

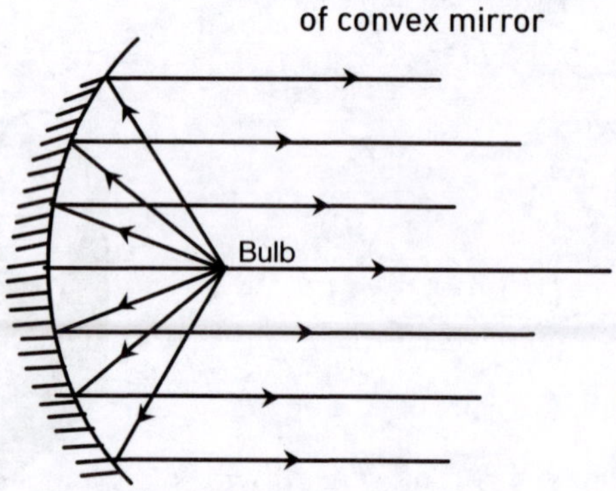

Figure 7.29 Figure to show how a concave mirror can be used to obtain parallel beam of light rays

EXAMPLE 7.2 Find the position of the image of an object placed at a distance of 150 cm from a convex mirror of a focal length 50 cm.

SOLUTION

In the given problem object distance $u = -150$ cm (by using sign convention). The focal length of the convex mirror, f = 50 cm.

From the mirror formula,

$$\frac{1}{f} = \frac{1}{u} + \frac{1}{v}$$

$$\frac{1}{50} = \frac{1}{-150} + \frac{1}{v}$$

Rearranging to find v:

$$\frac{1}{v} = \frac{1}{50} + \frac{1}{150} = \frac{4}{150}$$

$$v = \frac{150}{4} = 37.5\text{cm}$$

∴ The image distance is 37.5 cm.

EXAMPLE 7.3 An object of height 2 cm is placed on a principal axis at a distance of 10 cm from the pole of concave mirror. The image height is 5 cm. Find the image distance and the focal length of the concave mirror if the image is real and inverted.

SOLUTION

In the given problem,

The height of the object h_o = 2 cm

The height of the image h_i = – 5 cm (using sign convention)

The object distance u = – 10 cm (by using sign convention)

Since the image is real, image distance is negative = – v.

$$\therefore \text{Magnification} = \frac{h_i}{h_o} = \frac{v}{u}$$

$$= \frac{-5}{2} = \frac{-v}{-10}$$

$$= \frac{-5 \times -10}{2} = -v$$

$$v = -25 \text{ cm}$$

The focal length of the mirror

$$\frac{1}{f} = \frac{1}{u} + \frac{1}{v} \text{ (mirror formula)}$$

$$\therefore \frac{1}{f} = \frac{1}{-10} + \frac{1}{-25}$$

$$\therefore \frac{1}{f} = \frac{-25-10}{25 \times 10}$$

$$\frac{1}{f} = \left(\frac{-35}{250}\right) \text{ or } f = \left(-\frac{250}{35}\right) = -7.14 \text{ cm}$$

Refraction

Place a newspaper below a thick glass slab such that a portion of the paper lies outside the glass slab. View normally from the top of the glass slab. Portion of text lying below the glass slab appears closer than the portion outside the slab. Similarly, when a spoon is placed in a glass bowl, the spoon appears to be bent or discontinuous at air-water interface.

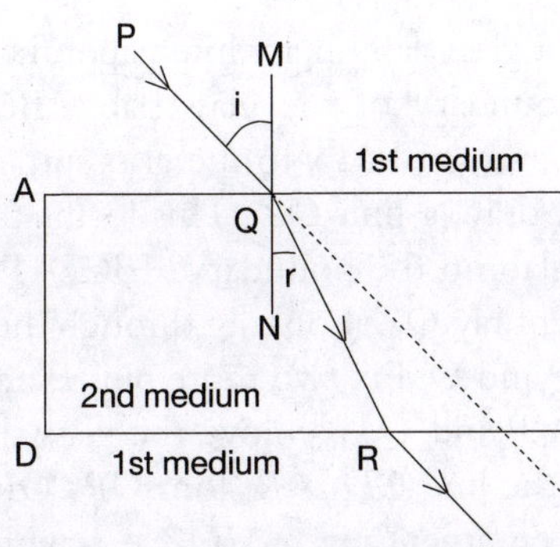

Figure 7.30 Refraction of a light ray traveling from air medium to glass medium

This perceived closeness of the text and the apparent bending of spoon is due to the refraction of a light. When light ray travels from one transparent medium to another, there is a deviation in the path of the light ray. This phenomenon is known as **refraction**. Refraction is due to change in speed of light while going from one medium to another.

PQ is the incident ray.

QR is the refracted ray.

MN is the normal to the refracting surface AB.

$\angle PQM = \angle i$ which is the angle of incidence.

$\angle RQN = r$ which is the angle of refraction.

Q is the point of incidence.

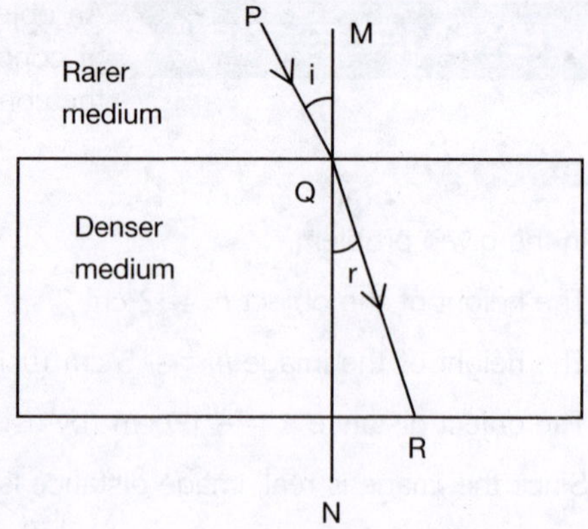

Figure 7.31 Refraction of a light ray traveling from rarer medium to a denser medium

When a diving board is seen from inside a pool of water, it appears to be at a greater height than it actually is. This is because light ray travelling from rarer to denser medium bends towards the normal and the object appears to be farther. The angle of incidence is greater than the angle of refraction if the light is incident from the rarer to the denser medium.

Due to the above-said reason, the sun appears to be at a higher position than its actual position during the sun rise and the sunset.

The floor of the swimming pool or a fish in water appears to be closer than they actually are when viewed from outside. This is because the light ray traveling from denser medium (water) to rarer medium (air) bends away from the normal, hence, the object appears to be nearer.

The angle of incidence is lesser than the angle of refraction $\angle i < \angle r$, when light travels from denser to rarer medium.

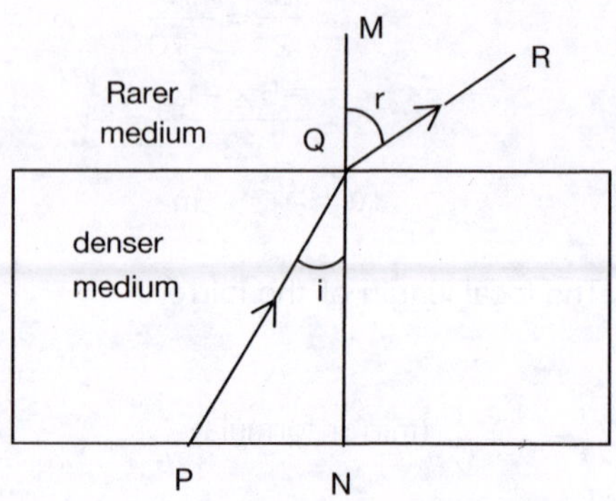

Figure 7.32 Refraction of a light ray traveling from a denser medium to a rarer medium

The Laws of Refraction

The refraction of light occurs in accordance with the following two laws of refraction.

1. The incident ray, the refracted ray and the normal to the refracting surface at the point of incidence, all lie in the same plane.
2. For a given pair of media and for the light of a given wavelength, the ratio of the sine of the angle of incidence to the sine of angle of refraction is a constant. This law is known as **Snell's law of refraction**.

$$\frac{\sin i}{\sin r} = \text{Constant}$$

Info Bytes!

When light is incident along the normal, the ray passes without deviation.

Refraction Through a Glass Slab

Place a glass slab on a white paper fixed to a drawing board. Mark the boundary of the glass slab $ABCD$. Remove the glass slab. Draw a normal MN to the glass surface AB. Taking suitable acute angle, draw a line OZ. This forms the incident ray. Replace the glass-slab on the boundary $ABCD$. Fix two pins P and Q on the incident ray OZ. Looking through the face CD, find the images of pins P and Q. Fix two more pins P' and Q' in line with the images of pin P and Q. Remove the glass slab. Join P' and Q' so that it meet the line CD at R. Join OR. OR is the refracted ray and RS is the emergent ray. $\angle MOZ = i$, which is the angle of incidence. $\angle NOR = r$, which is the angle of refraction and $\angle TRS$ is the angle of emergence.

Measure the angle of incidence, angle of refraction and angle of emergence.

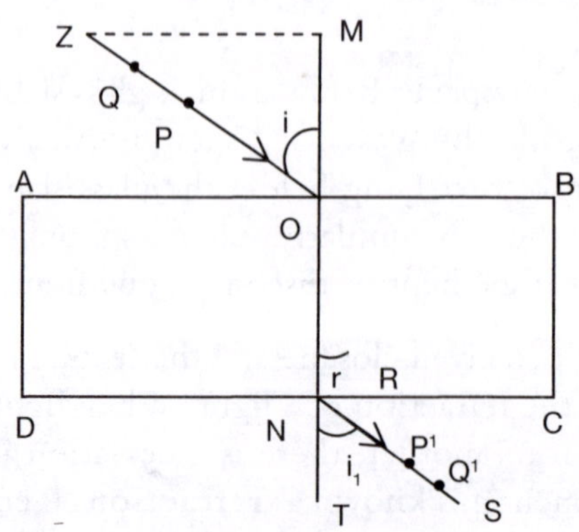

Figure 7.33 Refraction of light through glass slab

Calculate sin i and sin r and find their ratio.

The above experiment can be repeated for different angle of incidence and the result is tabulated.

Trial No.	Angle of incidence = $\angle i$	Angle of refraction = $\angle r$	sin i	sin r	$\frac{\sin i}{\sin r}$

Observation

In the above experiment it is found that

1. the incident ray, the refracted ray and the normal all lie in the plane of the paper.
2. The ratio of the sine of the angle of incidence to the sine of the angle of refraction is found to be constant, i.e.,

$$\frac{\sin i}{\sin r} = \text{constant.}$$

3. It is also found that the angle of emergence is equal to the angle of incidence. ($\angle i_1 = \angle i$) But the emergent ray is slightly displaced and is parallel to the incident ray. The emergent ray is parallel to the incident ray only if the medium on both the sides of the glass slab is the same.

Refractive Index of a Medium

Light is considered to be travelling in the form of waves. A wave has characteristics like wavelength, frequency and velocity.

These three parameters (i.e., physical quantities required to be measured) are related as $v = n\lambda$ where v, n and λ are the velocity, frequency and the wavelength, respectively.

When light travels from one transparent medium to another, a change in the wavelength of the light occurs due to a change in the density (more specifically, optical density considered with reference to the motion of light) of the medium. But the frequency of light (i.e., the number of light waves produced in unit time) does not change. This results in the change in the velocity of light when it travels from one transparent medium to another.

For a given pair of media, the ratio of the velocity of light in the two media is constant, which is known as the '**refractive index**' of one medium with reference to the other medium.

Consider a light ray travelling from air or vaccum to glass. Let 'c' and 'v' be the velocity of light in air or vacuum and glass respectively. Then, the ratio (c/v) is constant and is known as the refractive index of glass. The standard symbol for denoting refractive index is 'μ'.

To calculate the refractive index of any medium, the standard medium which is taken as reference is air or vacuum. The velocity of light is greater in the rarer medium when compared to the velocity of light in the denser medium.

For a given pair of media, the refractive index is calculated for the denser medium with reference to the rarer medium.

If v_1 and v_2 are the velocities of light in the 1st medium which is rarer and the 2nd medium which is denser, respectively, then the refractive index of the 2nd medium with reference to the 1st medium is given by $\mu_{21} = \frac{v_1}{v_2}$. If '$c$' is the velocity of light in air or vacuum then, the refractive index of the 1st medium with respect to air or vacuum (or simply known as the refractive index of the 1st medium) is given by $\mu_1 = \frac{c}{v_1}$ and similarly the refractive index of the 2nd medium is given by $\mu_2 = \frac{c}{v_2}$.

Hence, $\mu_{21} = \frac{v_1}{v_2} \Rightarrow \mu_{21} = \frac{v_1}{v_2} \times \frac{c}{c}$

$$\Rightarrow \mu_{21} = \frac{c}{v_2} \times \frac{v_1}{c} = \frac{c}{v_2} \div \frac{c}{v_1} \Rightarrow \mu_{21} = \frac{\left(\frac{c}{v_2}\right)}{\left(\frac{c}{v_1}\right)}$$

$$\Rightarrow \mu_{21} = \frac{v_1}{v_2}$$

Hence, we can define the refractive index or **absolute refractive index** of a material as 'the ratio of velocity of light in air or vacuum to the velocity of light in the medium'.

Konnect

1. Optical density is the property of a material and refractive index is the measure of that property.
2. The more the refractive index of a material is the more the light bends while travelling in that medium.
3. Since refractive index is the ratio of velocity, it does not have any unit and is just a number.

EXAMPLE 7.4 The velocity of light in first medium is 2.8×10^8 m s^{-1} and that in the second medium is 2.3×10^8 m s^{-1}. Find the refractive index of medium 2 with respect to medium 1.

SOLUTION

In the given problem.

Velocity of light in medium 1, $v_1 = 2.8 \times 10^8$ m s^{-1}

Velocity of light in medium 2, $v_2 = 2.3 \times 10^8$

Refractive index of medium 2 with respect to medium is given by

$$\mu_{21} \text{ or } {}^1\mu_2 = \frac{v_1}{v_2}$$

$$\therefore {}^1\mu_2 = \frac{2.8 \times 10^8}{2.3 \times 10^8} = 1.2$$

EXAMPLE 7.5 Find the velocity of light in a given medium. The absolute refractive index of the medium is 1.5 (given velocity of light in vacuum or air = 3×10^8 m s^{-1}).

SOLUTION

In the given problem

Velocity of light in air or vacuum,

$$c = 3 \times 10^8 \text{ m s}^{-1}$$

Velocity of light in a given medium = ?

Absolute refractive index of the medium is $\mu = 1.5$

$$\mu = \frac{c}{v}$$

$$1.5 = \frac{3 \times 10^8}{v}$$

$$v = 1.5 = \frac{3 \times 10^8}{v} = 2 \times 10^8 \text{ m s}^{-1}.$$

$\therefore$ The velocity of light in the given medium is 2×10^8 m s^{-1}.

Apparent Depth—A Phenomenon Due to Refraction

Consider a glass slab of depth '*t*'; light rays travelling from the depth *t*, such as *OA* is refracted along *AB* and the refracted ray when produced backwards, meets at point *I*. The point *I* lies on the ray *OC* which travels normally to the interface and reaches the eye undeviated. Thus, the ray appears to come from *I* and not from *O*. *I* is the virtual image of *O* placed at depth '*t*'. *CI* is the apparent depth, i.e., the depth seen by us.

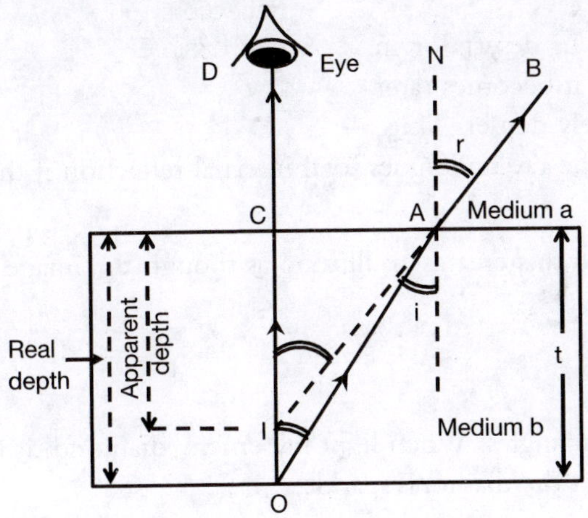

Figure 7.34 Apparent Depth

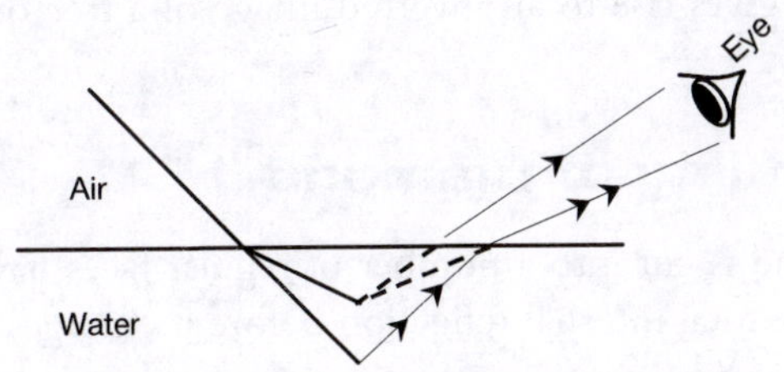

Figure 7.35 Apparent bent in a stick

When light enters from a denser medium to a rarer medium it bends away from the normal. As a consequence of this, the depth of a pond or the thickness of a glass slab appears to be less than the actual value (Figure 7.34). It is due to the same reason that a stick partially immersed in water appears to be bent (Figure 7.35) and short.

When a coin is placed in an empty beaker and water is poured into it, the coin appears to be raised. This happens due to the refraction of light. The depth of the coin due to optical illusion is known as 'apparent depth' and the actual depth is known as the 'real depth'.

Both apparent and real depths are related to the refractive index of water by the relation,

$$\mu = \frac{\text{Real depth}}{\text{Apparent depth}}$$

This equation is applicable not only to water but also to any other liquid in which refraction of light takes place.

Total Internal Reflection

When a light ray travels from a denser to rarer medium, the refracted ray bends away from the normal. When the angle of incidence is further increased, the angle of refraction also increases. At a particular angle of incidence, the refracted ray just grazes the surface separating the two media or in other words the angle of refraction is equal to 90°. The angle of incidence for which the angle of refraction is 90° is called **critical angle** and is denoted by 'c'. If the angle of incidence is greater than the critical angle, the light rays are not refracted but they are reflected back in the same denser medium. This phenomenon is known as **total internal reflection**.

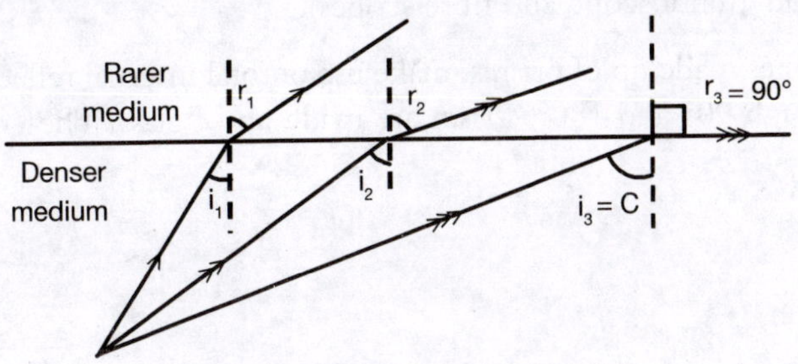

Figure 7.36 Critical angle

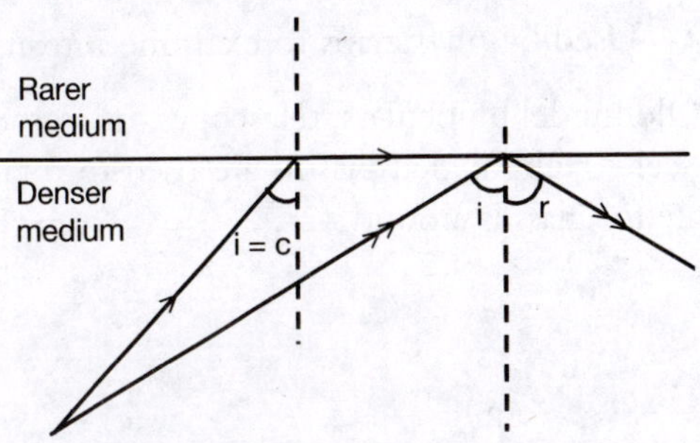

Figure 7.37 Total internal reflection

The conditions required for the total internal reflection to take place are:

1. Light rays should travel from the denser to the rarer medium and
2. The angle of incidence should be greater than the critical angle.

Info Bytes!

The formula of Total Internal Reflection:
$n = 1/\sin C$

Mirage

It is an optical illusion caused due to total internal reflection. In deserts or in peak summers the air above the earth surface gets heated up and it becomes rarer whereas the upper layers of in the atmosphere air are comparatively denser. Thus, the light from the sun travels from denser to rarer medium and the ray undergoes total internal reflection if the angle of incidence is greater than the critical angle of air.

This gives rise to an inverted image of a tree or any object and this creates an illusion as though the image is formed in water.

Sparkling of Diamond

Diamond is cut into a number of regular faces having appropriate angles. When light ray enters diamond, it undergoes multiple total internal reflection before it emerges out. This makes the diamond sparkle.

Bicycle Reflectors

A disc on the rear side of the bicycle which glows red when light is incident on it, works on the principle of total internal reflection. It is made up of a reflecting prism which make the disc's surface glitter which in turn makes the drivers vehicles approaching the bicycle take notice of its presence.

Optical Fibres

Optical fibres are used to transport images. An optical fibre consists of glass or plastic fibre which has a very small area of cross-section. A number of fibres are placed parallel to each other and clamped at the edges to form a cable. The ends of the cable or the fibres are highly polished. These cables or fibres are used to transport light in any desired path. Since the pipes have a small area of cross section, the incident ray strikes the fibre at a glancing angle. The light entering a fibre undergoes a series of total internal reflections before emerging out.

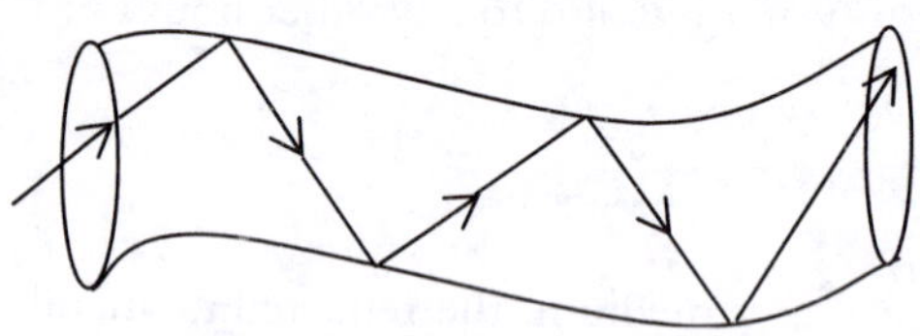

Figure 7.38 Optical fibre

Uses

1. Used in communication of images and sound.
2. Used by physicians to examine internal parts of the body (endoscope and fibre scopes).

Old model binoculars, telescopes, microscopes, and periscopes made up of prisms, make use of total internal reflection. Isosceles right angled prisms are used to rotate the light through 90° and 180°. Prism are made up of glass. The critical angle for glass is around 42°.

Refraction through a Prism

A prism is a solid with triangular surfaces at two ends and bounded by three rectangular lateral surfaces (Fig. 7.39). Any section perpendicular to the rectangular surface is called principal section.

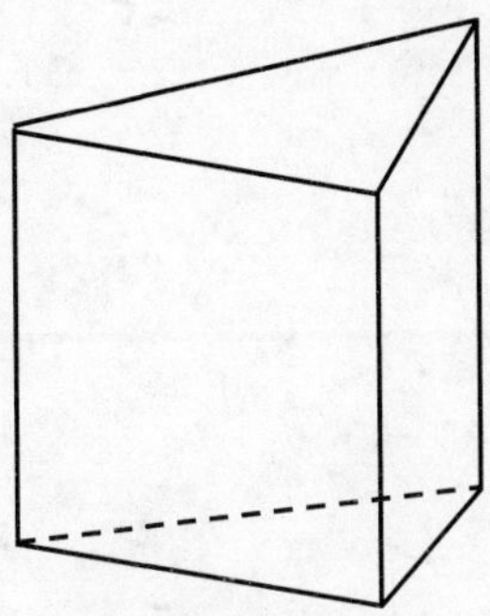

Figure 7.39 Prism

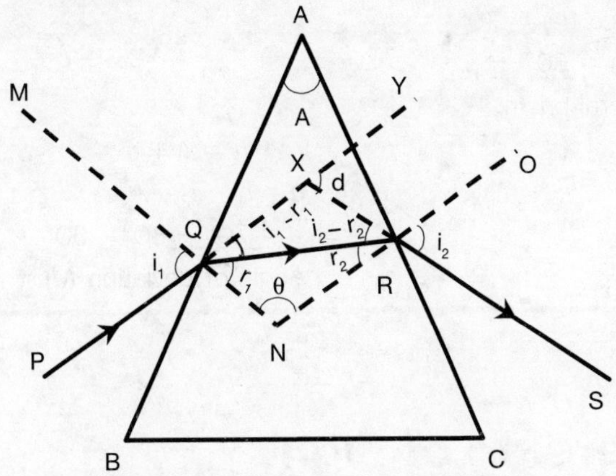

Figure 7.40 Refraction through glass prism

Consider the principal cross section of the prism ABC as shown in Fig. 7.40. BC is the base of the prism and AB, AC are the refracting surfaces. The angle between them, i.e., $\angle BAC = A$, is the angle of the prism. 'PQ' is the incident light ray at 'Q' on face AB of the prism. 'QR' is the refracted ray inside the prism and 'RS' is the emergent ray emerging from face AC. 'i_1' is the angle of incidence, 'i_2' is the angle of emergence 'r_1' is the angle of refraction on face 'AB' and 'r_2' is the angle of incidence inside the prism on the face 'AC'. In the absence of the prism, the light ray would travel along the path '$PQXY$'. Due to the presence of the prism, it refracts at 'Q' and 'R' on the two faces and emerges in the direction 'RS'. The angle between incident ray (PQ) and emergent ray (RS), i.e., $\angle YXR$ (= d) is known as the angle of deviation. 'MN' and 'NO' are the normals at 'Q' and 'R' on faces 'AB' and 'AC', respectively. From the figure, in the quadrilateral $AQNR$, $A + \theta = 180°$, and in ΔQRN, $r_1 + r_2 + \theta = 180°$.

Thus, $$A + \theta = r_1 + r_2 + \theta$$

$\therefore$ $$A = r_1 + r_2 \qquad (7.1)$$

In ΔXQR, $$\begin{aligned} d &= (i_1 - r_1) + (i_2 - r_2) \\ &= i_1 - r_1 + i_2 - r_2 \\ &= (i_1 + i_2) - (r_1 + r_2) \\ &= (i_1 + i_2) - A \end{aligned}$$

Thus, we have $$i_1 + i_2 = A + d \qquad (7.2)$$

Rotation of Light Rays using Different Prisms

Rotates through 90°

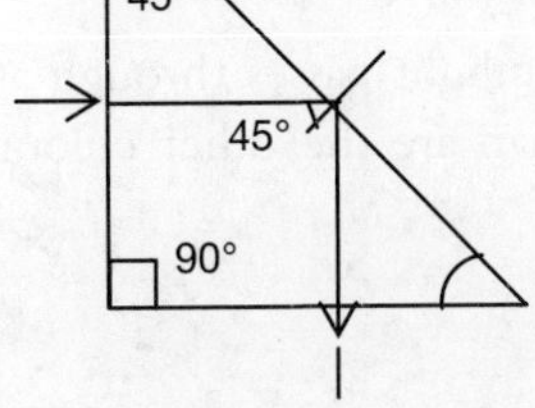

Rotates the light through 180°

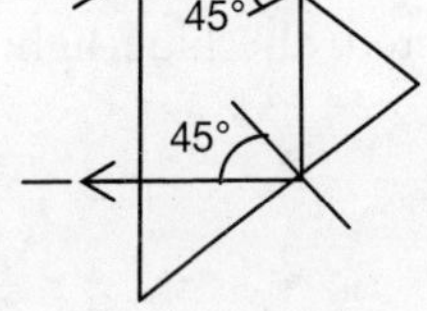

Figure 7.41 Right angled isosceles prism and Equilateral prism

EXAMPLE 7.6 A light ray incidents on an equilateral triangle with an angle of 30°. Find the angle of deviation of the emergent light ray if the angle of emergence from the second surface is 70°.

SOLUTION

Angle of incidence (i_1) = 30°
Angle of emergence (i_2) = 70°
Angle of prism (A) = 60°
since it an equilateral prism,

$$i_1 + i_2 = A + d$$
$$d = i_1 + i_2 - A$$
$$\Rightarrow d = 70° + 30° - 60°$$
$$\Rightarrow \text{Angle of deviation } (d) = 40°$$

Dispersion of Light

When sunlight (white light) is made to pass through a prism, it is found that the ray of white light splits into its constituent colours. This phenomenon is called **dispersion of light**.

As discussed earlier the refractive index of a medium is different for different wavelengths (colours). When a ray of white light falls on a refracting surface like a prism, although the angle of incidence is the same for all colours, the angle of refraction is different for different colours. This causes the white light to split into its constituent colours (Figure 7.42).

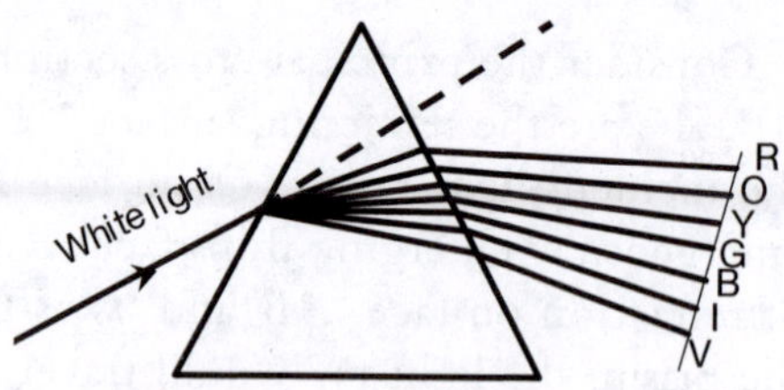

Figure 7.42 Dispersion of light

Spectrum

The visible light consists of seven colours. The band of these seven colours is called visible **spectrum**.

Rainbow

The formation of a rainbow is due to the dispersion of the sunlight by water droplets. When sunlight falls on water droplets, light undergoes dispersion. Water droplets act as a dispersive medium. Some times two rainbows appear together. The inner rainbow is called **primary rainbow** and the outer rainbow is called **secondary rainbow**. The primary rainbow is narrower and brighter than the secondary rainbow. Rainbow is due to dispersion, refraction and total internal reflection.

Scattering of light

When light falls on dust and other minute particles present in the atmosphere it undergoes irregular reflection and spreads. This is called **scattering of light**.

Blue Colour of the Sky

The colour of the sky is blue due to dispersion and scattering. When sunlight passes through atmosphere it undergoes refraction. When light gets refracted, the blue light is scattered more than are the other colours by the air molecules. Hence, the sky appears blue.

Lenses

A **lens** is a transparent medium bound by two refracting surfaces. A lens can be bounded by two curved surfaces or one plane surface and one curved surface. There are many types of lenses, as shown in Figure 7.43.

(a) plano-convex lens (b) plano-concave lens (c) biconcave (or simply, concave) lens (d) biconvex (or simply, convex) lens (e) convex-concave lens

Figure 7.43 Types of lenses

A biconvex lens can be considered to be formed from the combination of two glass spheres, as shown in Fig. 7.44. Since it is formed from two spheres, it will have two centres of curvature and correspondingly two radii of curvature (whose values need not always be equal). A convex surface having a larger radius of curvature is less curved. (If the curvature is zero, i.e., if the surface is plane, the radius of curvature is infinity). An imaginary line passing through the two centres of curvature of the two surfaces of a lens is known as the '**principal axis**' of the lens.

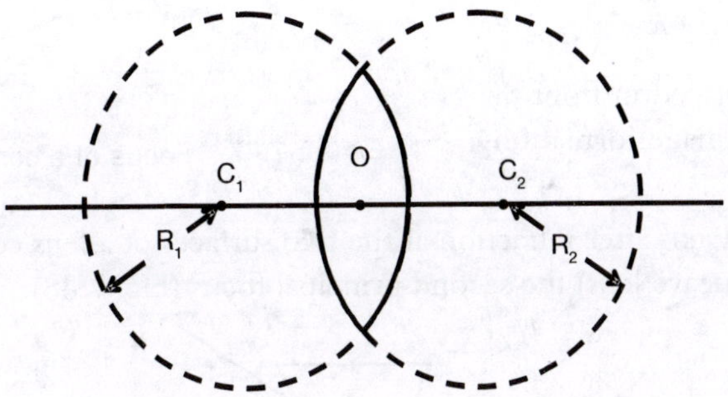

Figure 7.44 Formation of a convex lens

> **Info Bytes!**
>
> Contact lenses work on the principle of refraction to correct vision.

The mid-point of the line segment 'C_1C_2' (shown as 'O' in Fig. 7.44) is known as the **optic centre** of the lens. For a thin lens and for all practical purposes, the distance from the optic centre to the centre of curvature is treated as the **radius of curvature**.

A biconcave lens is considered to be formed by filling the space between two imaginary spheres with glass, as shown in (Fig. 7.45).

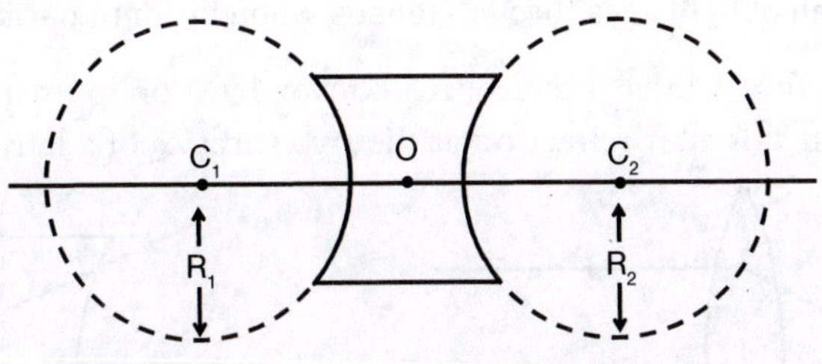

Figure 7.45 Formation of a concave lens

Similar to a convex lens, the centres and the radii of curvature of the two concave surfaces and the optic centre and principal axis are shown in (Fig. 7.45).

When a beam of light parallel to the principal axis is incident on a lens, it refracts at the two surfaces and after refraction at the two surfaces, it converges at (in the case of a convex lens) or appears to diverge from (in the case of a concave lens) a point on the principal axis, which is known as the **principal focus** *(F)*.

Thus, a convex lens is also known as a converging lens and a concave lens is also known as a diverging lens. Converging lenses are generally the thickest in the middle while diverging lens are thinnest in the middle.

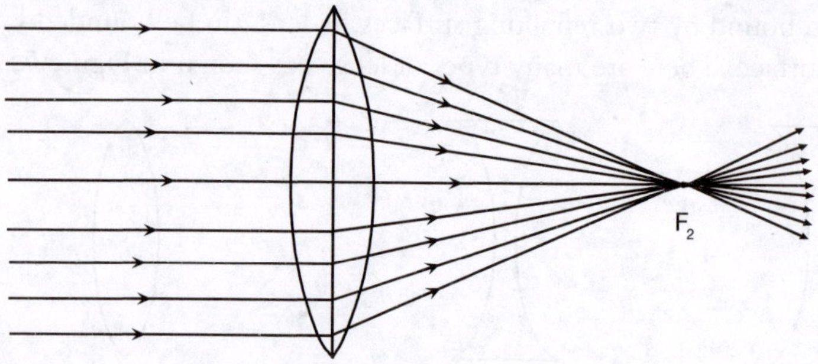

Figure 7.46 Focus of a convex lens

The distance of an object from the optic centre of a lens is known as the object distance (denoted by '*u*'), the distance of an image from the optic centre of a lens is known as the image distance (denoted by '*v*') and the distance of principal focus from the optic centre of a lens is known as the '**focal length**' (denoted by '*f*').

Since a lens has two refracting surfaces, like two centres and radii of curvature, it has two principal foci and focal lengths, each on either side of the lens.

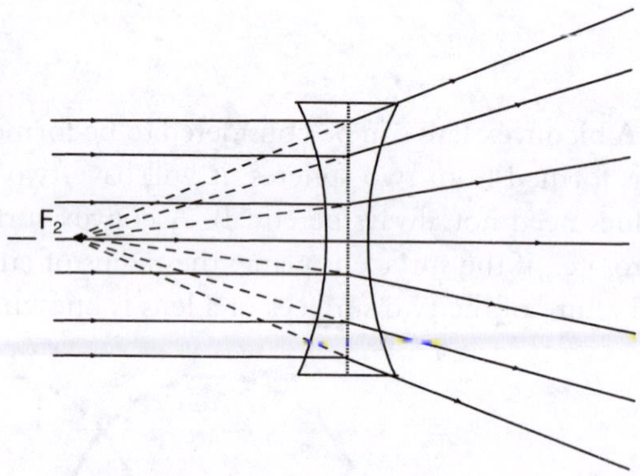

Figure 7.47 Focus of a concave lens

Refraction by Spherical Lenses

Any two of the following rays coming from an object placed in front of a lens are taken into consideration to know about the image formation in lenses.

1. A light ray from an object parallel to the principal axis after refraction at the two surfaces of a lens converges at (in a convex lens) or appears to diverge from (in a concave lens) the second principal focus (Fig. 7.48).

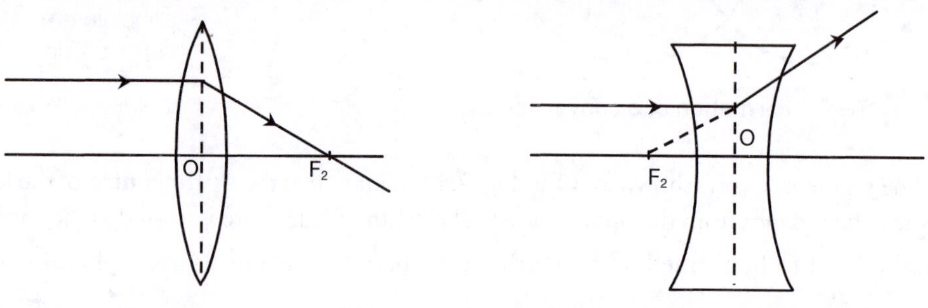

Figure 7.48 Refraction of light rays through lenses when incident parallel to principal axis

2. A light ray passing through the first principal focus (in a convex lens) or appearing to meet at it (in a concave lens) emerges parallel to the principal axis after refraction at the two surfaces of a lens (Fig. 7.49).

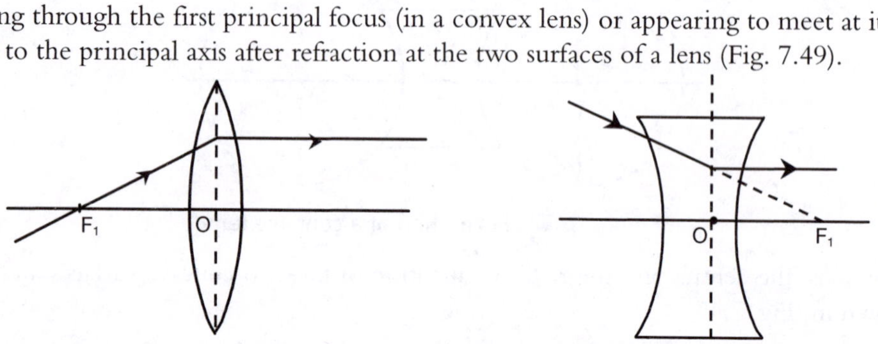

Figure 7.49 Refraction of light rays through lenses when incident light rays pass through or appear to pass through focus

3. A ray of light passing through the optical centre of a lens, emerges without any deviation after refraction at the two surfaces of the lens (Fig. 7.50).

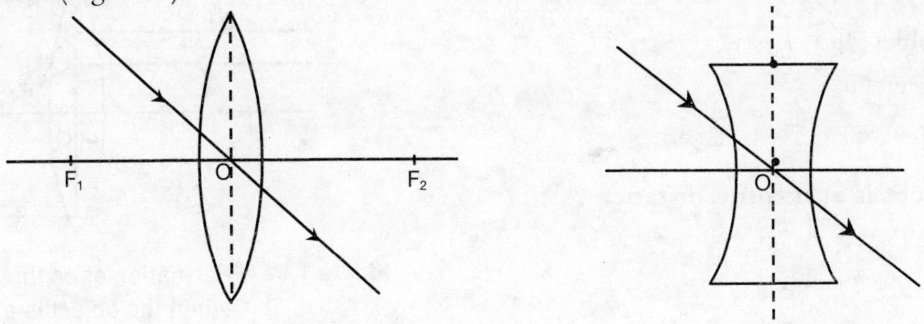

Figure 7.50 Refraction of light rays through lenses when incident light rays pass through Optic center

Sign Convention for Lenses

1. All distances parallel to the principal axis are measured from the optic centre of the lens.

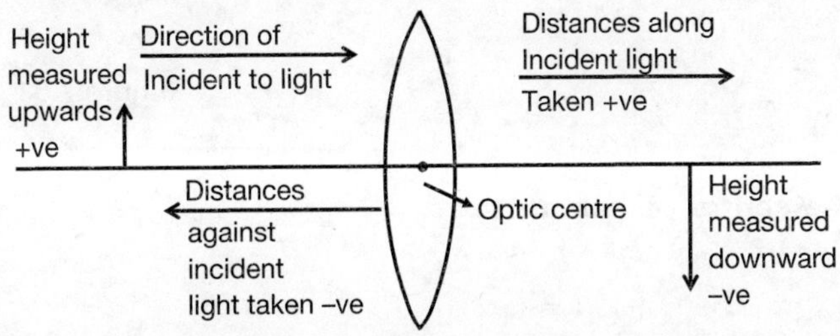

Figure 7.51 Sign convention in lenses

2. The distances measured in the direction of incident light are considered to be positive.
3. The distances measured in the direction opposite to the direction of incident light are taken as negative.
4. The heights of objects or images measured upwards (above the principal axis) and perpendicular to it are considered as positive.
5. The height of objects or images measured downwards (below the principal axis) and perpendicular to it are considered as negative.

Lens Formula

The relation between object distance (u), image distance (v) and focal length of a lens (f) is given by the expression $\frac{1}{f} = \frac{1}{v} - \frac{1}{u}$. This expression is known as **lens formula**, and is applicable to both convex as well as concave lenses.

Magnification in case of spherical lens is given by,

$$m = \frac{h_i}{h_0} = \frac{v}{u}$$

Formation of Images by a Convex Lens

The image of an object placed in front of a convex lens depends on the distance of the object from the lens. The distances of the object and its image from the lens are measured from optic centre of the lens.

When the object is at infinite distance from the lens, the image is formed on the other side of the lens, highly diminished, real and inverted. As the object moves nearer to the lens, the image moves away from the lens gradually and even the size of the image formed increases.

The following figures illustrate the formation of images by a convex lens when an object is at different positions.

Symbols used:

$OF_1 = OF_2 =$ Focal length $= f$

$OA =$ object distance $= u$

$OA_1 =$ image distance $= v$

1. When the object is at infinite distance

The image is

(i) Formed at the focus (F_2)

(ii) Real

(iii) Inverted and

(iv) Highly diminished (Fig. 7.52).

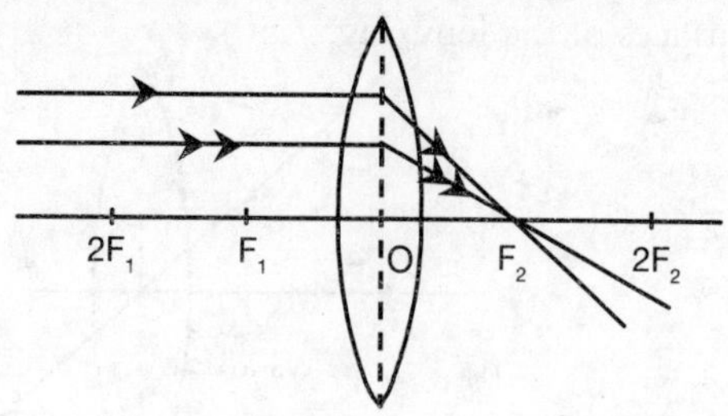

Figure 7.52 Formation of an image by a convex lens when the object is placed at infinity

2. When the object is beyond the centre of curvature

The image is

(i) Formed between F_2 and $2F_2$

(ii) Real

(iii) Inverted and

(iv) Diminished (Fig. 7.53)

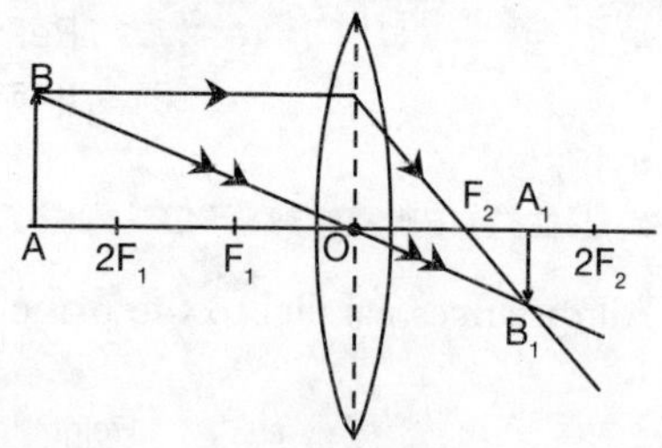

Figure 7.53 Figure showing the formation of an image by a convex lens when the object is placed at the center of curvature

3. When the object is at the centre of curvature

The image is

(i) Formed at $2F_2$,

(ii) Real,

(iii) Inverted, and

(iv) Same size as that of the object (Fig. 7.54).

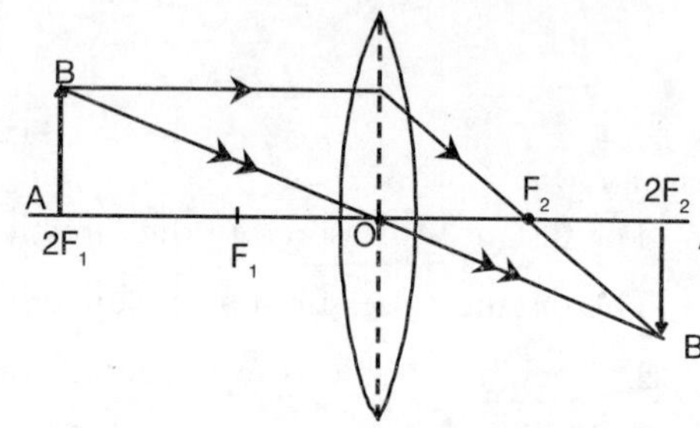

Figure 7.54 Figure showing the formation of an image by a convex lens when the object is placed at the center of curvature

4. When the object is between the principal focus and centre of curvature

The image is

(i) Formed beyond $2F_2$,

(ii) Real,

(iii) Inverted, and

(iv) Magnified (Fig. 7.55)

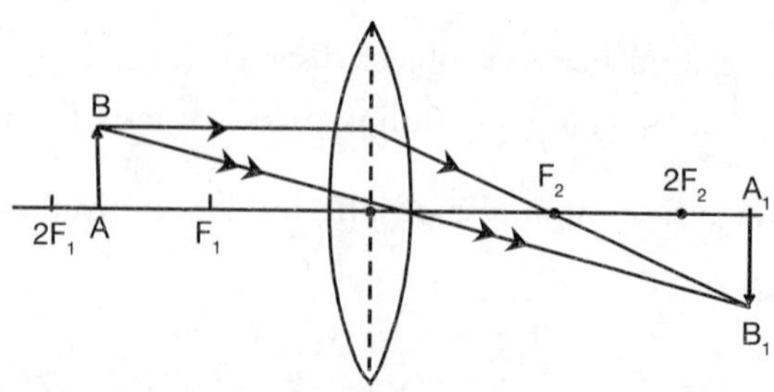

Figure 7.55 Formation of an image by a convex lens when the object is placed between focus and the center of curvature

5. When the object is at the principal focus

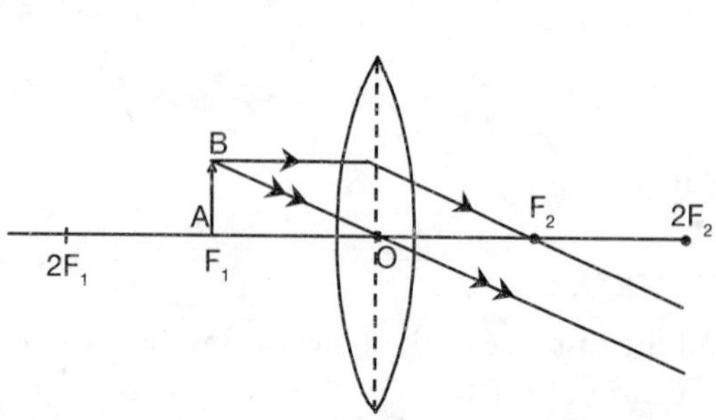

Figure 7.56 Formation of an image by a convex lens when the object is placed at the focus of the lens

The image is
- (i) Formed at infinity,
- (ii) Real,
- (iii) Inverted, and
- (iv) Highly magnified (Fig. 7.56).

6. **When the object is placed between the optic centre and the principal focus**
In this case the refracted rays are diverging, and hence, a real image cannot be formed. When the diverging rays are produced backward, they meet at a point and the position where these divergent rays appear to meet is the position of the image. Hence, the image is erect, virtual and magnified. Here the image is formed on the same side of the lens, i.e., on the side where the object lies. (Fig. 7.57).

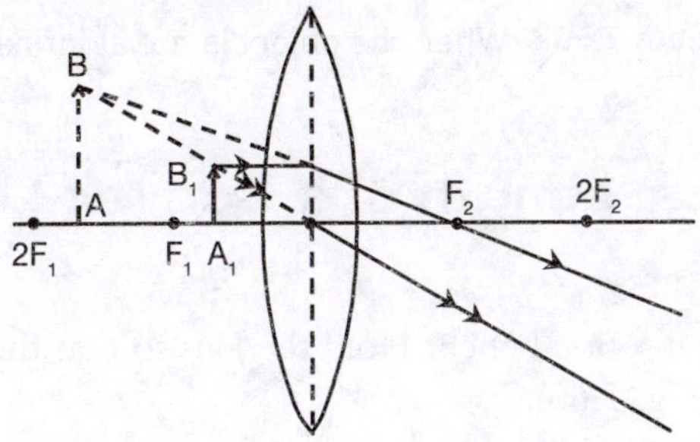

Figure 7.57 Formation of an image by a convex lens when the object is placed in between focus and the optic center

The above information can be summarized in the table 7.2:

Table 7.2 Nature of images formed by convex lens

Object distance	Image distance	Nature of image
$u = \infty$	$v = f$	Real, inverted and highly diminished
$2f < u < \infty$	$f < v < 2f$	Real, inverted and diminished
$u = 2f$	$v = 2f$	Real, inverted and of the same size as that of the object
$f < u < 2f$	$v > 2f$	Inverted, real and magnified
$u = f$	$v = \infty$	Real, inverted and highly magnified
$u < f$	–	Virtual, erect, magnified and formed on the same side of the lens on the side where the object lies.

Formation of Image by a Concave Lens

In the case of a concave lens, the nature of the image does not change with a change in the object distance, as illustrated in the following Figs, 7.58 and 7.59 except that there will be a slight difference in the magnification. When the object is at infinity the image is highly diminished and is formed at F_2. When the object is at other places, it is diminished, and is formed between O and F_2.

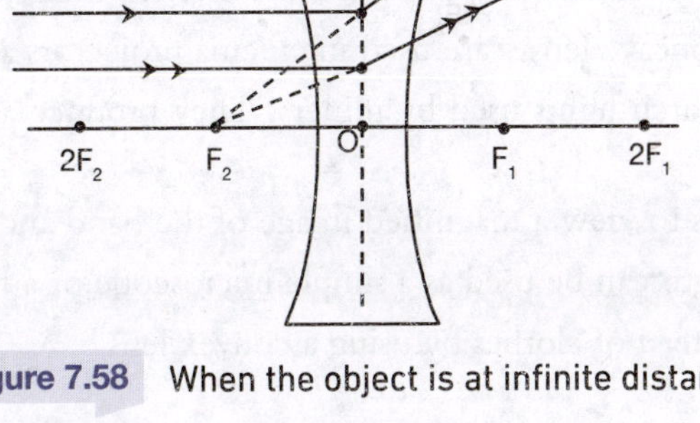

Figure 7.58 When the object is at infinite distance

The nature of the image is always virtual, diminished, erect and formed on the same side of the lens as the object. Due to this nature of a concave lens, it is used in Galileo telescope and for correcting short sightedness.

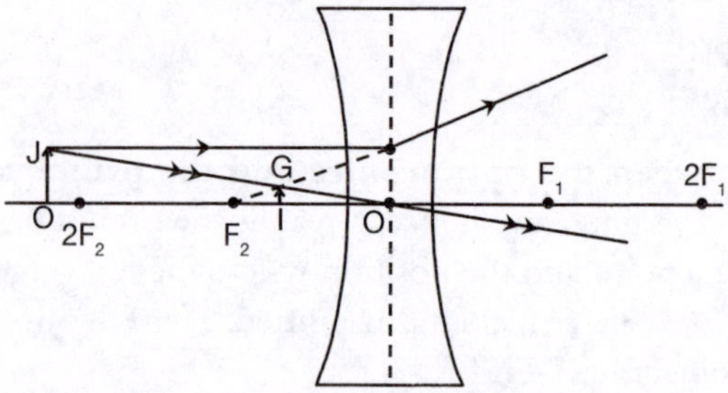

Figure 7.59 When the object is not at infinity

Determination of the Focal Length of a Convex Lens

Using a Distant Object

Mount a convex lens and a screen on an optic bench. Hold the lens so that the rays of light from the sun fall directly upon it. Focus the image on the screen (Fig. 7.60).

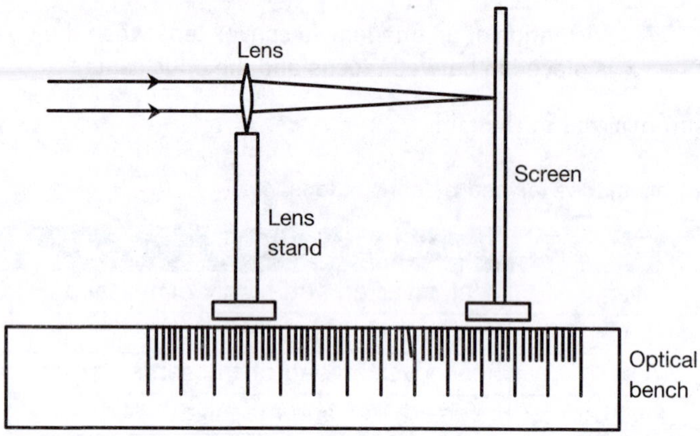

Figure 7.60 Experimental arrangement to determine the focal length of a particular convex lens

Measure the distance of the image from the optical centre of the lens. Since the object distance is infinity, the image distance would be equal to the focal length.

Uses of Lenses

1. A convex lens having short focal length can be used to focus light coming from the sun at a point and can be used for burning.
2. A convex lens is used in photographic cameras.
3. A convex lens can be used in a terrestrial telescope to make the inverted images erect, and is known as an erecting lens.
4. A combination of convex and concave lenses are used in cinema projectors and LCD projectors.
5. Convex lenses can be used in search lights used by miners. They produce a parallel beam of light when a bulb is placed at the principal focus.
6. A convex lens is used by palmists to view a magnified image of the hand and to study it.
7. A convex lens of short focal length can be used as a simple microscope or a hand-lens to read fine prints.
8. We can observe the weaving pattern of clothes by using a convex lens.

9. A convex lens of appropriate focal length can be used for correcting long sightedness.
10. A concave lens of appropriate focal length can be used for correcting short-sightedness.
11. A concave lens is also used as an eye lens in a Galileo telescope.

Human Eye

The human eye has some limitations, a few of which are listed below.

1. Inability to see clearly far off objects like stars.
2. Inability to see very small objects like bacterial cells.
3. The images formed are temporary and cannot be stored permanently.

Also due to ageing and due to several other reasons, a person may be unable to see nearby or distant objects clearly.

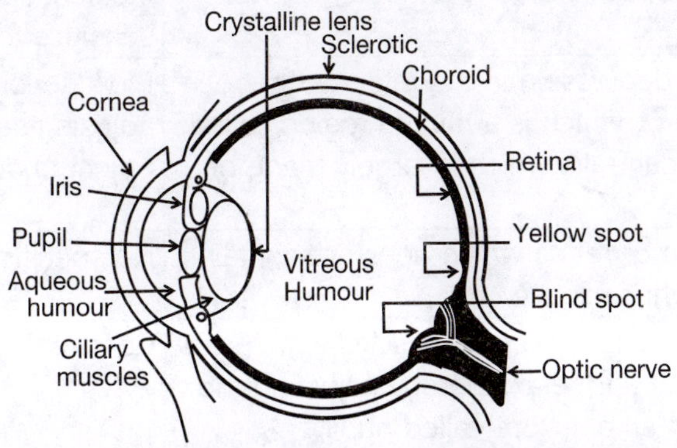

Figure 7.61 Human Eye

To overcome these limitations and defects, several optical instruments like spectacles, microscopes, telescopes and camera were invented.

These optical instruments help us to see better. Before we discuss how different optical instruments help us in doing that, we discuss the functioning of a human eye.

A normal human eye is a spherical ball having a diameter of about 2.5 cm, with a slight bulge in the front portion.

The table 7.3 below gives the different parts of an eye, their description and their function.

Table 7.3 Parts of an eye, their description and functionality

Part of eye	Description	Function
Sclerotic	A thick, white and opaque fibrous tissue covering the exterior part of the eye ball.	Gives a definite shape to the eye and protects the interior parts.
Choroid	A dull grey membrane between sclerotic and retina.	Keeps the interior part of the eye ball dark by preventing internal reflections.
Cornea	Tough and transparent membrane covering the front part of the eye.	Allows the light to enter the eye.
Aqueous humor	A transparent liquid present in the region behind cornea.	Keeps the cornea moist and gives definite shape to the eye ball.
Crystalline lens	A capsule containing a fibrous jelly. Hard at the centre and softer at outer portions.	Acts as a double convex lens and helps focusing the image on the retina.
Ciliary muscles	A ring of muscles which hold the lens in place.	Relax and contract, thereby changing the focal length of the lens.

(Continue)

Table 7.3 Continued

Part of eye	Description	Function
Vitreous humor	Thin jelly like fluid consisting largely of water. Present behind the lens.	Prevents the eye ball from collapsing.
Optic nerve	A bunch of thousands of nerves which originate from the brain.	Helps in transmitting optical impulses to the brain.
Retina	The ends of thousands of nerves of optical fibres form a hemispherical delicate film on the inner surface of the eye. This film is called retina.	Converts the image that is formed on it into optical impulses.
Rods and cones	Special type of cells on retina which are rod shaped and cone shaped.	Rod cells respond to the intensity of incident light, whereas cone cells are sensitive to colours.
Yellow spot or Macula	Slight depression in the retina at the centre of which is a minute region called fovea centralis which is largely made of cones.	Most sensitive part of the eye, the lens adjusts itself such that the image of an object under observation falls on fovea.
Blind spot	Portion of retina which does not contain any light sensitive cells.	No specific function.
Iris and pupil	Iris comprises several muscles which can contract and relax, thereby adjusting the size of an aperture called pupil.	Control the amount of light entering the eye.

Formation of Image on the Retina

The rays coming from an object enter the eye through the pupil. The size automatically dilates if the brightness is low and decreases when brightness is high. This ability of the eye to adapt to changes in brightness is called adaptation of the eye. The light entering through the eye falls on the lens, which being a converging lens, converges the rays on to the retina, forming an inverted and real image. The optical nerves convert the image into optical impulses and then pass on the image to the brain.

As discussed earlier, a human eye has a unique ability to adjust its focal length. The focal length of the lens is varied by relaxing or contracting the ciliary muscles. This process of altering the focal length of the lens is known as the **accommodation of eye**.

When objects near the eye are being viewed, the ciliary muscles contract, making the lens more convex, this helps in decreasing the focal length of the lens.

When distant objects are being viewed, the ciliary muscles relax; this makes the lens less convex, and hence increases the focal length, of the lens.

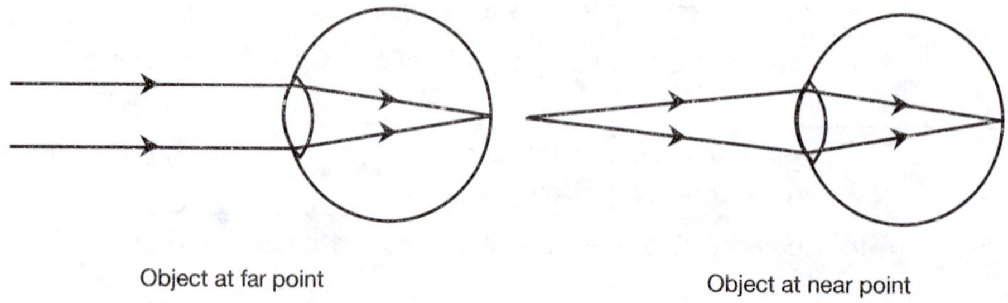

Figure 7.62 Focusing of ray for normal eye

But the variations in focal length of the eye is limited, the minimum distance at which an object can be clearly viewed is called **near point**. Similarly, the farthest point at which an object can be viewed clearly is called **far point**. The far point for a normal human eye is at infinity. The near point for a normal human eye or the least distance of distinct vision is approximately 25 cm.

Defects of Eye

If the ciliary muscles are unable to alter the focal length of the eye lens, the eye lens cannot focus either near objects or far off objects clearly on the retina. Then the eye is said to be defective.

Long-Sightedness or Hypermetropia

Hypermetropia is a defect due to which a person can see distant objects clearly but is unable to see objects which are near to the eye clearly. This happens as the rays from a near object are focused behind the retina.

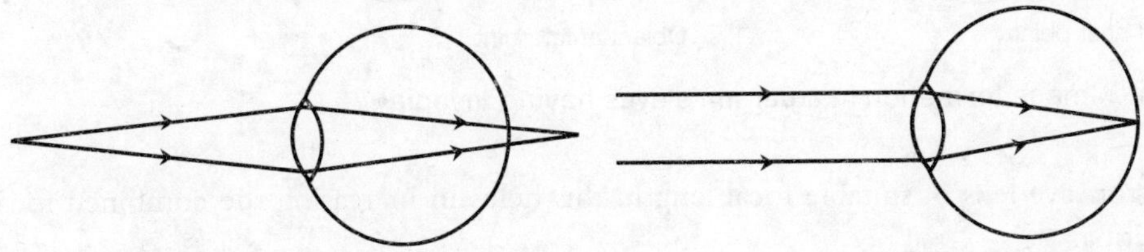

Object at near point Object at far point

Figure 7.63 Image formation in a person's eyes having hypermetropia

Hypermetropia can be corrected by using a convex lens of suitable focal length, this helps in decreasing the combined focal length, thus forming the image on the retina.

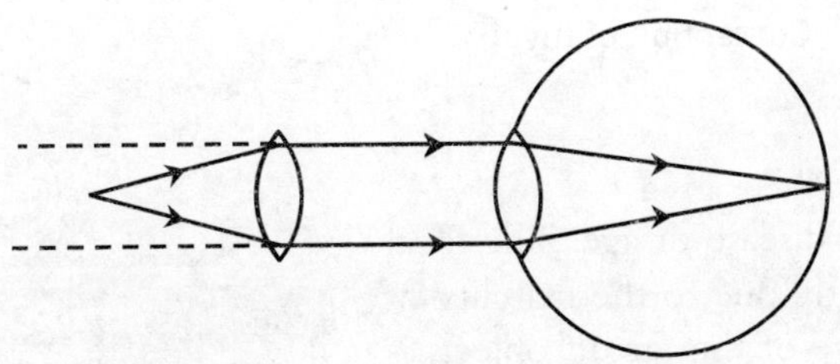

Figure 7.64 Correction of hypermetropia

Info Bytes!

Some persons are visually handicapped either they are born with no or poor eye-sight, or in some instances they would have lost their eyesight due to an accident or a disease.
However, such people use other sensory organs like touch, hearing, speech to identify, listen, talk and communicate.
There are either Non-optical aids (Hearing Aids, Braille Kit, Audio cassettes/CDs etc) or Optical Aids (Lenses, Spectacles, Bifocals).

Causes for Long-Sightedness

1. As we grow old or due to some disease, ciliary muscles becomes hard, and hence, they cannot contract. As a result the curvature and the focal length of the eye lens cannot be decreased as required. The image is formed behind the retina.
2. The eyeball shortens or the focal length of the eye lens increases due to some disease, and hence, the image is formed behind the retina.

EXAMPLE 7.7 A person has least distance of distinct vision of 75 cm. What should be the focal length of the lens that is required for him to read a news paper at a distance of 25 cm?

SOLUTION

The person near point is 75 cm, i.e., he could not see objects never than 75 cm. This defect is called hypermetropia and this can be rectified using convex lans.

$$\frac{1}{f} = \frac{1}{v} - \frac{1}{u}$$

$u = -25 \text{ cm} = -0.25 \text{ m}$

$\therefore v = -75 \text{ cm} = -0.75 \text{ m}$

Short-Sightedness or Myopia

Myopia is a defect due to which a person can see the objects nearby clearly but is unable to see the objects at a distance clearly. This happens as the rays from a distant object are focused before they reach the retina.

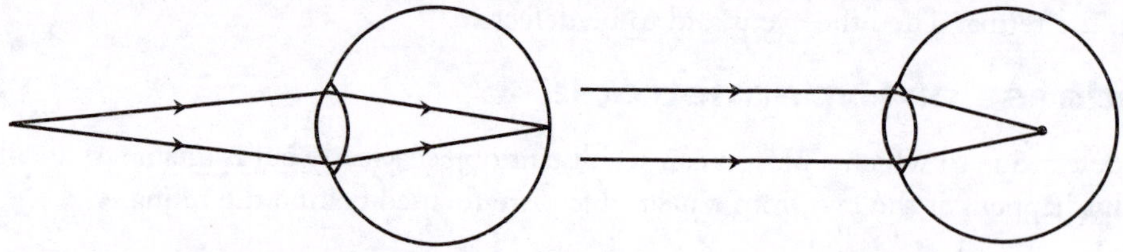

Figure 7.65 Image formation in a person's eyes having myopia

Myopia can be corrected by using a concave lens of suitable focal length, this helps in increasing the combined focal length thus forming the image on the retina.

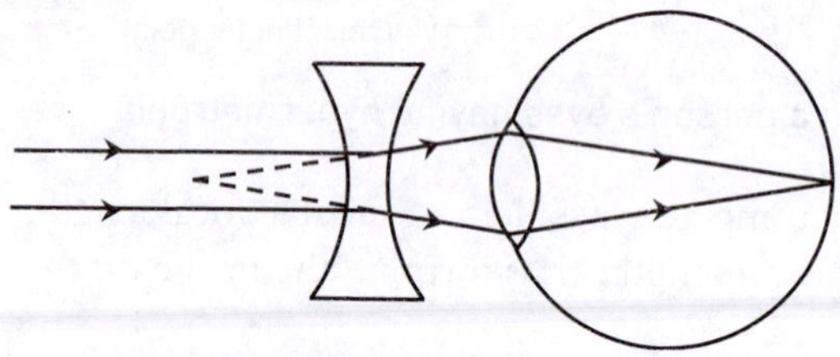

Figure 7.66 Correction of myopia

Causes of Short-Sightedness

1. Ciliary muscles become weak as a result of some disease or age. The focal length of the eye lens does not increases sufficiently due to the inability of ciliary muscles to pull outward. Hence, the image of the far off objects is formed in front of the retina.
2. If the eyeball gets bulged, then the focal length of the eye lens becomes short. As a result, the image of a distant object is formed in front of the retina.

Info Bytes!

Care and precautions should be taken to protect the eyes against any possible damages or injuries.

When we see the eyes of cat and cattle in the dark, their eyes sparkle due to reflection of light. This is due to the presence of a reflecting layer called tapetum which is present behind the retina.

Optical Instruments

Some of the optical instruments are discussed below.

Photographic Camera

A **camera** is an optical instrument which helps us to create permanent images of objects. A photographic camera consists of a convex lens, a dark chamber and a photosensitive film.

The convex lens is fitted at the front portion of the dark box and at the other end is the photographic film. The distance between the lens and the film can be changed using a knob. The box is blackened from inside to prevent internal reflections. Behind the lens, a circular plate having an aperture called diaphragm is placed.

The diameter of the aperture can be adjusted to control the light entering the camera. In dim light, the size of the aperture is increased to obtain a clear image. To control the exposure time, a shutter is provided whose speed can be controlled.

To take the photograph of an object, the distance between the lens and the film is adjusted, so as to get a clear image in the view finder. The size of the aperture and the shutter speed is adjusted depending upon the intensity of the light. When the 'click' button is pressed, the shutter opens briefly and the light enters the camera through the lens and falls on the film. The exposed film is then treated chemically in a process known as development and then prints are taken on a photographic paper.

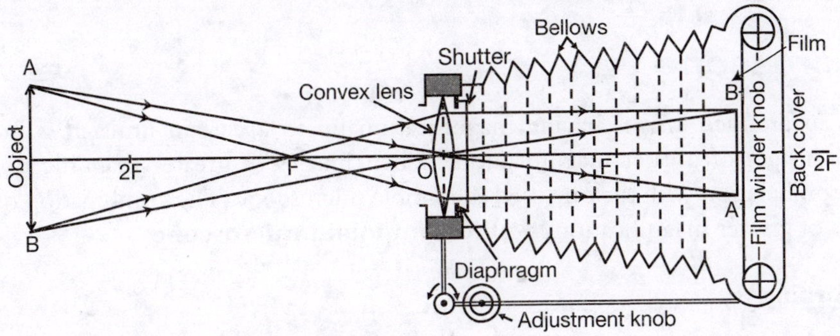

Figure 7.67 Camera

Similarities between the Eye and the Camera

1. In both the cases, the image formation takes place by means of a convex lens.
2. The image is real and inverted in both the cases.
3. The amount of light entering the dark chamber can be controlled in both cases. In the case of the eye, the pupil controls the light entering the eye whereas in the case of a camera, the diaphragm plays a similar role.
4. Incase of eye, eyelid controls the time of exposure of light whereas in a camera, the time of exposure is controlled by the shutter.

Dissimilarities between the Eye and the Camera

1. The eye lens can adjust its focal length, whereas the lens in a camera cannot vary its focal length.
2. Focussing in the case of an eye is done by changing the shape of the lens, whereas in the case of a camera, focusing is done by changing the distance between the lens and the film.
3. Image formed on the retina is temporary whereas in a camera, the image formed is permanent.
4. The eye lens is made up of a transparent and flexible substance whereas the camera lens is made up of glass.

Microscopes

A **microscope** is an instrument which is used to obtain magnified images of minute objects which cannot be otherwise viewed clearly by the naked eye.

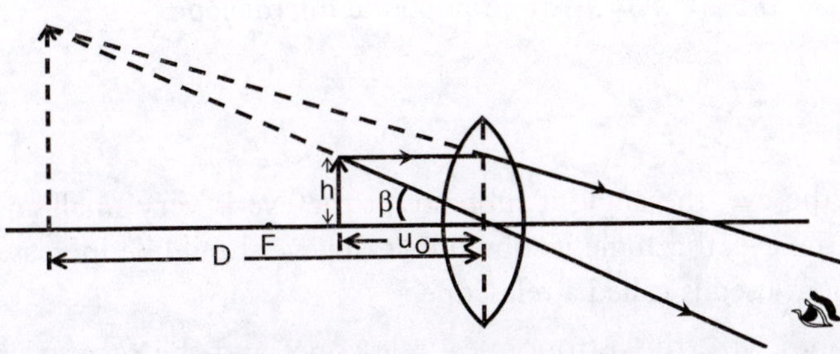

Figure 7.68 Simple microscope

A convex lens of short focal length can be used to observe small objects, this lens is known as a simple microscope or a magnifying glass. A simple microscope works on the principle of angular magnification. By placing a convex lens of short focal length between the eye and the object, such that the object lies within the focal length of the lens, the rays coming from the object can be made to form a larger angle than that which would have formed without the use of the lens. The image obtained by using a simple microscope is virtual, erect and magnified.

Compound Microscope

A simple microscope can produce images having magnification up to a certain limit. It is not possible for a simple microscope to produce images of greater magnification. When images of greater magnification are required, we use another convex lens in combination with the one used as a simple microscope. The combination of these two lenses which is used to obtain images of greater magnification is called **compound microscope**.

Construction and Working

The two lenses that are used in a compound microscope are each fixed to the outer ends of two hollow tubes that can slide one over the other such that their principal axes coincide. The lens that faces the object is called an objective and is of smaller focal length when compared to the focal length of the other lens which faces the eye and is called eye-piece.

A screw is provided so that on rotating, the distance between the objective and the eye-piece can be adjusted.

An object AA_1 is placed beyond the principal focus of the objective and its image BB_1 is formed between the objective and the eye-piece. The first image formed (BB_1) is inverted, real and magnified with respect to the object. This first image acts as an object to the second convex lens, i.e., eye-piece. The distance of the first image 'BB_1' from the eye-piece is less than the focal length of the eye-piece. So, it is further magnified and final image 'CC_1' is formed beyond 'BB_1'. The final image is inverted with respect to the object and virtual. It is magnified when compared to the first image.

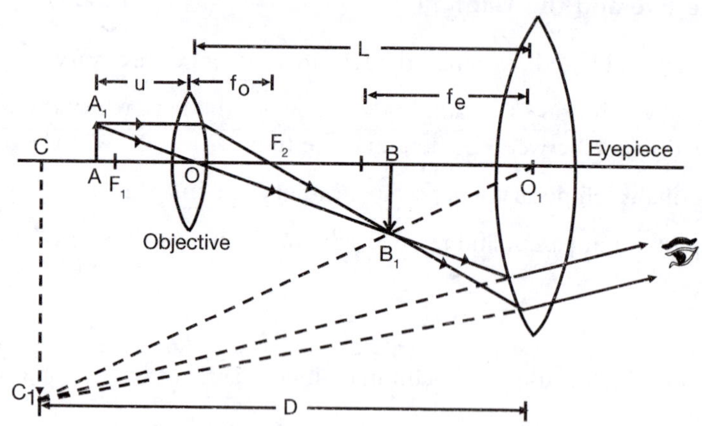

Figure 7.69 Compound microscope

Telescopes

When an object is very far from the eye, the angle it subtends at the eye is very small and so it appears to be small. To make the object appear nearer to the eye, the angle it subtends at the eye should be increased. To make the distant objects appear nearer, the optical instrument used is called a telescope.

There are two types of telescopes, viz., the astronomical telescopes and the terrestrial telescopes. The astronomical telescopes are used to observe the celestial bodies, like planets, comets, etc., and the terrestrial telescopes are used to observe distant objects on the earth's surface, like distant mountains, etc.

Astronomical Telescope

An astronomical telescope has the same construction as that of a compound microscope, but the focal length of the objective is larger compared to the focal length of the eye-piece.

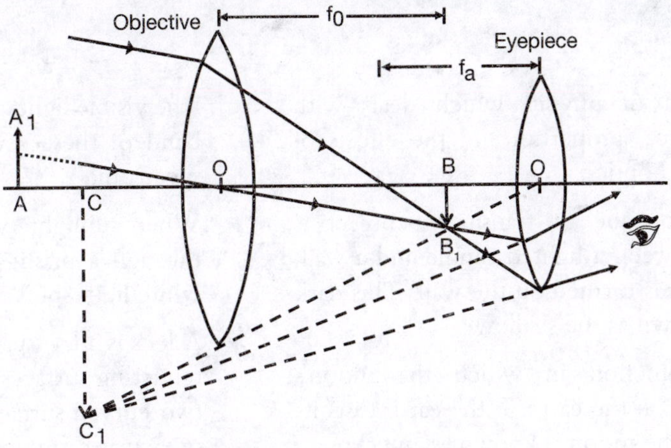

Figure 7.70 Astronomical Telescope

Working of Telescope

A parallel beam of light rays from a distant object (AA_1) almost parallel to the principal axis of the objective is incident on the objective and an image (BB_1) of the object is formed between the objective and the eye piece. This first image which is diminished, inverted and real acts as an object for the eye-piece. The distance between the first image and the eye-piece is less than the focal length of the eye-piece. So, a magnified and a virtual image (CC_1) is formed on the same side of the eye-piece as the first image. The final image is erect with respect to the first image but is inverted with respect to the object. The angle subtended by the final image at the eye-piece, and so at the eye, is larger than that of the angle subtended by the object at the eye. So, the final image is magnified and appears to be having larger size than that of the object.

Info Bytes!

The Hubble Space Telescope has provided some of the most detailed images of distant galaxies ever captured.

Info Bytes!

The Braille script is an alphabet set used by the blind people for reading and writing. Six dots arranged in a matrix forms each character of Braille. These combinations of raised and flat dots is used to encode the alphabets.

POINTS TO REMEMBER

- ✔ The branch of physics which deals with nature, source, properties and the effects of light is called optics.
- ✔ When an opaque or translucent object is brought between a lighted candle and a wall, a dark patch is formed on the wall. This dark patch is known as the shadow.
- ✔ The phenomenon in which the moon's shadow falls on the earth or the earth casts its shadow on the moon is known as an eclipse.
- ✔ Mirrors which are used by dentists, mirrors used as rear view mirrors in automobiles, and mirrors used for shaving are not plane mirrors. These are called spherical mirrors.
- ✔ The ratio of the size of an image to the size of its object is known as magnification.
- ✔ Bouncing of light into the same medium, from which the light ray is incident, is called reflection.
- ✔ When light ray travels from one transparent medium to another, there is a deviation in the path of the light ray. This phenomenon is known as refraction.
- ✔ If the angle of incidence is greater than the critical angle, the light rays are not refracted but they are reflected back in the same denser medium. This phenomenon is known as total internal reflection.
- ✔ When sunlight (white light) is made to pass through a prism, it is found that the ray of white light splits into its constituent colours. This phenomenon is called dispersion.
- ✔ The visible light consists of seven colours. The band of these seven colours is called visible spectrum.
- ✔ When sunlight (white light) is made to pass through a prism, it is found that the ray of white light splits into its constituent colours.
- ✔ A lens is a transparent medium bound by two refracting surfaces. A lens can be bounded by two curved surfaces or one plane surface and one curved surface.
- ✔ Hypermetropia is a defect due to which a person can see distant objects clearly but is unable to see objects which are near to the eye clearly.
- ✔ Myopia is a defect due to which a person can see the objects nearby clearly but is unable to see the objects at a distance clearly.
- ✔ A microscope is an instrument which is used to obtain magnified images of minute objects which cannot be otherwise viewed clearly by the naked eye
- ✔ A simple microscope can produce images having magnification up to a certain limit.
- ✔ The combination of these two lenses which is used to obtain images of greater magnification is called compound microscope.
- ✔ To make the distant objects appear nearer, the optical instrument used is called a telescope.
- ✔ An astronomical telescope has the same construction as that of a compound microscope.

CLASSROOM WING

PRACTICE QUESTIONS

Very Short Answer Type Questions

Directions for questions from 1 to 7:
Fill in the blanks.

1. A light ray incident on a reflecting surface with an angle of incident of 30°. The angle of deviation is ________.
2. The periscopes in which mirrors are used, ________ takes place.
3. Glow worm is an example of ______ source of light.
4. Formation of shadows is a consequence of ______ light.
5. The degree to which the light bends as it passes from one medium to another medium depends on the ________.
6. Kaleidoscope works on the principle of ______ of plane mirrors.
7. The focal length of the defective eye lens of a person is less than the diameter of the eyeball. Then the person is suffering from ________.

Directions for 8 to 25:
Answer the following questions:

8. Define the focal length of a spherical mirror.
9. State Snell's law.
10. Define irregular reflection of light.
11. What is magnification?
12. What are optical fibres?
13. What is a translucent medium?
14. Define the principal focus of a spherical mirror.
15. What is the function of the ciliary muscles?
16. Are the laws of refraction applicable to the refraction taking place at curved surfaces?
17. What is the nature of the image formed by a plane mirror?
18. The focal length of an eye lens is *f*. What is the value of the diameter of the eyeball?
19. Define the principal focus of a lens.
20. Why is a concave lens called a diverging lens?
21. When an object is moved away from a convex mirror, what happens to the image?
22. Why is a concave mirror called converging mirror?
23. What is meant by the far point of the eye?
24. What is the nature of the image of an object formed by a convex mirror?
25. What is the number of images formed, when the angle between two mirrors is 72°?

Short Answer Type Questions

26. Explain the principle of a photographic camera.
27. Describe the construction and working of a periscope.
28. Why does it take some time to see surroundings clearly in a dark cinema hall when a person enters from bright sunlight?
29. Draw the ray diagrams to show the defective eye and the corrected eye for long sightedness.
30. Why does the sky appear blue?
31. If a plane mirror and an object placed in front of it, both move towards each other by 10 cm, find the shift in the position of the image.
32. When two plane mirrors are placed at an angle of 30° with their reflecting surfaces towards each other, and an object is placed between them, how many images of the object can be observed?
33. A student has constructed a reflecting periscope by arranging two plane mirrors as shown in the figure.

What is the nature of the image of an object viewed through this periscope?

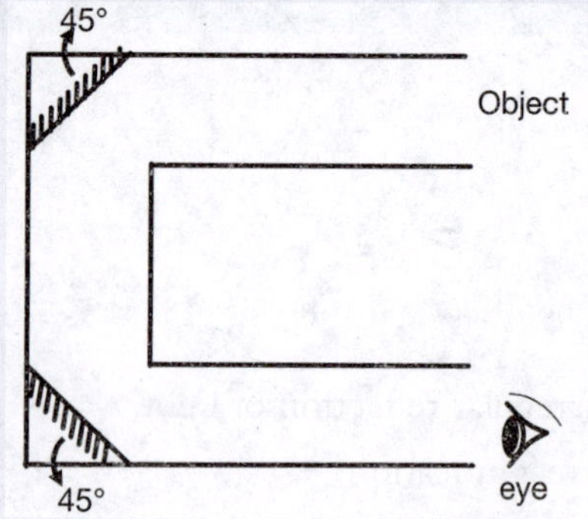

34. State and explain the rules for construction of ray diagrams for lenses.

35. A thin single glass plate is transparent. If number of such glass plates are arranged in the form of a stack, is the arrangement still transparent? Explain.

36. How does a concave lens help to correct the short sightedness in a person?

37. State and explain the formation of images in a convex mirror with the help of ray diagrams.

38. In which of the following cases, a bright image is produced (1) the image formed by a concave mirror (2) the image formed by a convex lens (3) the image formed due to total internal reflection of light.

39. Velocity of light in air is 3×10^8 m s^{-1} and of that in a given medium is 1.875×10^8 m s^{-1}. Find the refractive index of the given medium.

40. State the laws of reflection.

41. What is a divergent beam of light?

42. A light ray travelling from medium 'A' to medium 'B' undergoes refraction and another light ray travelling from 'A' to 'C' undergoes reflection. If A, B and C are transparent media and μ_A, μ_B and μ_C are their refractive indices, then what can be the relation between their refractive indices?

43. A light ray travels through three media A, B, and C as shown below. If v_A, v_B and v_C are the velocities of light in A, B, and C respectively, then

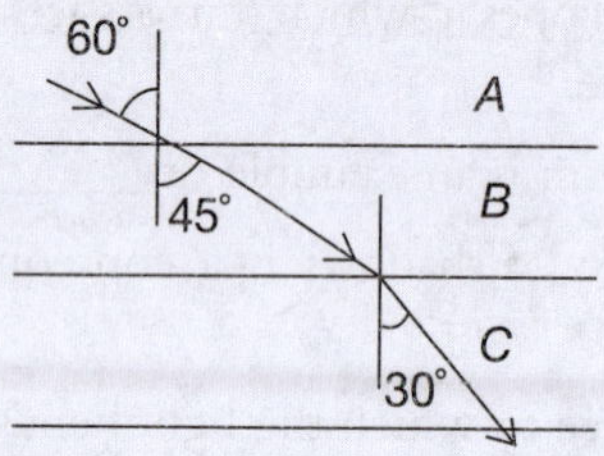

44. When a light ray incident on a reflecting surface, the angle of deviation is found to be 90°. What is the value of the angle of reflection?

Essay Answer Type Questions

45. Describe an experiment to find the focal length of a concave mirror and to find the nature of the image when the object is at finite distance.

46. Explain the construction and working of a compound microscope.

47. Describe an experiment to verify laws of reflection.

48. What is a point source of light?

49. Bring out the differences between myopia and hypermetropia.

COMPETITION WING

PRACTICE QUESTIONS

Level 1: Apply your Concepts

Directions for questions 1 to 12:
State whether the following statements are true or false.

1. In Prism periscopes, total internal reflection takes place.
2. Eclipse appears only when Moon cast its shadow on sun.
3. Concave mirror can produced magnified image.
4. Luminous bodies cannot emit light.
5. Angle of incidence is greater than critical angle in total internal reflection.
6. Virtual images are formed by diverging rays.
7. When a ray of light travels from water ($\mu = 4/3$) to glass ($\mu = 1.5$), it bends towards the normal.
8. The size of the images produced by any mirror is of the same as that of the object.
9. The focal length of a lens is same for all the colours in visible spectrum.
10. The nearest point upto which an eye can see objects clearly is called near point of the eye.
11. Transparent objects do not cast shadows.
12. Rainbow formation is due to combined effect of refraction, total internal reflection and dispersion.

Directions for questions 13 to 19:
Fill in the blanks

13. Image formed on a convex mirror is __________(real/virtual) and __________(magnified/diminished).
14. When a light ray travels from a medium P to Q, it undergoes total internal reflection. Then, avoiding normal incidence __________.
15. ______________ helps in transmitting optical impulses to the brain.
16. The portion of a mirror from which reflection of light actually takes place is ______________.
17. Lateral displacement depends on ________ of the glass slab.
18. The ratio of velocity of light in first medium to that of velocity of light in second medium is ________.
19. Irregular reflection ________ laws of reflection.

Directions for question 20:
Match the entries in Column A with the appropriate ones in Column B.

20. Match the statements of Column A with those of Column B.

Column A	Column B
(A) Blue colour of the sky	(a) Total internal reflection
(B) Mirage	(b) Scattering of light
(C) Twinkling of stars	(c) Dispersion
(D) Formation of rainbow	(d) Refraction

Directions for questions 21 to 42:
For each of the questions, four choices have been provided. Select the correct alternative.

21. When an object is moved away from a convex mirror, the image
    (a) becomes smaller
    (b) moves closer to the focus
    (c) becomes inverted
    (d) Both (a) and (b)
22. Light travels in straight line because
    (a) its velocity is very high.
    (b) bending effect is negligible, due to its small wavelength.
    (c) it is not absorbed by atmosphere.
    (d) it consist of all wave lengths
23. A man stands in front of a mirror and finds that his image is larger than himself. The mirror is a ________ mirror.

(a) convex

(b) concave

(c) plane

(d) Both (a) and (b)

24. Total internal reflection may occur when light travels from ______.

(a) vacuum to air (b) water to glass

(c) air to glass (d) glass to water

25. Real images are formed by______.

(a) converging rays

(b) diverging rays

(c) Both (a) and (b)

(d) Neither (a) nor (b)

26. Velocity of light in medium 1 is 2.4×10^7 m s^{-1} and velocity of light in medium 2 is 1.8×10^7 m s^{-1}, then the refractive index of medium 2 with respect to medium 1 is

(a) $\frac{3}{4}$ (b) $\frac{4}{3}$

(c) $\frac{1}{3}$ (d) $\frac{1}{4}$

27. A ray of light passing through the principal focus of a convex lens after refraction

(a) passes through the optic centre.

(b) emerges parallel to the principal axis.

(c) emerges without any deviation.

(d) None of these

28. The sun is seen before the actual sun rise because of:

(a) reflection

(b) refraction

(c) scattering of light

(d) rectilinear propagation of light

29. In a convex lens, we get virtual image when the object is______.

(a) between F and 2F

(b) beyond 2F

(c) between F and optic center

(d) None of these

30. When white light is incident on a hollow prism,

(a) the light emerges from the prism and gives rise to spectrum.

(b) the light emerges giving no spectrum.

(c) the light doesn't emerges from the prism and spectrum is not observed.

(d) the light emerges from the prism and gives spectrum, but all colours bend towards the base.

31. By using a concave mirror, image of a tree is focused on a screen. The distance between the screen and the mirror is ______.

(a) equal to radius of curvature of the mirror.

(b) equal to half the radius of curvature of the spherical mirror.

(c) equal to twice the focal length of the mirror.

(d) equal to one fourth the focal length of the mirror.

32. The object or image distance is taken as positive

(a) if the length is measured opposite to the direction of the incident ray.

(b) if the length is measured in the direction of the incident ray.

(c) if the length is measured opposite to the direction of the refracted ray.

(d) None of these

33. The convex lens of larger focal length used in a compound microscope is called

(a) objective.

(b) eye piece.

(c) erector lens.

(d) None of these

34. A concave mirror forms an erect image twice the size of a object. The object distance from the mirror is:

(a) $\frac{f}{2}$ (b) $2f$

(c) $\frac{3f}{2}$ (d) $\frac{2f}{3}$

35. If the real depth of a coin in water ($\mu = 4/3$) is 4 cm, the apparent depth is

(a) 3 cm (b) $\frac{1}{3}$ cm

(c) $\frac{16}{3}$ (d) None of these

36. Five spherical mirrors are made from the same sphere. The uncommon thing among the mirrors is ______.

(a) radius of curvature (b) focal length

(c) pole (d) None of these

37. When an extended source of light moves towards a stationary opaque body, where the extended source is bigger than the opaque body, then on a stationary screen placed behind the object the

(a) penumbra and umbra, both increase.

(b) penumbra and umbra, both decrease.

(c) penumbra increases and the umbra decreases.

(d) penumbra decreases and the umbra increases.

38. Arrange the following steps of an experiment in sequential order to prove the rectilinear propagation of light.

(A) Place a lighted candle towards the wooden upright C facing the hole.

(B) The candle flame is clearly visible which would disappear if one of the uprights is moved.

(C) Take three wooden uprights *A*, *B* and *C* and make a small hole at the same height from the base on each of *A*, *B* and *C* such that they are in a straight line.

(D) Now, look through the hole of upright *A*.

(a) C A D B

(b) C D A B

(c) A C B D

(d) A D C B

39. Arrange the following steps of an experiment in sequential order to calculate the focal length of a concave mirror when the object is at a small distance.

(A) Mount a concave mirror on the mirror stand and place an object in front of it at a certain distance.

(B) Adjust the position of the screen and the mirror until a bright and sharp image is obtained on the screen.

(C) Measure the distance between the object and the mirror. This distance gives the object distance u.

(D) Place the screen between the object and mirror but not in line with them.

(E) Measure the distance between the concave mirror and the screen. This gives the image distance v.

(F) The focal length of the given concave mirror can be found out using the mirror formula with proper signs.

(G) Repeat the experiment for different values of u and v and tabulate the results.

(a) A D B C E G F (b) A C E B D G F

(c) A B C D E F G (d) A B D E C G F

40. **Assertion (A):** Convex mirrors are used as rear view mirrors in vehicles.

Reason (R): The field view of convex mirrors is maximum and they form diminished images.

(a) Both A and R are correct, and R is the correct explanation of A.

(b) Both A and R are correct, but R is not the correct explanation of A.

(c) A is correct but R is incorrect.

(d) Both A and R are incorrect.

41. **Assertion (A):** A rainbow is formed when white light is incident on raindrops.

Reason (R): White light contains seven colours and it undergoes dispersion inside a raindrop.

(a) Both A and R are correct, and R is the correct explanation of A.

(b) Both A and R are correct, but R is not the correct explanation of A.

(c) A is correct but R is incorrect.

(d) Both A and R are incorrect.

42. **Assertion (A):** A convex lens placed in the air always forms a real image.

Reason (R): Any light ray passing through a convex lens is converged.

(a) A and R both are correct, and R is correct explanation of A.

(b) A and R both are correct, and R is incorrect explanation of A.

(c) A is correct but R is incorrect.

(d) A is incorrect but R is correct.

Level 2: Review your Concepts

43. A convex mirror and a plane mirror are arranged facing an object as shown in the figure below. If there is no parallax between the images formed by the two mirrors, then find the radius of curvature of the convex mirror?

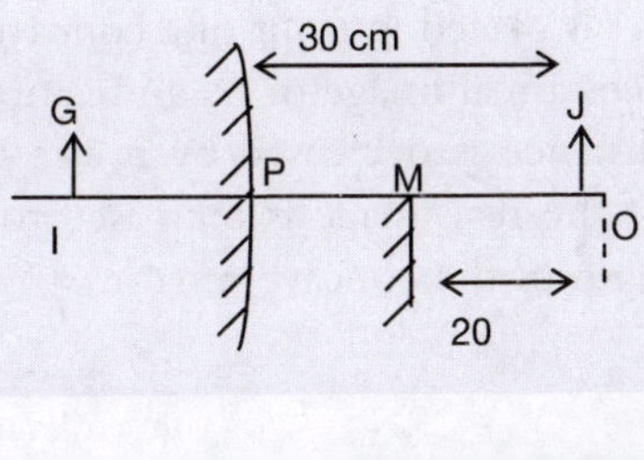

44. If a plane mirror shifts through a distance of 5 cm towards an object and the object shifts through 10 cm towards the mirror, then find the shift in the position of an image.

45. In the given figure below, *AB* is the object and *CD* is its image. If a spherical mirror is used to get the image, name the type of spherical mirror used and locate the position of focus of the mirror by drawing a ray diagram. '*P*' is the pole of the mirror.

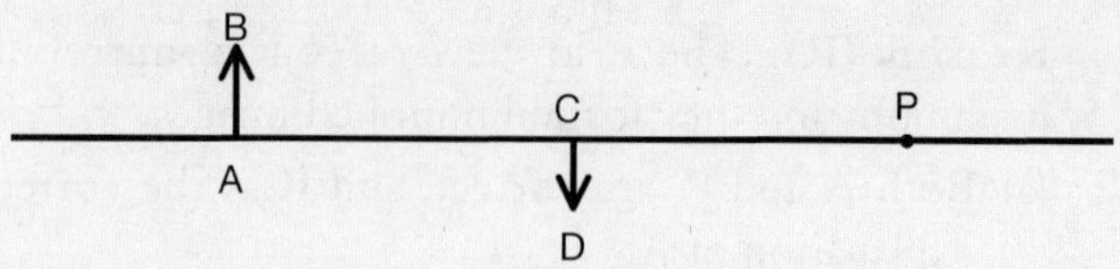

46. Two convex lenses, of focal lengths 20 cm and 10 cm, respectively are separated by a distance of *x* cm. If a parallel beam of light remain parallel after refraction through both the lenses find *x*.

47. Are all animals equally sensitive to same intensity of light? Explain.

48. A jar contains two immiscible liquids *A* and *B* with a coin at its bottom. The depths of liquid *A* and liquid *B* are 6 cm and 8 cm, respectively. If the apparent depth of the coin is 9 cm and refractive index of liquid *A* is 1.5, what is the refractive index of liquid *B*?

49. A bird came closer to the periscope at an instant of time as shown in the figure. What is the shortest distance of the bird from the observer at that instant of time?

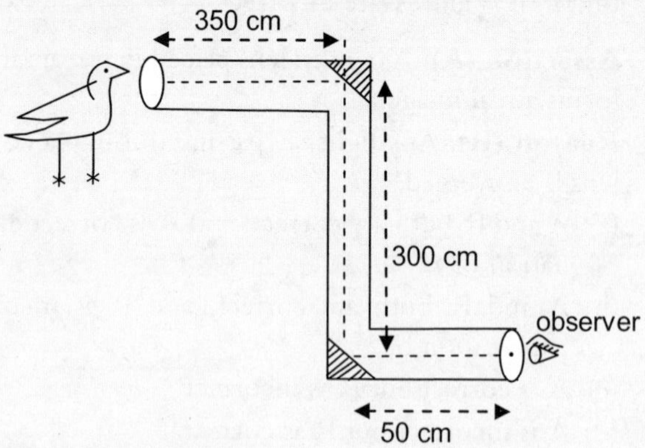

50. For a person sitting near a fire, why the objects like trees and houses on the other side of the fire appear shifting?

51. An object is placed in front of a concave mirror and it produces a real image of magnification 1.5. If the object distance is decreased by 5 cm, the magnification of the real image is increased to 4. Find the focal length of the concave mirror.

52. A man places a rectangular glass slab of thickness 9 cm on a newspaper. On the top of the glass slab he places a glass beaker of negligible wall thickness containing water up to a height of 6 cm. If refractive index of glass is 1.5 and refractive index of water is (4/3), what is the apparent depth of the newspaper?

53. A source of light and screen are separated by a distance of 50 cm. A sharp image of the source is produced by lens when placed at two positions between the source and the screen. If the distance of separations of the lens between the two positions is 20 cm, find the focal length of the lens.

54. A glass slab of thickness 5 cm and refractive 3/2 is placed over a photo. Calculate the apparent shift in position of the photo.

55. Two plane mirrors are inclined at an angle of 50°. A ray is incident on one of the mirrors with certain angle of incidence. The reflected ray from this mirror is incident on the second mirror such that it gets reflected parallel to the first mirror. Find the angle of incidence at the two mirrors. Also show that the sum of angles of incidence on first and second mirrors is equal to the angle of inclination between the two mirrors.

56. Two plane mirrors *AB* and *CD* each of length 2 m are arranged parallel to each other $\sqrt{3}$ m apart and a ray of light is incident at '*A*' as shown in the figure. How many reflections does the ray of light undergo?

What is the distance travelled by the ray of light between the two mirrors? What is the angle of deviation?

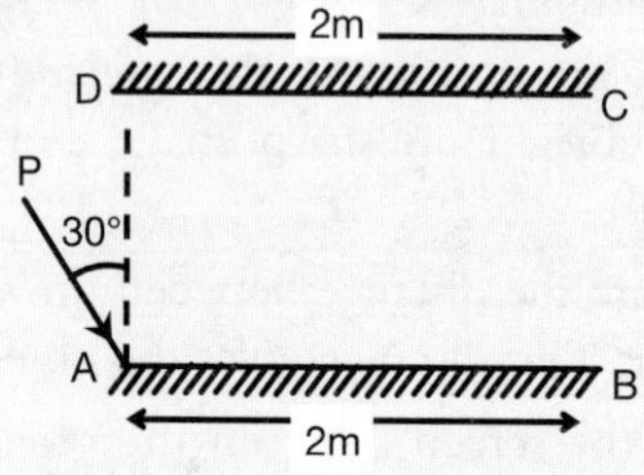

57. A concave mirror and a plane mirror are arranged facing each other and an object *AB* is placed between them as shown in the figure.

What is the distance between the object and its inverted, virtual image formed in plane mirror?

58. In the figure given below, *OB* is the object and *IG* is the image formed. A spherical mirror with *P* as the pole of the mirror is used to form image *IG*. Identify the type of spherical mirror used and also

locate the position of focus of the mirror using the ray diagram.

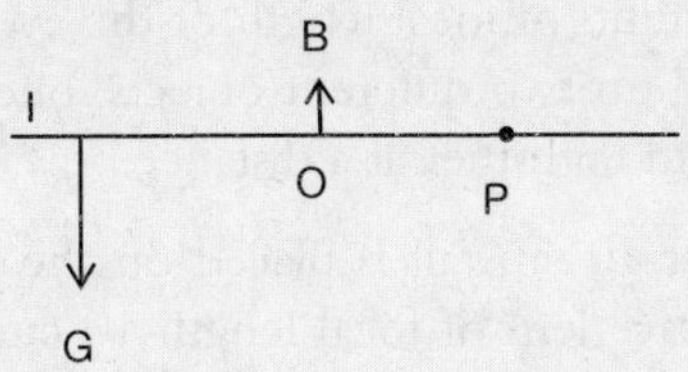

59. If the mirror moves away from the object with speed v units, then find the speed of the image that moves away from the object.

60. Mahesh wanted to know whether the decrease in the number of images of an object placed between two mirrors would vary proportionally to the rate at which the angle between them increases. So, he arranged two plane mirrors facing each other in such a way that they were inclined at an angle of 5°. They were arranged such that the angle between them increased uniformly at 1° per second. What is his inference?

61. Siddharth wanted to see his inverted image in a plane mirror. So, he stood between a concave mirror and a plane mirror facing each other as shown in the figure. Knowing the focal length of the concave mirror, he found the distance between him and his inverted virtual image, formed in the plane mirror. What is his answer?

62. Two identical objects 'P' and 'Q' are placed at a distance of 10 cm in front of a concave mirror and convex mirror respectively. The focal length of each spherical mirror is 20 cm. Find the image distance, magnification and hence the nature of images of 'P' and 'Q'.

63. A concave mirror of focal length 'f' forms an erect image twice the size of an object. Find the object distance from the mirror.

64. Srikar focussed separately on two objects of different sizes using a photographic camera. He found that the sizes of the images of the two objects, one kept at a distance of 200 m and the other at a distance of 2 m is the same. How did he achieve this? Explain.

Level 3: Assess Your Concepts

65. A thin rectangular silver sheet acts as a plane mirror. A person who can see his face in it, holds it vertically, such that the length of the sheet is perpendicular to the ground. How does his image in the silver sheet change if the sheet is bent in a semi-circular way,

(a) along the length such that it bulges towards the face.

(b) along the length such that it bulges away from the face.

(c) along the breadth such that it bulges towards the face.

(d) along the breadth such that it bulges away from the face.

66. Velocity of light in medium 1 is 2.4×10^8 m s^{-1} and velocity of light in medium 2 is 1.8×10^8 m s^{-1}, then calculate:

(a) absolute refractive indices of the media 1 and 2.

(b) refractive index of medium 2 with respect to medium 1.

67. 'Objects in the mirror are closer than they appear'. This statement is printed on the rear view mirrors of vehicles. What is its significance?

68. Three plane mirrors are mounted on three walls forming an isosceles right triangle as shown in the figure. How many images are formed in all? Draw a diagram and indicate the positions of the images.

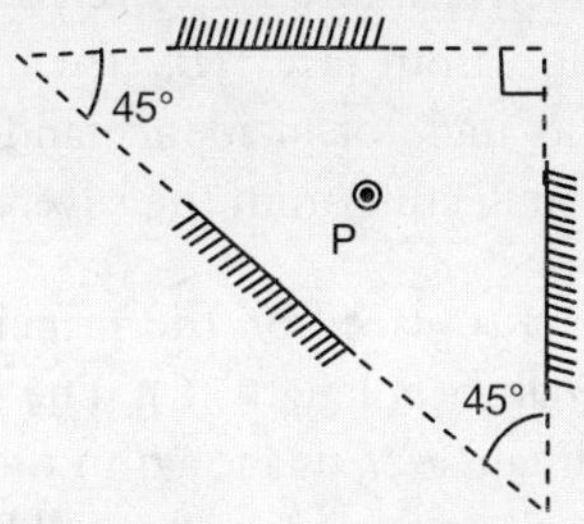

69. If v is the velocity of light in air or vacuum, find the time taken by the light to travel through a glass slab of thickness x and having refraction index μ.

70. An object of height 5 cm is placed in front of a convex lens of focal length 20 cm at a distance of 30 cm. What is the height of the image (in cm)?

71. A ray of light changes its wavelength from 6000 A° to 3000 A°, when it travels from one medium to another medium. What is the critical angle of the denser medium with respect to the rarer medium?

[Given sin 0° = 0, sin 30° = $\frac{1}{2}$, sin 45° = $\frac{1}{\sqrt{2}}$,

$\sin 60° = \dfrac{\sqrt{3}}{2}$, $\sin 90° = 1$]

72. If a convex lens and a plane mirror are arranged in the way shown in figure and the final image is 3 cm behind the plane mirror. Then, find the focal length of the convex lens.

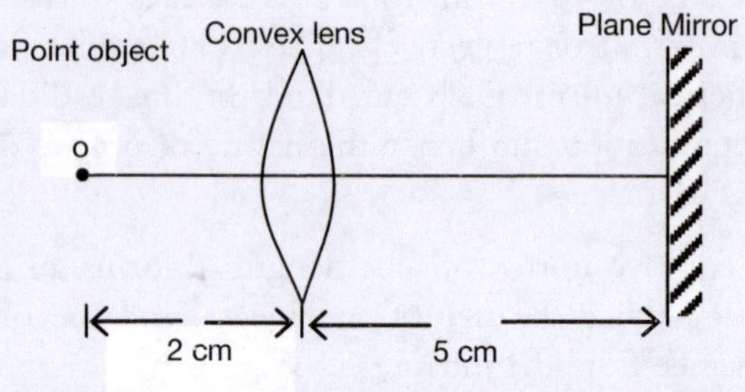

73. A ray of light PQ is incident on the face AB of an equilateral glass prism ABC as shown in the figure. Show that angle of emergence = angle of deviation. Also, with a ray diagram, trace the path of the emergent ray.

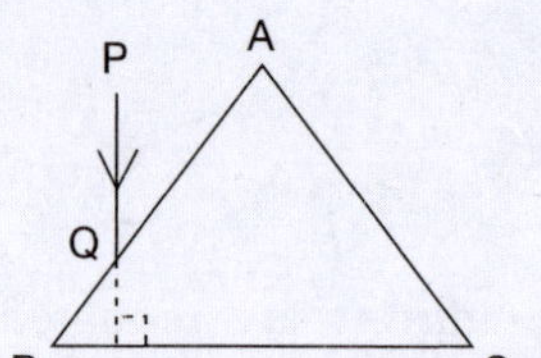

74. The face AC of the prism ABC of refracting angle 30° and refractive index 2 is silvered. A ray of light, after refraction from face AB, strike the face AC at 90°. Find the angle of incidence and path traced by the ray after reflecting from the silvered surface.

75. An object AB is placed on the principal axis of two lenses of equal focal length (f). The lenses are separated by a distance $2f$, as shown in the fi gure. Using ray diagram locate the image formed by each lens and state their nature.

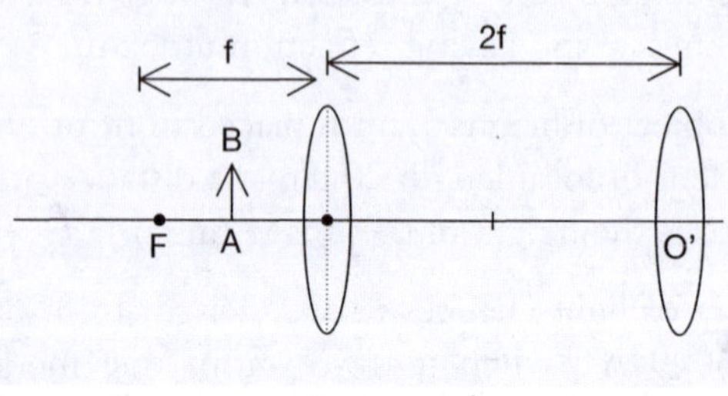

76. The ciliary muscles can change the focal length of the eye lens. The diameter of the normal eye is 2.5 cm. Find the ratio of focal length of the eye lens when it is focused on two different objects, one at a distance of 3 m and the other at a distance of 2 m.

77. An object 10 cm tall is placed on the principal axis of a concave lens of focal length 10 cm at a distance of 15 cm from it. Find the position and nature of the image formed by the lens and draw the ray diagram.

78. A ray of light making an angle 50° with the horizontal is incident on a plane mirror, which itself is inclined to the horizontal at an angle 10°as shown in the figure. Determine the angle made by the reflected ray with the horizontal ______.

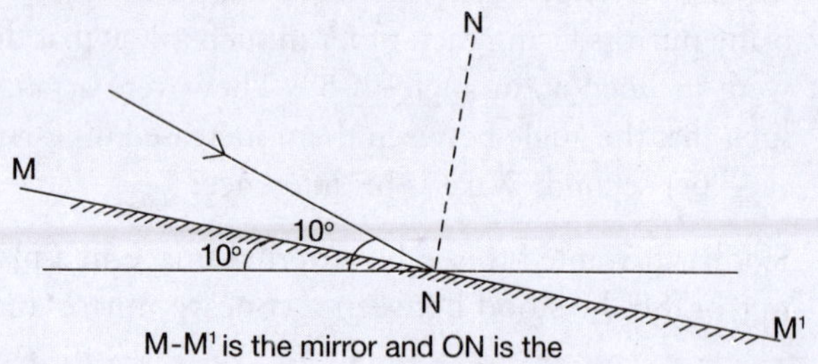

79. An object is placed in front of a convex mirror at a distance equal to the focal length of the mirror. If its focal length is 20 cm, the distance of the image from the mirror is ______ cm.

(a) 10 (b) 20
(c) 40 (d) infinity

80. An object is first placed at a distance of 24 cm from the lens and then at a distance of 16 cm from the lens. If the magnification of the image formed in both the cases is same, determine the focal length of the lens

81. When an object of height 3 cm is placed in front of a convex lens of focal length 20 cm, the height of the real image is found to be 6 cm. What is the distance between the object and image?

82. A convex mirror of radius of curvature 20 cm forms an image which is half the size of the object. Determine the position of the object from the pole of the mirror.

JEE-NEET SPECIAL WING

PRACTICE QUESTIONS

Multiple-Answer Type Questions

Directions for questions 1 to 5:

Select one or more correct alternative(s) from the given choices.

1. Pick out the translucent bodies from the following.
   (a) Glass
   (b) Frosted glass
   (c) Tissue
   (d) Ice
2. If an extended source of light is used to cast the shadow.
   (a) Umbra is formed.
   (b) Penumbra is formed.
   (c) Penumbra is formed, umbra is not formed.
   (d) Umbra is formed, penumbra is not formed.
3. Which of the following statements are true?
   (a) Light requires a material medium to travel.
   (b) Light changes the properties of medium through which it passes.
   (c) Light travels in a straight line.
   (d) When light travels from denser to rarer medium, the velocity of light increases.
4. The total number of images formed is given by
   (a) $n = \left[\frac{360°}{\theta} - 1\right]$
   (b) $n = \left[\frac{\theta}{360°} - 1\right]$
   (c) $n = \left[\frac{\theta - 360°}{360°}\right]$
   (d) $n\theta = 360° - \theta$
5. The colour of the sky is due to
   (a) Dispersion
   (b) Reflection
   (c) Scattering
   (d) Refraction

Comprehension-Based Questions

Directions for questions 6 to 10:

These questions are based on the following information.

Refraction:
When a light ray travels from a transparent medium to another, there is a deviation in the path of the light ray due to difference in the speed of light in different media. The greater the change in speed, the more the light is bent. A ray of light incident normal to the surface passes straight without being refracted.

6. The swimming pool appears shallower because the light ray bends
   (a) away from normal
   (b) towards normal
   (c) normally
   (d) None of the above.
7. Refractive index is a measure of
   (a) Frequency
   (b) Temperature
   (c) Optical density
   (d) Material density
8. The S. I. unit of refractive index is
   (a) $m\ s^{-1}$
   (b) $m^{-1}\ s$
   (c) $kg\ m^{-3}$
   (d) No unit
9. The real depth and apparent depth are related to refractive index (μ) by the relation
   (a) $\mu = \frac{\text{apparent depth}}{\text{real depth}}$

(b) $\mu = \dfrac{\text{real depth}}{\text{apparent depth}}$

(c) μ = real depth × apparent depth

(d) real depth$= \dfrac{\mu}{\text{apparent depth}}$

10. If the absolute refractive index of a medium is 2 then the velocity of light in the given medium is (in m s^{-1})

(a) 1×10^8 (b) 1.33×10^8

(c) 1.5×10^8 (d) 2×10^8

Directions for questions 11 to 15:

These questions are based on the following information.

Total Internal Reflection (TIR):

Total internal reflection is the phenomenon of reflection of ray to same medium when it passes from denser to rarer medium such that the angle of incidence is greater that its critical angle. Thus, TIR refers to the complete reflection of light within a transparent medium. TIR allows the light to be contained and guided along very thin fibres and hence is the basic principle for optic fibre communication.

11. In TIR, the critical angle will be maximum when the light passes

(a) from water to air

(b) from glass to air

(c) from diamond to air

(d) from glass to water

12. When a light ray incident at critical angle when it travels from denser to rarer medium then angle of refraction

(a) $r = 0°$

(b) $r = 90°$

(c) $r = 180°$

(d) $r = 360°$

13. The critical angle of a glass prism whose refractive index is 1.4 will be

(a) 30°

(b) 60°

(c) 45°

(d) 90°

14. The relation corresponding to refraction through a glass prism is given by

(a) $i_1 + i_2 = A + d$

(b) $i_1 - i_2 = A + d$

(c) $i_1 + A = i_2 + d$

(d) $i_1 - i_2 = A - d$

15. If a light ray is incident on an equilateral triangular prism at an angle 45° and the angle of emergence from second face be 80° then the angle of deviation of the emergent ray is

(a) 35°

(b) 50°

(c) 65°

(d) 90°

Match the Column

Directions for question 16:

The question is based on the following information.

Lenses and its Image Formation

Lens is a transmissive optical device that disperses or concentrate light rays while passing through them, by the phenomenon of refraction. It is bound by two surfaces out of which at least one will be a curved surface. Some of them are shown below.

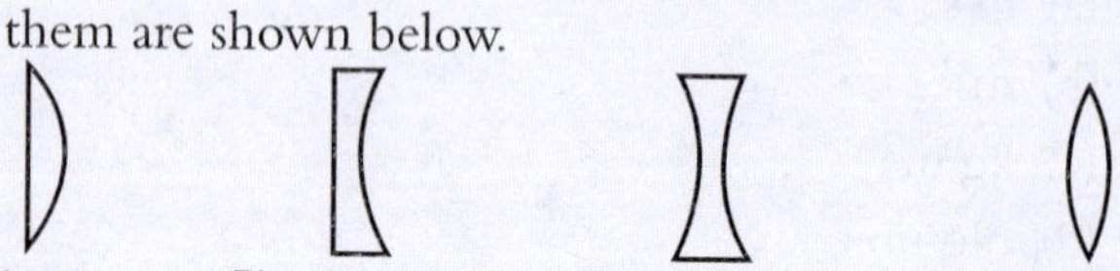

Plano convex lens   Plano concave lens   Concave lens   Convex lens

Some data regarding image formed by convex lens are given.

16. Match the values in List - I with those in List - II:

List - I	List - II
A. u = ∞	a. v = 2f
B. 2f < u < ∞	b. v > 2f
C. u = 2f	c. v = f
D. f < u < 2f	d. v = ∞
E. u = f	e. f < v < 2f

(a) A - d, B - e, C - b, D - a, E - c

(b) A - c, B - e, C - a, D - b, E - d

(c) A - b, B - c, C - d, D - e, E - a

(d) A - a, B - d, C - b, D - c, E - e

ANSWER KEYS

Crossword

Across

1. Infinity
5. Directly proportional
7. Glancing angle
8. Umbra
9. Candle
10. Periscope
13. Lens
14. Refraction

Down

2. Negative
3. Ultraviolet
4. Concave
6. Regular reflection
11. Cyan
12. Convex

Classroom Wing

Very Short Answer Type Questions

1. 120°
2. Refraction
3. Natural
4. Rectilinear propagation
5. Refractive index of the medium
6. Multiple reflections
7. Short-sightedness
17. virtual
18. f
25. 5
44. $r = 45°$

Competition Wing

Level 1: Apply your Concepts

1. True
2. False
3. True
4. False
5. True
6. True
7. True
8. False
9. False
10. True
11. True
12. True
13. Virtual and diminished
15. Optic nerve
16. Aperture
17. Thickness
18. Refractive index of second medium with respect to first medium.
19. Obeys
20. A : b, B : a, C : d, D : c
23. (b)
24. (d)
25. (a)
26. (b)
27. (b)
28. (b)
29. (c)
30. (b)
31. (b)
32. (b)
33. (a)
34. (a)
35. (a)
36. (c)
37. (c)
38. (a)
39. (a)
40. (a)
41. (a)
42. (d)

Level 2: Review your Concepts

49. 500 cm
54. 5/3 cm
61. 6 m
62. 6.66 cm
63. $\frac{f}{2}$
64. 100 times more

Level 3: Assess Your Concepts

65. 10 cm
66. $\frac{4}{3}$
70. 10 cm
71. 30°
72. 1 cm
74. 45°
76. 243:242
77. –6 cm
79. 10 cm
80. 20 cm
81. 90 cm
82. –10 cm

JEE-NEET Special Wing

Multiple-Answer Type Questions

1. (b) and (c)
2. (a) and (b)
3. (c) and (d)
4. (a) and (d)
5. (c)

Comprehension-Based Questions

6. (a)
7. (c)
8. (d)
9. (b)
10. (c)
11. (d)
12. (b)
13. (c)
14. (a)
15. (c)

Match the Column

16. (b)

For answer key of Classroom wing and Competition wing, refer to Hints and Solutions

Hints and Explanations

Classroom Wing

Very Short Answer Type Question

1. 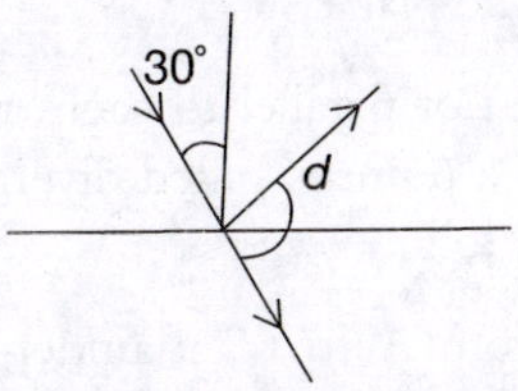

At from the figure $d = 180 - 60 = 120°$

2. Refraction takes place in mirror periscopes.
3. natural
4. Rectilinear propagation
5. Refractive index of the medium
6. Multiple reflections
7. As the focal length is less than the diameter of eyeball, the image is formed in front of the retina, and hence, the person is suffering from short-sightedness.
8. The distance between the pole and the principal focus.
9. $\frac{\sin i}{\sin r} = \mu$
10. Reflection taking place on uneven surface is the irregular reflection of light.
11. Ratio of image distance to object distance is magnification.
12. An optical fibre consists of glass or plastic fibre which has a very small area of cross-section. Optical fibres are used to transport images.
13. The medium which allows only a part of the light to travel through it.
14. The fixed point at which the paraxial rays converge or appear to diverge after reflection.
15. They change the focal length of the lens.
16. Yes
17. Image formed by a plane mirror is virtual.
18. Focal length = diameter of eyeball = f
19. A beam of light parallel to principal axis is incident on a lens, it refracts at the two surfaces and after refraction at the two surfaces, converges at or appears to diverge from a point on the principal axis known as principal focus.
20. Because this type of lens is thin in the middle and rays of light that pass through the lens spread out(diverge).
21. The image becomes smaller and moves closer to the focus when the object moves away from the convex mirror.
22. The incident rays parallel to the principal axis after reflection from the spherical mirror converges through principal focus.
23. The farthest point at which an object can be viewed clearly.
24. Virtual
25. $\frac{360}{\theta} = \frac{360}{72} = 5$

Short Answer Type Questions

Note: This is how you should frame your answer covering.

26. Camera is used to form permanent images. The position of object is adjusted such that the image is formed between F and 2F, is real, inverted and diminished.
27. (a) Two plane mirrors
    (b) Bent tube
    (c) Blackened
    (d) Reflected
    (e) Image at the other end
28. (i) Functioning of part of eye that controls different amounts of light entering the eye
    (ii) Adjustment of a pupil for different amounts of sunlight entering the eye.
30. Due to dispersion and scattering
31. (i) Ray diagram, Difference in the initial distance between object and the mirror and final distance between them.
    (ii) Use the laws of reflection and a diagram, representing the position of the mirror, object and the image.

Determine the final object-distance with respect to the initial object-distance.

Determine the distance between the initial position of the image and the final position of the mirror and subtract the final image-distance from it.

That is $(x - 2y) - (x + y)$ where x is the initial object-distance and y is the distance through which the mirror is moved.

32. $n = \frac{360}{\theta} - 1$

33. (i) Trace the path of two light rays each from the top and the bottom of the object and compare he final reflected ray with the incident ray.
(ii) Now find the nature of the object.

34. (1) A light ray from an object parallel to the principal axis after refraction at the two surfaces of a lens converge or appears to diverge from the second principal focus.
(2) A light ray passing through the first principal focus or appearing to meet at it emerges parallel to the principal axis after refraction at the two surfaces of a lens.
(3) A ray of light passing through the optical centre of a lens emerges without any deviation after refraction at the two surfaces of the lens.

35. Compare the transparency of a thin glass plate with that of a thick glass plate.
Why is the intensity of light coming out from a thick glass plate less than that from a thin glass plate?

36. Cause for the defect of short sightedness and how it can be rectified.

37. (i) When object is at infinity or near to the mirror—image formed is erect, virtual and diminished.
(ii) But the image formed by object at infinity is highly diminished and at the principal focus.
(iii) For other positions of object, position of image is between focus and pole of the mirror.

38. Images formed by TIR (Total Internal Reflection) are brighter than those formed by either convex or concave mirror. The reason is that in the TIR, 100 % of the incident light is reflected back into the same medium without the loss of intensity (as the intensity is lost always in case of convex and concave mirror.)

39. $\mu = \frac{V_{air}}{V_{medium}}$

40. (i) The angle of incidence is always equal to angle of reflection.
(ii) The angle of incidence, angle of reflection and the normal all lie in the same plane.

41. The rays of light which are not parallel to each other and which spread out from a point is called divergent beam of light.

42. When a light ray travels from A to C, it undergoes reflection (T. I. R). Therefore, A is denser and C is rarer. No other conclusions can be made.

$\therefore \mu_A > \mu_C$

43. As the angle of refraction in medium C is greater than the angle of incidence in medium A, the correct relation is $V_c > V_A$.

44. Angle of deviation, $d = 180 - 2i$
$= 180 - 2r$; $90 = 180 - 2r$
$2r = 90$; $r = 45°$

Essay Answer Type Questions

This is how you should frame your answer covering:

45. (a) Object and source (candle)
(b) Screen in between
(c) Object distance
(d) Sharp image

46. (a) Objective
(b) Eye piece
(c) Convex lens
(d) Object at principal focus
(e) First image within principal focus of the eye piece
(d) Magnified

47. (a) Plane mirror (b) Normal
(c) Acute angles (d) Pins
(e) Image

48. The light that emerges though a pin hole

49. (a) Nearby object (b) Far objects
(c) Convex lens (d) Concave lens

Competition Wing

Level 1: Apply your Concepts

13. Image formed by convex mirror is virtual and diminished.

14. $m = \frac{1}{\sin^C} = \frac{2V}{V} = 2$

$Sin\,C = \frac{1}{2}$

20. Blue colour of the sky is due to the scattering of light.

$A \rightarrow b$

Mirages are formed due to total internal reflection.

$B \rightarrow a$

Twinkling of stars is due to the refraction.

$C \rightarrow d$

Formation of a rainbow is due to the dispersion of light.

$D \rightarrow c$.

36. As spherical mirror is a part of sphere, the focal length and radius of curvature for all the mirrors will remain same, but depending on the length of (arc of sphere) mirror, the position of pole changes.

Hence, the correct answer is (c).

37. In case an extended source of light is bigger than an opaque body, and the extended source moves towards the opaque body or screen moves away from the opaque body, the umbra decreases and penumbra increases. When the extended source moves away from the opaque body or the screen moves towards the opaque body, umbra increases and penumbra decreases.

Hence, the correct answer is (c).

38. (A) Take three wooden uprights *A*, *B* and *C* and make a small hole at the same height from the base on each of *A*, *B* and *C* such that they are in a straight line.(*c*)

(B) Place a lighted candle towards the upright *C* facing the hole (*a*).

(C) Now, look through the hole of upright A (*d*).

(D) The candle flame is clearly visible which would disappear if one of the uprights is moved (*b*).

Hence, the correct answer is (d).

39. (A) Mount a concave mirror on the mirror and place an object in front of it at a certain distance (*a*).

(B) Place the screen between the object and mirror but not in line with them (*d*).

(C) Adjust the position of the screen and the mirror until a bright and sharp image is obtained on the screen (*b*).

(D) Measure the distance between the object and the mirror. This distance gives the object distance *u* (*c*).

(E) Measure the distance between the concave mirror and the screen. This gives the image distance *v* (*e*).

(F) Repeat the experiment for different values of u and v and tabulate the results (*g*).

(G) The focal length of the given concave mirror can be found out using the mirror formula with proper signs (*f*).

Hence, the correct answer is (a).

40. Convex mirrors are used as rear view mirrors in vehicles because the field view of a convex mirror is large and it forms a diminished image so that the vehicles coming from behind can be observed. So, *A* and *R* are correct, and *R* is the correct explanation of *A*.

Hence, the correct answer is (a).

41. White light contains all the seven colours of light. When white passes through light raindrops, under certain conditions it undergoes dispersion and forms a rainbow. So, *A* and *R* are correct and *R* is the correct explanation of *A*.

Hence, the correct answer is (a).

42. Convex lens forms both virtual and real image.

Hence, the correct answer is (d).

Level 2: Review your Concepts

Note: This is how you should frame your answer covering.

43. (a) Relation between object distance and image distance for a plane mirror.

(b) Mirror formula for a convex mirror

(c) Relation between focal length and radius of curvature.

44. (i) Recall and identify the position of mirror object and its corresponding images, respectively.

(ii) To answer, find the shift in the image by using the characteristics of a plane mirror.

45. (i) Recall the for the ray diagrams

(ii) Observe the position of the object and the type of image formed.

Recall the nature of image formed by different mirrors.

Which mirror is used here–concave mirror or convex mirror?

Draw the ray diagram to obtain the type of image shown in the question. Compare this ray diagram with the given figure and analyze to locate the position of the principal focus.

46. (a) Condition for emergent beam to remain parallel after refraction through both the lens in terms of their foci.

(b) Foci of two lens coincide.

47. (a) Relation between refractive index and wavelength of light.

(b) Which part of the eye is responsible for the sensitivity towards the light rays?

Is it the same for all animals?

48. $\mu = \dfrac{\text{real depth}}{\text{appaarent depth}}$

49. $x^2 = 400^2 + 300^2$

$x = 500$ cm

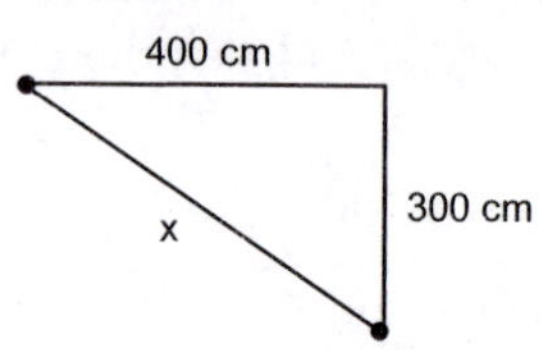

50. (i) Relation between refractive index and wavelength of light.

(ii) ${}^{2}\mu_1 = \dfrac{\mu_2}{\mu_1} = \dfrac{\lambda_1}{\lambda_2}$

Find $\angle i$

51. (i) Mirror formula.

(ii) By using the relation between object-distance, image-distance and the magnification, $m = \dfrac{v}{u}$. In both cases find u, then find the image-distance. Use the relation between focal length, object-distance and the image-distance and find the focal length of the mirror using the mirror formula $\left(\dfrac{1}{f} = \dfrac{1}{u} + \dfrac{1}{v}\right)$.

52. (i) Displacement = real depth – apparent depth.

(ii) Use the relation, $\mu = \dfrac{\text{Real depth}}{\text{Apparent depth}}$.

(iii) The position of the image shifts twice, when the light rays pass through the two media.

53. (i) Identifying the lens that produces conjugate positions of object and image.

(ii) The image is formed in two positions of the convex lens where these two positions are conjugate positions.

54. Thickness = 5 cm

$$\mu = \frac{\text{real thickness}}{\text{apparent thickness}}$$

$$\frac{3}{2} = \frac{5}{x};\ x = \left(\frac{10}{3}\right)$$

$$\text{Shift} = \frac{5-10}{3} = \frac{15-10}{3} = \frac{5}{3}\text{ cm}$$

55. (i) Draw a ray diagram.

(ii) Using a ray diagram, find the incident rays of the light ray on two mirrors and also find the sum of these incident rays.

56. (1) Laws of reflection of light

(2) Equilateral triangle

57. (i) Mirror formula

(ii) Find the image-distance formed by the concave mirror using the formula $\dfrac{1}{f} = \dfrac{1}{u} + \dfrac{1}{v}$

(use Cartesian signs)

(iii) Is the image formed by the concave mirror inverted?

(iv) The inverted image of the concave mirror acts as virtual object to the plane mirror.

(v) Find the distance of the virtual object from the plane mirror $(50 + 30 - v) = u^1$

(vi) Now find the image distance, (v^1) formed by plane mirror $(v^1 = u^1)$

(vii) Now find the distance between the original object and the image formed in the plane mirror.

58. Using the rules for constructing ray diagrams drawing the ray diagram.

59. If the mirror moves away from the object with a speed v units, then the image moves away from the object with a speed of 2v units.

$\therefore$ OI' = x + v + x + v = 2x + 2v

OI = x + x = 2x

As v is the velocity of the mirror, it travels through a distance 'v' in one second.

$\therefore$ Distance moved by image from object in one second = 2x + 2v – 2x = 2v units.

Thus, the speed of the image = 2v.

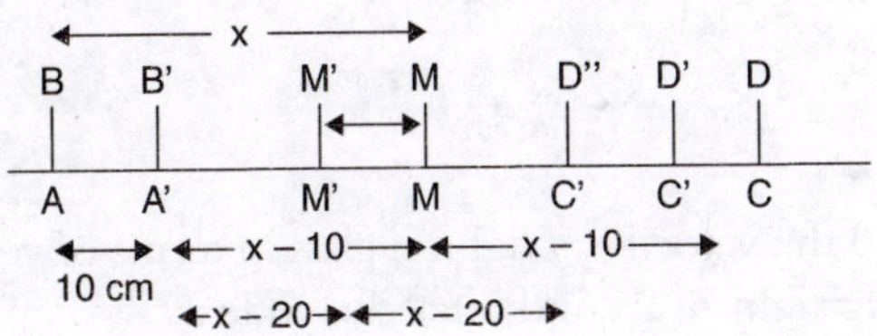

60.

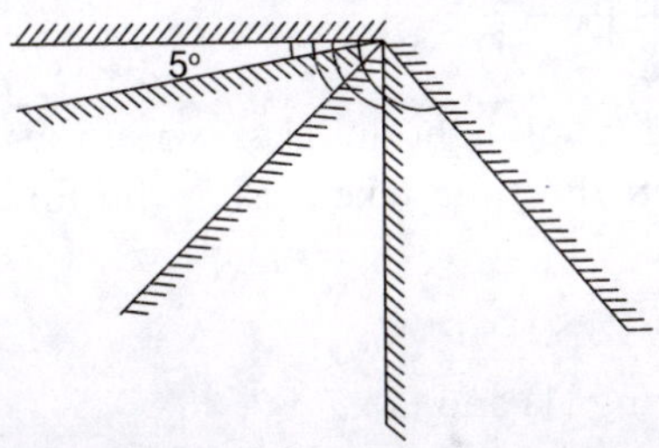

Time in second	Angle between mirrors	Number of images	Decrease in number of images
0	5°	71	-
5	10°	35	36
10	15°	23	12
15	20°	17	6

From the above table, it can be concluded that, the decrease in the number of images formed is not equal in equal intervals of time; whereas the angle between the mirrors increases uniformly. So, the decrease in the number of images is not proportional to the rate at which the angle between the mirrors increase.

61.

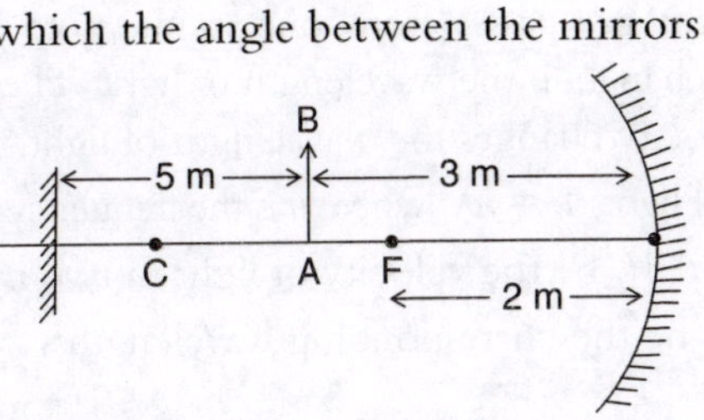

Given $f = -2\text{m}$, $u = -3\text{m}$

$$\frac{1}{f} = \frac{1}{u} + \frac{1}{v} \Rightarrow \frac{-uf}{u-f} = \frac{-3 \times -2}{-3+2} = \frac{-6}{-1} = 6\text{m}$$

An inverted, magnified and real image forms at 6 m from the concave mirror and this acts as an object to the plane mirror. Hence, the inverted virtual image is formed at a distance of 5 + 3 – 6 = 2 m, behind the plane mirror. So, the distance of the object and its virtual, inverted image is 2 + 5 = 7 m.

62. Object P: Placed in front of a Concave Mirror

Focal length, f = –20 cm (taking the sign convention)

Object distance, u = –10 cm (taking the sign convention)

Mirror formula:

$$\frac{1}{f} = \frac{1}{v} + \frac{1}{u}$$

$$\Rightarrow \frac{1}{v} = \frac{1}{f} - \frac{1}{u}$$

$$= \frac{1}{-20} - \frac{1}{-10} = \frac{1}{10} - \frac{1}{20} = \frac{1}{20}$$

$$\Rightarrow v = 20\,\text{cm}$$

Magnification:

$$m = -\frac{v}{u} = -\frac{20}{-10} = 2$$

Hence, image is at 20 cm from the pole of the mirror behind the mirror. It is virtual, erect and magnified.

Object Q: Placed in front of a Convex Mirror

Focal length, f = 20 cm (taking the sign convention)

Object distance, u = –10 cm (taking the sign convention)

Mirror formula:

$$\frac{1}{f} = \frac{1}{v} + \frac{1}{u} \Rightarrow \frac{1}{v} = \frac{1}{f} - \frac{1}{u}$$

$$= \frac{1}{20} - \frac{1}{-10} = \frac{1}{20} + \frac{1}{10} = \frac{3}{20}$$

$$\Rightarrow v = \frac{20}{3}\,\text{cm} = 6.66\,\text{cm}$$

Magnification:

$$m = -\frac{v}{u} = -\frac{\frac{20}{3}}{-10} = \frac{2}{3} = 0.66$$

Hence, image is at 6.66 cm from the pole of the mirror behind the mirror. It is virtual, erect and diminished.

63. For concave mirror: $h_i = 2 \times h_o$

$$\frac{h_1}{h_0} = 2 = \text{m} = \frac{-v}{u} \Rightarrow v = -2u.$$

$$\frac{1}{f}=\frac{1}{u}+\frac{1}{v}$$

$$\frac{-1}{f}=\frac{1}{-2u}+\frac{1}{u}$$

($\because$ Applying sing convention)

$$\frac{-1}{f}=\frac{-1+2}{-2u};\frac{-1}{2u};u=\frac{-f}{2}$$

negative sign indicates that the object is placed along the side of principal focus of the mirror.

$\therefore$ object distance from the mirror $\frac{f}{2}$.

64. Given that an object is placed at 200 m and another object at 2 m, respectively. The size of the images formed due to two objects are also equal. The distance between the lens and the images formed due to the two objects are also equal, i.e., image distance (v) is equal. Hence, let m_1 be the magnification of 1st object at 200 m and m_2 be the magnification of 2nd object at 2 m.

$$\therefore m_1=\frac{h_i}{h_{o_1}}=\frac{v}{u_1}\Rightarrow\frac{h_1}{h_{o_1}}=\frac{v}{200} \quad (1)$$

$$\therefore m_2=\frac{h_i}{h_{o2}}=\frac{v}{u_2}\Rightarrow\frac{h_1}{h_{o2}}=\frac{v}{2} \quad (2)$$

Dividing (1) by (2)

$$\frac{h_i}{h_{o1}}\times\frac{h_{o2}}{h_i}=\frac{v}{200}=\frac{2}{v}\Rightarrow\frac{h_{o2}}{h_{o1}}=\frac{1}{100}(or)$$

$$ho_1 = 100\ ho_2$$

$\therefore$ The height or the size of 1st object is 100 times more than the size or the height of 2nd object.

Level 3: Assess Your Concepts

Note: This is how you should frame your answer covering.

65. (i) Identify the shape of the mirror in each case after it is bent.

(ii) Characteristics of the nature of the images for concave and convex mirrors.

66. $^1\mu_2=\frac{V_1}{V_2}=\frac{2.4\times10^7}{1.8\times10^7}$

$$^1\mu_2=\frac{4}{3}$$

67. Recall the nature of the image formed by different mirrors.

Which mirror can produce a diminished real image of a distant object?

What is the relation between the image distance and the magnification?

68. (i) Find the number of images formed when two plane mirrors are placed at some angle in each case.

(ii) Add all the images excluding the images that have overlapped.

(iii) Number of images formed $=\frac{360}{\theta}-1$

69. (i) $\mu=\frac{v_1}{v_2}$

(ii) Find the velocity of light in glass in terms of velocity of light in air and refractive index.

Using the formula $\mu=\frac{c}{v}$ (1)

Relate the velocity of light in glass with the distance traveled and the time taken using the formula

$$v=\frac{x}{t} \quad (2)$$

Find t by comparing (1) and (2)

70. Height of the object = 5 cm

f = 20 cm u = –30 cm

$$\frac{1}{f}=\frac{1}{v}=\frac{1}{u}$$

$$\frac{1}{20}=\frac{1}{v}+\frac{1}{30}$$

$$\frac{1}{v}=\frac{1}{20}-\frac{1}{30}\frac{30-20}{600}v=\frac{60\text{ cm}}{1}$$

$$\text{Magnification}=\frac{h_i}{h_o}=\frac{v}{u}\Rightarrow\frac{h_i}{5}=\frac{60}{30}$$

h_i = 10 cm

71. When light ray passes from one medium to another there is a change in the wavelength of light. The change in the velocity changes the wavelength of light.

Velocity of light, $V = n\lambda$, where n is the frequency of light.

Let V_1 and V_2 be the velocity of light in two media.

λ_1 and λ_2 be the corresponding wavelengths.

$$V_1 = n\lambda_1$$

$$V_2 = n\lambda_2$$

$$\frac{V_1}{V_2}=\frac{\lambda_1}{\lambda_2}=\frac{6000}{3000}=2$$

Refractive in index of medium

$$= \frac{V_1}{V_2} = 2. \text{ Sin } \angle c = \frac{1}{\mu}; \text{Sin } \angle c \frac{1}{2} \therefore \angle c = 30^o$$

72. For a plane mirror u = v therefore u = 3 cm.

This object for plane mirror is the image formed due convex lens.

Distance between convex lens and mirror is 5 cm.

⇒ distance between lens and object of mirror is 2 cm.

⇒ $v_{lens} = 2$ cm

⇒ $u_{lens} = -2$ cm

u = v

⇒ object is placed at radius of curvature

⇒ R = 2 cm.

∴ f = 1 cm

73.

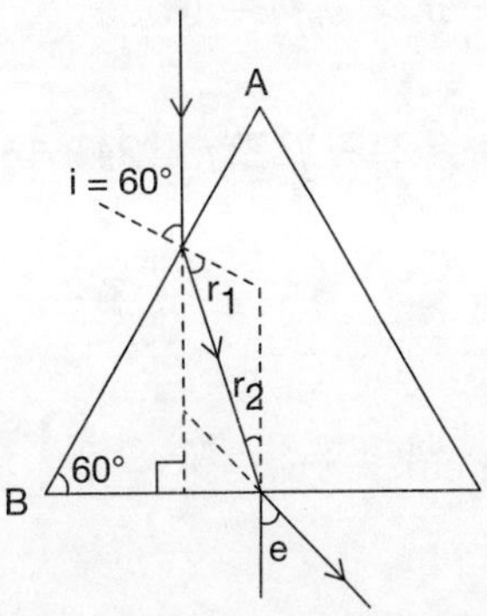

Here, *B* is the vertex of the prism and ∠*B* is the angle of prism.

$i + e = B + D$.

From geometry we have $B = 60°$, $i = 60°$.

$\therefore e = D$.

74. *PQ* is the incident ray incident at an angle *i*, *QR* the refracted ray refracted at an angle *r*.

From geometry (in triangle *AQR*)

$\angle AQR = 60°$

∠ angle of refraction $r = 90° - 60° = 30°$

From Snell's law

$$\mu = \frac{\sin i}{\sin r}$$

$(\mu = \sqrt{2}$ given)

$$\sqrt{2} = \frac{\sin i}{\sin 30}; \sqrt{2} = \frac{\sin i}{\frac{1}{2}}$$

$$\sin i = \frac{\sqrt{2}}{2} = \frac{1}{\sqrt{2}}$$

$$i = 45^o$$

∴ angle of incidence = 45°

Since the ray strikes the mirror normally, it retraces its path.

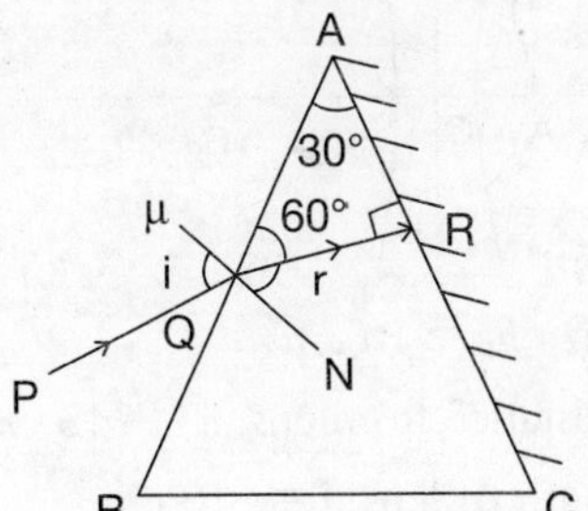

(i)

75.

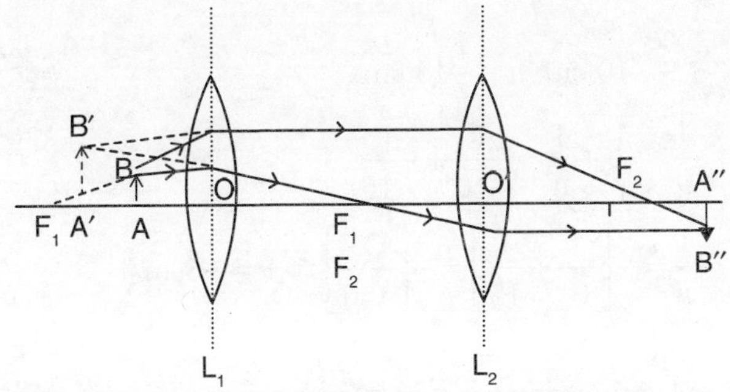

Let F_{11} and F_{12} be the principal foci of the first lens L_1, and F_{21} and F_{22} be the principal foci of the second lens L_2. From the construction of the ray diagram it is evident that two images would be formed, *A'B'* image formed by the first lens which would become the object for the second lens, and *A"B"*, final image formed by the second lens. *A'B'* – virtual, erect, on the same side as object *AB*, and magnified. *A'B'* – real, inverted, diminished (compared to *A'B'*) and on the far side of the combination of lens.

76. $\frac{1}{f} = \frac{1}{v_1} - \frac{1}{u}$

$$\frac{1}{f_1} = \frac{1}{2.5} - \frac{1}{-300}$$

$$= \frac{10}{25} + \frac{1}{300} = \frac{120+1}{300}$$

$$\therefore f_1 = \frac{300}{121}$$

$$\frac{1}{f_2} = \frac{1}{v_2} - \frac{1}{v_1} = \frac{10}{25} - \frac{1}{-200} = \frac{80+1}{200}$$

$$\therefore f_2 = \frac{200}{81}$$

$$\text{Ratio} = \frac{f_1}{f_2} = \frac{300}{121} \times \frac{81}{200} = \frac{243}{242}$$

243:242.

77.

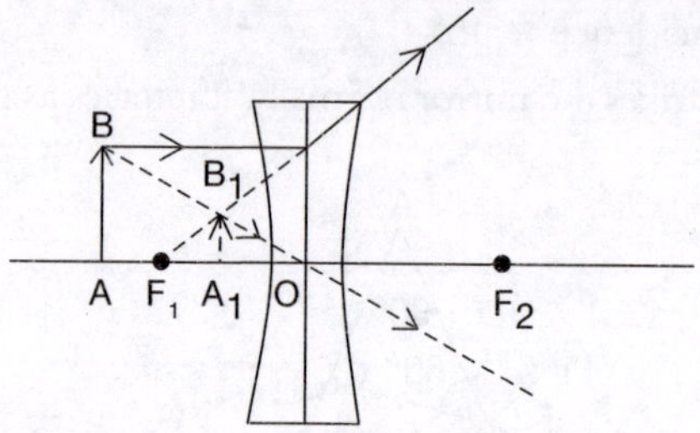

Object size $h_O = 10$ cm

Object distance fromlens, $u = -15$ cm.

Focal length of lens, $f = -10$ cm.

We know $\frac{1}{f} = \frac{1}{v} - \frac{1}{u}$

$f = -10$ cm; $u = -15$ cm

$$\frac{1}{v} = \frac{1}{f} + \frac{1}{u} = \frac{1}{-10} + \frac{1}{-15}$$

$$\frac{1}{v} = -\left[\frac{1}{10} + \frac{1}{15}\right] = -\left[\frac{25}{150}\right] \Rightarrow v = -6\text{cm}$$

Magnification, m $= \frac{v}{u} = \frac{-6}{-15} = \frac{2}{5}$

$$\Rightarrow m = \frac{h_i}{h_o} \Rightarrow \frac{2}{5} = \frac{h_i}{10}$$

$$\Rightarrow h_i = \frac{20}{5} = 4 \text{ cm}$$

∴ image distance, $v = -6$ cm.

The nature of images formes is virtual, erect and diminished compared to the object size.

78.

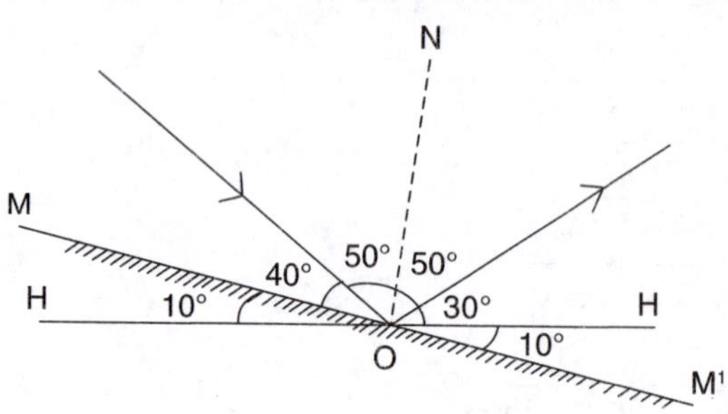

79. $\frac{1}{f} = \frac{1}{u} + \frac{1}{v}, f = 20 \text{ cm}, u = -20 \text{ cm}$

$$\frac{1}{20} = \frac{-1}{20} + \frac{1}{v}; \frac{1}{v} = \frac{1}{20} + \frac{1}{20} = \frac{2}{20}$$

$v = 10$ cm

80. In the first case the image is real

$$\frac{1}{f} = \frac{1}{u} + \frac{1}{v}, \ u = -ve, \ v = +ve$$

$$\frac{1}{f} = \frac{1}{u} + \frac{1}{v}, \ m = \frac{v}{u}; \ \frac{u}{f} = \frac{u}{v} + 1, \ \frac{u}{v} = \frac{u}{f} - 1 = \frac{u-f}{f}$$

$$m = \frac{f}{u-f}, \ m = \frac{f}{24-f} \quad (1)$$

In the 2nd case the image is virtual

$u = -ve, v = -ve$

$$\frac{1}{f} = \frac{1}{v} - \frac{1}{u}, \ \frac{1}{f} = \frac{-1}{v} + \frac{1}{u}; \ \frac{u}{f} = \frac{-u}{v} + 1, \ \frac{u}{v} = 1 - \frac{u}{f}$$

$$\frac{1}{m} = \frac{u}{v} = \frac{f-v}{f}, \ m = \frac{f}{f-u}, \ m = \frac{f}{f-16} \quad (2)$$

$$\frac{f}{24-f} = \frac{f}{f-16}, \ f - 16 = 24 - f, \ 2f = 24 + 16$$

$$f = \frac{40}{2} = 20 \text{ cm}$$

81. Height of the object = 3 cm

Focal length = 20 cm

Height of the image = 6 cm

$$\frac{hi}{ho} = \frac{v}{u} = \frac{6}{3} = \frac{v}{u}\frac{1}{2} = \frac{v}{u}$$

$u = 2v$

$$\frac{1}{f} = \frac{1}{v} = \frac{1}{u}$$

$$\frac{1}{20} = \frac{1}{v} + \frac{1}{2v}; \ \frac{1}{20} = \frac{2+1}{2v}$$

$V = 30$ cm

$u = 60$ cm; $u + v = 90$ cm.

82. Since convex mirror always forms a virtual image, magnification, m is positive.

$$m = -\frac{v}{u} = \frac{1}{2}\frac{v}{u} = \frac{h_i}{h_o} \text{ where } v \text{ is image}$$

distance, u is object distance, h_i is height of the image and h_O is height of the object.

$$v = -\frac{u}{2} \quad (1)$$

Radius of curvature, R = 20cm

$$\text{Focal length, } f = \frac{R}{2} = \frac{20}{2} \quad 10\text{cm}$$

From mirror formula

$$\frac{1}{f} = \frac{1}{u} + \frac{1}{v}$$

$$\frac{1}{10} = \frac{1}{u} + \frac{1}{-\frac{u}{2}}$$

$$\frac{1}{10} = \frac{1-2}{u}$$

or $u = -10$ cm.

Therefore, the object is at 10 cm from the pole of the mirror.

JEE-NEET Special Wing

Multiple-Answer Type Questions

1. Glass and ice are transparent bodies.
Hence, the correct option is (b) and (c).

2. If an extended source of light is used, both umbra and penumbra are formed.
Hence, the correct option is (a) and (b).

3. Light does not require any material medium to propagate. It can travel through vacuum. Light does not affect the properties of the medium through which it pass.
Hence, the correct option is (c) and (d).

4. $n = \left[\frac{360°}{\theta} - 1\right]$

$= \left[\frac{360° - \theta}{\theta}\right]$

$n\theta = 360° - \theta$

Hence, the correct option is (a) and (d).

5. The colour of sky is due to scattering.
Hence, the correct option is (c).

Comprehension-Based Questions

6. Light ray travels from water (denser medium) to air (rarer medium) bends away from the normal. Thus, the object appears to be nearer.
Hence, the correct option is (a).

7. Refractive index is a measure of optical density.
Hence, the correct option is (c).

8. It is the ratio of velocities, hence no unit.
Hence, the correct option is (d).

9. $\mu = \frac{\text{real depth}}{\text{apparent depth}}$

Hence, the correct option is (b).

10. Absolute ref. index $= \frac{\text{velocity of light in vacuum/air}}{\text{velocity of light in medium}}$

$\mu = \frac{c}{v}$

$v = \frac{c}{\mu} = \frac{3 \times 10^8}{2}$

$= 1.5 \times 10^8 \text{ m s}^{-1}$

Hence, the correct option is (c).

11. The critical angle will be maximum when light travels from glass to water.
Hence, the correct option is (d).

12. The angle of incidence for which the angle of refraction is 90° is called the critical angle.
Hence, the correct option is (b).

13. $n = \frac{1}{\sin C}$

$\sin C = \frac{1}{n}$

$= \frac{1}{1.4}$

$= 0.71428$

$C = \sin^{-1}(0.71428)$

$= 45.58$

$\approx 45°$

Hence, the correct option is (c).

14. $i_1 + i_2 = A + d$
Hence, the correct option is (a).

15. $i_1 + i_2 = A + d$

$d = i_1 + i_2 - A$

$= 45 + 80 - 60$ ($\because$ for an equilateral triangle $A = 60°$)

$= 65°$

Hence, the correct option is (c).

Match the Column

15. **Choice (b) follows.**

(A) If $u = \infty$, $v = f$ (at focus)

(B) If $2f < u < \infty$, object is beyond C, v is between C and F.

(C) If $u = 2f$ (at C), then v is also at C.

(D) If $f < u < 2f$, ie., object between C and F, then image is beyond C ($v > 2f$)

(E) If $u = f$ (at focus), then image is at infinity ($v = \infty$).

Electricity

CHAPTER

8

Key Ideas

After completing this chapter, you should be able to:

- learn about Thale's and Gilbert's experiments.
- study structure of an atom and models related.
- define terms, such as electrification, electrostatic force, atmospheric electricity, etc.
- learn properties of charges, methods of charging a body, detection and testing of charges.
- learn about electric current and cause of electric current, resistance and factors affecting resistance, EMF, primary and secondary cells, conductors and insulators.
- discuss about electrical circuits (series and parallel), electrical energy, power, and applications of electricity.

Remember

Before beginning this chapter, you should be able to:

- discuss the nature of electric charges at rest.
- discuss the construction and working of cells and the heating effect, chemical effect and magnetic effect of electricity.

Scientific Crypt

A Tribute to William Gilbert (1544–1603)

William Gilbert, English scientist and physician, was born in Colchester, Suffolk, on 24th May, 1544 to a prosperous magistrate. He completed B.A from Cambridge university in 1561, received an M.A degree in 1564. He studied medicine at St. John's College, Cambridge, and completed graduation in 1573. Later, started practicing medicine and became a member of the Royal College of Physicians. In 1600, he was elected President of the Group of Royal College of Physicians. He became a successful medical practioner and was elected as one of the queen Elizabeth I's personal physician from 1600 – 1603. Later, served her successor King James I as physician up to November of that year when he died of plague.

He studied magnetism and Lodestones for nearly two decades, to explain the behaviour of magnetic compasses. In 1600, Gilbert published De Magnate (on magnets) the first major scientific work produced in England. In this book, Gilbert's attitude towards scientific investigation is reflected. Gilbert mostly relied on sense experiments and his own observations and experiments and demeaned others authoritative opinions and deductive philosophies.

He gathered and not only received critically older knowledge on the behaviour of the magnet and electrified bodies and tried to explain on the basis of his own researches. Gilbert concluded that earth was a huge magnet with its north and south poles coinciding with the geographical poles and suggested that electrostatic force of attraction was due to a subtle electric effluvium emitted by charged bodies.

This early period scientist, made a tremendous break through in the field of science with his innovative ideology. This versatile, physician cum physicist left the world on 30th November, 1603 as a viction of the plague epidemic.

Crossword

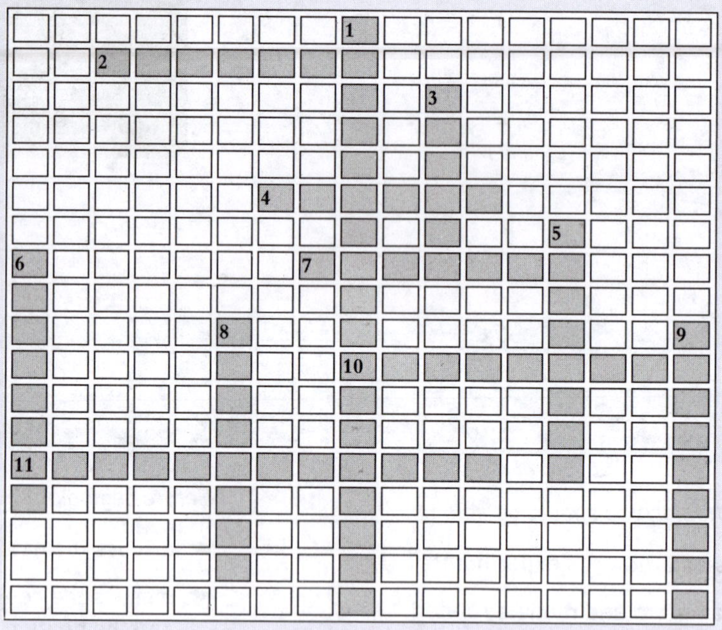

Across

2. A cell in which electrolyte used in the form of paste.

4. If one of the bulbs in this combination is removed the other bulbs do not work.

7. 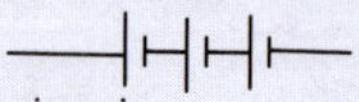 is the symbol of ______ in a circuit.

10. Name of the process of charging in which body acquires the same charge as that of source.

11. It is used to control the electric current in a household electric circuit.

Down

1. Work done by cell.

3. Unit of electric current.

5. When a glass rod is rubbed with silk cloth, they get charged due to.

6. When the bulbs are connected in this manner the bulbs glow with the same e.m.f.

8. Material used as heating element.

9. A material through which electric charges cannot pass.

INTRODUCTION

The initial research and study made by scientists like Gilbert, Thale, Benjamin Franklin, Ampere, Faraday, etc., laid the foundation for perhaps the most important branch of Science and Engineering, i.e., Electricity.

Today it is difficult to imagine life without electricity. From lighting in a room to agriculture, communication and media to medical field, transport to computers, almost every field depends heavily on electricity and electrical engineering, and it has become important to understand some basic concepts of this branch of physics.

Electricity is a form of energy that can be easily transformed into other forms of energy and also transmitted over large distances with minimum loss. For better understanding of thisform of energy, we divide the study of this topic into electrostatics and current electricity.

Study of electric charges at rest and their cause and effect constitutes electrostatics, whereas current electricity deals with the cause and effect of moving charges. We shall initiate the study of electrostatics by reviewing the structure of an atom.

Structure of Atom

A study of the structure of an atom reveals that there exist fundamental particles namely protons, electrons and neutrons in it. Protons and neutrons lie in the central part of the atom and its whole mass is concentrated at the central part, which is also known as 'nucleus'. Electrons are the fundamental particles that revolve round the nucleus in orbits. There is a force of attraction between protons present in the nucleus of an atom and the electrons that revolve round the nucleus.

This force of attraction decreases as the distance between the orbits in which electrons revolve and the nucleus increases. Thus, the electrons present in the outermost orbit or its sublevels known as 'orbitals' are loosely bound to the nucleus of the atom. These outermost orbitals are called **valence orbitals** and the electrons present in them are called **valence electrons**.

Electrification

When a body is rubbed over another, transfer of the valence electrons takes place between the two bodies and the two bodies are said to be 'electrically charged'. **'Charge'** is defined as the amount of electricity present in a body and is denoted by 'Q' or 'q'. In an atom, the electrons are considered to be negatively-charged and protons are considered to be positively-charged while the neutrons do not possess any charge. So, when a body A is rubbed over another body 'B', electron transfer takes place, say from 'A' to 'B'. 'A' is positively-charged due to depletion of electrons and 'B' is negatively-charged due to the presence of excess number of electrons. This means that a body losing electrons is losing some negative charge, so it becomes a positively-charged body. Similarly, a body gaining electrons is gaining some extra negative charge, so it becomes a negatively-charged body. The transfer of electrons from one body to another takes place when these two bodies are rubbed and the cause of electron transfer is friction between the two bodies. The process of charging a body is known as **electrification** and when it is done by rubbing one body over the other, it is called electrification by friction. The charge thus obtained is called **frictional charge**.

Thale's Experiment

The word 'electricity' was coined about 600 years before the birth of Christ. Greek philosopher and scientist Thale conducted an experiment with 'amber', which is a resinous material and called electron in Greek language. He rubbed a substance made of amber with fur cloth and found that both these materials developed a special property of attracting some other small bodies like pieces of paper, thread, etc. Hence, amber and fur were considered to have acquired electrical property and the process was called electrification.

Gilbert's Experiment

An experiment similar to that conducted earlier by Thale was conducted by a British physicist Gilbert in the early years of 16th century.

Gilbert showed that not only amber, but also other materials like a glass rod or an ebonite rod when rubbed with silk cloth or cat's skin, respectively developed the property of attracting small pieces of paper, etc. Two glass rods rubbed with silk cloth were found to repel each other. So, it was concluded that these two glass rods acquired a similar electric charge, and that bodies with like charge repel each other, whereas bodies with unlike charge attract each other.

When a glass rod is rubbed with a silk cloth, transfer of electrons takes place from the glass rod to the silk cloth. Since electrons are negatively-charged, the glass rod loses some negative charge and is charged positively. Similarly the silk cloth contains more electrons than the number of protons and so it contains more negative charge than positive charge on it. So, the silk cloth is said to be charged negatively. Thus, there are two types of charges, namely positive and negative.

Unit of Electric Charge

The unit of electric charge in S.I. system is **'coulomb'** named after the scientist **Coulomb**. It is denoted by 'C'.

Info Bytes!

Like charges repel, unlike charges attract. This simple yet fundamental principle governs how everything from atoms to galaxies interact!

Properties of Charges

The following are the properties of electric charges:

- There are two types of charges, namely positive and negative.
- Like charges repel and unlike charges attract each other.
- On losing electrons, a neutral body acquires a positive charge.
- On gaining electrons, a neutral body acquires a negative charge.
- The amount of charge present in a body, either positive or negative, is expressed in terms of an integral number of the charge of an electron, which is considered the elementary entity of an electric charge.
- The magnitude of charge of an electron is equal to the magnitude of charge of a proton.
- The charge on a body gives the information about the excess or deficiency of electrons in the body but does not refer to the total charge, either positive or negative, present in the body.
- When no charge is supplied to or removed from a body, it is said to be electrically neutral and then the amount of positive charge present in it is equal to the amount of negative charge in it.
- When two bodies are rubbed together, and if one body acquires a positive charge by losing some electrons, the second body acquires a negative charge of equal magnitude by gaining the same number of electrons as those lost by the first body (as shown in figure 8.1). Thus, the total electric charge on both the bodies put together, before and after electrification remains the same. Thus, the charge is said to be conserved. This is known as the **law of conservation of charge**, according to which 'charge can only be transferred from one body to another, and can be neither created nor destroyed'.

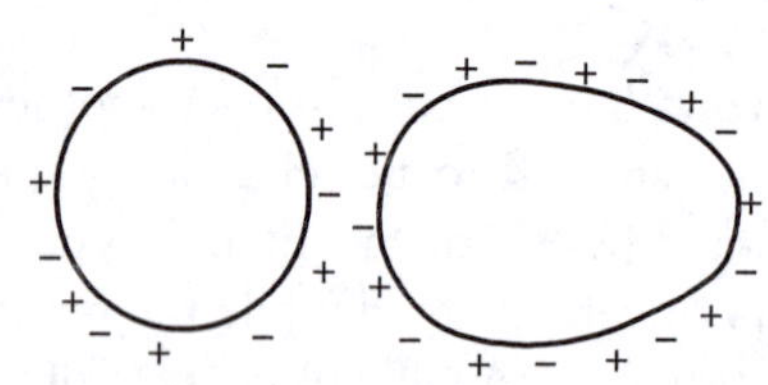

Figure 8.1 Acquiring of charge from one body to another

- If a spherical conductor is supplied some amount of charge, the charge gets distributed over its surface uniformly, no matter at what point the charge is supplied. The amount of charge present per unit surface area is called **surface charge density** and is generally denoted by 'σ' (Greek alphabet sigma). Surface charge density is measured in C m^{-2} or C cm^{-2}. For spherical conductors the surface charge density is equal at all places. But if the surface of a conductor has more sharply curved surfaces or has pointed tips, at those positions, the surface charge density is higher.
- The charge supplied to an insulator is not distributed over its entire surface and remains stationary at the supplied position on the insulator.
- The charge supplied to a conductor always resides on its outer surface and is not present inside the body.

Methods of Charging a Body

The process of supplying an electric charge to a body is known as **'charging'**. A body can be charged in different ways.

Charging by Friction

When a body is rubbed over another, transfer of electrons from one body to another takes place due to friction. Thus, one body acquires a net negative charge and the other acquires a net positive charge. This method of charging is known as charging or electrification by friction. A substance when rubbed with a substance coming after it in the following list gets positively-charged.

- Cat's skin
- Fur
- Glass
- Cotton
- Silk
- Wood
- Rubber
- Resin
- Amber
- Sulphur and
- Ebonite

Konnect

Properties of Electric Charge are as follows

(i) Scalar : Charges are Additive in Nature

(ii) Conserved Electric charge can neither be created nor be destroyed but remains constant.

(iii) Quantized : Net charge of a system is the algebraic sum of individual charges.

Charging by Conduction

Consider a small metallic sphere placed on a wooden stand as shown in Figure 8.2. Let a glass rod be rubbed with a silk cloth and then brought into contact with the metallic sphere placed on the wooden stand. The glass rod, when rubbed with a silk cloth, acquires a positive charge. When this positively-charged glass rod is brought into contact with the metallic sphere, some of the electrons get transferred from the metallic sphere to the glass rod. Thereby the metallic sphere acquires some positive charge as shown in Figure 8.2. This process of electrically charging a conductor by bringing it into contact with another charged body is known as **'charging by conduction'**.

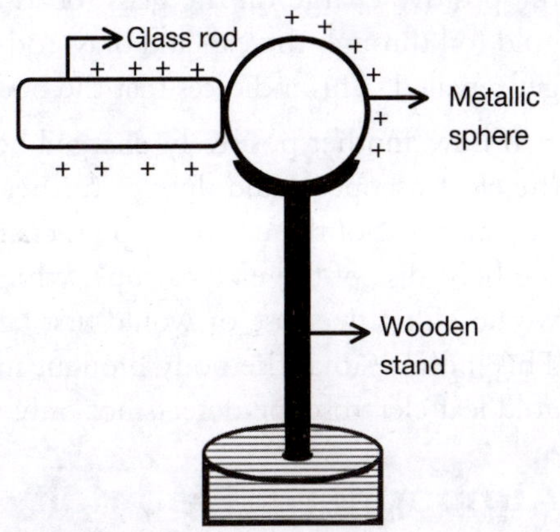

Figure 8.2 Charging by conduction

Charging by Induction

Consider a small metallic sphere placed on a wooden stand. The metallic sphere, being neutral, contains equal amounts of both positive and negative charges. When a glass rod rubbed with a silk cloth is brought near the metallic sphere, an opposite charge is induced on the surface of the metallic sphere closer to the glass rod, and similar charge is induced on the sphere at the far end. The glass rod, when rubbed with a silk cloth, acquires a positive charge. When this positively-charged glass rod is brought near the metallic sphere, the positive charge on the glass rod attracts the negative charges present on the sphere and repels the positive charges. Thus, the charges on the metallic sphere rearrange themselves in such a way that the negative charges are nearer to the glass rod and the positive charges are away from it. Now, if by some means, we take away the positive charges accumulated at the far end of the metallic sphere, it would have excess negative charges and we say that the metallic sphere is charged negatively as shown in Figure 8.3. This process of electrically charging a body by bringing another charged body near it (and without making physical contact) is known as **'charging by induction'**.

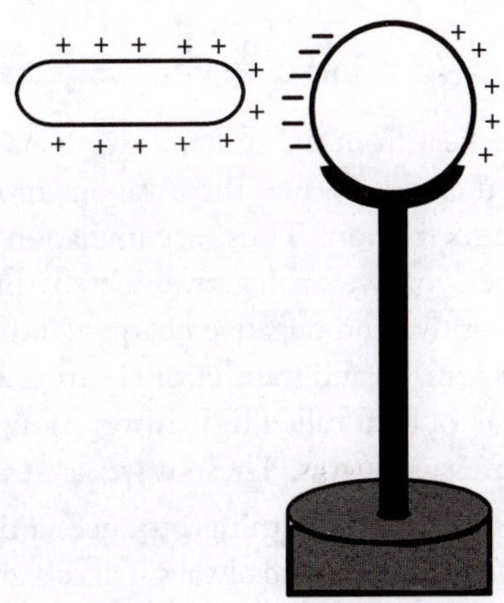

Figure 8.3 Charging by induction

Detection and Testing of Charges

Electroscope

Electroscope is an instrument to check whether a body is electrically charged or not and also to find the nature of the charge, i.e., positive or negative, present on the body. The most popular electroscope is the gold leaf electroscope.

Gold Leaf Electroscope

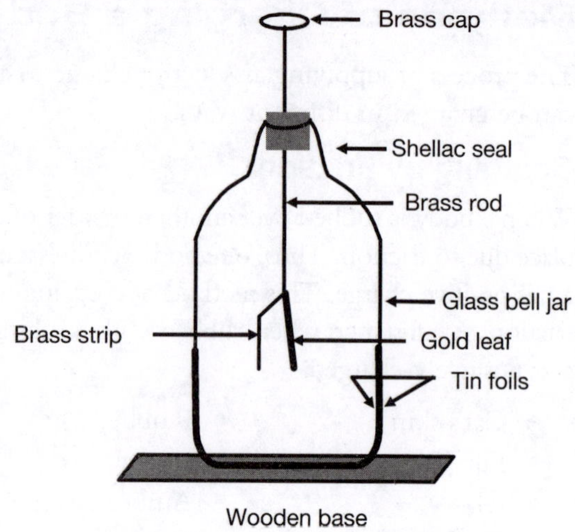

Figure 8.4 Gold leaf electroscope

A gold leaf electroscope consists of a glass jar placed on a non-conducting surface like wood. The mouth of the glass jar is closed with a cork and sealed with shellac material. This serves as an insulator and also supports a brass rod passing through it. Inside the jar, the lower end of the brass rod is fitted with a brass strip and a small gold foil loosely held to the strip. An aluminum foil may be used instead of the gold foil as shown in Figure 8.4.

At the bottom and lower lateral sides of the jar, tin foils which are earthed are fixed which help the charge to remain on the gold foil for a longer time, thus increasing the sensitivity of the electroscope. A brass cap is provided at the upper end of the brass rod.

Working: Initially, the brass cap of the electroscope is earthed to remove any charge present on the foils and the brass rod. Now, if the brass cap of the electroscope is touched with a glass rod rubbed with a silk cloth, the positive charge on the glass rod is transferred to the brass plate and gold foil through the cap and brass rod. Both the brass strip and the gold foil acquire the positive charge and the gold foil get repelled. This indicates that the body which is brought into contact with the brass disc of the electroscope is charged.

If now another positively-charged body is brought into contact with the brass disc of the electroscope, the gold leaf of the electroscope would diverge further away from the brass strip. This indicates that the body brought into contact with the brass disc of the electroscope is charged positively. Similarly, if a negatively-charged body is brought into contact with the brass disc of the electroscope, which is already charged positively, the divergence of the gold leaf from the brass strip would either decrease or would first fall back and charge again depending on the amount of negative charge on the rod. This indicates that the body brought into contact with the brass disc of the electroscope is charged negatively. Thus, the gold leaf electroscope detects not only whether a body is charged or not, but also the type of the charge on the body.

Atmospheric Electricity

Benjamin Franklin was the first scientist to discover that atmosphere surrounding the earth too contains electric charges. He discovered that clouds contain electric charges through his experiment with a kite made of silk cloth.

Franklin made a kite with thin silk cloth and used iron wires as the cross-wires of the kite. He attached a silk thread to the central spar of the kite. To the other end of the silk thread, he tied a key made of iron. Then he flew the kite on a certain day when the sky was overcast. When it was not raining and only dark clouds were present, nothing happened when he brought his hand close to the metallic key which was attached to the lower end of the silk string. But when it started raining and he brought his hand close to the metallic key again, he observed bright sparks between the key and his fingers giving him an electric shock. He concluded that clouds contain electric charge and it was transferred to his hand through the silk kite, the silk thread and the key.

Clouds and their Electric Charge

The heat from the sun and warm air cause water from water bodies to vaporize. These vapours accumulate in the sky and form clouds. When these vapour molecules rub against the air molecules or other vapour molecules, they acquire charge due to friction. Thus, accumulation of these molecules cause accumulation of a huge amount of static electric charge, either positive or negative, thereby increasing the electric potential of the clouds. When two clouds having huge amount of positive and negative charges (and consequently high potential) come close to each other, the air present between them gets ionized and transfer of electrons takes place from one cloud to another, resulting in the production of a dazzling white streak of light called **lightning**. Along with the lightning a large amount of heat is produced which results in the production of pressure waves. These waves are transmitted in all directions and produce a loud sound, which is called **thunder**.

Sometimes lightning produces a devastating effect. Whenever lightning occurs, it tends to conduct the charge to the surface of earth and always strikes a conductor that is closer to the clouds. This means, lightning strikes a conductor whose height from the surface of earth is maximum at that place; for example tall buildings and trees. A negatively-charged cloud induces a positive charge on the top surface of a tall building and a negative charge at its ground level. When it rains, the moist air between the cloud and the building creates a conducting path between the two, so that the electrons on the cloud flow to the building through the path. When the electrons from the cloud reach the top of the building, high electric current flows through the building, thus setting the building on fire. Thus, lightning sometimes produces a destructive effect. To protect such tall buildings from lightning, generally lighting rods are provided at the top (the highest point) of the buildings. A lightning rod is a good conductor of electricity through which charge can flow. This lightning rod is connected to the earth by means of the thick strip of conductor. The lightning conductor has sharp points at its top so as to receive the lightning charge at the specific point. Once the charge is received at the conductor, it passes to the ground through the conducting strip; thus the building is safeguarded from damage.

Info Bytes!

Generally copper is used for the lightning conductor and the thick strip.

Electric Current

All the materials can be classified into either conductors or insulators with respect to electricity. The **conductor** is a material which allows an electric charge to flow through it.

All metals in solid form and aqueous solutions of salts are examples of conductors. Gases generally do not conduct electricity under normal conditions of temperature and pressure. They conduct electricity only under certain special conditions.

An **insulator** is a material that does not allow electric charge to flow through it. All plastic materials, glass, rubber, wood, ebonite, etc., are examples of insulators in solid state. Pure water is an example of insulator in liquid state. As mentioned earlier, gases in general are insulators.

The rate at which electric charge flows through a conductor is known as **electric current**. It is denoted by '*i*', and is measured in units of 'ampere' (A).

Mathematically, $i = \frac{q}{t}$. Here '*q*' is the total charge that flows through a conductor in a given time '*t*', which denotes the time of flow.

$$\text{Unit of electric current} = \frac{\text{Unit of electric charge}}{\text{Unit of time}}$$

$$\Rightarrow \text{ampere} = \frac{\text{coulomb}}{\text{second}}$$

Thus, if one coulomb of charge flows across a conductor in one second of time, the electric current passing through the conductor is said to be **one ampere**.

EXAMPLE 8.1 A device is connected to a battery for 45 seconds, and during this time, a total charge of 135 C flows through it. Find the electric current passing through the device.

SOLUTION

We know that electric current (I) is the rate at which charge (*Q*) flows in a given time (*t*). Given, the total charge flowing through the device in 45 seconds is 135 C.

Therefore, the charge that flows in 1 second = 135C/45s = 3 Cs^{-1} = 3A

Using the formula, *I* = *Q*/*t*, where I represents the electric current, *Q* is the total charge, and *t* is the time taken:

$I = \frac{135C}{45s} = 3Cs^{-1} = 3AI$ = 135C/45s = 3 C s – 1 = 3A

∴ The electric current passing through the device = 3A.

EXAMPLE 8.2 In a motor, a current of 10A flows for 45 minutes. Determine the amount of charge that has passed through the motor.

SOLUTION

From the definition of electric current, we have, $I = Q/t$

$I = 10A$

$T = 45$ min $= 2700$ seconds

$\therefore Q = I \times t$

$= (10A) \times (2700\ s)$

$= 27000$ C

$= 27$ kC.

EXAMPLE 8.3 An electric fan draws a current of 1.5A when turned on. Determine the number of electrons passing through the fan in 100 minutes.

SOLUTION

We are given,

$I = 1.5A$ and $t = 100$ minutes $= 100 \times 60$ s $= 6000$ s

$\therefore Q = It$

$= (1.5A) \times (6000\ s) = 9000$ C

1 C charge corresponds to 6.25×10^{18} electrons

$\therefore$ 9000 C charge corresponding to $9000 \times 6.25 \times 10^{18}$ electrons

$= 56250 \times 10^{18}$ electrons

$= 56.2 \times 10^{21}$ electrons.

The Cause of Electric Current

Electric current through a conductor can be understood easily by an analogy of flow of water. Consider two cylindrical tanks 'A' and 'B' having different diameters containing water at different levels, as shown in the Fig. 8.5.

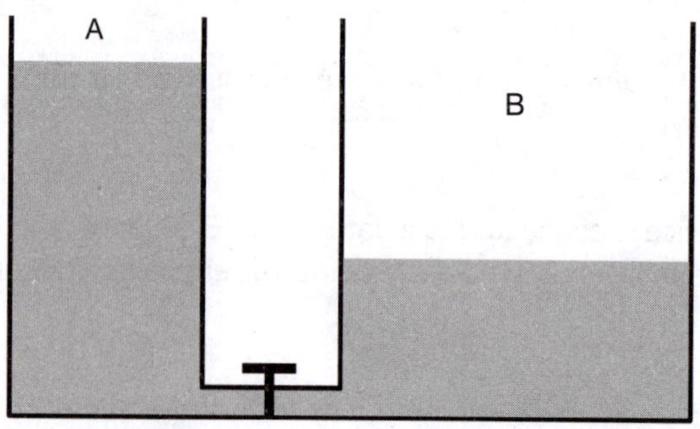

Figure 8.5 liquid flows due to the difference in water levels in the tanks

The level of water in tank 'A' is higher than the level of water in tank 'B'. The bottom of the two tanks are connected with the help of a pipe with a tap in between. When the tap is opened water flows from tank 'A' to tank 'B' until the levels are equal in both the tanks, irrespective of the quantity of water present in the two tanks. So, it is the level of water that decides the direction of water flow from one tank to another and not the amount of water present in them. Also waterflow ceases when the level of water in both the tanks is equal.

Similarly, in an electric conductor, the electric charge flows from one end to another end of the conductor, only when an electric potential difference exists between the two ends of the conductor. Thus, an **electric potential difference** is the condition required for a conductor to have an electric charge travelling through it from one end to another and is measured in volts. If the potential difference across two ends of a conductor is zero, there exists no electric current through the conductor.

Positively-charged bodies are considered to be at a higher potential and negatively-charged bodies to be at a lower potential. So, when a positively-charged body and a negatively-charged body are connected by means of a conductor, there exists a potential difference across the ends of the conductor and so an electric charge flows through the conductor from a positively-charged body to a negatively-charged body. Initially, it was considered that the flow of positive charges constituted an electric current. Later, it was discovered that it is not the movement of positive charges that cause electric current, but the flow of electrons that causes electric current in a conductor. So, when a positively-charged body is connected to the earth by means of a conductor, electrons flow from the earth to the body through the conductor till all the positive charge on the body is neutralized. Similarly, if a negatively-charged body is connected to the earth by means of an electric conductor, the excess electrons present in the body pass through the conductor to the earth until it loses all the excess electrons and becomes electrically neutral. Thus, the earth has the capacity to both supply or absorb electrons to or from a body. So, the earth is considered to be at zero electric potential.

When it was discovered that the flow of electrons constituted the electric current in a conductor, many theories and laws regarding electricity were proposed. So, these laws were not changed again and electric current was classified into two types. One type of electric current is the flow of charge from a body at a high potential (positively-charged body), to a body at a low potential (negatively-charged body) as assumed before and is called **conventional electric current**. The second type of electric current is the actual current which is, due to the movement of negative charges from a negatively-charged body to a positively-charged body, called **electronic current**.

Conductors and Insulators

Substances which allow electric current to pass through them readily are called **electric conductors**. All metals are good conductors. Substances which do not allow electric current to pass through them are called **electric insulators**.

Example: plastic, wood, rubber, etc.

Electric Cell

Consider the two cylindrical tanks containing water, as shown in Fig. 8.5. It is obvious that water flows from tank 'A' to tank 'B' as long as there is a difference in the level of water in both the tanks. If we need to have a continuous flow of water from tank 'A' to tank 'B', we need to maintain the difference in levels of water in both tanks continuously. In order to maintain a constant difference in the levels of water in both the tanks, we need to do some work and spend some energy. This may be achieved by pumping back water continuously from tank 'B' to tank 'A'.

Similar to the condition required for flow of water from one tank to another, the condition required to have a continuous flow of charge through a conductor is to have a difference in the potential maintained across its ends.

Similar to the energy spent in maintaining the difference in water level in both water tanks, as discussed earlier, energy has to be spent to maintain the potential difference across the ends of a conductor. The device which maintains an electric potential difference across the ends of a conductor is known as an **electric cell**.

An electric cell converts chemical energy into electrical energy. These kinds of cells are known as **'primary cells'**. Voltaic cell and Leclanche cell are examples of primary cells. In the process of supplying electrical energy, the composition of the chemicals in these cells changes gradually and the chemicals are said to be used up. It is not possible to retain the original composition of chemicals in these types of cells and the old cells have to be replaced by new cells, once all the chemical energy is used up.

In certain cells, it is possible to restore the original composition of chemicals by passing electric current in the cell in a direction opposite to the direction of current established by the cell and use the cell again whenever required. The process of restoring the original composition in the cells by passing electricity in opposite direction is known as 'charging' and these kinds of cells in which charging can be done are known as **'secondary cells'**. A lead-acid storage battery used in motor vehicles is an example of a secondary cell.

Electro Motive Force (EMF)

An electric cell has two terminals. These two terminals have different potentials and when a conductor of electricity is connected to these two terminals, electric charge flows through the conductor and an electric current is established in it. So, an electric cell does some work in driving electric charge through the conductors connected across its terminals. Thus, some energy is spent in moving electric charge through the conductor connected across the terminals of a cell. The amount of energy spent or work done in moving a unit positive charge through the conductors connected across the terminals of a cell is known as **electro motive force (EMF)** and it is measured in volts (V).

Voltaic Cell

Voltaic cell consists of a glass vessel, with dilute sulphuric acid (H_2SO_4) present in it which is also called an 'electrolyte'. Two plates, one made of zinc and another of copper, are immersed in the electrolyte and these two plates are connected with a conducting wire with a bulb in between, as shown in the Figure 8.6. The two plates immersed are known as **electrodes**.

Info Bytes!

Voltaic cell was invented by an Italian Scientist Alessandro Volta in the 18th century.

The dilute sulphuric acid present in the glass vessel is in the ionized state; i.e., the acid is dissociated into its ions.

$$H_2SO_4 \rightleftharpoons 2H^+ + SO_4^{2-}$$

The zinc plate, being more electroposi-tive compared to copper plate, loses electrons and gets ionized

$$Zn \longrightarrow Zn^{2+} + 2e^-.$$

Thus, when each zinc atom gets ionized, two free electrons are produced. So, negative charges are produced. The negative charges are accumulated over the zinc plate and, thus, it is called negative electrode. The positive zinc ions (Zn^{2+}), formed due to the ionization of zinc plate, move into the electrolyte and, thus, repel the hydrogen ions (H^+) and force them to get accumulated on the copper plate.

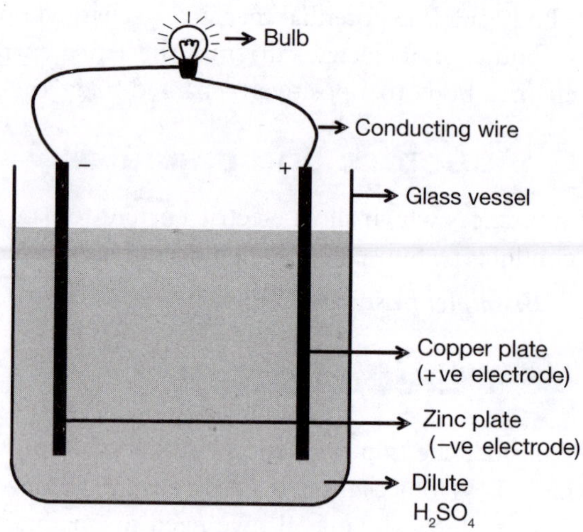

Figure 8.6 Voltaic cell

Thus, the positive charges are accumulated over the copper plate, which becomes the positive electrode. The free electrons accumulated at the zinc plate pass through the external conducting wire through the bulb, making it glow, and reach the copper plate. At the copper plate, these electrons combine with positive hydrogen ions and neutralize them to form molecular hydrogen and evolve as gas. The zinc ions (Zn^{2+}) that move into the electrolyte from zinc plate combine with sulphate ions (SO_4^{2-}) to form zinc sulphate.

$$Zn^{2+} + SO_4^{2-} \longrightarrow ZnSO_4.$$

Since negative charges are accumulated at the zinc plate, it is at a lower potential and similarly the copper plate is at a higher potential. Thus, this potential difference makes possible the flow of electrons through the external conducting wire and an electric current is established. After some time, the whole of sulphuric acid (H_2SO_4) is consumed gradually and simultaneously there is a gradual increase in the concentration of zinc sulphate ($ZnSO_4$). Thus, the electric current is established in the external conducting wire until all the sulphuric acid is used up.

Konnect

In a cell, the conventional electric current in the external circuit is from positive electrode to negative electrode whereas the electronic current is from negative electrode to positive electrode

Disadvantages

As the amount of hydrogen gas formed at the copper plate increases, the gas forms a layer of hydrogen gas over the copper electrode, which hinders the charge flow and, thereby, the potential difference between the electrodes and the electric current decreases with time. This effect is known as **'polarization'**.

If any metal pieces other than zinc are present on the zinc plate as impurities, the chemical reactions take place continuously in the cell, which causes the zinc plate to wear away faster than when electric current is extracted in the external conducting wires. This causes loss in the electric current that can be extracted from the cell. This effect is called **local effect** or **local action**.

The voltaic cell is not convenient to carry from one place to another, and has to be kept always in an upright position. It has to be handled carefully since an acid is used as electrolyte.

Daniel Cell

The Daniel cell was invented by J. F. Daniel in 19th century. Some of the disadvantages of the voltaic cell were overcome in this cell. It consists of a glass container which is divided into two equal portions by a porous membrane as shown in the Figure 8.7.

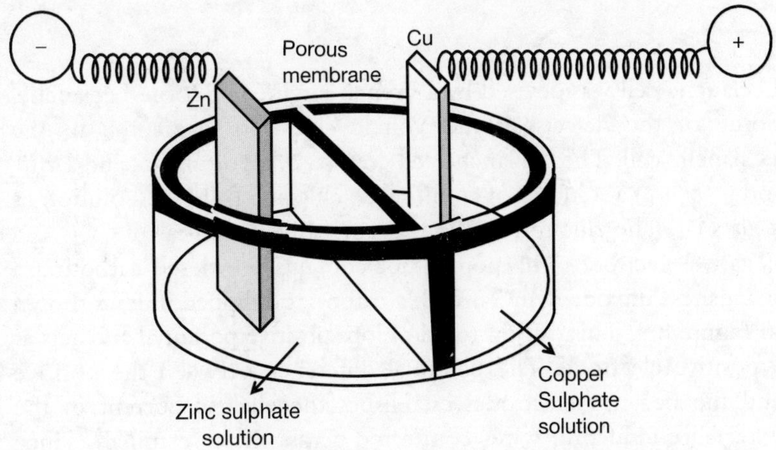

Figure 8.7 'Daniel cell'

One portion of the container consists of zinc sulphate solution and a zinc rod or a zinc plate dipped in it. The other portion of the container consists of a copper sulphate solution with a copper rod or a copper plate dipped in it. These two solutions present in the two parts of the container constitute electrolytes of the cells and the two rods or plates dipped in them are the electrodes. At the zinc rod (dipped in zinc sulphate solution) the zinc atoms lose two electrons and convert into ions that move into the zinc sulphate solution.

$$Zn \longrightarrow Zn^{2+} + 2e^-$$

Thus, electrons (negative charges) get accumulated over the zinc rod and so it is at a negative (lower) potential. The dissociated copper ions (Cu^{2+}) in the copper sulphate solution get accumulated on the copper rod in the other portion of the cell. Thus, positive charges get accumulated over the copper rod and it is at a positive (higher) potential. When these two rods are connected externally by conducting wires, flow of electrons from zinc rod to copper rod takes place establishing electric current in the external conducting wires. The electrons which reach the copper electrode combine with copper ions and neutralize to form copper atoms that get deposited over the copper electrode.

As electric current is established in the external conducting wires connected between the zinc and copper rods, gradual dissociation of zinc atoms to zinc ions increases and thereby, the size and mass of zinc rod gradually decreases.

Simultaneously, the accumulation of copper atoms on the copper electrode increases, resulting in the increase in zinc ions in the zinc sulphate solution and sulphate ions in copper sulphate solution. The porous membrane present between the two solutions plays an important role, allowing the excess sulphate ions in the copper sulphate solution to permeate through the membrane and combine with zinc ions in the zinc sulphate solution. Thus, gradually, the concentration of zinc sulphate solution increases and, simultaneously, the concentration of copper sulphate solution decreases. Thus, the electric current is established by the cell as long as the zinc rod does not wear out completely or the concentration of zinc sulphate solution does not reach a saturation point.

The Daniel cell is not portable and cannot be carried to any desired place easily and care has to be taken that the electrolytes do not spill out and it has to be placed always in the upright position.

Bichromate Cell

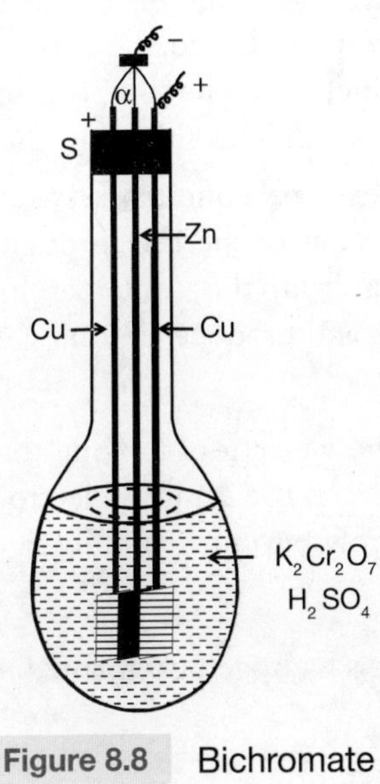

Figure 8.8 Bichromate cell

Bichromate cell consists of a mixture of two solutions as an electrolyte, unlike a Voltaic cell or a Daniel cell. The electrolyte in the cell is a mixture of sulphuric acid ($H_2 SO_4$) and Potassium dichromate ($K_2 Cr_2O_7$) solutions. The electrolyte is placed in a glass vessel. A lid is fitted to the vessel and three electrodes are fitted to the lid, as shown in Figure 8.8. Out of the three electrodes that are immersed in the electrolyte the middle one is made of zinc and acts as a negative electrode developing negative potential. The other two electrodes are made of copper and act as positive electrodes developing positive potential. These two electrodes are connected by a conducting wire and it is treated as the positive terminal of the cell whereas the conducting wire connected to the zinc electrode is the negative terminal of the cell. The difference in potential at these two terminals establishes the electric current in the conducting wires connected across them.

Leclanche Cell

Leclanche cell was devised by a French engineer George Leclanche. Some of the defects of the Voltaic cell were overcome in the Leclanche cell. The Leclanche cell consists of a porous pot and a zinc rod placed in a solution of ammonium chloride (NH_4Cl) solution in a glass jar. The zinc rod develops the negative potential and acts as a negative electrode. The porous pot contains powdered carbon and manganese dioxide (MnO_2) with a carbon rod dipped in it, as shown in Figure 8.9. This carbon rod develops positive potential and acts as a positive electrode. The potential difference between the positive and the negative electrodes establishes the electric current in the external conducting wires connected across these terminals. Since the electrolyte used in the Leaclanche cell is in the liquid form, this cell also is not convenient to move from one place to another and it cannot be placed in any desired position.

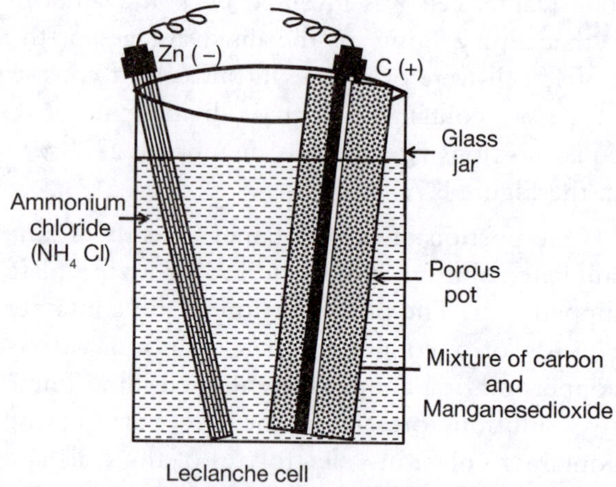

Figure 8.9 Leclanche cell

Dry Cell

To overcome the disadvantage of the cell invented by him, Leaclanche has modified it further, replacing the electrolyte in the liquid form with an electrolyte in the form of a paste. Thus, a dry cell is not completely dry as the name implies. Since the electrolyte is in the paste form, there is no danger of the spilling of electrolyte from the cell while in motion and it is also convenient to keep the cell in any desired position since the cell is portable.

Construction of a Dry Cell: A zinc cylindrical container consists of a chemical in the form of a paste. The chemical is a mixture of ammonium chloride (NH_4Cl) and zinc chloride ($ZnCl_2$) with manganese dioxide (MnO_2) and powdered carbon present in it. A carbon rod is present in the centre of the cylindrical container surrounded by the chemical mentioned above. The chemical which is in the form of a paste is the electrolyte, the zinc container itself is the negative electrode on which negative charges are accumulated and the carbon rod at the centre is the positive electrode on which positive charges are accumulated. A brass cap is provided to the carbon rod at its top to improve the electrical conductivity. The top portion of the cylindrical container is sealed and made airtight as shown in the figure 8.10.

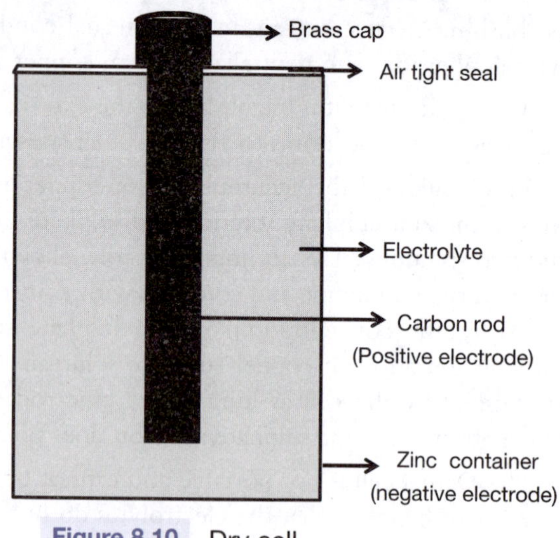

Figure 8.10 Dry cell

If external conducting wires are connected to the positive and negative electrodes of the cell through an electrical device like a bulb, the zinc atoms from the container lose electrons to the external conducting wires and produce an ion.

$$Zn \longrightarrow Zn^{2+} + 2e^-$$

These electrons flowing through the wire connected to the cell externally causes electric current, make the bulb glow and reach the positive electrode, i.e., carbon rod. These electrons combine with ammonium ions (NH_4^+) present in the electrolyte to form ammonia (NH_3) and hydrogen gas (H_2).

$$2NH_4^+ + 2e^- \longrightarrow 2NH_3 + H_2$$

This hydrogen gas formed reacts readily with manganese dioxide (MnO_2) to form manganese oxide (Mn_2O_3) and water.

$$H_2 + 2MnO_2 \longrightarrow H_2O + Mn_2O_3$$

The zinc ions (Zn^{2+}) formed in the electrolyte react with chlorine ions (Cl^-) originated from ammonium chloride to form zinc chloride.

$$Zn^{2+} + 2Cl^- \longrightarrow ZnCl_2$$

The powdered carbon present in the electrolyte enhances the flow of charge through it. When the cell is used for a long time continuously, the amount of hydrogen gas produced will be larger than the amount of hydrogen reacted with manganese dioxide and thus this excess of hydrogen gets accumulated over the carbon causing a restriction to the flow of charges within the electrolyte. Thus, the efficiency of the cell is reduced. When the cell is used intermittently (giving a gap after usage for some time), the time gap given is sufficient for the excess of hydrogen formed to react with manganese dioxide and thus the restriction to the charge flow is decreased. Thus, the dry cell can be used more efficiently. Once, the total amount of chemical is used up, the cell has to be replaced with a fresh one, as the original chemical composition cannot be regained.

A dry cell, which is widely used in many electronic appliances, generally produces an electro motive force (EMF) of 1.5 volt. If an emf of more than 1.5 volt is required a combination of more than one cell is used, as shown in Figure 8.11, such a combination of cells used to produce more emf is known as a **'battery'**.

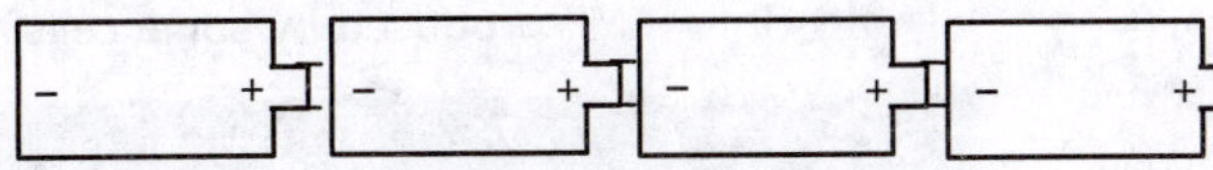

Figure 8.11 A battery

Even when the dry cell is not in use, the ammonium chloride continues to react with zinc (even though it is a slow process) and wears away the zinc can. Thus, the life span of a dry cell is not very long. If the zinc of the can is corroded, it causes the chemicals (electrolyte) in the cell to leak out.

If not checked, the leaked out electrolyte destroys the external connections of the electronic device which uses the dry cell. Thus, the dry cell should be taken out from an appliance when it is not in use for a long time.

Lead-acid Storage Battery

The cells discussed so far are primary cells, that is once the chemical (electrolyte) is used up, it is not possible to regain the original composition of the electrolyte for its further use. But, in a secondary cell, the original composition of the electrolyte can be restored by passing electric current through the cell in a direction opposite to the direction in which electric current is established by the cell. Such a secondary cell was invented by a French scientist Gaston Planet. Generally, a single secondary cell is not used. A number of secondary cells are connected with each other similar to the combination of cells in a battery; and usually a battery consists of a combination of six cells. The electrolyte most commonly used in these batteries is dilute sulphuric acid and the electrodes are made of lead oxide plates or spongy lead. Hence, these batteries are generally referred to as lead-acid storage batteries or accumulators. These are generally used in automobiles and inverters.

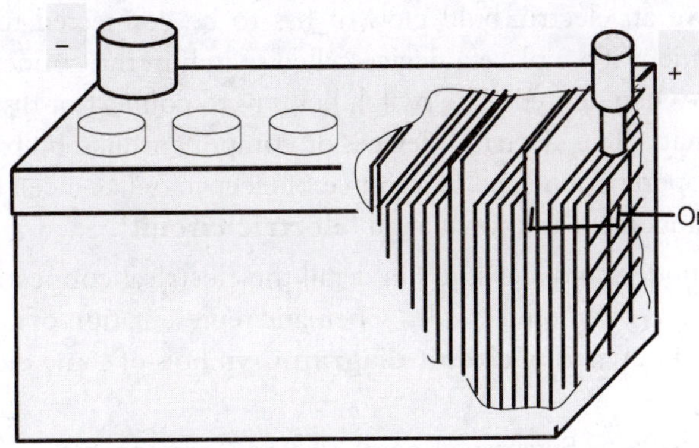

Figure 8.12 Lead-acid storage battery

Button Cell

The cells used in wrist watches, hearing aids, calculators, etc., are button shaped, hence, they are called **button cells**. They are small, compact and have long life. A mercury oxide cell and a silver oxide cell are example of button cells. Mercury oxide and silver oxide in the respective cells act as cathodes and zinc acts as anode in both of them.

The working of all cells which we have studied is more or less similar. All have zinc as negative electrode, either copper or carbon as positive electrode and sulphuric acid or ammonium chloride paste as electrolytes. Zinc reacts with electrolytes giving positively-charged hydrogen ions, which migrate towards the cathode. Zinc itself becomes the negative electrode due to the deposition of electrons on it. In this way the potential at copper or carbon increases whereas at zinc it decreases. When the cell is not connected to an external circuit, the potential difference between the positive and the negative terminals of the cell is called electromotive force or EMF. The **EMF** is defined as the work done in driving a unit positive charge through the external circuit and inside the cell itself. It is measured in volts (V).

The chemical reaction taking place in a cell can be summarized as follows.

$$Zn + [H_2SO_4 \text{ or } 2(NH_4CI)] \longrightarrow [ZnSO_4 \text{ or } ZnCl_2] + 2\,[H^+ \text{ or } NH^+] + e^-$$

$$e^- + Zn \longrightarrow Zn^-$$

$$[H^+ \text{ or } NH_4^+] + [Cu \text{ or } C] \longrightarrow [Cu^{++} \text{ or } C^{++}] + H_2\uparrow \text{ (gas)}$$

Table 8.1 EMF produced by some cells

S. No.	Name of cell	Negative electrode	Positive electrode	Electrolyte	EMF (volts) developed
1.	Voltaic cell	Zinc	Copper	H_2SO_4 (Dilute)	1.08
2.	Leclanche cell	Zinc	Carbon	NH_4Cl	1.5
3.	Bichromate cell	Zinc	Carbon	$K_2Cr_2O_7$ + H_2SO_4	2
4.	Dry cell	Zinc	Carbon	NH_4Cl (Paste)	1.5

Electric Circuit

To have an electric bulb glow, it has to be connected to a source of electricity like a cell by conducting wires. It is convenient if we place a device called switch in the connection. So, we can disconnect the bulb from the electric source as and when desired. The switch helps us to connect or disconnect the bulb or any other electrical device to the source of electricity. The electrical devices or components like bulb, switch, etc., are arranged in an orderly manner and then they are properly connected to a source of electricity like a cell or a battery by conducting wires to get the desired result. Such an arrangement is known as an **'electric circuit'**.

To understand and study in detail the electrical connections made between various electrical components, a schematic diagram is often used. Such a schematic representation of an electric circuit on paper showing the symbols for components used is known as a **'circuit diagram'** symbols of some electrical components.

Table 8.2 Symbols of some electrical components.

Components	Symbol
Cell (source of electricity)	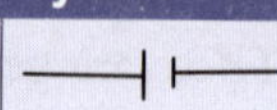
A battery (source of electricity)	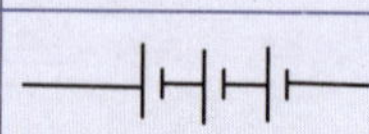
Plug key (switch) in closed condition	
Plug key in open condition	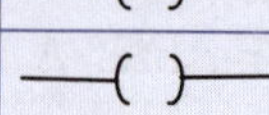
Tap key (switch) in open condition	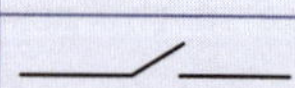
Tap key in closed condition	

(Continued)

Table 8.2 Continued

Components	Symbol
Bulb	
Ammeter (electric current measuring device)	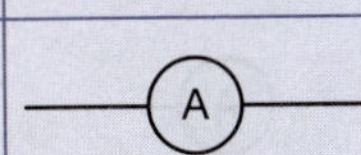
Example of a simple circuit:-	
E ⟶ Cell (source of electricity) B ⟶ Bulb K ⟶ Plug key	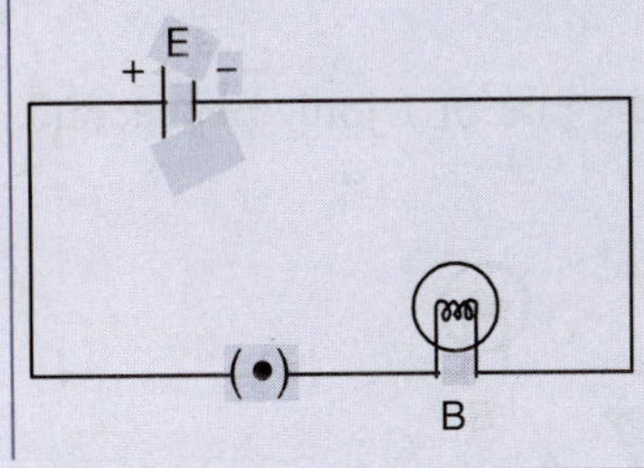

Series Circuit

An electric circuit in which all components are connected one after the other such that same current flows through them is called **series circuit**.

As seen in the figure 8.13, two bulbs are connected one after the other with one terminal each of the first bulb and the last bulb connected to the positive and the negative terminal of the battery. A switch can also be connected in series as shown in the following circuit diagram.

When the switch *S* is closed, the same current *I* flows through each of the bulbs making them glow. If any one of the bulbs is removed or if fuses, there is a break in the circuit, i.e., there is discontinuity in the electric current passing through the circuit and none of the other bulbs glow though they are in working condition.

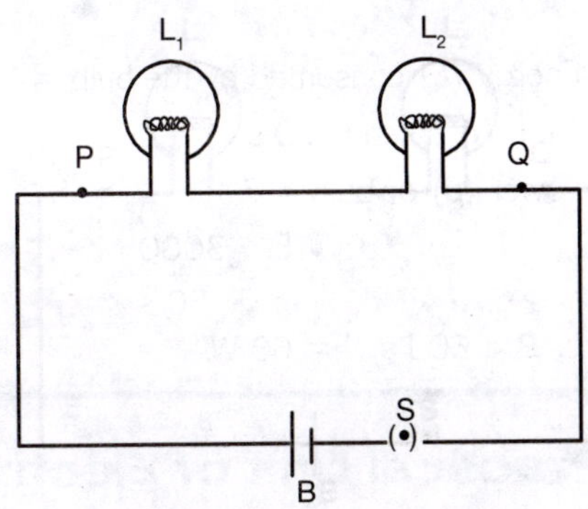

Figure 8.13 Series circuit

Parallel Circuits

A circuit in which different components are individually connected to the battery thus forming different branches in circuit is called **parallel circuit**. In each branch, the current flowing might be same or different depending upon the resistance to the flow of current that each branch offers.

From the Figure 8.14, it can be seen that each bulb is connected to both the terminals of battery independently so that even if one bulb is removed or if fuses, other bulbs are not affected. This is the reason why electricity appliances at homes and offices are connected in parallel so that they can be independently switched off and on.

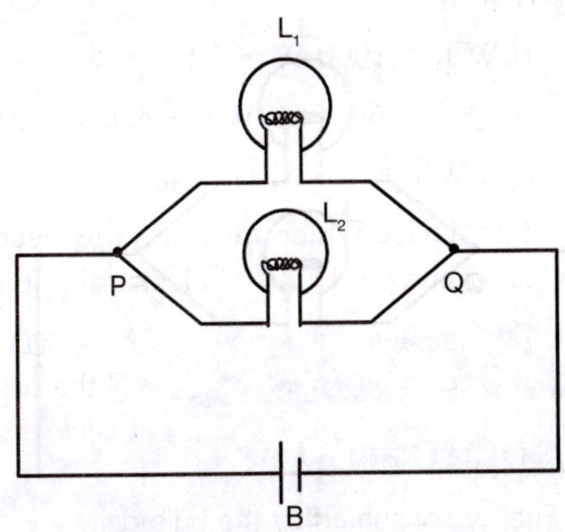

Figure 8.14 Parallel circuit

Electrical Energy

Electricity is a form of energy. It can be converted to various other forms of energy and vice versa. The S.I. unit of electric energy is, therefore, joule (J). Usually higher units like kilojoule or megajoule are used.

1kJ = 1000 J

1 MJ = 10^6 J

Electric Power

Power is the rate of doing work. When current flows through a circuit, work is done in moving the charges, during which some electric energy is utilized. The rate at which the electric energy is used is called **electric power**.

$$\therefore \text{Electric power} = \frac{\text{Electric energy used}}{\text{time}}$$

$$P = \frac{E}{t}$$

The S.I. unit of electric power is joule per second [$J\,s^{-1}$] which is called Watt (W) named after the English physicist James Watt.

If a device uses energy at the rate of 1 joule per second, its power is said to be 1 watt. The higher units of power are kilowatt and megawatt.

1 kW = 1000 W

1 MW = 10^6 W

EXAMPLE 8.4 A bulb uses 3000 J of energy in 50 s. Calculate its power.

SOLUTION

Energy (***E***) consumed by the bulb = 3000 J.

Time (***t***) taken = 50 s.

Power (***p***) of bulb = ?

$$P = \frac{E}{t} = \frac{3000\ J}{50\ s}$$

$\therefore$ ***P*** = 60 J s^{-1} = 60 W.

Practical Unit of Electrical Energy

The amount of electrical energy used daily in our household is quite large and a special unit has to be used to measure it. This unit is kilowatt hour (kW h). If 1000 J of energy per second is used continuously for 1hour, the energy consumed is 1kW h.

1kW h = 1000 W × 1 h

= 1000 × 60 × 60 W s = 3.6 × 10^6 J

$\therefore$1kW h = 3.6 M J

The device which measures the electrical energy being consumed in a household is called **kW h meter**, and 1 kW h is referred to as 1 unit of electrical energy.

EXAMPLE 8.5 A 60 W bulb is switched on for 5 hours daily. If the cost of electricity is ₹ 3 per unit, calculate the bill for the month of April.

SOLUTION

Energy consumed by the bulb daily

= 60 W × 5 h

= 300 W h

Energy consumed in the month of April is 300 W h × 30

= 9000 W h

= 9 kW h

$\therefore$ cost = 9 kW h × ₹ 3 = ₹ 27

Electricity and its Effects

As discussed earlier, electricity is the most convenient form of energy that can be transformed into other forms. It has innumerable applications and has become a part of human life. Different applications of electricity are possible due to different **effects that electricity can produce**. Electricity can produce magnetism and the effect is called **magnetic effect** of electricity. Similarly, if electricity brings out chemical changes in a substance, the effect produced is called **chemical effect of electricity**. Likewise, if electricity brings out heat in a substance, the effect produced is called **heating effect of electricity**.

Chemical Effects of Electricity

We have studied the production of electricity through chemicals in voltaic and other types of cells. In those cells, chemical reactions take place in the electrolytes and cause flow of charges in the external circuit. Similarly, electricity flowing through an electrolyte (electrical conductor in liquid form) taken in a container can cause chemical reactions in the electrolytes. This is known as **Chemical Effect of Electricity**. The most commonly occurring chemical reaction in an electrolyte, when an electric current passes through it, is the 'chemical decomposition reaction'. **Chemical decomposition** is the process of splitting of a compound into its constituent ions or elem ɔmposition of a compound by passing electricity through the compound is kr ugh which electricity passes is called **electrolyte**.

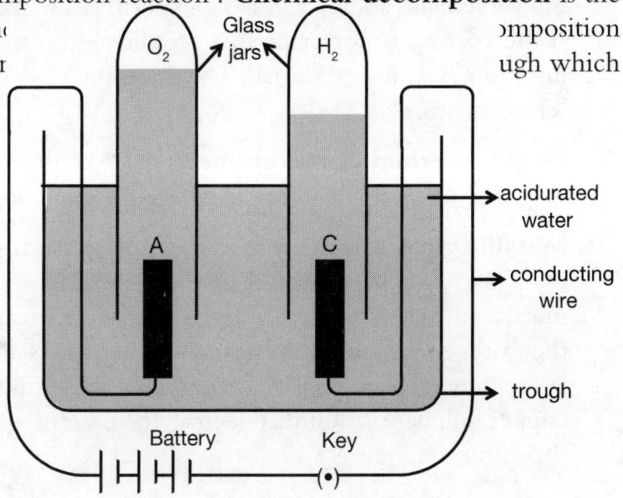

Figure 8.15 Electrolysis of water

Electrolysis of Water

Water, being a weak electrolyte, cannot get ionized. So, pure water cannot conduct electricity. So, to make water an electric conductor and ionize it, some amount of sulphuric acid is added to it and then the water is called acidulated water. Take some acidulated water in a trough and immerse two copper rods or copper plates in the trough as shown in the Figure 8.15. The copper rods are connected to a battery and a plug key by conducting wires. The copper rod connected to positive terminal of the battery is called positive electrode or anode and it develops a positive potential. Similarly, the copper rod connected to the negative terminal of the battery via plug key is called negative electrode or cathode and it develops a negative potential.

Acidulated water is in the ionized state and contains hydrogen ions (H^+) and oxygen ions (O^{2-}). Since hydrogen ions are positively-charged entities, they move towards the negative electrode and got accumulated over it. Similarly, oxygen ions, being negatively-charged entities move towards the positive electrode and accumulate over it. Since hydrogen and oxygen are gases, they can be collected by downward displacement of water in the inverted glass jars placed above the respective electrodes as shown in the figure. The chemical equation corresponding to the dissociation of water into ions is $H_2O \longrightarrow 2H^+ + O^{2-}$.

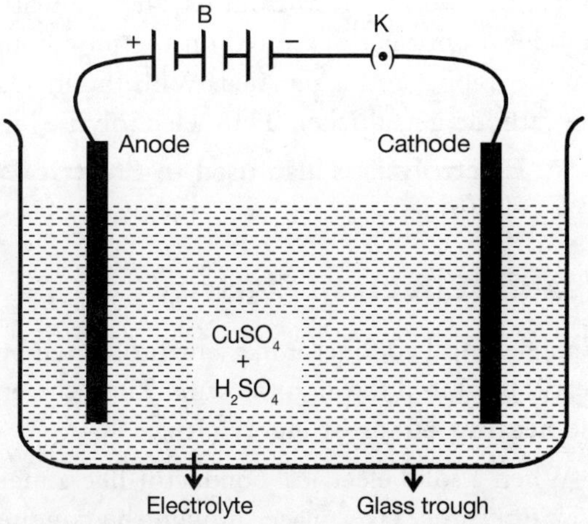

Figure 8.16 Electrolysis of $CuSO_4$

Electrolysis of Copper Sulphate ($CuSO_4$)

Take some aqueous copper sulphate solution in a trough and add some sulphuric acid (H_2SO_4) to it. Addition of the sulphuric acid to the copper sulphate solution increases the ionization of the copper sulphate, thus increasing the electric conduction through the electrolyte. Insert two metallic rods or plates in the trough containing the electrolyte and connect them to a battery (B) via a plug key (K) by conduction wires, as shown in Figure 8.16.

The two metallic rods are the electrodes. The rod connected to the positive terminal of the battery is anode and the rod connected to the negative terminal of the battery is the cathode. Copper sulphate in the solution dissociates to form copper ions (Cu^{2+}) and sulphate ions (SO_4^{2-}).

$$CuSO_4 \longrightarrow Cu^{2+} + SO_4^{2-}$$

Since sulphate ions are negatively-charged anions, they move towards anode. Similarly, since copper ions are positively-charged cations, they move towards cathode, absorb electrons from the cathode, neutralize and thus form a deposit of copper over the cathode. Thus, as the electric current increases or the electrolyte increases, the amount of copper deposited on the cathode also increases.

Applications of Electrolysis

The chemical effect of electricity, namely electrolysis has a wide variety of applications. Some of them are mentioned below.

1. **Electroplating:** Generally items made of iron get rusted. To avoid rusting of iron items, they are coated with nickel or chromium. This coating can be observed mostly on the handle bars and wheel rims of two wheeler motor vehicles and bicycles. This coating of nickel or chromium on these items is done by means of electrolysis. If the coating is not made in a proper method, we can observe that the coating peels off the item after some duration, say few months. The method of coating of iron items with nickel or chromium is known as 'electroplating'.

2. **Gold Covering:** Some ornaments made of low cost metals like brass or copper can be coated with gold to make imitation jewellery. The coating of gold on such ornaments is done by the process of electrolysis.

3. **Metallurgical Applications:** Electrolysis has utmost importance in metallurgy, the branch of science which deals with the properties of metals. In metallurgy, electrolysis is used to extract the metals from their ores and to purify the extracted metals. As an example, consider an impure copper rod of certain thickness immersed in acidified copper sulphate solution (electrolyte) present in a glass trough, as shown in the Figure 8.17.

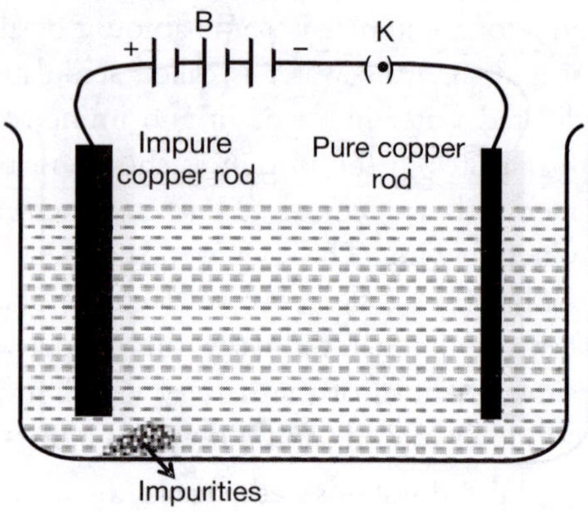

Figure 8.17 Purification of copper

This impure rod is connected to the positive terminal of a battery (B) and thus acts as the anode. A thin rod of pure copper is immersed in the same solution and is connected to the negative terminal of the battery and serves as the cathode. The copper at the anode is dissociated into ions (Cu^{2+}). After that, it moves through the solution and gets deposited at the cathode by taking two electrons from it. The impurities in the impure copper rod (anode) do not get deposited on the pure copper rod (cathode). Thus, the impure copper rod is purified. With the increase in the time of passage of electric current, the anode gets thinner and the cathode gets thicker. Thus, electrolysis is used in the purification of metals.

4. **Electrolysis is also used in Electric Printing:** This is done by selecting suitable electrolytes and corresponding electrodes.

Heating Effects of Electricity

If an electrical conductor like a nichrome wire is connected to the terminals of a battery, we observe that, after some time, heat is produced through the wire. Thus, the energy is transformed from electrical form into heat form. This is known as the **heating effect of electricity**.

When a solid electrical conductor like a metallic wire is connected to the terminals of a battery, electric current, i.e., flow of charge, takes place through the conductor by way of the motion of free electrons present in it from one end to the other end. While the free electrons of the wire are in motion through it, they collide with atoms or molecules of the substance giving rise to restriction to their free flow. This restriction to the flow of charges in a conductor is known as its

'resistance' or more precisely 'electrical resistance'. Due to the collision of free electrons in the conductor with its atoms or molecules, their kinetic energy increases and this increase in the kinetic energy is exhibited in the form of heat. Thus, we can say the more the electrical resistance of a conductor, the more is the heat produced. It is found that the resistance of a conductor is directly proportional to its length and inversely proportional to its area of cross section.

If 'l' and 'a' are respectively the length and the area of cross section of a conductor whose resistance is 'R', then mathematically, $R \propto l$ and $R \propto \frac{1}{a}$. Thus, $R \propto \frac{l}{a}$

The heating effect of electric current has a wide variety of applications. Some of them are discussed below.

1. **An Electric Bulb:** It was invented by Thomas Alva Edison. It is a glass bulb, spherical at the bottom portion and extended to cylindrical shape at the top. It contains an inert gas like argon or helium at low pressures. Inside the glass bulb, a tiny conducting coiled coil of tungsten wire having high resistance is fitted and is called filament of the bulb.

   The filament rests on two tiny wires called supporters and its ends are connected to leads through which electric current passes. The leads and filament supporters are fixed to a glass support, as shown in figure 8.18 and the upper portion is sealed with glass. Above the seal, an aluminium cap is attached and the leads are connected to the top of the cap as two terminals. On the lateral sides of the aluminium cap, two small projections are provided diametrically opposite to each other to help in fixing the bulb to its holder. As the resistance of the filament is much higher, it gets red hot and then emits light when electricity is passed through it.

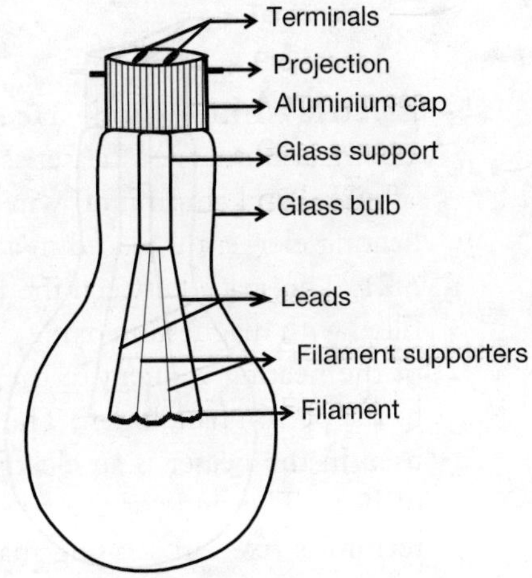

Figure 8.18 An electric bulb

2. **An Electric Stove:** An electric stove consists of a porcelain base fixed in a casing and a filament fixed in the groove of the base. The filament is a long thin coiled wire and has high resistance. The ends of the thin filament is connected to the terminals by means of leads as shown in figure 8.19. When electric current passes through the filament, it gets red hot and generates heat, which can be used for cooking.

Figure 8.19 An electric stove

3. **An Electric Iron:** An electric iron contains a heating element, usually made of nichrome (an alloy of nickel and chromium) placed between two mica sheets. These sheets are placed on an iron base. Above the mica sheets in which heating element is placed, an asbestos sheet is placed and above that a dome is placed and fixed to the iron base. The ends of the heating element are connected to the mains through connecting wires. The mica sheets placed on either side of the heating element do not conduct electricity but transfer the heat. Thus, the iron base is heated and transfers the heat to the clothes being pressed. The asbestos sheet, placed above the mica sheet being a bad conductor of heat, does not allow the heat to move in the upward direction. A handle preferably made of ebonite is attached to the dome.

4. **A Soldering Gun or Soldering Iron:** In a Soldering gun so many wires are connected at so many places in a complex electric circuit. The connections are perfect when the joints of the wires are perfect. To have a perfect joint, the ends of the wires have to be joined in a molten state or a fused state. When the wires are made of less fusible material, in order to make the joint a perfect one, we use another fusible material, which is an alloy, to join the edges of the less fusible materials. This fusible alloy is called **solder** and the process of joining the wires with a solder is called **soldering**. For this purpose a metallic rod is used; which is called soldering gun or soldering iron. One end of the rod is pointed and wedge-shaped and the other end is fixed to a hollow metallic tube. A heating element is placed inside the hollow tube and is in contact with the rod, as shown in the figure 8.20. To the other end of the rod, a handle preferably made of bakelite material is attached.

The heating element in the soldering iron is connected to the mains by means of a connecting wire through the handle.

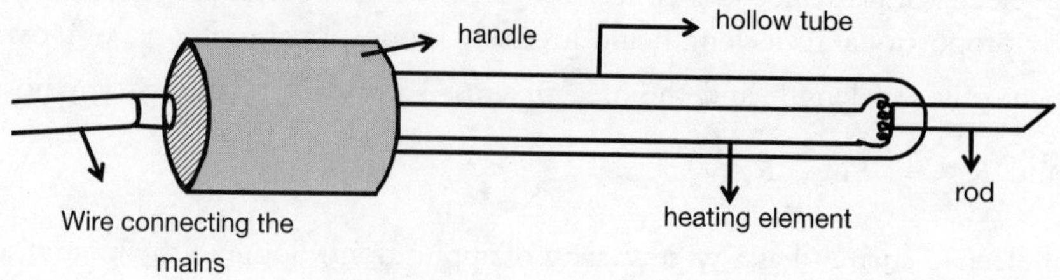

Figure 8.20 A Soldering iron

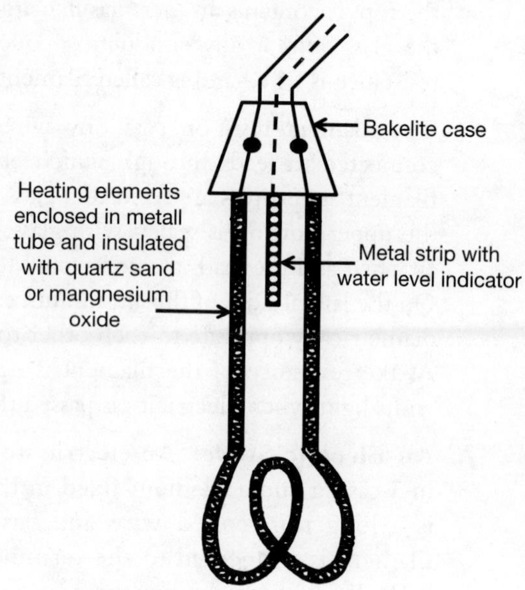

Figure 8.21 Immersion heater

5. **Electric Immersion Heater:** The heating element in an electrical immersion heater is usually made of nichrome (an alloy of nickel and chromium) wire wound in the form of a spring. The heating element is placed in a hollow brass tube as shown in figure 8.21. The space between the brass tube and the heating element is filled with magnesium oxide or quartz sand. This avoids the contact of the heating element to the brass tube and avoids electric shock to the person handling it. The magnesium oxide or the quartz sand used in the heater is an electric insulator but is a good conductor of heat. The ends of the heating element are connected to brass terminals fixed in a casing made of bakelite and the terminals are connected to the mains through a plug and wire. Nichrome has high electrical resistance and so it is the most preferred material for the preparation of heating elements.
6. **Electric Fuse:** It is the device used in the household electric wiring that protects appliances from high current. Fuse wire is connected between the mains and leads of the primary circuit of an electric appliance. When excess amount of electricity passes through the wire, the fuse wire gets heated and the heat produced fuses or melts the wire breaking the power supply to the circuit of the appliance. Thus, the electric appliance is protected from the passage of high electric current which destroys the appliance.

POINTS TO REMEMBER

- A study of the structure of an atom reveals that there exist fundamental particles namely protons, electrons and neutrons in it.
- The process of charging a body is known as electrification and when it is done by rubbing one body over the other, it is called electrification by friction.
- The charge thus obtained is called frictional charge.
- The process of supplying an electric charge to a body is known as 'charging'. A body can be charged in different ways.

  i. Charging by Friction

  ii. Charging by Conduction

  iii. Charging by Induction
- Electroscope is an instrument to check whether a body is electrically charged or not and also to find the nature of the charge, i.e., positive or negative, present on the body.
- The rate at which electric charge flows through a conductor is known as electric current.
- An electric cell converts chemical energy into electrical energy. These kinds of cells are known as 'primary cells'. Voltaic cell and Leclanche cell are examples of primary cells.
- The process of restoring the original composition in the cells by passing electricity in opposite direction is known as 'charging' and these kinds of cells in which charging can be done are known as 'secondary cells'. A lead-acid storage battery used in motor vehicles is an example of a secondary cell.
- The amount of energy spent or work done in moving a unit positive charge through the conductors connected across the terminals of a cell is known as electro motive force (EMF) and it is measured in volts (V).
- Substances which allow electric current to pass through them readily are called electric conductors
- An electric circuit in which all components are connected one after the other such that same current flows through them is called series circuit.
- A circuit in which different components are individually connected to the battery thus forming different branches in circuit is called parallel circuit.
- Power is the rate of doing work.
- Electricity flowing through an electrolyte taken in a container can cause chemical reactions in the electrolytes known as chemical effect of electricity.
- This restriction to the flow of charges in a conductor is known as its 'resistance' or more precisely 'electrical resistance.'

CLASSROOM WING

PRACTICE QUESTIONS

Very Short Answer Type Questions

Directions for questions from 1 to 3:
Fill in the blanks.

1. The process due to which an uncharged insulated metallic conductor gets electrically charged when held near a charged body is called ___________.

2. In a dry cell, the cylindrical container made of zinc acts as a__________ terminal of the cell.

3. The commercial unit of electrical energy is _________.

Directions for questions 4 to 25:
Answer the following questions

4. What happens when a glass rod is rubbed with silk cloth?

5. What is the use of magnesium oxide used in an immersion heater?

6. What is an electric cell? What is a primary and a secondary cell?.

7. What is electricity?

8. A body gains 25×10^{18} electrons, by rubbing it with another body. Find the charge on the body.

9. What causes a body to become electrically charged when rubbed over another body?

10. What is meant by charging a secondary cell?

11. How many types of the charges are there? State the unit of charge?

12. A body contains 3 C of positive charge. Does this refer to the total number of protons or positively-charged particles present in the body?

13. State SI and practical units of electrical energy.

14. What is meant by charging a body?

15. If two charged bodies attract each other, what could the nature of charges present on them be?

16. In which of the following: telephones, electroplating, electric bell, and electric motor; the principle of chemical effects of electricity is used?

17. What is an electrolyte?

18. What happens when an ebonite rod is rubbed with fur?

19. What is electric potential difference? State its units.

20. What is electrolysis?

21. If a stream of He^{2+} ions passes through a cross-section at the rate 2 10^{19} ions per second, then calculate the electric current due to the flow of ions.

22. What is the heating effect of electricity?

23. An electric geyser consumes 10,000 J of electrical energy in 300 s to boil water. What is the power of the electrical greaser?

24. What is the electrolyte in a voltaic cell? Mention the electrolytes used in
    (1) Daniel cell.
    (2) Leclanche cell.
    (3) Bichromate cell.
    (4) Dry cell.

25. Define electric current. Define the unit of electric current?

Short Answer Type Questions

26. Leclanché cell consists of a porous pot and a zinc rod placed in a solution of NH_4Cl in a glass jar, the porous pot contains powdered carbon and MnO_2 with a carbon rod dipped in it. Which out of A and B are true?
    (A) Carbon rod acts as a positive electrode.
    (B) Zinc rod acts as a negative electrode.
27. Explain the construction of an electric stove.
28. A charged body of charge −100°C is connected to the ground. Then what would the direction of conventional and electronic current flow be?
29. Explain the construction of an electric soldering iron.
30. What is meant by charging a body? Describe charging by conduction and charging by induction.
31. Differentiate between primary and secondary cells.
32. Explain an electric fuse and its use.
33. Explain the cause of electric current in a conductor.
34. Explain electric circuit and draw a simple electric circuit.
35. A person takes out a woollen cap from his head and observes the hair on his head rising up. Explain the reason for this?
36. What is lightning? Explain the phenomenon.
37. Explain the applications of electrolysis.
38. Why do we use a thin and long tungsten wire as a filament in bulb?
39. Two identical copper coins are melted and two wires 'A' and 'B' are made out of them. What is the resistance of B, if the length of A is twice that of B?
40. Explain the construction of an electric bulb.
41. What is the charge of an electron? How many electrons make a coulomb of charge?
42. Out of A and B, which are the correct statement(s)?
    (A) In a dry cell, the powdered carbon present in the electrolyte enhances the flow of charge through it.
    (B) In lead–acid storage batteries, the electrodes are made up of zinc or carbon.
43. An electron revolves around the nucleus of an atom in an orbit of radius '*r*' with a speed '*u*'. What is the electric current due to the motion of the electron? (charge of the electron is represented as '*e*')
44. Why a small quantity of sulphuric acid is added to water for its electrolysis?
45. Five bulbs '*A*', '*B*', '*C*', '*D*' *and* '*E*' are connected to each other as shown in the figure. Which bulbs are in series and which are in parallel?

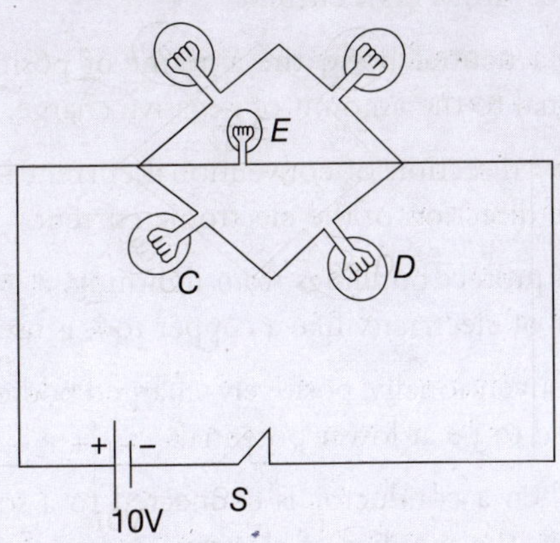

Essay Answer Type Questions

46. Explain the construction and working of a gold leaf electroscope.
47. Explain the construction and working of a dry cell.
48. Explain atmospheric electricity. How did Benjamin Franklin prove that lighting strikes dues to atmospheric electricity?
49. Explain the electrolysis of water.
50. Explain the construction and working of a voltaic cell.

COMPETITION WING

PRACTICE QUESTIONS

Level 1: Apply your Concepts

Directions for questions from 1 to 12:
State whether the following statements are true or false.

1. A Daniel cell consists of a glass container which is divided into two unequal portions by a porous membrane.
2. Conventional current assumes that current flows out of the negative terminal through the circuit and into the negative terminal of source.
3. To enhance the flow of charge through it powdered carbon is present in the electrolyte of a dry cell.
4. Sulphuric acid does not dissociate to produce ions which in turn increase conductivity during electrolysis.
5. Electric fuse is used to protect the electrical appliances from high current.
6. In a neutral body, the amount of positive charge is equal to the amount of negative charge.
7. The direction of conventional current is the same as the direction of the electronic current.
8. To protect buildings from lightning, a good conductor of electricity like a copper rod, is used.
9. Conventionally, positively-charged bodies are considered to be at lower potential.
10. When a conductor is connected to a source of current, the number of electrons entering at one end of the conductor is equal to the number of electrons leaving the conductor from the other end, per second
11. An uncharged gold leaf electroscope can detect the nature of charge present on the charged body.
12. When bulbs are connected in series, same current flows through them.

Directions for questions 13 to 19:
Fill in the blanks.

13. The types of cells in which it is possible to restore the chemicals are called ___________.
14. Nichrome is used as a heating element as it has ___________.
15. Glass does not allow ___________ to flow through it.
16. Inside a cell, the conventional current flows from the ______terminal to the ______terminal.
17. When an ebonite rod is rubbed with cat's skin, the cat's skin ___________ the electrons.
18. The lengths of two silver rods 'A' and 'B', having the same mass, are in the ratio 2 : 3 and the resistance of *A* is _________ times the resistance of *B*.
19. An electric fan consumes 1500 J of electrical energy in half-minute. The power of the fan is _________.

Directions for question 20:
Match the entries in Column A with the appropriate entries in Column B.

20.

	Column A		Column B
A.	Transfer of electrons	a.	Addition of H_2SO_4
B.	Dry cell	b.	Method of charging a body
C.	Electrolysis of $CuSO_4$	c.	———( )———
D.	Induction	d.	Watt
E.	Resistance	e.	Valence electrons
F.	Lower potential	f.	———(•)———
G.	Open key	g.	Carbon as a positive electrode
H.	Closed key	h.	Depends on length of the conductor.
I.	Power	i.	Heating effects of electricity.
J.	Electric iron	j.	Negatively-charged body

Directions for questions 21 to 45:
For each of the questions, four choices have been provided. Select the correct alternative.

21. 1 kWh = ________ MJ.
(a) 36 (b) 0.36
(c) 3.6 (d) 360

22. A gold leaf electroscope is used to
(a) detect the presence of charge on a body
(b) know the nature of charge on a charged body
(c) find the amount of charge present on a charged body
(d) Both (a) and (b)

23. Which of the following can be reused after charging?
(a) Dry cell (b) Leclanche cell
(c) Voltaic cell (d) Lead acid cell

24. Volt is the unit of ________.
(a) emf (b) current
(c) resistance (d) charge

25. The process of electrolysis is used in________.
(a) gold covering (b) metallurgy
(c) electric printing (d) All the above

26. Clouds get electrically charged when
(a) the ultraviolet rays of sun falls on them.
(b) air molecules rub against water molecules.
(c) cold currents of air rub against hot currents of air.
(d) Both (b) and (d)

27. During electrification by friction
(a) protons are transferred from one body to another body.
(b) neutrons are transferred from one body to another body.
(c) electrons are transferred from one body to another body.
(d) None of the above

28. The electrical energy consumed by a 30 W bulb in 5 minutes is ________.
(a) 9000 kJ (b) 9 kJ
(c) 9000 MJ (d) 9 MJ

29. The S.I. unit of electric charge is________.
(a) ampere (b) volt
(c) joule (d) coulomb

30. The S.I. unit of surface charge density is ________.
(a) C cm^{-2} (b) A m^{-2}
(c) A cm^{-2} (d) C m^{-2}

31. If 2 A of current flows through a conductor, the charge that flows in one minute is ________C.
(a) 12 (b) 120
(c) 60 (d) 16

32. When no charge is supplied to or removed from a neutral body, then the amount of ________.
(a) positive charge = negative charge present in it
(b) positive charge > negative charge present in it
(c) positive charge < negative charge present in it
(d) no charge is present in the body initially.

33. Two wires of same material and length have the radii of their cross sections as r and $2r$, respectively. The ratio of their resistances
(a) 2 : 1 (b) 4 : 1
(c) 1 : 4 (d) 3 : 2

34. Which among the following has carbon as the positive electrode?
(a) Lechanche (b) Bichromate cell
(c) Dry cell (d) All of the above

35. The charge supplied to a good conductor always resides
(a) at the supplied position itself.
(b) on its outer surface.
(c) inside the body.
(d) All the above.

36. In a circuit, a battery can be represented by
(a) 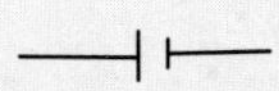 (b) 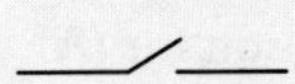
(c) 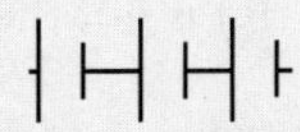 (d) 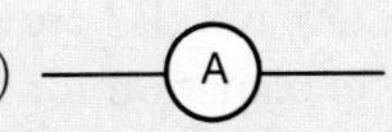

37. An electric current of 6 A flows through a circuit for 10 minutes. Write the following steps in sequential order to find the electrons that would pass through the circuit in 10 minutes.
(A) Note the given data about current (i) and time (t).
(B) The number of electrons (n) flowing through the circuit can be found using, $Q = ne$ (2)
(C) Find the charge (Q) that flows through the circuit using, $Q = it$ (1)
(D) Equate (a) and (b), to find n.

(a) A D B C (b) A B C D
(c) B C A D (d) A C B D

38. In a factory, 100 bulbs of 100 W, 100 fans of 60 W and 100 tube lights of 40 W are used for 10 h per day for 30 days. Arrange the following steps to calculate the total energy consumed, in a proper sequence.
(A) Find the energy consumed by bulbs, fans and tube lights.
(B) Find the wattage of different electrical appliances from the given data.
(C) Find the total number of hours they are used in 30 days.
(D) Add all the energies consumed by all appliances to get total energy.
(E) Use $P = E/t$
(a) BCEAD (b) ABECD
(c) DABCE (d) CDBAE

39. **Assertion (A):** All the bulbs connected in parallel glow brightly.
Reason (R): All the bulbs are connected directly to a battery anzd derive the required electrical energy.
(a) (A) and (R) are correct and (R) is correct explanation for (A).
(b) (A) and (R) are correct but (R) is not the correct explanation for (A).
(c) (A) is correct but (R) is not correct.
(d) Both (A) and (R) are not correct.

40. **Assertion (A):** A 200 W bulb consumes 2 units of electrical energy when it is used for 10 hours.
Reason (R): 1 unit of electrical energy = 1000 kWh.
(a) (A) and (R) are correct and (R) is correct explanation for (A).
(b) (A) and (R) are correct but (R) is not the correct explanation for (A).
(c) (A) is correct but (R) is not correct.
(d) Both (A) and (R) are not correct.

41. **Assertion (A):** Mica sheets are placed on either side of the heating element.
Reason (R): Mica does not conduct electricity but transfers the heat.
(a) A and R both are correct, and R is correct explanation of A.
(b) A and R both are correct, and R is incorrect explanation of A.
(c) A is correct but R is incorrect.
(d) A is incorrect but R is correct.

42. When a positively-charged body and a negatively-charged body with equal magnitude of charge are brought simultaneously in contact with the cap of a positively-charged electroscope, then the strips
(a) move apart.
(b) come closer.
(c) remain uneffected.
(d) Cannot be determined.

43. A current carrying metallic comb is placed close to small iron filings, then the
(a) iron filings will fly away from the comb, when switch is turned off.
(b) iron filings align in the direction of the magnetic field produced around the metallic comb.
(c) iron filings will be attracted by the comb.
(d) Both (b) and (c).

44. Choose the correct statement:
When the same current(i) flows through two circuits as shown in the figures, then (assume that all bulbs are identical)
(A) bulbs in first combination glow with more brightness.
(B) bulbs in second combination glow with more brightness.
(C) bulbs in both the combination glow with equal brightness.

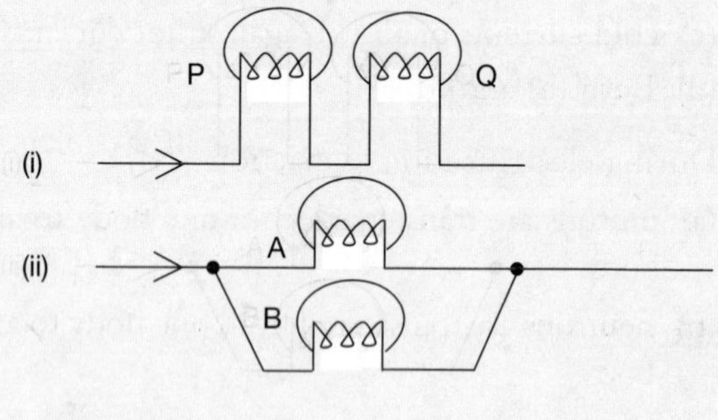

(a) Only (A) is true
(b) Only (B) is true
(c) Only (C) is true
(d) Cannot be determined

45. A magnet is brought close to a current carrying conductor, as shown in figure, then,
(a) it will be repelled by the conductor.
(b) it will be attracted by the conductor.
(c) it will not show any effect.
(d) it will be just deflected.

Level 2: Review your Concepts

46. The length (16 cm) and area of cross section (4 cm^2) of a copper wire are increased by 25% each. If the resistance of original wire is 8 Ω, find the new resistance.

47. A charged thermocol ball is suspended by means of a nylon thread. When a neutral body is brought nearer to it the thermocol ball is first attracted by it and then flies away from it. Explain by giving the reason.

48. What is the direction of conventional and electronic current flow, when two identical bodies 'A' and 'B', which have +10 C and +5 C, respectively, are connected to each other by means of a metal wire?

49. Explain why electrical appliances in a house are connected in parallel and not in series.

50. When we mention the charge of body we indicate only the deficit or excess of electrons in it but not protons. Why?

51. Gasoline (explosive) transport trucks generally carry long chains of metal hanging down and touching the ground. Why?

52. In an electric circuit, explain why a fuse is always connected in series.

53. When a glass rod is rubbed with resin, a mass of 27.3×10^{-14} *g* is transferred from glass rod to resin. Find the amount charge acquired by the glass rod. What is the nature of the charge? (Charge of electron $= 1.6 \times 10^{-19}$ C, Mass of electron $= 9.1 \times 10^{-31}$ kg)

54. Two copper wires have equal length but the thickness of one is twice that of the other. If the resistance of the thin wire is 10 Ω, find the resistance of the thick wire.

55. A body 'P' contains 50 electrons and 45 protons and a body 'Q' contains 72 electrons and 77 protons after electrification by friction between the bodies. Find the number of electrons and protons in 'P' and 'Q' before electrification. Also find the number of electrons transferred between them.

56. A fluorescent lamp of 20 W and an incandescent bulb of 150 W are used for 5 hours per day in the month of February 2008. If the cost of one unit of electrical energy is ₹ 1.5, which of the two is more economical to use and by how much?

57. How much money can be saved per month by using a compact fluorescent lamp of 15 W in place of an incandescent bulb of 100 W if they are used 8 hours per day for 30 days? (Take the cost of one unit of electrical energy as ₹ 2)

58. What is the difference between the current in the external circuit and inside an electric cell?

59. During the electrolysis process 4 A electric current flows through a copper sulphate solution for 5 minutes. Determine the number of copper atoms deposited at the cathode.

60. What are the differences between the flow of electric current through metal conductors and electrolytes?

61. If 36.4×10^{-15} g of mass is transferred when fur is rubbed with silk, find the number of electrons lost by fur? (mass of electron $= 9.1 \times 10^{-31}$ kg).

62. The electrical energy consumed by an electric heater in a duration of 3 h is 0.6 kW h. What is the power consumed by the heater?

63. Two spheres of equal charge densities have charges in the ratio 1 : 4 on their surfaces. Then the ratio of their volumes

64. A cube of side 20 cm gained a charge of 15×10^{-16} C. Is there any gain in mass of the cube? If so, what is the gain in the mass of cube?

65. Two bulbs P and Q are connected in series to a battery. If the resistance offered by the bulb P is more than that of bulb Q and 6 A of current is passed through the P, then what is the current through Q?

66. Number of excess electrons present on a conducting body A is 6.25×10^{18}. When it is brought in contact with another identical conducting body of charge – 5 coulomb, find the charge present on each body.

Level 3: Assess Your Concepts

67. What is the use of glass bulb in an electric bulb? Can we use an electric bulb without the glass bulb in space?

68. Can a charged body 'A' having a very small charge on it, be used to charge an uncharged body 'B', such

that the charge acquired by 'B' is many times more than that on 'A'? If so, how? Explain.

69. A spherical shaped metallic body of radius 5 cm gained 15×10^6 electrons. Find the surface charge density of sphere in SI system.

70. A copper wire of mass 20 *g* carries a current of 6.023 A. What fraction of the total number of free electrons present in copper wire flows through the cross-section of the copper wire in 2 s?

(Gram atomic weight of copper = 63.5 g)

71. A, B and C are three identical metallic spheres having positive, negative and positive charges, respectively. The deficiency or excess of electrons present in A, B and C are 10, 20 and 31, respectively. Initially the spheres A and B are brought in contact and then B and C are brought together. Determine the magnitude and nature of charge present on the bodies after bringing them in contact. (Take charge of electron as 1.6×10^{-19} C).

72. The tyres of air craft are made of special rubber which make them slightly conducting. Explain the reasons for using special rubber.

73. Divij wants to check his current bill generated for the month of December which was billed at an amount of ₹ 4800. The cost of each unit is ₹ 5. The list of electrical components and their details are tabulated below. Is the bill generated, correct? If not, what is the difference in the amount he found?

Component	Quantity	Usage per day in hour
100 W Bulbs	6	6
200 W Fans	5	8
2500 W Refrigerator	1	8

74. 'A' is a conducting rod connected to a cell as shown in the diagram.

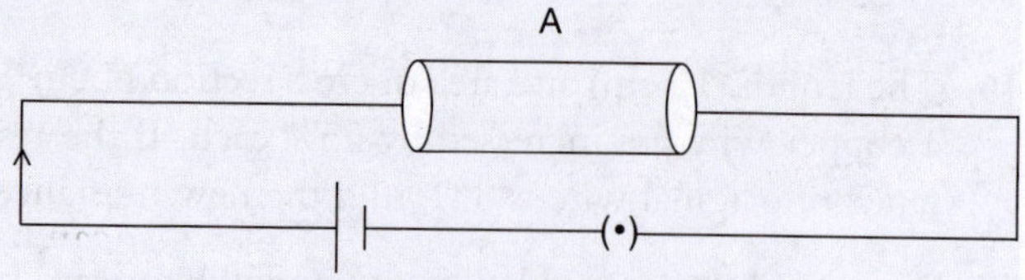

If 5 A of current passes through the circuit for 5 s, find the amount charge accumulated on 'A'.

75. In an atom, electrons revolve around the nucleus in circular orbits. Can this be treated as electric current? If an electron revolves around the nucleus 2000 times in one second, what is the equivalent current? Given charge of the electron as 1.6×10^{-19}C.

76. Bharat takes five identical bulbs B_1, B_2, B_3, B_4 and B_5 and connects them to a cell as shown in the figure. He compares

(i) the current passing through the different bulbs and

(ii) the potential difference across different bulbs when the circuit is closed.

What does he conclude?

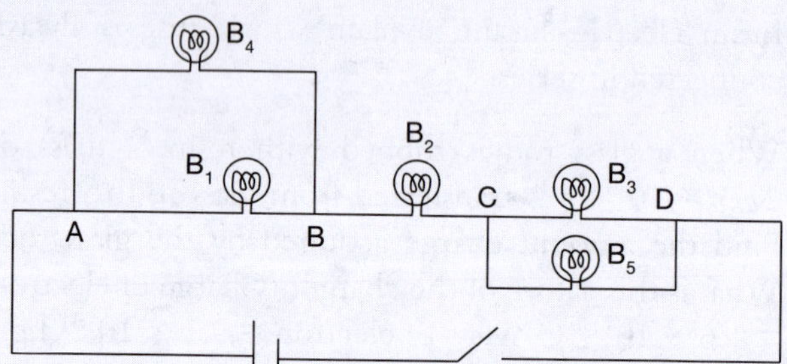

77. During an electrolysis process, 10^{20} ions of copper (Cu^{2+}) are found to get drawn to the cathode in 16 s. Calculate the equivalent current due to the movement of copper ions through the electrolyte.

78. The following table provides the list of different appliances used by two families A and B in April 2010. If the charge per unit is ₹4/–, calculate their monthly bill for April 2010.

	100 W Bulbs	Usage Per Day (in hours)	Electric Fans of 200 W	Usage Per Day (in hours)	Refrigerator 2500 W	Usage Per Day (in hours)	Washing Machine 2000 W	Usage Per Day (in hours)
Family A	3	5	4	8	1	3	1	2
Family B	4	4	5	6	1	3	1	2

79. Seeta says that a compact fluorescent lamp uses less electrical energy compared to that of an incandescent bulb. But Geeta, her friend, does not agree with this. Seeta proves it by calculating the money that can be saved per month by using a compact fluorescent lamp of 15 W in place of an incandescent bulb of 100 W if they are used 8 hours per day for 30 days. How did she prove this? (The cost of one unit of electrical energy is ₹2)

80. A student connected two conductors 'P' and 'Q' of areas of cross-section 'a', '2a' and lengths l, $l/2$ respectively to two different sources providing the same potential difference. What will be the ratio of currents in the conductors 'P' and 'Q'?

AT

JEE-NEET SPECIAL WING

PRACTICE QUESTIONS

Multiple-Answer Type Questions

Directions for questions 1 to 5:

Select one or more correct alternative(s) from the given choices.

1. Identify the insulators from the following.
   (a) Pure water
   (b) Ebonite
   (c) Nitrogen
   (d) Graphite

2. In a circuit consisting of a bulb, a current of 6A flows for 1 hour. The amount of charge that passes through the bulb is
   (a) 21600 C
   (b) 2.16×10^4 A s
   (c) 3600 C
   (d) 3.6×10^3 A s

3. Identify the disadvantage of a voltaic cell
   (a) Produce electricity as a redox reaction occurs
   (b) Polarization
   (c) Has to be kept in an upright position
   (d) Local action

4. The S. I. unit of electric power is
   (a) J s (b) $J s^{-1}$
   (c) A (d) W

5. Consider two bulbs B_1 and B_2 which offers resistances R_1 and R_2 respectively ($R_1 > R_2$) are connected as shown in figure. Then,

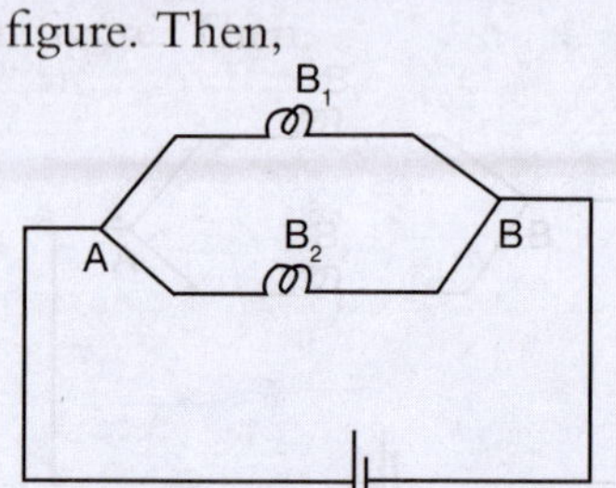

   (a) Current through both bulbs are same.
   (b) Current through each bulb is different.
   (c) Potential across each bulb is different.
   (d) Potential across both bulbs are the same.

Comprehension-Based Questions

Directions for questions 6 to 10:

These questions are based on the following information.

Electrical Energy

The flow of charged particles like electrons through a conductor constitute electrical energy. It is one of the most commonly used forms of energy in the world. When current flows through a conductor some work is done to move the charges and rate of this work is called electrical power. The charge can build upon a capacitor and store electrical energy.

6. If a device uses energy at the rate of 3 J in 1 minute, its power is
   (a) 1 W (b) 0.5 W
   (c) 0.05 W (d) 0.25 W

7. 1 MW = ________ W
   (a) 10^3 (b) 10^6
   (c) 10^9 (d) 10^{12}

8. The device which measures electrical energy being consumed in a household is
   (a) kWh meter
   (b) Wh meter
   (c) Joule meter
   (d) MWh meter

9. If 3000 J of energy per second is used continuously for 2 hours, the energy consumed is
   (a) 2 kWh (b) 3 kWh
   (c) 4 kWh (d) 6 kWh

10. A 100 W bulb is switched on for 5 hours daily. If the cost of electricity is ₹ 3 per unit, then the bill for the month of June is

(a) ₹ 15 (b) ₹ 25
(c) ₹ 35 (d) ₹ 45

Directions for questions 11 to 15:

These questions are based on the following information.

Chemical effects of electricity

If electricity brings out chemical changes in a substance, the effect produced is called chemical effects of electricity. Some of the chemical changes involving electricity are electrolysis, electroplating etc. Apart from chemical effects, there are other two effects of electric current i.e., heating effect and magnetic effect.

11. The process of splitting of compounds to its constituent ions is called

(a) Electrolysis
(b) Electroplating
(c) Chemical decomposition
(d) Electrolyte

12. The process of producing chemical decomposition by passing electricity through compound is

(a) Electrolysis
(b) Electroplating
(c) Electrolytic splitting
(d) None of these

13. The chemical equation corresponding to the dissociation of water into ions is

(a) $H_2O \rightarrow H^+ + O^-$
(b) $H_2O \rightarrow H^{2+} + O^-$
(c) $H_2O \rightarrow H^{2+} + 2O^-$
(d) $H_2O \rightarrow 2H^+ + O^{2-}$

14. The rod connected to the positive terminal of the battery is

(a) Cathode (b) Anode
(c) Anion (d) Cation

15. Identify the process shown in the diagram

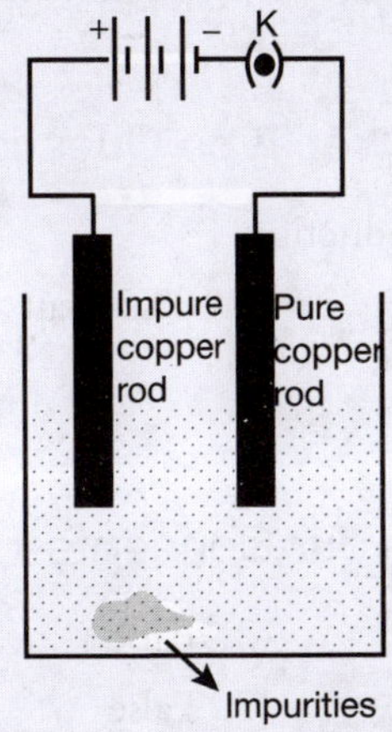

(a) Electroplating
(b) Double decomposition
(c) Metallurgy
(d) Reduction of copper oxide.

Match the Column

Directions for questions 16:

The question is based on the following information.

Electric Cell

An electric cell is actually an electric power supply in which stored chemical energy is converted into potential energy. It has two terminals with different potentials. There are different types of electric cells like primary cells, secondary cells and fuel cells. A battery is a collection of cells.

List - I	List - II
A. Voltaic cell	a. $ZnSO_4$ solution and $CuSO_4$ solution
B. Daniel cell	b. NH_4Cl (paste)
C. Bichromate cell	c. dil. H_2SO_4
D. Leclanché cell	d. $K_2Cr_2O_7 + H_2SO_4$
E. Dry cell	e. NH_4Cl

(a) A - c, B - a, C - d, D - e, E - b
(b) A - b, B - c, C - d, D - e, E – a
(c) A - a, B - b, C - c, D - d, E - e
(d) A - d, B - e, C - b, D - c, E - a

ANSWER KEYS

Crossword

Across

2. Dry cell 4. Series 7. Ammeter 10. Induction 11. Electric fuse

Down

1. Electromotive force 3. Ampere 5. Friction 6. Parallel 8. Nichrome
9. Insulator

Classroom Wing

Very Short Answer Type Questions

1. Electrostatic induction 2. Negative 3. kilowatt hour 16. Electroplating
21. 21m 23. 33.3 watt

Competition Wing

Level 1: Apply your Concepts

1. False 2. False 3. True 4. False 5. True
6. True 7. False 8. True 9. False 10. True
11. False 12. True 13. Secondary cells 14. High resistivity 15. Electric charge
16. Negative, positive. 17. Loses 18. 4/9 19. 50 Watt
20. A : e, B : g, C : a, D : b, E : h, F : j, G : c, H : f, I : d, J : i 21. (c) 22. (d)
23. (d) 24. (a) 25. (d) 26. (d) 27. (c)
28. (b) 29. (d) 30. (d) 31. (b) 32. (a)
33. (b) 34. (d) 35. (b) 36. (c) 37. (d)
38. (a) 39. (a) 40. (c) 41. (a) 42. (b)
43. (b) 44. (a) 45. (d)

Level 2: Review your Concepts

47. 8 Ω 54. 2.5 Ω 56. ₹28.25 57. ₹40.80 61. 4×10^{13}
62. 200 W 63. 1 : 8 64. 8.54×10^{-27} kg 66. – 3 C

Level 3: Assess Your Concepts

70. 7.64×10^{-11} C m^{-2} 73. ₹98 75. 3.2×10^{-16} A 77. 2 A
78. ₹2292 79. ₹40.8 80. 4:1

JEE-NEET Special Wing

Multiple-Answer Type Questions

1. (a), (b) and (c) 2. (a) and (b) 3. (b), (c) and (d) 4. (b) and (d) 5. (b) and (d)

Comprehension-Based Questions

6. (c) 7. (b) 8. (a) 9. (d) 10. (d)
11. (c) 12. (a) 13. (d) 14. (b) 15. (c)

Match the Column

16. (a)

For answer key of Classroom wing and Competition wing, refer to Hints and Solutions

Hints and Explanations

Classroom Wing

Very Short Answer Type Questions

1. Electrostatic induction
2. Negative
3. kilowatt hour
4. When silk cloth and glass rod are rubbed with each other, the electrons flow from the glass rod to the cotton cloth. Because of this, the cotton cloth, due to excess of electrons, becomes negatively charged and the glass rod, due to lack of electrons, becomes positively charged.
5. Magnesium oxide or quartz sand is filled between the heating element and brass tube which may be in contact with the person who is using it.
   Magnesium oxide or quartz sand is a good conductor of heat.
6. Electric cells are the devices which convert chemical energy into electrical energy. The electric cells which once used cannot be charged again are called primary cells whereas the cells which can be charged again and again even after use are called secondary cells.
7. Electricity is a form of energy that can be easily transformed into other forms of energy and also transmitted over large distances with minimum loss.
8. Charge of an electron $(\bar{e})$
   $$= -1.602 \times 10^{-19}\text{ C.}$$
   The charge gained $= n \times \bar{e}$
9. When one body rubs against another, there is a transfer of valence electrons from one to the other due to friction. This electron transfer results in one body becoming positively charged (losing electrons) and the other becoming negatively charged (gaining electrons).
10. To use a secondary cell again the original composition of the electrolyte should be replaced.
11. (i) Two types of the charges are there i.e., Positive, negative.
    (ii) Coulomb.
12. A body can be charged positively by removing electrons and charged negatively by adding electrons.
    The charge of a fundamental particle is 1.602×10^{-19} C.
13. The SI unit of energy is the same irrespective of the forms of energy. One unit of energy is the energy utilized by a device of power 1 kW in one hour.
    $$\text{Electric power} = \frac{\text{electric energy}}{\text{time}}$$
    Unit of electrical energy is the unit of electric power × unit of time.
14. Supplying electric charge to a body charging a body.
15. Like charges repel each other and unlike charges attract each other.
16. The principle of chemical effects of electricity is used in electroplating.
17. Liquid state electric conductors.
18. The electrons flow from the fur to the ebonite rod.
19. Work done on electric charges to move from one point to another point in electric field. S.I unit of potential difference is volts.
20. The process of producing chemical decomposition of a compound by passing electricity through the compound is known as electrolysis.
21. $S = ut = \frac{1}{2}at^2$
    $$S_4 = 0 \times 4 + \frac{1}{2} \times 6 \times 4^2 = 48\text{ m}$$
    $$S_3 = 0 \times 3 + \frac{1}{2} \times 6 \times 3^2 = 27\text{ m}$$
    ∴ Displacement in 4th second is = 48 – 27 = 21 m
22. The conversion of electrical energy into heat energy when an electrical conductor is connected to the terminals of a battery is known as the heating effect of electricity.
23. $P = \frac{w}{t} = \frac{EE}{t} = \frac{10{,}000\text{ J}}{300\text{ s}} = 33.\bar{3}\text{ Js}^{-1} = 33.3$ watt.
24. Dilute sulphuric acid.
    Electrolyte used in Daniel cell is
    (1) Zinc sulphate and copper sulphate.
    Electrolyte used in Leclanche cell is
    (2) Ammonium chloride.
    Electrolyte used in Bichromate cell is
    (3) Mixture of sulphuric acid and potassium dichromate solutions.
    Electrolyte used in Dry cell is

(4) Mixture of ammonium chloride and zinc chloride with manganese dioxide and powdered carbon.

25. The rate at which electric charge flows through a conductor is known as electric current. It is measured in ampere(A) and the current is said to be 1 ampere when 1 coulomb of charge flows across a conductor in one second of time.

Short Answer Type Questions

26. Carbon and zinc rods act as positive and negative electrodes, respectively.

27. The different parts of electric stove and their uses.

28. The body is at a lower potential when compared to the ground. So, the electrons flow from the body to the ground. The conventional current flows from the ground to the body.

29. The different parts of soldering gun and their uses.

30. The process of supplying charge to a body. If a charged body is brought in contact with an uncharged body flow of electric charge takes place, this is called 'charging by conduction'.

The process of electrically charging a body by bringing another charged body near it (and without making physical contact) is known as 'charging by induction'.

31. Definition of primary and secondary cells.

32. Fuse wire is used to protect the electrical appliances from high current.

The fuse wire breaks when excess of electric current flows through the circuit.

33. Metallic conductors consist of many free electrons. They are free to move throughout the conductor.

34. The components of electric circuit are connecting wires, load to utilize the electrical energy, source of electricity. Representation of the different parts of electric circuit with the help of symbols.

35. (1) electrification by friction

(2) Like charges repel

36. Clouds contain large amount of positive and negative charges. It can ionize the air present between them and during the discharge the white streak of light is observed.

37. Applications of electrolysis are:

1) Iron is coated with nickel or chromium to prevent it from rusting.

2) Low cost metals can be covered with gold.

3) Extraction of metals by electrolysis.

38. Factors affecting resistance

$R \propto \ell$

$R \propto \frac{1}{A}$

39. $V = l_1 a_1 = l_2 a_2$

Given, $l_1 = 2 l_2$

$\Rightarrow a_2 = \frac{l_1 a_1}{l_2} = 2a_1$

$\frac{R_1}{R_2} = \frac{l_1/a_1}{l_2/a_2} = \frac{2l_2}{a_1} \times \frac{2a_1}{l_2} = \frac{4}{1} \Rightarrow R_2 = \frac{R_1}{4}$

40. The different parts of electric bulb and their uses.

41. The magnitude of charge of any fundamental particle is 1.602×10^{-19} C.

$Q = 1C = n\,e$

Where n is the number of electrons and e is the charge of an electron.

42. Powdered carbon in a dry cell enhances the flow charges through electrolytes and lead oxide plates or spongy lead are used as electrodes in a lead acid storage battery.

43. Electric current, $i = \frac{q}{t} = \frac{e}{t}$

Speed, $v = \frac{\text{distance}}{\text{time}} = \frac{2\pi r}{t}$

$t = \frac{2\pi r}{v}$

$\therefore \quad i = \frac{e}{\frac{2\pi r}{v}} = \frac{ev}{2\pi r}.$

44. Because sulphuric acid dissociates to produce ions which in turn increase conductivity during electrolysis.

45. Bulbs A and B are in series, and Bulbs C and D are in series. The bulb E is parallel to bulbs A, B, C and D.

Essay Answer Type Questions

46. The different parts of gold leaf electroscope are glass jar, brass cap, tin foil, brass strip, gold leaf, wooden base.

47. The different parts are zinc container, brass cap, air tight seal, carbon rod, electrolyte in the form of paste.

48. Kite with thin silk cloth, silk thread, iron key and dry cloth.

49. Water mixed with salt or acid electrodes, connecting wires, battery, key glass jars, trough.

50. The different parts are glass beaker or a trough, dilute sulphuric acid, zinc plate, copper plate, connecting wires.

Competition Wing

Level 1: Apply your Concepts

1. False, A Daniel cell is divided into two equal portions by a porous membrane.

9. Bulbs A and B are connected in series.

18. Given, $l_A : l_B = 2 : 3$

$$\frac{R_A}{R_B} = \frac{l_A}{a_A} \times \frac{a_B}{l_B} = \frac{2}{3} \times \frac{2}{3} = \frac{4}{9}$$

19. $P = \frac{w}{t} = \frac{EE}{t} = \frac{1500\text{ J}}{30\text{ s}} = 50\text{ Js}^{-1} = 50\text{ Watt}$

36. A group of cells is called battery. The battery can be represented as 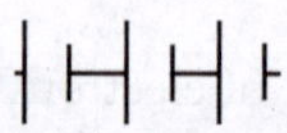

Hence, the correct answer is (c).

37. Construct your answer as follows:
(i) Note the given data about current (i) and time (t).
(ii) Find the charge (Q) that flows through the circuit using,

$$Q = it \quad (1)$$

(iii) The number of electrons (n) flowing through the circuit can be found using,

$$Q = ne \quad (2)$$

(iv) Equate (1) and (2), to find n.

Hence, the correct answer is (d).

38. $E_{total} = 100 \times 100W$; $wfans = 100 \times 60W$

$W_{TLS} = 100 \times 40W \to$ (B)

$\Rightarrow$ Total time, $t = 30 \times 10 = 300h \to$ (C)

$P = \frac{\in}{t} \to$ (E)

$E = P \times t$

$E_{\text{Bulbs}} = 100 \times 100 \times 10\text{ J}$

$E_{\text{Fans}} = 100 \times 60 \times 10\text{ J}$

$E_{TLS} = 100 \times 40 \times 10\text{ J} \to$ (A)

$E_{Total} = E_{bulbs} + E_{fans} + E_{TLS} \to$ (D)

Hence, the correct order is BCEAD.

Hence, the correct answer is (a).

39. All the bulbs connected in parallel glow brightly because all the bulbs are connected directly to a battery, and derive the required electrical energy

Hence, the correct answer is (a).

40. We know $P = Q/t$

$$\Rightarrow Q = P \times t$$

$$Q = 200\ W \times 10\ h$$

$$= 2000\text{ Wh}$$

$$= 2\text{ k Wh } (\because 1\text{ unit} = 1\text{ kWh})$$

$$= 2\text{ electrical units}$$

Hence, A is correct but R is not correct.

Hence, the correct answer is (c).

41. Mica sheets are placed on either side of the heating element because mica does not conduct electricity but transfers the heat.

Hence, the correct answer is (a).

42. When positively-charged and negatively-charged bodies are brought in contact with the brass cap of the gold leaf electroscope both the charges neutralize each other and the net charge will be zero on the cap of electroscope, and hence, the charge on strips flows to the bodies brought in contact with the cap and due to this the gap between the strips decreases.

Hence, the correct answer is (b).

43. As the switch is turned on, the current flows through the circuit and magnetic field will be produced around it. All iron filings will align in the direction of a magnetic field. But the metallic comb will not behave like an electro magnet, and hence, the iron filings will neither be attracted nor repelled.

Hence, the correct answer is (b).

44. When same current flows through the circuit the bulbs in series combination glow with more brightness than the bulbs in parallel combination.

Hence, the correct answer is (a).

45. When a current is allowed to pass through a conductor, it produces a magnetic field around it, and hence, when a magnet is brought closer to it, it will

be deflected by the field produced by the current carrying conductor.

Hence, the correct answer is (d).

Level 2: Review your Concepts

Note: This is how you should frame your answer covering.

46. (i) $R \propto \ell/A$

(ii) $\frac{R_1}{R_2} = \frac{\ell_1}{\ell_2} \times \frac{A_2}{A_1}$

(iii) $\ell_2 = \ell_1 + 0.25\ell_1$

$A_2 = A_1 + 0.25\ A_1$

(iv) 8 Ω

47. What happens when a charged body is brought in contact with an uncharged metallic body?

What happens to the electrons present on the surface of an uncharged body when a positively-charged body is brought in contact with it?

48. Here, body A is at higher potential when compared to body B. The positive charges flow from A to B, i.e., conventional current flows from A to B or electronic current flows from B to A.

49. Because each appliance gets full voltage as the resistance in the parallel arrangement is low.

50. (i) Protons present inside the nucleus

(ii) Protons bound to the nucleus

51. What happens to the charge on a body when it is connected to the ground?

What is the consequence if a gasoline transport truck is charged by friction?

52. Fuses are used to control the current in an electric circuit. When more current enters the circuit, the fuse wire fuses out and the circuit becomes an open circuit.

Will the circuit be open if the fuse wire is connected parallely?

53. (i) $m = n \times m_e$

(ii) $Q = ne$

(iii) 49.6 μC, positive charge.

54. (i) Resistance $R \propto \frac{1}{A}$. Determine the resistance of the wire using the formula, $\frac{R_1}{R_2} = \frac{A_2}{A_1}$

(ii) 2.5 Ω

55. (i) During electrification, transfer of only valence electrons but not protons.

(ii) Number of electrons = Number of protons in a neutral body.

(iii) P – 45 e, 45 P

Q – 77 e, 77 P

P gained 5 electrons.

56. Fluorescent lamp, ₹ 28.25

57. (i) One commercial unit of electrical energy is equal to 1 kilowatt hour.

The number of units of electrical energy used in a month can be calculated as $E = p \times t \times 30$.

where 't' is in hours.

The cost of the electrical energy can be determined from the equation, cost = energy × cost per unit.

Compare the cost of electrical energy in both the cases.

(ii) ₹ 40.80

58. Electrons flow from negative electrode towards positive electrode when an electric circuit is connected across the cell. However, inside the cell, the negatively charged ions are attracted towards negative electrode because it is depleted of electrons.

59. Current $I = \frac{q}{t}$

60. Compare the electric current carriers in conductors and electrolytes.

What is the role of electrodes in an electrolyte?

How do the anions and cations move inside an electrolyte?

Compare it with the movement of electrons in conductors.

61. $m = 36.4 \times 10^{-15}\ g = 36.4 \times 10^{-18}$ kg

$M_e = 9.1 \times 10^{-31}$ kg

$m = n \times m_e$

$$n = \frac{m}{m_e} = \frac{36.4 \times 10^{-18}}{9.1 \times 10^{-31}}$$

$n = 4 \times 10^{13}$

62. The duration for which an electric heater used $t = 3$ h.

Energy consumed (E) = 0.6 kW h.

∴ Power of the heater (P) = ?

We know that power $(P) = \frac{\text{energy consumed}}{\text{time taken}}$

$$\Rightarrow P = \frac{0.6 \text{ kW h}}{3\text{h}} = 0.2\text{kW} = 0.2 \times 1000\text{W}$$

$$= 200 \text{ W}$$

∴ Power of the heater (P) = 200 W.

63. Let the charge densities of two spheres be $\sigma_1 = \sigma_2 = \sigma$ $= \frac{q}{A}$. For given two spheres, the charge density is the same.

$$\therefore \sigma = \text{constant} = \frac{q}{A} \Rightarrow q \propto A \rightarrow \quad (1)$$

Ratio of charges $q_1 : q_2 = 1 : 4$.

$$\therefore (1) \Rightarrow \frac{q_1}{q_2} = \frac{A_1}{A_2} = \frac{1}{4}$$

$$\frac{4\pi r_1^2}{4\pi r_2^2} = \frac{1}{4}$$

$$\frac{r_1}{r_2} = \sqrt{\frac{1}{4}} = \frac{1}{2}$$

$$\therefore \text{Ratio of their volumes} = \frac{v_1}{v_2} = \frac{\left(\frac{4}{3}\right)\pi r_1^3}{\left(\frac{4}{3}\right)\pi r_2^3}$$

$$\frac{v_1}{v_2} = \left(\frac{r_1}{r_2}\right)^3 = \left(\frac{1}{2}\right)^3$$

$$v_1 : v_2 = 1 : 8$$

∴ Ratio of their volumes = 1: 8.

64. Charge gained by given cube, Q = 15 × 10^{-16} C.
Number of electrons gained, n = Q / e; e = charge of electron

n = 15 × 10^{-16} C / 1.6 × 10^{-19} C

n = 9.375 × 10^3

n = 9375.

Since electrons are gained, mass of cube increases.

Mass of electron, me = 9.11 × 10^{-31} kg

Total mass gained, M = n × m_e

M = 9375 × 9.11 × 10^{-31} kg

M = 8.54 × 10^{-27} kg

65. Here P and Q are connected in series. So, current through P and Q are same. If 6A current pases through P, then current through Q is also 6A.

66. Number of excess electrons present on the body 'A', n = 6.25 × 10^{18}.

Charge of each electron (e) = 1.6 × 10^{-19} C.

∴ Total charge present on the body 'A' is Q = $n \times e$.

Q = 6.25 × 10^{18} × –1.6 × 10^{-19}

= –10 × 10^{-1} = –1 coulomb

The charge present on body 'B' = – 5 coulomb.

When these two bodies are brought in contact, the charge distributes uniformly over its surface. (both are identical)

∴ Total charge = – [1 C + 5 C] = – 6 C

∴ Charge on each body = – 3 C.

Level 3: Assess Your Concepts

67. Filament should not be in contact with oxygen

68. Use another body and charge it by using A.
The charge on the body can be transferred to B. What happens to the charge on B and A if we repeat this process?

69. Radius of given sphere, r = 5 cm; r = 5 × 10^{-2} m

Number of electrons gained n = 15 × 10^6

Charge of electron, e = 1.6 × 10^{-19} C

Total charge on the sphere, Q = n × e

Q = 15 × 10^6 × 1.6 × 10^{-19} C

Q = 24 × 10^{-13} C

Surface area of sphere, A = $4\pi r^2$

A = 4 × (22/7) × (5 × 10^{-2})^2 m^2

A = (22/7) × 10^{-2} m^2

Surface charge density, σ = Q / A

σ = 24 × 10^{-13} C / (22/7) × 10^{-2} m^2

σ = 7.64 × 10^{-11} C m^{-2}.

70. (i) Number of atoms (n) = mass of the substance × number of atoms in one gram.
Number of electrons = n × no. of electrons in each atom

$$i = \frac{Q}{t}$$

$$q = n\bar{e}$$

(ii) $\frac{127}{64 \times 10^4}$

71. (i) Charge each conductor when they brought together = $\frac{q_1 + q_2}{2}$ where q_1 and q_2 are the charge on each body.

(ii) A $\longrightarrow -8 \times 10^{-19}$ C

B and C + 20.8×10^{-19} C

73. Electrical energy consumed by:

i) Bulbs: 6 × 100 W × 6 h = 3600 W h = 3.6 kW h

ii) Fans: 5 × 200 W × 8 h = 8000 W h = 8 kW h

iii) Refrigerator: 1 × 2500 W × 8 h = 20,000 W h = 20 kW h

Total number of units (kW h) of electrical energy consumed,

E = E bulbs + E fans + E refrigerator

E = (3.6 + 8 + 20) kW h = 31.6 kW h.

December month has 31 days.

Number of units of electrical energy consumed in December,

N = 31.6 × 31 = 979.6

Given: Cost of each unit of electrical energy = ₹ 5

Cost of 979.6 units = 979.6 × 5 = ₹ 4898

Given: Bill amount = ₹ 4800

Difference in amount found by Divij

= ₹ 4898 – ₹ 4800 = ₹ 98.

74. When current passes through a conducting rod, accumulation of charge do not take place. Hence, the charge accumulated on A is zero.

75. If the electron makes 2000 revolutions in one second, it is equivalent to movement of 2000 electrons across any point in one second.

$i = q/t = ne/t$

$$= \frac{2000 \times 1.6 \times 10^{-19}}{1} = 3.2 \times 10^{-16}\ \text{A}.$$

76. When the circuit is closed, current starts flowing from the positive electrode of the cell. At '*A*' the total current splits, a part passes through 'B_1' and other part passes through 'B_4'. As all the bulbs are identical, the resistance offered by them is the same. If the total current flowing in the circuit is *i*, at A it splits into two equal halves, and a current of '*i*/2' passes through B_1 and B_4. Here, B_1 and B_4 are connected in parallel between A and B. As B_2 is connected in series the current that passes through it is '*i*'. Similarly, B_3 and B_5 are connected in parallel between C and D. Hence, '*i*/2' current passes through both of them. Their potential difference depends on the current that passes through the different bulbs. As shown, the potential drop across B_1, B_4, B_3 and B_5 is equal and the potential drop across B_2 is twice that of the others.

77. Number of Cu^{2+} ions, n = 10^{20}

Time, t = 16 s

Charge on each copper ion, q = +2 units

= $2 \times 1.6 \times 10^{-19}$ C

Charge of 10^{20} Copper ions, Q = n × q

Q = $10^{20} \times 2 \times 1.6 \times 10^{-19}$ C

Q = 32 C

Equivalent current, I = Q / t

I = 32 C / 16 s

I = 2 C s^{-1} = 2 A.

78. For family 'A' the total energy consumed in watt hour every day

= (3 × 5 × 100) + (4 × 8 × 200) + (1 × 3 × 2500) + (1 × 2 × 2000)

= 1500 + 6400 + 7500 + 4000 = 19400 watt hour.

The energy consumed in kilowatt hour (units)for 30 days

$$= \frac{19400 \times 30}{1000} = 582\ \text{units}.$$

The electricity bill for April = 582 × 4 = ₹2328.

For family '*B*' the total electrical energy consumed in watt hours every day

= (4 × 4 × 100) + (5 × 6 × 200) + (1 × 3 × 2500) + (1 × 2 × 2000)

= 1600 + 6000 + 7500 + 4000 = 19100 w h.

The energy consumed in kilowatt hour (units) for 30 days

$$= \frac{19100 \times 30}{1000} = 573\ \text{units}.$$

The electricity bill for April = 573 × 4 = ₹2292.

79. The energy consumed in operating a fluorescent lamp = 15 × 8 × 60 × 60 × 30 J

$$= \frac{15 \times 8 \times 36 \times 3 \times 10^5}{36 \times 10^5}\ \text{kW h} = 3.6\ \text{kW h}.$$

The cost = 2 × 3.6 = ₹7.2.

The energy consumed by the bulb = 100 × 8× 60 × 60 × 30 J

$$= \frac{8 \times 36 \times 3 \times 10^3}{36 \times 10^5} \text{kW h} = 24 \text{ kW h.}$$

The cost = 2 × 24 = ₹48.

Saving = 48 − 7.2 = ₹40.8.

80. For conductor P:

Area, A_P = a

Length, l_p=

For conductor Q:

Area, A_Q = 2a

Length, $l_Q = l/2$

Resistance of a conductor is directly proportional to its length and inversely proportional to its area of cross-section.

R ∝ l ------ (1)

R ∝ 1/A ------ (2)

Combining (1) & (2)

$$R \propto \frac{l}{A}$$

$$R = \frac{kl}{A}$$ ------ (3); k is proportionality constant

When the applied potential difference is the same,

Current ∝ 1/ Resistance

$i \propto 1/R$

$i_P : i_Q = R_Q : R_P$

$$R_Q : R_P = k\frac{l_Q}{A_Q} : k\frac{l_P}{A_P}; \text{using (3)}$$

$$= \frac{l_Q}{A_Q} : \frac{l_P}{A_P}$$

$$= \frac{\frac{l}{2}}{2a} : \frac{l}{a}$$

$$= \frac{1}{4} : 1$$

$$= 4 : 1$$

Hence, $i_P : i_Q = 4:1$

JEE-NEET Special Wing

Multiple-Answer Type Questions

1. Graphite is a form of carbon and is a conductor of electricity.
Hence, the correct option is (a), (b) and (c).

2. $I = \frac{q}{t}$
$q = I \times t$
$= 6A \times 1$ hr
$= 6 \times 60 \times 60$ s
$= 6 \times 3600$
$= 21{,}600$ C
$= 2.16 \times 10^4$ C
1 C = 1 A s
Hence, the correct option is (a) and (b).

3. Polarization - Formation of a layer of hydrogen gas over Cu electrode which reduce current flow. This occurs due to impurities in zinc.
Local Action - Loss in current extracted from cell due to wear in zinc plate.
Hence, the correct option is (b), (c) and (d).

4. The S. I. unit of electric power is J s^{-1} which is also called watt (W).
Hence, the correct option is (b) and (d).

5. Since the bulbs are connected in parallel between the same points A and B, the potential across both will be the same. As the resistance offered by each bulb is different, the current through each bulb is different.
We have $i = \frac{V}{R}$, as resistance changes the value of current changes.
Hence, the correct option is (b) and (d).

Comprehension-Based Questions

6. $P = \frac{E}{t}$
$= \frac{3}{60\,s} = 0.05$ W
Hence, the correct option is (c).

7. 1 MW = 10^6 W
Hence, the correct option is (b).

8. 1 kWh = 1 unit of electrical energy
Hence, the correct option is (a).

9. E = P×t
= 3000 J s^{-1}×2h
= 3000 W×2 h
= 3 kW×2h
= 6 kWh
Hence, the correct option is (d).

10. Energy consumed in a day $= \frac{100}{1000} kW \times 5h$
= 0.1×5 = 0.5 kWh
Energy consumed in the month of June
= 0.5×30 = 15 kWh
∴ cost = 15×₹ 3 = ₹ 45
Hence, the correct option is (d).

11. The process of splitting of compounds to its constituent ions is called chemical decomposition.
Hence, the correct option is (c).

12. The process of producing chemical decomposition by passing electricity through compound is electrolysis.
Hence, the correct option is (a).

13. (d) $H_2O \rightarrow 2H^+ + O^{2-}$
Hence, the correct option is (d).

14. The rod connected to the positive terminal of the battery is anode.
Hence, the correct option is (b).

15. The figure shows the purification of copper. In metallurgy, electrolysis is used to extract the metals from their ores and to purify the extracted metals.
Hence, the correct option is (c).

Match the Column

15. **Choice (a) follows.**
The electrolytes used in some cells are provided.

Magnetism

CHAPTER

9

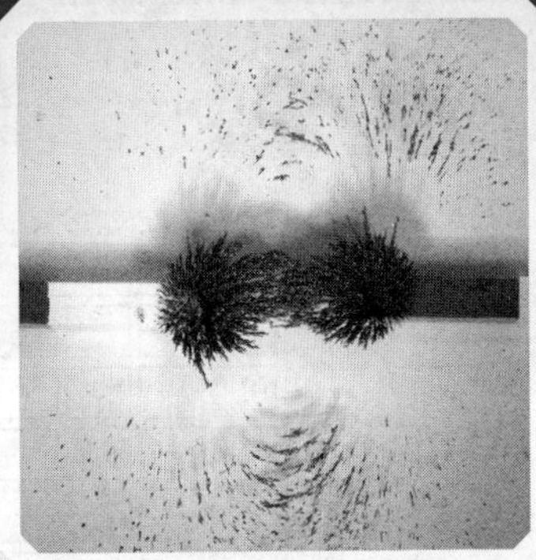

Key Ideas

After completing this chapter, you should be able to:

- learn about the properties of magnets and study magnetic Induction.
- learn artificial magnets, bar magnet, etc.
- understand magnetic field lines and their properties.
- study methods of magnetization, methods of demagnetization, Ewing's molecular theory and terrestrial magnetism.

Remember

Before beginning this chapter, you should be able to:

- define electric charge, electricity, current, etc.
- discuss magnetic effect of electricity and conclude basic concept of magnetism.

Scientific Crypt

A Tribute to Wilhelm Eduard Weber (1804—1891)

A Wilhelm Eduard Weber was a German physicist, born on 24th October, 1804, in Wittenberg, Germany. His father was a theologian and his family migrated to Halle. Weber completed his university education and received his doctorate degree in physics in 1826. This German physicist was much interested in magnetism and electricity and had shown his excellence in these topics. His contributions were appreciated and proved very vital in the development of electromagnetic theory. He was given professorship in physics at Gottingen, in 1831. There he worked with another physicist Carl Friedrich Gauss whose interest was also in electricity and magnetism. Their close collaboration proved very fruitful when they worked on terrestrial magnetism and developed several magnetic devices, including the electrodynamometer which measures small electrical currents. In 1843, he was appointed as physics professor in Leipzig. There, Weber published Electro Dynamical Measurements and established an absolute system of electrical units. In 1948 he returned to his former position at Gottingen, and worked on the ratio between the electro dynamic and electro static units of charge which became basis for development of electromagnetic theory. Weber wrote on subject called mechanics of the human walking tool along with his brother named Eduard Friedrich Weber. With another brother, Ernst Heinrich Weber, he wrote a book on wave motion.

He died on 23rd June, 1891 at age of 86. This loss is always felt in the field of science and technology for his ceaseless contribution. His life was always an inspiration for aspirants in science. After his demise, a magnetic unit was measured in 'Webber' in honour of him.

Crossword

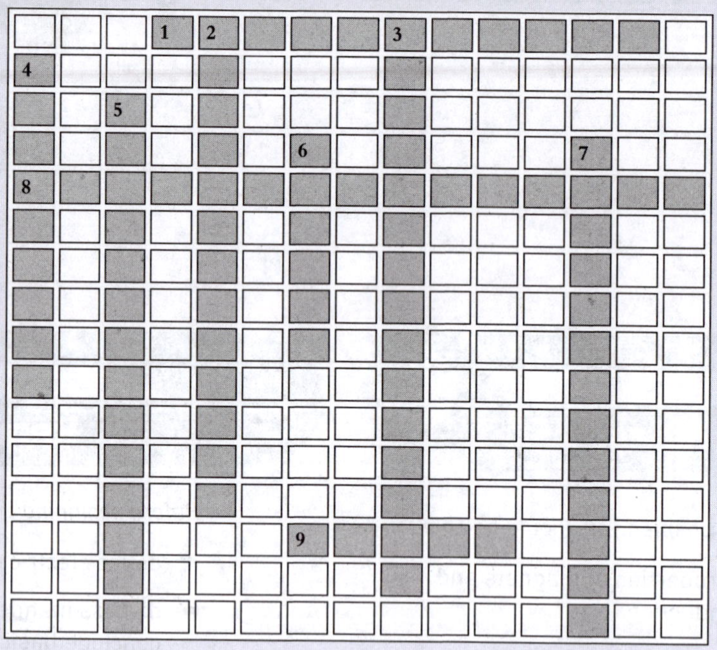

Across

1. Unit of pole strength
8. Device used to test polarity of magnet
9. Example of diamagnetic substance

Down

2. More attractive strength of a magnet is concentrated at ______.
3. Distance between north pole and south pole of a magnet
4. induced magnetism in steel
5. The product of pole strength and effective length of the magnet
6. Metal used in making magnet
7. Region where angle of dip is 90 degrees

INTRODUCTION

As early as 600 b.c. the Greeks knew that a certain form of iron ore had the property of attracting small pieces of iron. The iron ore called magnetite or lodestone, was found in Magnesia in Asia minor. Later during the middle ages, crude navigational compasses were made by attaching pieces of lodestone to wooden splints floating in bowls of water. These splints were always found to come to rest in a North–South direction, and were the forerunners of the modern aircraft and ship compasses. The word lodestone was derived from an old English word meaning way, and refers to the directional property of the stone.

Magnets

Naturally occurring substances which have the property of attracting pieces of iron, cobalt, nickel, etc., are called natural magnets. Lodestone is a natural magnet. On rubbing a piece of iron with lodestone, the piece of iron acquires magnetic properties and behaves like a magnet. These type of magnets are known as artificial magnets. There are several other ways of producing artificial magnets.

There are several kinds of artificial magnets. Some generally used artificial magnets are discussed below.

1. **Bar Magnet:** A magnet in the form of a bar having either a rectangular or a circular cross section is called bar magnet as shown in the figure 9.1 and 9.2.

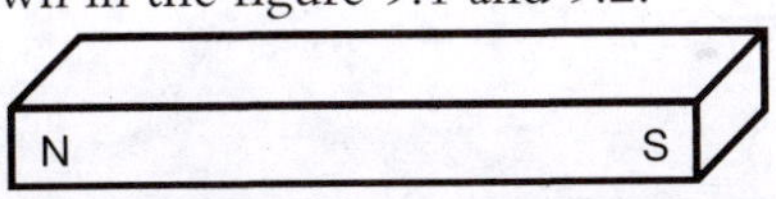

Figure 9.1 Bar magnet

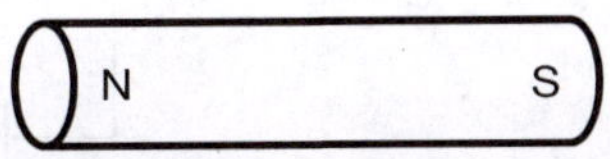

Figure 9.2 Cylindrical magnet

2. **Horseshoe Magnet:** A magnet which is U shaped and resembles a horseshoe is called horseshoe magnet, shown in the figure below.

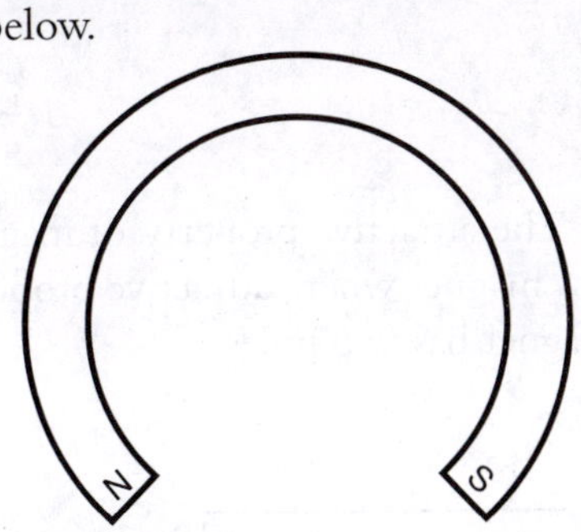

Figure 9.3 Horse shoe magnet

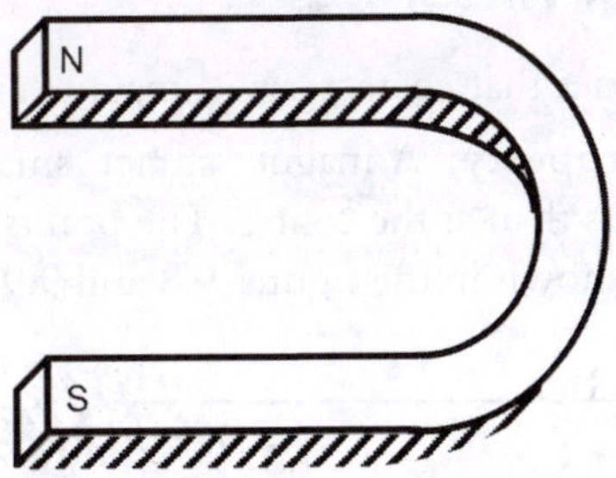

Figure 9.4 Horse shoe magnet

3. **Magnetic Needle:** A magnet in the form of a bar which is tapered from the centre towards the ends and is pivoted at its centre on a stand is called magnetic needle, shown in the figure below.

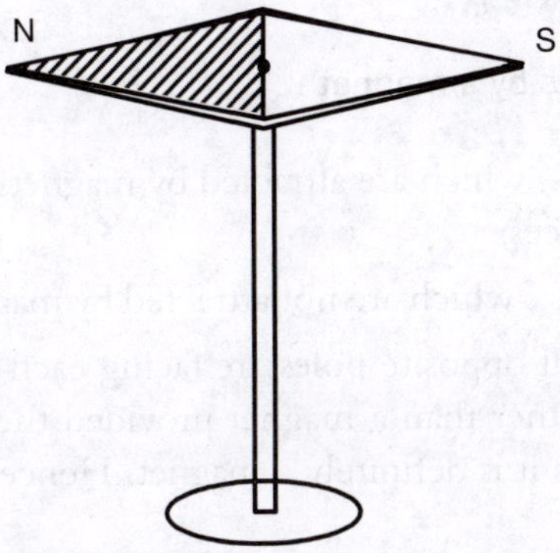

Figure 9.5 Magnetic needle

Info Bytes!

The north pole of the needle is generally coloured red.

4. **Magnetic Compass:** A magnetic compass consists of a small magnetic needle pivoted at the centre and encased in a small brass box with a glass top. It can be used to find the direction of a magnetic field at a place and also to test the polarity of a magnet as shown in figure 9.6.

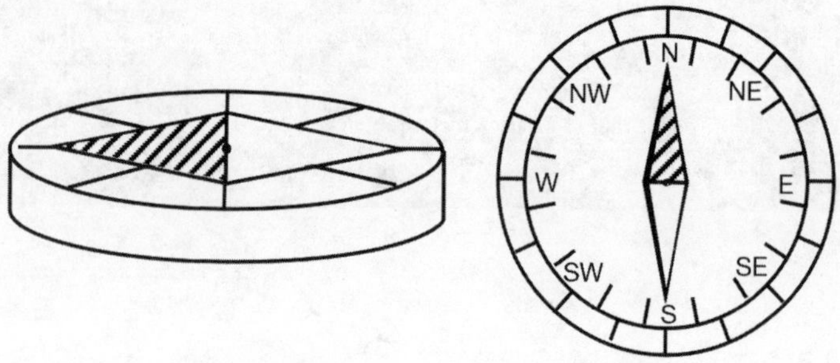

Figure 9.6 Magnetic compass

5. **Electromagnet:** An electromagnet consists of a soft iron core with a wire wound around it. The soft iron piece acts as a magnet as long as current passes through the coil as shown in figure 9.7.

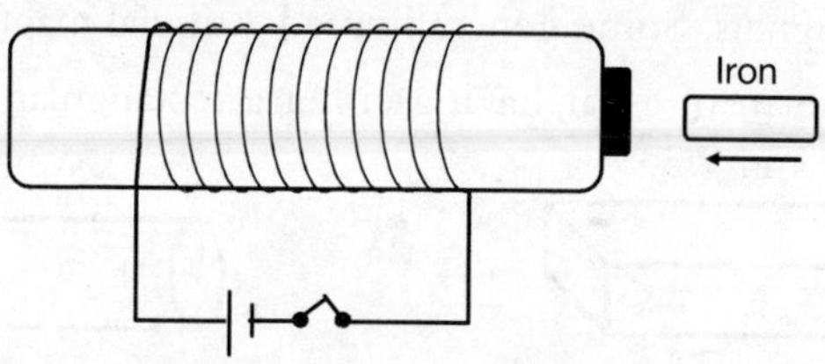

Figure 9.7 Electromagnet

Properties of Magnets

The physical properties that characterize a magnet are:

1. **Attractive Property:** A magnet attracts small pieces of iron. The attractive property of magnets is concentrated more at its ends than at the centre. The points near the ends of a magnet where attractive property is maximum are called **poles** (shown in the figures 9.8 and 9.9). Thus, every magnet has two poles.

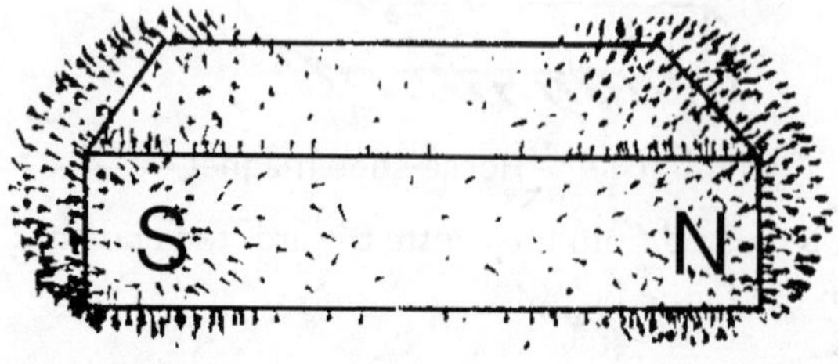

Figure 9.8 Attraction of iron filings by a magnet

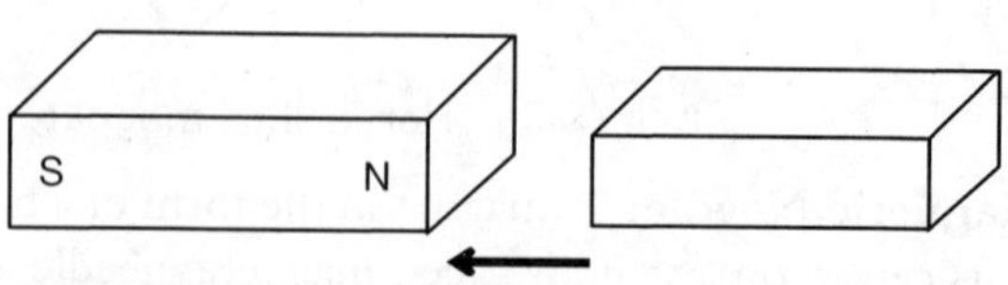

Figure 9.9 Attraction of magnetic substance by a magnet

Substances like iron, nickel, cobalt, etc., which are attracted by magnets are called **magnetic substances**. Artificial magnets are made of magnetic substances.

Substances like wood, paper, plastic, etc., which are not attracted by magnets are called **non-magnetic substances**.

A magnet can attract another magnet if opposite poles are facing each other, or it can attract magnetic substances. Magnets cannot repel any substance other than a magnet provided their like poles face each other. Thus, when a substance is repelled by a magnet, then it is definitely a magnet. Hence, repulsion is a sure test for magnetism.

2. **Directive Property:** A freely suspended bar magnet always points in the north–south direction. Even if it is disturbed, it will oscillate for some time and come to rest in the north–south direction. The end of a magnet which points in the north direction is called north-seeking pole or north pole. The other end which points in the south direction is called south-seeking pole or south pole.
3. **Law of Magnetic Poles:** When two magnets are brought near each other such that either their north poles or south poles face each other, they repel each other. When the north pole of a magnet is brought near the south pole of another magnet, they attract each other. Thus, like poles repel and unlike poles attract each other. This is called law of magnetic poles.
4. **Pair Property**
Magnetic poles always exist in pairs. It is not possible to have an isolated north pole or south pole. Even when a magnet is cut into a number of small pieces, each piece has both the poles, no matter what the size of the piece is. Even at the molecular level every molecule of a magnetic substance possesses two poles. See figure 9.10.

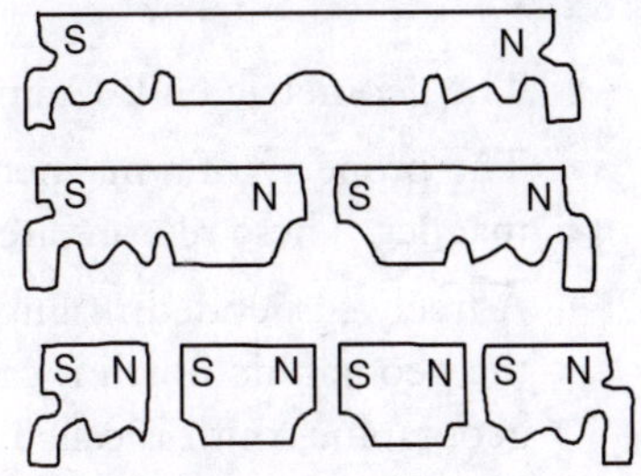

Figure 9.10 Pair property

Magnetic Induction

Take a soft iron bar and fix it vertically to a stand. Place a bowl full of iron filings below the iron bar. The iron filings cling to the iron bar when a bar magnet is brought near it indicating that it has become a magnet itself. When the bar magnet is removed the iron filings which were attached to the iron bar fall back into the bowl indicating that the soft iron bar has lost its magnetism as shown in the Figure. 9.11.

When this experiment is repeated by replacing the soft iron bar with a steel bar, it is found that steel attracts less than soft iron, but holds the iron filings even when the magnet is removed. (Fig. 9.12)

The process in which a magnetic substance becomes a magnet when it is kept near a magnet without there being physical contact between them, is called **magnetic induction**.

When we bring a magnet near a magnetic substance like a steel rod, the nearer end of the magnetic substance attains an opposite polarity. Hence, the steel rod gets attracted towards the magnet. Thus, magnetic induction precedes attraction.

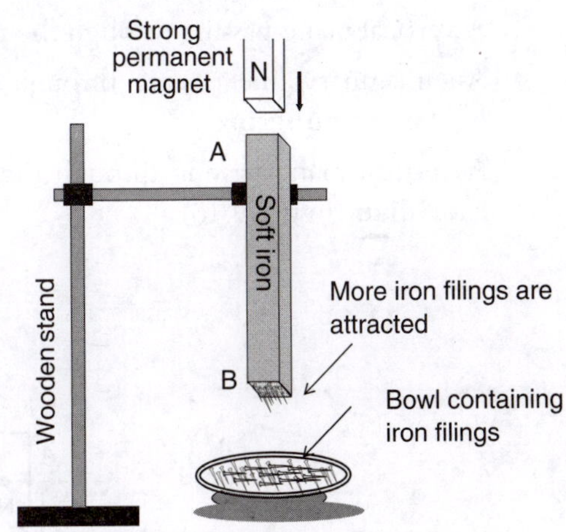

Figure 9.11 Soft iron bar behaves like a magnet due to induction

We note that,

- induced magnetism in soft iron is temporary.
- induced magnetism in steel is permanent.
- the degree of magnetization in the case of steel is less than that in the case of soft iron.
- soft iron is used for making temporary magnets.
- steel is used for making permanent magnets.
- a steel bar, when magnetized, does not lose magnetism easily and retains magnetism for a long time, i.e., its retentivity is high.
- the retentivity for soft iron is very low.

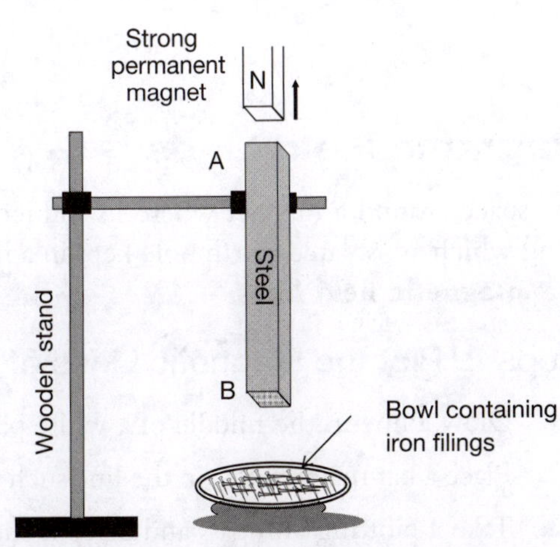

Figure 9.12 Steel bar does not get magnetized easily by induction method

Factors Affecting Magnetic Induction

1. More powerful magnets can produce a high induced magnetism in a magnetic substance.

2. Magnetic induction is inversely proportional to the distance between inducing magnet and the magnetic substance.
3. It also depends upon the nature of magnetic substance.

Bar Magnet

- The geometric ends (A and B) of a bar magnet are called its **geometric poles.**
- The property of a magnet to attract small pieces of iron seems to be very high, in small regions at each end of the magnet. These regions are called **magnetic poles.** These poles lie slightly within the ends of a magnet.
- A freely suspended magnet aligns itself in the north-south direction. The end of the magnet which points towards the geographic north is called north seeking pole or **magnetic north pole** and the end which points towards the geographic south is called south seeking pole or **magnetic south pole.**
- The line joining the north pole and the south pole of a magnet is called **axis of the magnet.**
- The distance (ℓ) between any one of the magnetic poles and the centre of the magnet is called **length of the magnet.** The distance between the north pole and the south pole of the magnet is called **effective length of the magnet.** This is slightly less than the physical length of the magnet and is taken to be equal to 2ℓ .
- The product of pole strength and the length of the magnet is called **magnetic moment.**
- A vertical plane passing through the magnetic axis of a freely suspended magnet is called its **magnetic meridian.**
- An imaginary line passing through the centre of the magnet and perpendicular to the magnetic axis is called **magnetic equator.**
- A vertical plane passing through the magnetic equator of a freely suspended bar magnet is called its **equatorial meridian** (figure 9.13).

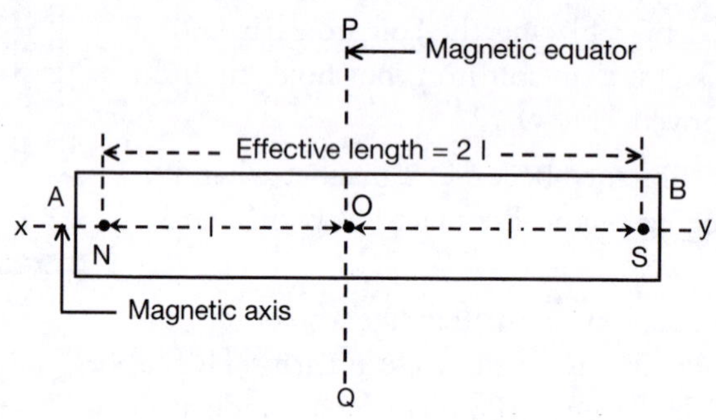

Figure 9.13 Bar magnet

Magnetic Field Lines

The space around a magnet where its influence can be felt is called **magnetic field.** Line of force is an imaginary line along which an isolated north pole kept in a magnetic field tends to move. Lines of force, more appropriately, are referred to as **magnetic field lines.**

Steps to Plot the Magnetic Lines of Force Around a Bar Magnet

1. Draw a line in the middle of a white paper fixed on a drawing board.
2. Place a bar magnet NS on the line such that its axial line coincides with the line on the paper and mark its boundary.
3. Take a plotting compass and place it such that its S-pole is directed towards point 0 at the edge of the bar magnet, and mark the point 1 in the direction in which the north pole of the plotting compass points (figure 9.14).
4. Repeat the procedure described in step(3), by shifting the compass and plot the points 2, 3, 4, etc.
5. Join the points 0, 1, 2, 3, ...by a smooth curve.

The magnetic line of force for a bar magnet is a closed continuous curve along which a unit north pole will move, and its direction is given by the direction in which a free N–pole would point. The lines of force due to a bar magnet is shown in Figure 9.15. The lines start at the north pole and end at the south pole.

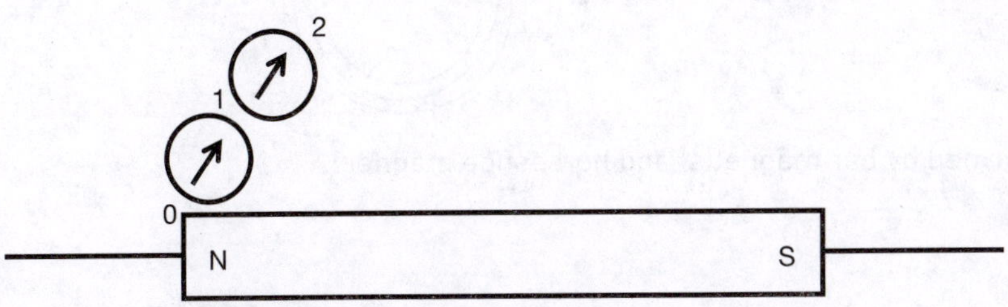

Figure 9.14 Mapping magnetic field lines

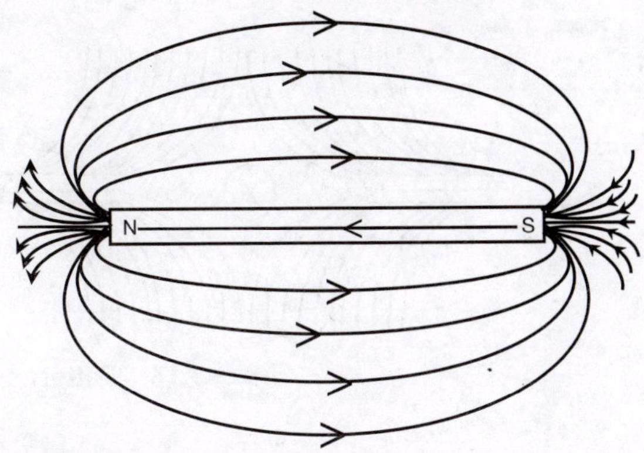

Figure 9.15 Magnetic field lines around a bar magnet

Sprinkle some iron filings on a piece of paper and place it over a magnet. The iron filings arrange themselves in a certain pattern. It can be seen that the lines of force will be crowded near the poles.

Properties of Lines of Force

- They are closed, continuous curves.
- Magnetic lines of force start at the north pole and end at the south pole outside the magnet. Inside the magnet, the lines of force move from the south pole to the north pole.
- Two lines of force can never meet each other.
- They are crowded near the poles.
- The strength of the field is more where the lines of forces are crowded.
- The lines of force have longitudinal tension and lateral pressure.
- Number of magnetic lines of force per unit area gives the intensity of the magnetic field at a point.

Konnect

The number of magnetic lines of force passing perpendicularly through a certain area gives the magnetic flux.

Patterns of Lines of Force

Place a cardboard on a magnet or a set of magnets and scatter some iron fillings uniformly over the cardboard. Now slightly tap the board. It will be observed that the filings arrange themselves in curved lines forming a pattern. We will discuss the pattern of lines of force in some standard cases, as shown in the figures below.

(a) Pattern due to single bar magnet

(b) Pattern due to two bar magnets with opposite poles facing each other

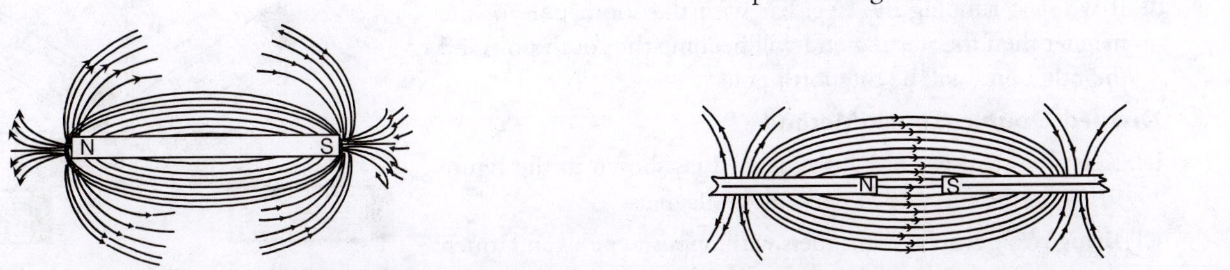

Figure 9.16 Patterns formed by bar magnet(s)

(a) Pattern due to two bar magnets with similar poles facing each other

(b) Pattern due to a horseshoe magnet

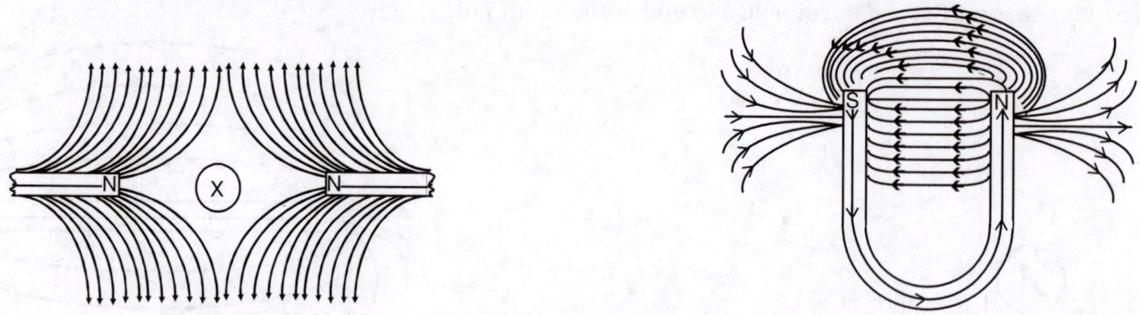

Figure 9.17 Patterns formed by bar magnet(s) and horseshoe magnet

Uses of Magnets

- The directive property of magnets is used in the construction of a magnetic needle and magnetic compass.
- Permanent magnets are used in dynamos, electric motors, generators, electron accelerators, door locks, etc.
- Electromagnets are used widely in electric bells, electric cranes, tape recorders, speakers, etc.
- Magnets are used in separating iron particles from solid mixtures using the method of magnetic separation.

Konnect

A neutral point (X) is obtained in between the two poles. The space between two opposing magnetic fields, where the resulting magnetic effect is zero is called neutral point.

Methods of Magnetization

The process used for inducing the magnetism (the magnetic properties) of a magnet is called **magnetization**.

Following are some of the methods of magnetization:

1. **Single-Touch Method**
   (a) Keep the steel bar to be magnetized on a wooden table.
   (b) Take a strong permanent magnet and bring one pole (say north pole) of the magnet near one end of the steel bar and gently rub from one end to the other as shown in the Fig. 9.18.
   (c) Once it has reached the other end, lift the magnet gently away from the steel bar and again bring it to the starting end.
   (d) Repeat this process several times.
   (e) Now, the steel bar will be magnetized with the starting end as the north pole and the other end as the south pole.
   (f) If we start rubbing the steel bar with the south pole of the magnet then the starting end will become the south pole and the other end will be the north pole.

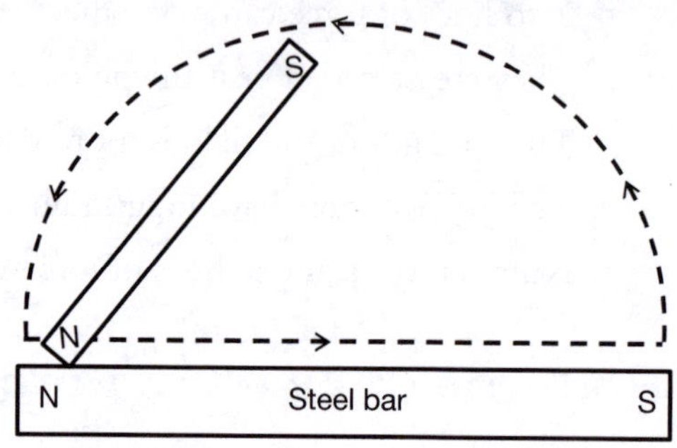

Figure 9.18 Set up for single-touch method

2. **Divided Double-Touch Method**
   (a) Keep the steel bar to be magnetized (as shown in the figure 9.19) on the top of two permanent magnets.
   (b) Bring two permanent magnets with opposite poles and touch the middle of the steel bar and rub and move as shown in the Fig. 9.19.

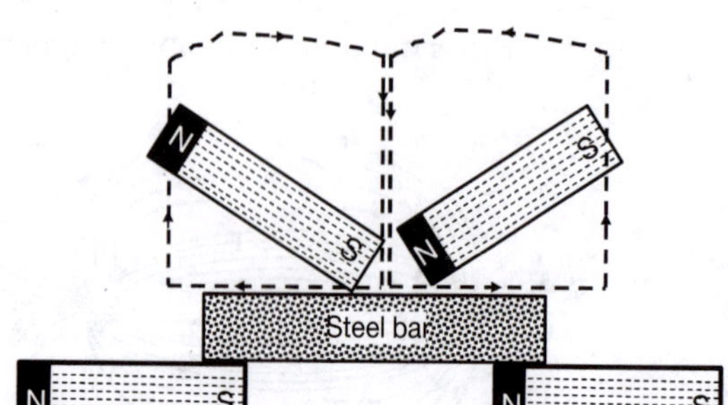

Figure 9.19 Set up for divided double-touch method

(c) Repeat this several times.

(d) The end of the steel bar at which the south pole of the magnet leaves becomes the north pole. The end of the steel bar at which the north pole of the magnet leaves becomes the south pole.

3. **Double-Touch Method**

(a) Two permanent magnets separated by a piece of wood or cork are held together, such that their opposite poles are together.

(b) This combination is placed on a piece of soft iron or steel in the centre and moved to and fro from one end to the other end without lifting.

(c) The polarities of the magnetized bar is opposite to that of the nearest stroking magnets as shown in the Figure 9.20.

(d) For better and stronger magnetization, the piece to be magnetized may be placed over two permanent magnets as shown.

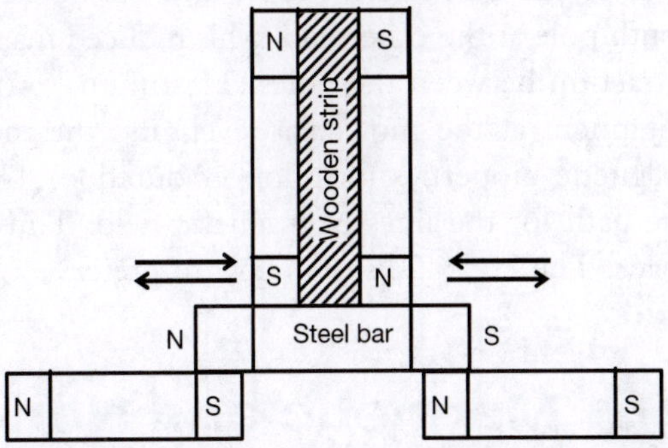

Figure 9.20 Set up for double-touch method

4. **Electrical Method**

(a) Keep the steel bar to be magnetized inside a long coil of insulated copper wire.

(b) Pass a strong direct current through the coil for some time.

(c) The specimen of steel bar will get magnetized.

(d) The end at which current enters in an anti-clockwise direction will become the north pole and the other end becomes the south pole (see figure 9.21).

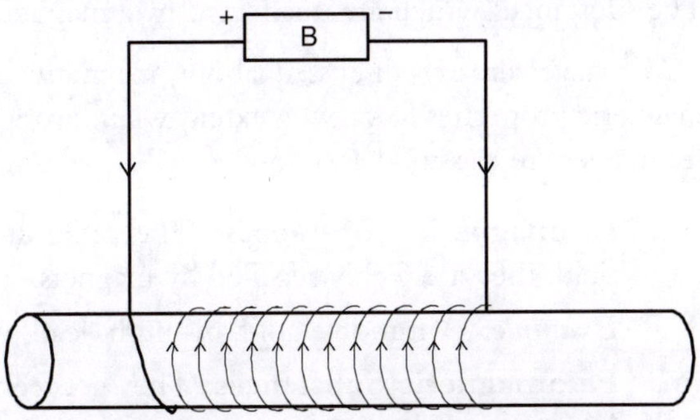

Figure 9.21 Set up for electrical method

Methods of Demagnetization

The process used for destroying the magnetism (the magnetic properties) of a magnet is called **demagnetization**.

Following are some of the methods of demagnetization:

1. By rough handling.
2. Heating the magnet and allowing it to cool while it is lying in east–west direction.
3. By passing high frequency electric current.
4. A magnet may lose its magnetism by self-induction.

Konnect

Instead of a steel bar if we keep a soft iron bar, it acts as a magnet as long as there is a current in the coil. Once the current stops flowing, it loses its magnetic effect. These type of magnets are known as temporary magnets. They are also called electromagnets.

Magnetic Keepers

If we keep the magnet for a long time, we find that it loses its magnetic property. It becomes weak. Due to self induction, opposite poles are induced which results in the loss of magnetic force. The earth's magnetic field also induces its own poles which weakens the magnetic strength of the magnet.

In order to prevent loss of magnetism, we use a soft iron piece between the poles of the magnet. This soft iron piece is called **magnetic keeper**.

How Magnetic Keepers Prevent Loss of Magnetism?

The magnet induces opposite polarity at the ends of the keeper, generally soft iron pieces, in contact with it. The south pole of the magnet induces a north pole at one end of the keeper and the north pole of the magnet induces a south pole at the other end. This induced magnetism in the keeper results in attraction between the poles. This mutual attraction improves the magnetic alignment at the molecular level, and the magnet is also able to retain its magnetic properties for a longer duration. The magnetic keepers complete the path for the lines of magnetic field. Thus, they screen the surrounding space. The Fig. 9.22 shows how to preserve a horseshoe magnet.

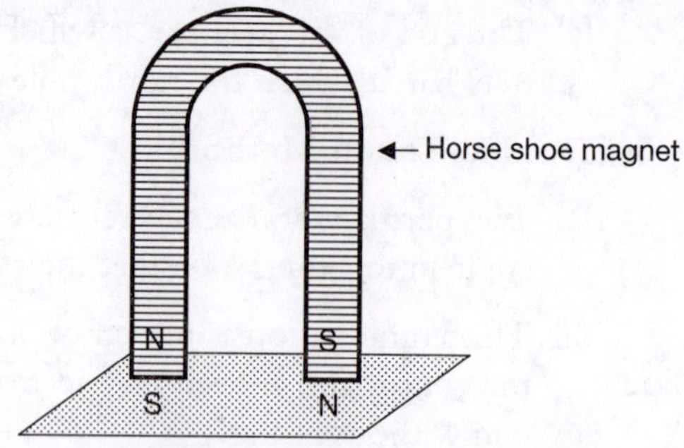

Figure 9.22 Magnetic keeper

Magnetic and Non-Magnetic Substances

The substances which can be magnetized or the substances which are either attracted or repelled by a magnet are called **magnetic substances**. For example, an iron bar can be called magnetic substance, even though it may not be magnetized. The substances which are unaffected by a magnet are called **non-magnetic substances.**

We have already discussed about magnetic and non-magnetic substances. Different magnetic substances exhibit magnetic properties to varying extent when brought under the influence of strong magnetic field. Based on this, magnetic substances are classified as follows.

1. **Diamagnetic Substances:** They exhibit practically no magnetic properties. However, in a powerful magnetic field, they are feebly repelled by magnets.

   Example: Antimony, gold, bismuth, lead, water, etc.

2. **Paramagnetic Substances:** They get feebly magnetized in a powerful magnetic field, and are feebly attracted by powerful magnets.

   Example: Platinum, chromium, aluminium, etc.

3. **Ferromagnetic Substances:** They are easily magnetized by an external magnetic field and are strongly attracted by magnets. They are used to make artificial magnets.

   Example: Iron, nickel, cobalt, etc.

Molecular Theory

James Ewing proposed a molecular theory to explain the origin of magnetism and various magnetic phenomena. According to this theory molecules of all magnetic substances behave like tiny magnets known as **molecular magnets**, each having a north and south pole.

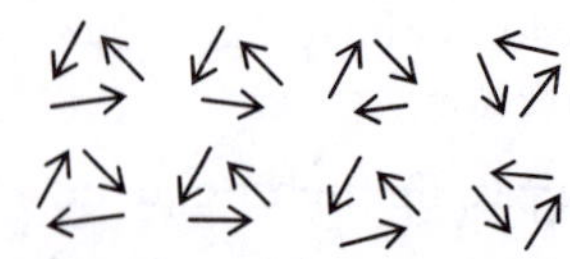

Figure 9.23 Molecular magnets in a demagnetized substance

Normally, in a magnetic substance such as a bar of soft iron, the molecular magnets are randomly oriented forming closed chains as shown in the Fig. 9.23 and 9.24. The magnetic fields of molecules cancel out each other and the net magnetic field due to the iron bar is zero.

When this iron bar is magnetized, molecules lose their random orientations and arrange themselves such that all the north poles point in one direction and south poles point in the opposite direction. The magnetic fields of all molecular magnets add giving the magnetized iron bar a net magnetic field.

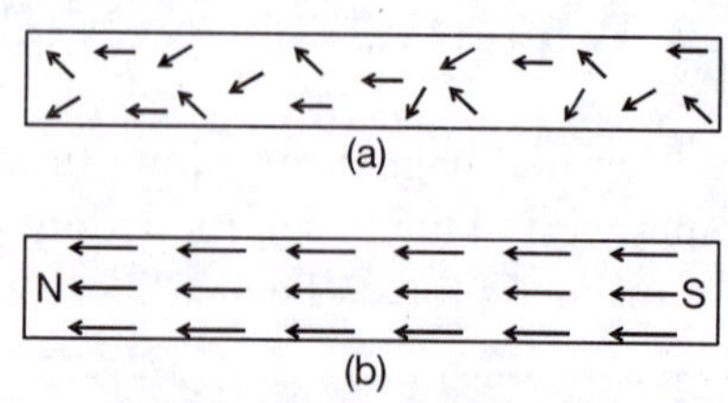

Figure 9.24 Orientation of molecular magnets in (a) Non-magnetized material and (b) Magnetic material

Following facts can be explained on the basis of Ewing's molecular theory.

1. When an iron piece is magnetized, the closed molecular chains break down and all molecules begin to align themselves in the direction of

the external magnetic field. As the magnetising field is increased, more molecular magnets align in the given orientation. Thus, magnetic strength of the iron piece increases with the increase in the strength of external magnetic field. When all molecules of the iron piece have aligned themselves there is no further increase in its magnetic strength even if the strength of external magnetic field is increased. This is called **saturation point**.

2. Molecular theory explains why each piece of a magnet cut into number of pieces has a north and south pole, i.e., each piece, however small, is a complete magnet.
3. It also explains how a magnet loses its magnetism when hammered, heated, handled roughly, etc. In all the cases, molecular magnets gain energy and their orderly alignment is disturbed. Hence, the magnet loses its magnetic properties.

Earth as a Magnet

A freely suspended magnet always points in the north–south direction. It means some force is acting on the magnet which keeps it in the north–south direction. This indicates that the earth acts like a huge magnet. North pole of a magnet points towards geographical north indicating the presence of magnetic south pole of the earth there. Similarly, the magnetic north pole of the earth is near the earth's geographic south pole, as the south pole of all magnets points towards geographic south. Thus, the earth behaves like a huge bar magnet with its south pole near its geographic north and vice versa.

The region where the effect of earth's magnetism is felt is called **earth's magnetic field**. An imaginary line joining the earth's geographic north and south poles is called **geographic axis**. An imaginary plane containing geographic north, south poles and a given place is called **geographic meridian** at the given place as shown in the figure 9.25.

An imaginary line joining the earth's magnetic north and south poles is called **magnetic axis**. The earth's magnetic axis makes an angle of about 17° with its geographic axis. An imaginary vertical plane passing through the given place and containing the earth's magnetic poles is called **magnetic meridian**.

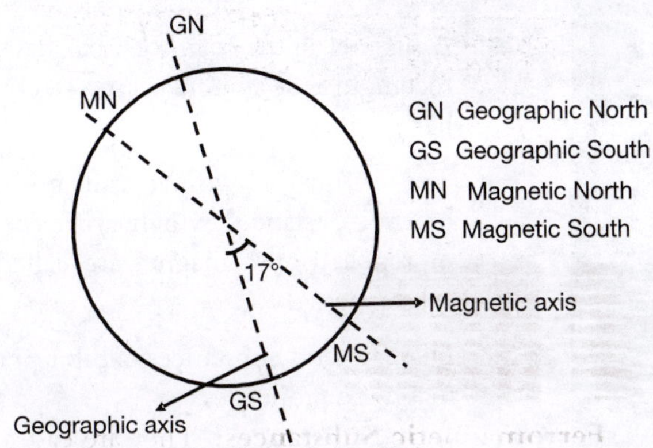

Figure 9.25 Magnetic and Geographic axis of Earth

Angle of Dip

At a given place, the earth's magnetic field can be resolved into horizontal and vertical components. The angle made by the earth's magnetic field with its horizontal component is called **angle of dip** or angle of inclination. It varies from place to place. Its value is zero at the magnetic equator and maximum, i.e., 90° at the earth's magnetic poles. The angle of dip at a given place can be measured with the help of a device called **dip circle**.

Angle of Declination

The angle between the earth's magnetic meridian and the geographic meridian at a given place is called **angle of declination**. It varies form place to place on the earth.

POINTS TO REMEMBER

- ✔ The physical properties that characterise a magnet are (i) attractive property, (ii) directive property (iii) law of magnetic poles and (iv) pair property.
- ✔ The space around a magnet where its influence can be felt is called magnetic field.
- ✔ Line of force is an imaginary line along which an isolated north pole kept in a magnetic field tends to move. Lines of force, more appropriately, are referred to as magnetic field lines.
- ✔ A magnet in the form of a bar having either a rectangular or a circular cross-section is called bar magnet.
- ✔ The substances which can be magnetized or the substances which are either attracted or repelled by a magnet are called magnetic substances.
- ✔ Diamagnetic Substances exhibit practically no magnetic properties.
- ✔ Paramagnetic Substances get feebly magnetized in a powerful magnetic field, and are feebly attracted by powerful magnets.
- ✔ Ferromagnetic Substances are easily magnetized by an external magnetic field and are strongly attracted by magnets.
- ✔ Like poles repel and unlike poles attract each other. This is called law of magnetic poles.
- ✔ The process used for destroying the magnetism (the magnetic properties) of a magnet is called demagnetization.
- ✔ The region where the effect of earth's magnetism is felt is called earth's magnetic field.
- ✔ An imaginary line joining the earth's geographic north and south poles is called geographic axis. An imaginary plane containing geographic north, south poles and a given place is called geographic meridian at the given place.
- ✔ An imaginary line joining the earth's magnetic north and south poles is called magnetic axis.
- ✔ An imaginary vertical plane passing through the given place and containing the earth's magnetic poles is called magnetic meridian.
- ✔ The angle made by the earth's magnetic field with its horizontal component is called angle of dip or angle of inclination.
- ✔ The angle of dip at a given place can be measured with the help of a device called dip circle.
- ✔ The angle between the earth's magnetic meridian and the geographic meridian at a given place is called angle of declination.

CLASSROOM WING

PRACTICE QUESTIONS

Very Short Answer Type Questions

Directions for questions from 1 to 8:
Fill in the blanks.

1. A substance which is feebly repelled by a magnet is a __________.
2. The equatorial meridian of a magnet bisects the magnetic axis __________.
3. A substance placed near a strong magnet is attracted by it, the substance can be ________.
4. Diamagnetic substances are __________ by strong magnets.
5. When a magnet is broken into two parts, each part will have __________ poles.
6. When an iron bar is placed nearer to the north pole of a magnet the south poles of the molecular magnets in the iron bar point towards ________.
7. A freely suspended magnet aligns itself in __________ direction.
8. In the presence of a magnet, an iron bar acts as a magnet due to __________.

Directions for questions from 9 to 25:
Answer the following questions

9. What is magnetic induction?
10. What is a lodestone?
11. What is a magnetic meridian?
12. What is an artificial magnet?
13. What is the effective length of a bar magnet?
14. What is a magnetic pole?
15. From the figure given below, in which points is the net magnetic field induction zero?

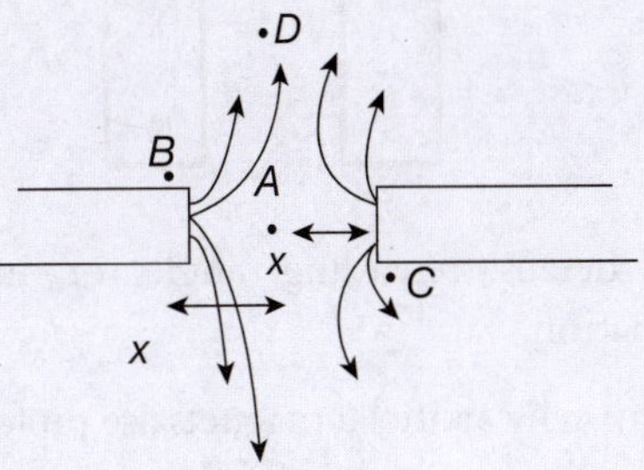

16. Which is more powerful between a bar magnet and a horseshoe magnet?
17. Which is more powerful between a magnetic compass needle and a bar magnet?
18. Is magnetic line of force a continuous curve?
19. What is the difference between magnetic axis and magnetic meridian?
20. In double touch method of magnetization, what is the polarity of the end of an iron bar at which the magnetizing magnet leaves?
21. Which property of a magnet is used to determine the polarity of the magnet?
22. What is meant by saturation point?
23. What happens when a magnet is broken into two parts?
24. On which factors does the magnetic induction depend?
25. What is meant by demagnetization?

Short Answer Type Questions

26. Write a short note on the earth's magnetic field.
27. Describe terrestrial magnetism.
28. Give two properties of lines of force.
29. How are the molecular magnets of a magnet affected, when the magnet is demagnetized?
30. Why can't lines of force intersect each other?

31. Draw the lines of force due to two bar magnets, north pole of one facing the south pole of the other.

32. Why does north pole of a magnet points toward geographical north?

33. Draw a neat diagram of lines of force around two bar magnets placed as shown in the figure.

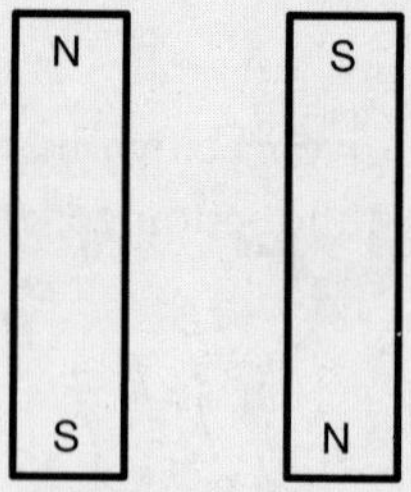

34. Give details regarding angle of inclination and declination.

35. Explain why artificial magnets are preferred to natural magnets.

36. How can a magnet be demagnetized?

37. Explain why ferromagnetic substances are used to make permanent magnets.

38. Why does the value of dip increase as we move from equator to pole?

39. Write a short note on magnetic keepers.

40. Magnetic induction precedes attraction. Explain.

41. Define equatorial line of a bar magnet.

42. What is meant by self induction?

43. What is a geographic meridian?

44. What is the difference between geographic axis and geographic meridian?

45. What happens to the orientations of the molecules of a magnetized iron bar?

Essay Answer Type Questions

46. What properties of magnetic substances are explained on the basis of molecular theory?

47. Draw the lines of force of a bar magnet neglecting the earth's magnetic field.

48. Describe the method to magnetize a steel rod by divided double touch method.

49. What are the properties of lines of force?

50. Draw the lines of force due to two bar magnets, the north pole of one facing the north pole of the other.

COMPETITION WING

PRACTICE QUESTIONS

Level 1: Apply your Concepts

Directions for questions 1 to 12:
State whether the following statements are true or false.

1. A substance which is feebly repelled by a magnet is a __________.
2. Opposite poles are induced in a magnet due to self induction.
3. An imaginary plane containing geographic north, south poles and a given place is called geographic meridian at the given place.
4. An imaginary line joining the earth's geographic east and south poles is called geographic axis.
5. The angle of declination is constant.
6. The earth can be considered as a huge bar magnet.
7. A magnetic compass does not show any particular direction at the magnetic poles.
8. In an electrical method of magnetization, a direct current is used.
9. The polarity of an electromagnet can be changed by changing the direction of electric current through the coil.
10. Cobalt is strongly attracted by a magnet.
11. Isolated north pole can be produced.
12. Natural magnets are stronger than artificial magnets.

Directions for questions 13 to 19:
Fill in the blanks.

13. Effective length of a magnet is __________ than its actual length.
14. In order to prevent loss of magnetism, __________ are used.
15. Magnetic lines of force are directed from __________ pole to __________ pole, in the magnetic field.
16. The space surrounding a magnet within which the effect of magnet is present is called __________.
17. The point beyond which a magnet cannot be magnetized any further is called ______.
18. The end of a freely suspended magnet which points to the magnetic north of earth is __________.
19. When a bar magnet is brought near an iron rod __________ precedes __________.

Directions for question 20:
Match the entries in Column A with the appropriate ones in Column B.

20.

Column A	Column B
A. Directive property	a. Horseshoe magnet
B. Attractive property	b. Magnetic flux
C. Natural magnet	c. Resultant magnetic field is zero
D. Artificial magnet	d. Study of earth's magnetic field
E. Permanent magnet	e. Repulsion
F. Temporary magnet	f. Lodestone
G. Sure test of magnetism	g. Mariner's compass
H. Magnetic lines of force passing perpendicular to a given area	h. Steel
I. Null points	i. Magnetic separation
J. Terrestrial magnetism	j. Soft iron

Directions for questions 21 to 48:

For each of the questions, four choices have been provided. Select the correct alternative.

21. Magnetic lines of force are
    (a) directed from the north pole to south pole in the magnetic field.
    (b) directed from the south pole to north pole inside a magnet.
    (c) closed loops.
    (d) All the above

22. In which of the following devices temporary magnets are used?
    (a) Dynamo
    (b) Electric motors
    (c) Generators
    (d) Electric cranes

23. Which of the following properties of a magnet is/are used in navigation?
    (a) Pair property
    (b) Laws of magnetic poles
    (c) Directional property
    (d) Attractive property

24. Choose the correct match

A. Ferromagnetic	(a) water
B. Diamagnetic	(b) cobalt
C. Paramagnetic	(c) chromium
(a) A–b, B–c, C–a	(b) A–c, B–a, C–b
(c) A–b, B–a, C–c	(d) A–a, B–c, C–b

25. The direction of magnetic field at any point inside the field is given by ______.
    (a) perpendicular to the line of force
    (b) tangent to the line of force
    (c) the line of force itself
    (d) None of the above

26. Which of the following is not a magnetic substance?
    (a) Cobalt (b) Iron
    (c) Copper (d) Nickel

27. When an iron bar is moved over a bar magnet along its length the attractive force ______.
    (a) increases first and then decreases
    (b) decreases first and then increases
    (c) remains same
    (d) increase

28. The attracting power of a magnet is
    (a) evenly distributed along its length.
    (b) maximum at its centre.
    (c) maximum at its poles.
    (d) minimum at its poles.

29. 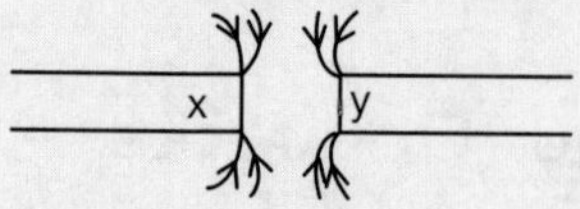

The above diagram is the pattern of magnetic lines of force obtained when two magnets are placed with their magnetic axes coinciding. The magnetic poles x and y are ______ and ______, respectively.
    (a) north, south (b) south, north
    (c) north, north (d) south, south

30. In the single touch method of magnetization, the north pole of a bar magnet is rubbed against a steel rod. Then the polarity of the end of the steel rod at which the magnet leaves
    (a) is the south.
    (b) is the north.
    (c) depends upon the material.
    (d) None of these

31. **Assertion (A):** Direct current (DC) and alternating current (AC) both are used for the electrical method of magnetisation.

    Reason (R): Direct current and alternating current produce a constant magnetic field.
    (a) A and R both are correct, and R is correct explanation of A.
    (b) A and R both are correct, and R is incorrect explanation of A.
    (c) A is correct but R is incorrect.
    (d) Both A and R are incorrect.

32. **Assertion (A):** Magnetic lines of force never intersect each other.

    Reason (R): If they intersect, there will be two directions for the magnetic field which is impossible.
    (a) A and R both are correct, and R is correct explanation of A.
    (b) A and R both are correct, and R is incorrect explanation of A.
    (c) A is correct but R is incorrect.
    (d) A is incorrect but R is correct.

33. **Assertion (A):** When an iron piece is magnetized, its length slightly increases.

Reason (R): The closed molecular chains break down and all molecules align themselves in the direction of an external magnetic field.

(a) A and R both are correct, and R is correct explanation of A.
(b) A and R both are correct, and R is incorrect explanation of A.
(c) A is correct but R is incorrect.
(d) A is incorrect but R is correct.

34. **Assertion (A):** Steel is used for making a permanent magnet.

Reason (R): Retentivity of steel is high.

(a) A and R both are correct, and R is correct explanation of A.
(b) A and R both are correct, and R is incorrect explanation of A.
(c) A is correct but R is incorrect.
(d) A is incorrect but R is correct.

35. A bar magnet is moved over a steel bar as shown in the figure below.

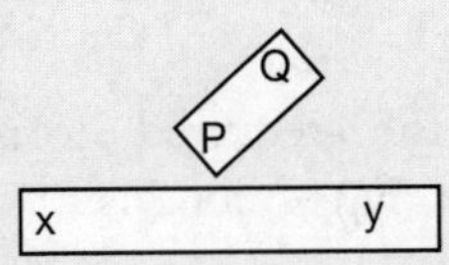

Choose the correct alternative from the following
(a) The end *x* becomes north pole if '*p*' is south pole when moved from the end *x* to *y*.
(b) the end *y* will become a south pole if *p* is a south pole and moved from the end *y* to *x*
(c) the end *x* will be a south pole if '*p*' is a south pole and moved from *x* to *y*
(d) Both (b) and (c)

36. When a magnet is broken into two parts,
(a) the bigger part acts like the north pole.
(b) the smaller part acts like the north pole.
(c) both the parts will have both the poles.
(d) polarity of each part depends upon the material.

37. In the electrical method of magnetization, the polarity of the end in which current flows in clockwise direction
(a) is the north pole.
(b) is the south pole.
(c) does not depend upon the direction of current flow.
(d) Cannot be determined.

38. An electric bell works on the principle of ________.
(a) magnetic induction
(b) attractive property of magnets
(c) electromagnetism
(d) All the above.

39. The angle of declination is ________.
(a) 90° at the poles
(b) 0° at the equator
(c) variable
(d) None of the above.

40. Ewing's molecular theory does not explain
(a) saturation point of magnetization.
(b) existence of two poles in a magnet.
(c) paramagnetism.
(d) None of the above.

41. Which of the following substances is repelled by strong magnet?

(a) Iron (b) Platinum
(c) Gold (d) Aluminium

42. In which of the following devices is a permanent magnet not used?

(a) Electric motor (b) Telegraph
(c) Generators (d) Particle accelerators

43. A substance placed near a strong magnet is attracted by it, the substance can be ________.
(a) a magnet
(b) paramagnetic substance
(c) ferromagnetic substance
(d) All the above.

44. In an unmagnetized iron bar, the molecules form:
(a) circular chains
(b) long straight chains
(c) closed chains
(d) opposite, parallel chains

45. Arrange the following statements in sequential order the process of plotting the lines of force around a bar magnet.

(A) Draw a line in the middle of a white paper fixed on a drawing board.

(B) Repeat the procedures described above, by shifting the compass and plot the points 2, 3, 4, etc.

(C) Place a bar magnet NS on the line so that its axial line coincides with the line on the paper and mark its boundary.

(D) Join the points 0, 1, 2, 3, ... by a smooth curve.

(E) Take a plotting compass and place it such that its south pole is directed towards point 0 at the edge of the bar magnet, and mark point 1 in the direction in which the north pole of the plotting compass points.

(a) A C E B D (b) A B C E D
(c) E B C A D (d) E A B C D

46. A bar magnet has a pole strength of 15 A m. If the distance from its centre to either of the poles is 15 cm, arrange the following steps in sequential order to find its magnetic moment in SI unit.

(A) Write the given value of pole strength (m) of the magnet.

(B) Substitute the values in the above formula to get the value of M.

(C) Find the value of length (ℓ) of the magnet from the problem and convert it into SI unit.

(D) Write the required formula, i.e., magnetic moment, (M) = $m \times 2\ell$.

(a) A C B D (b) C A B D
(c) A D C B (d) D B A C

47. Following are the steps to magnetize a steel bar. Arrange them in a sequential order.

(A) The end at which the current enters in an anti-clockwise direction will become the north pole and the other end will become the south pole.

(B) Keep the steel bar to be magnetized inside a long coil of insulated copper wire.

(C) Pass a strong direct current through the coil for some time.

(D) The specimen of the steel bar will get magnetized.

(a) ABCD (b) BCDA
(c) ACBD (d) DCBA

48. A bar magnet has a pole strength of 10 A-m. If the distance from its centre to either of the poles is 5 cm, arrange the following steps in sequential order to find its magnetic moment in the SI unit.

(A) Substitute the values in the above formula to get the value of M.

(B) Write the given value of pole strength (m) of the magnet.

(C) Find the value of the magnetic length (2ℓ) of the magnet from the problem and convert it into SI unit.

(D) Write the required formula, i.e., magnetic moment (M) = $mx\ 2l$

(a) BCAD (b) ABDC
(c) BCDA (d) ACDB

Level 2: Review your Concepts

49. In the figure shown below, if 'D' is a diamagnetic substance placed between two strong magnetic poles, map the magnetic lines of force.

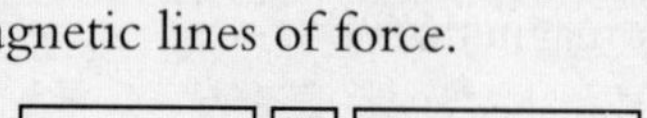

50. Explain why is it not possible to magnetize an iron rod beyond a certain limit?

51. Using a compass needle how would you distinguish between three bars similar in shape and appearance if one is brass, the second is an unmagnetized iron and the third is a permanent magnet?

52. Can we use a dip circle to identify the magnetic meridian of earth?

53. When an iron bar is magnetized, there will be a slight increase in its length. Explain.

54. Find the effective length of a bar magnet "A" of pole strength 5 A m and whose magnetic moment is twice the magnetic moment of another bar magnet "B" whose pole strength is 2 A m and effective length of 5 cm.

55. In which direction would a compass needle point when placed at the centre of the soft iron ring shown in the figure below? Substantiate your answer with reasons.

56. There are two identical bar magnets attached together as shown in the figure and suspended with the help of a thread. On being disturbed slightly, in which direction would the magnets point? Explain your answer.

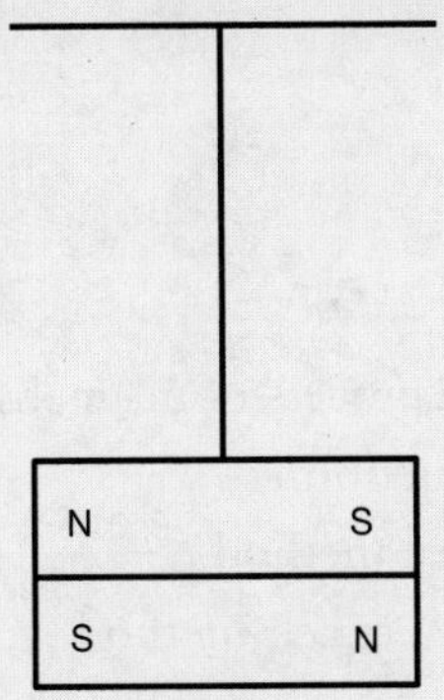

57. A bar magnet and a soft iron bar AB are placed close to each other as shown below.

Mark the polarity of induced magnetism in the soft iron bar with the help of lines of force. Explain by giving reasons for the polarity marked by you.

58. The angle between the geographical axis and the magnetic axis is 17°, then why does the value of angle of declination change from place to place?

59. A bar magnet of effective length 20 cm and pole strength of 12 A m is cut into 12 equal parts by cutting 4 equal parts parallel to axial line and 3 equal parts parallel to equatorial line. Then what is the relation between the magnetic moment of original magnet to that of each piece?

60. If a traveller using a compass needle follows the direction of the magnetic needle, would he be able to reach the geographic north pole? Explain in detail.

61. Explain why isolated magnetic poles do not exist?

62. In the following diagram if '*x*' is a neutral point, identify the magnetic poles A and B. Explain your answer.

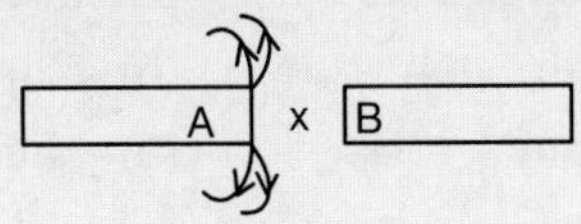

63. Explain the principle behind Maglev trains.

64. Where do we get neutral or null points when two bar magnets are aligned coaxially, such that their like poles face each other?

65. Two identical bar magnets are taken and one is cut along the axial line and another is cut along the equatorial line. Will there be any difference in the number of iron filings attracted by each piece of the magnets. Explain.

66. Explain why 'magnetic field lines never intersect with each other'.

Level 3: Assess Your Concepts

67. Explain how a magnet gets demagnetized when an alternative current is passed through a coil in which the magnet is placed.

68. If the length of a bar magnet is 4 cm and its pole strength is 20 A m, then what is the magnetic moment of the bar magnet?

69. How can the earth be considered a magnet when the exact cause for its magnetism cannot be ascertained?

70. An unmagnetized steel bar buried in earth in the north–south direction would, after a few days, exhibit magnetic properties, making it a weak magnet. Explain by giving reasons how this is possible. In what way will the effect be different if the steel bar is to be placed above the surface of earth?

71. How would mapping of the lines of force differ in two bar magnets of unequal pole strength? On the basis of this concept, explain the statement 'Magnetic induction is directly proportional to the strength of the inducing magnet'.

72. If the magnetic moment of a bar magnet is 4 A m^2, and its pole strength is 10 A m, then what is the magnetic length of the bar magnet?

JEE-NEET SPECIAL WING

PRACTICE QUESTIONS

Multiple-Answer Type Questions

Directions for questions 1 to 5:

Select one or more correct alternative(s) from the given choices.

1. Which among them is not a paramagnetic substance?
(a) Platinum (b) Chromium
(c) Antimony (d) Nickel

2. The angle of dip at the magnetic equator and magnetic poles are
(a) At magnetic equator, $\theta = 0°$
(b) At magnetic equator, $\theta = 90°$
(c) At magnetic poles, $\theta = 0°$
(d) At magnetic poles, $\theta = 90°$

3. Identify the process of magnetisation
(a) Self induction
(b) Electrical method
(c) Double - touch method
(d) Heating of the magnet

4. The magnet which loses its magnetism once the current stops flowing through it, is
(a) Temporary magnet. (b) Permanent magnet.
(c) Electromagnet. (d) Bar magnet.

5. Which are the factors affecting magnetic induction?
(a) Strength of magnet
(b) Distance between magnet and magnetic substance
(c) Nature of magnetic substance
(d) Magnetic meridian

Comprehension-Based Questions

Directions for questions 6 to 10:

These questions are based on the following information.

Magnetic Field Lines:
Magnetic field is the area around a magnet in which its influence is experienced. Magnetic field lines are imaginary lines used to represent magnetic field. These depict the strength and direction of magnetic field. The magnitude of magnetic field is indicated by its density and direction is taken to the direction in which a north pole of a compass needle moves inside it.

6. A student tried to plot the magnetic field lines around a magnet and couldn't trace it correctly. Given below are the order in which the student performed the task. Help the student by correcting the order of the steps to plot the field lines.
A. Take a compass and place such that the South pole is directed towards point zero at the edge of the magnet and mark 1 in the direction in which the North pole points.
B. Place a magnet NS on a line such that the axial line coincides with the line on paper and marks its boundary.
C. Repeat procedure, by shifting compass and plot the points 2, 3, 4, etc.
D. Draw a line in the middle of a white paper fixed on a drawing board.
E. Joint the points 0, 1, 2, 3,...... by a smooth curve.
(a) A, C, D, B, E (b) D, B, A, C, E
(c) B, C, A, D, B (d) D, B, C, A, E

7. The number of magnetic field lines passing perpendicularly through a certain area gives
(a) Magnetic meridian (b) Magnetic dip
(c) Magnetic flux (d) Magnetic strength

8. Pick out the patterns of lines of force due to two bar magnets with opposite poles facing each other.
(a)

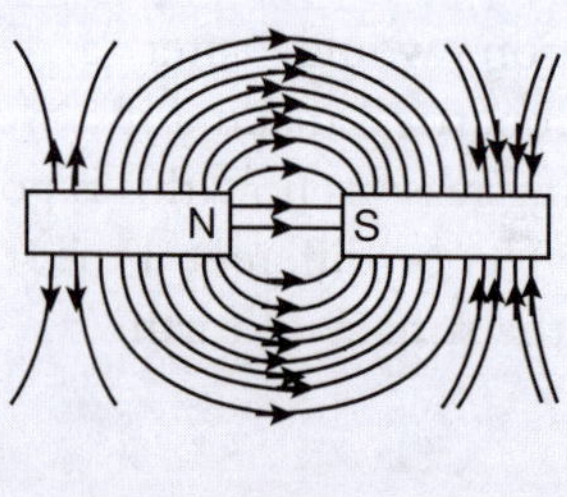

(b)

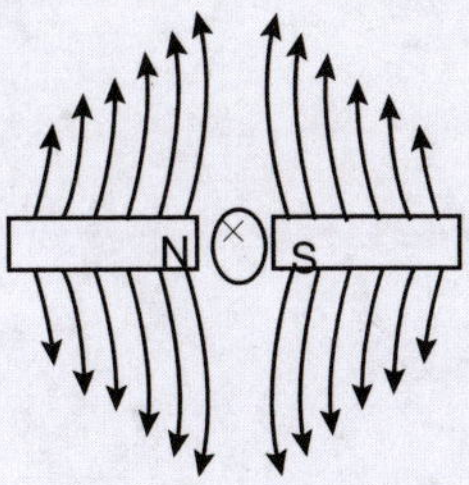

(c)

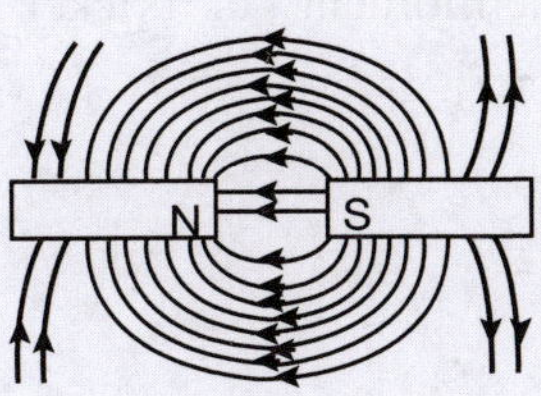

(d)

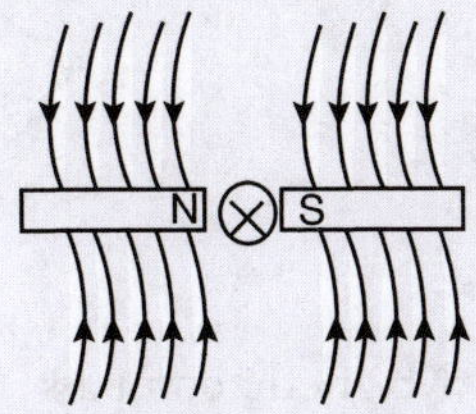

9. At neutral point the resulting magnetic field is

(a) maximum (b) minimum

(c) infinity (d) zero

10. Inside the magnet, the lines of force

(a) Move from South pole to North pole

(b) Move from North pole to South pole

(c) No field lines inside the magnet.

(d) Cannot be determined

Match the Column

Directions for question 11:

The question is based on the following information.

Magnets:

A magnet is a material which produces its own magnetic field around it. All magnets have two poles - a north pole and a south pole. There are natural magnets which occur naturally that have the property of attracting magnetic materials. Lodestone is a natural magnet. On the other hand, magnets are made from iron in different shapes and sizes based on its uses and are called artificial magnets.

11. Match the values in List - I with those in List - II:

List - I	List - II
A. Bar magnet	a. 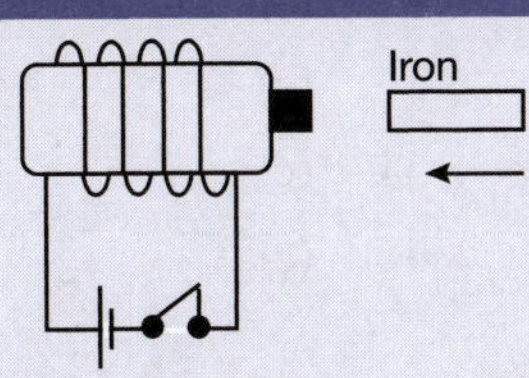
B. Horseshoe magnet	b. 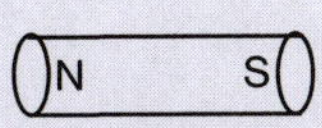
C. Magnetic needle	c. 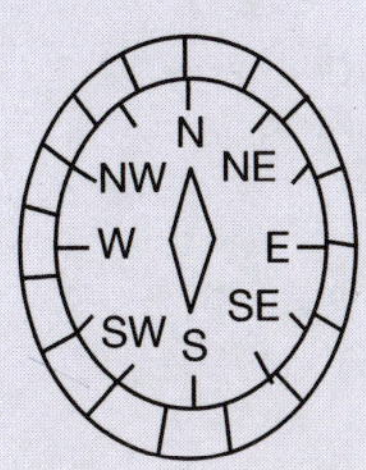
D. Magnetic compass	d. 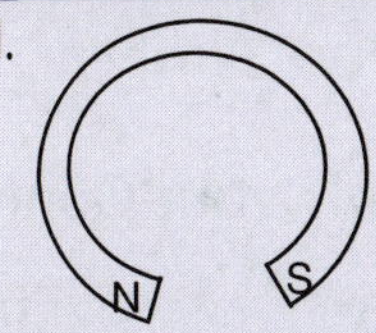
E. Electromagnet	e. 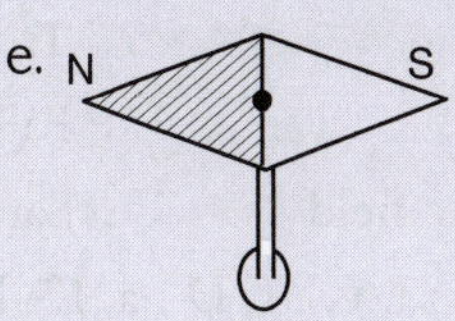

(a) A - b, B - c, C - a, D - d, E - e

(b) A - c, B - b, C - e, D - a, E - d

(c) A - b, B - d, C - e, D - c, E - a

(d) A - d, B - c, C - b, D - e, E - a

ANSWER KEYS

Crossword

Across

1. Ampere meter 8. Magnetic compass 9. Water

Down

2. Magnetic poles 3. Effective length 4. Permanent 5. Magnetic moment 6. Nickel
7. Magnetic poles

Classroom Wing

Very Short Answer Type Questions

1. Diamagnetic substance 2. Perpendicularly
3. A magnet, paramagnetic substance and ferromagnetic substance 4. Repelled
5. Both the parts will have both north and south poles. 6. North pole 7. North–south
8. Magnetic induction 15. point A

Competition Wing

Level 1: Apply your Concepts

1. False 2. True 3. True 4. False 5. False
6. True 7. True 8. True 9. True 10. True
11. False 12. False 13. Less 14. Magnetic keepers 15. North, south
16. Magnetic field 17. Saturation 18. South pole 19. Induction, attraction
20. A : g, B : i, C : f, D : a, E : h, F : j, G : e, H : b, I : c, J : d 21. (d) 22. (d)
23. (c) 24. (c) 25. (b) 26. (c) 27. (b)
28. (c) 29. (d) 30. (a) 31. (a) 32. (a)
33. (a) 34. (a) 35. (d) 36. (c) 37. (b)
38. (d) 39. (c) 40. (c) 41. (c) 42. (b)
43. (d) 44. (c) 45. (a) 46. (c) 47. (b)
48. (c)

Level 2: Review your Concepts

54. 4 cm 59. $\frac{12}{1}$

Level 3: Assess Your Concepts

68. 1.6 A m^2 72. 20 cm

JEE-NEET Special Wing

Multiple-Answer Type Questions

1. (c) and (d)
2. (a) and (d)
3. (b) and (c)
4. (a) and (c)
5. (a), (b) and (c)

Comprehension-Based Questions

6. (b)
7. (c)
8. (a)
9. (d)
10. (a)

Match the Column

11. (c)

For complete answer key of Classroom wing and Competition wing, refer to Hints and Solutions

Hints and Explanations

Classroom Wing

Very Short Answer Type Questions

1. A substance which is feebly repelled by a magnet is a diamagnetic substance.
2. The equatorial meridian of a magnet bisects the magnetic axis perpendicularly.
3. A magnet, paramagnetic substance and ferromagnetic substance
4. Repelled
5. Both the parts will have both north and south poles.
6. North pole
7. North–south
8. Magnetic induction
9. The process in which a magnetic substance becomes a magnet when it is kept near a magnet without there being physical contact between them, is called magnetic induction.
10. Lodestone is a natural magnet.
11. An imaginary vertical plane passing through a given place containing the earth's magnetic poles is called the magnetic meridian.
12. Man made magnets.
13. The distance between the north pole and south pole of the magnet is called effective length of the magnet.
14. The points near the ends of a magnet where attractive property is maximum are called poles.
15. Net magnetic field induction is zero at point A. i.e., it is a neutral point.
16. Horseshoe magnet.
17. Bar magnet.
18. Yes.
19. An imaginary line joining the earth's magnetic north and south poles is called magnetic axis.

    An imaginary vertical plane passing through the given place and containing the earth's magnetic poles is called the magnetic meridian.
20. Polarity of the bar is opposite to that of magnetizing magnet.
21. Magnetic repulsion.
22. When all the molecules of the iron piece have aligned themselves there is no further increase in its magnetic strength even if the strength of the external field is increased.
23. When a magnet is broken into any number of parts, each part will have both poles.
24. Magnetic induction depends on the strength of the inducing magnet and the nature of the magnetic substance.
25. The process used for destroying the magnetism (magnetic properties) of a magnet.

Short Answer Type Questions

26. Huge bar magnet, geographic and magnetic axes, geographic and magnetic meridians, angle of dip, angle of declination.
27. Geographical north lies near the magnetic south pole of the earth, dip, declination, axis, equator.
28. (i) Closed, continuous curves.

    (ii) Two lines of force can never meet each other.
29. Molecular magnets gain energy and their orderly alignment is disturbed.
30. At a point, the resultant magnetic field has only one direction and line of force will be along that direction.
31. Lines originating from north pole of one magnet.
32. Unlike poles attract each other.
33. You must know about what is the direction of magnetic lines of force around a magnet in a magnetic field?

    Outside a magnet, lines of force are directed from north to south.
34. The angle made by the earth's magnetic field with its horizontal component is called the angle of dip or inclination.

The angle between the earth's magnetic meridian and the geographic meridian at a given place is called the angle of declination. Both the angle varies from place to place on the earth.

35. (i) To answer this, you must state the advantages of artificial magnets.

(ii) Also, if it possible to make a horseshoe magnet from a natural magnet?

Is it possible to obtain a strong magnet from a natural magnet?

36. By rough handling, passing high frequency electric current, heating and allowing it to cool by keeping it in east-west direction.

37. (i) You must compare the effect of an external magnetic field on dia, para and ferromagnetic substances.

(ii) Also, you must state the main difference between a ferromagnetic substance and other magnetic substances? (i.e., is the ability to retain magnetism the same for all substances?

Also, the reason for the molecular magnets of a ferromagnetic substance align themselves in the presence and in the absence of an external magnetic field?

38. The magnetic field is horizontal at equator and vertical at poles. Value of dip increases from 0° to 90° when we move from equator to poles.

39. Soft iron piece is kept between the poles of the magnet to prevent loss of magnetism. This soft iron piece is called a magnetic keeper.

40. When a magnet is brought near a magnetic substance, nearer end of the magnetic substance attains opposite polarity and then gets attracted towards the magnet.

41. An imaginary line passing through centre of the magnet and perpendicular to the magnetic axis.

42. Opposite poles are induced in a magnet due to self induction.

43. An imaginary plane containing geographic north, south poles and a given place is called geographic meridian at the given place.

44. An imaginary line joining the earth's geographic north and south poles is called geographic axis. An imaginary plane containing geographic north, south poles and a given place is called geographic meridian.

45. Molecules lose their random orientations.

Essay Answer Type Questions

Note: This is how you should frame your answer covering.

46. You must explain in detail why the poles exist in pairs.

47. Lines of force leave the north pole and enter the south pole. (Refer to text on page 9.6)

48. Detail the reasons why the magnetising magnets move in opposite direction.

49. You must discuss in detail the given properties: Originate, terminate, intersect, crowded.

50. You must draw a neat diagram showing the given points: Neutral point, lines of force.

Competition Wing

Level 1: Apply your Concepts

5. False, The angle of declination is variable.

10. True, As cobalt is a ferromagnetic substance, so it is strongly attracted toward magnets.

31. Only direct current is used for the electrical method of magnetization. Alternating current demagnetize the magnet.

    Hence, the correct answer is (a).

32. If magnetic field lines intersect at a point, then there will be two directions for a magnetic field at a point which is impossible.

    Hence, the correct answer is (a).

33. When an iron piece is magnetized, all the molecules align themselves in the direction of an external magnetic field by breaking their closed-molecular chains, therefore, its length slightly increases.

    Hence, the correct answer is (a).

34. Steel is used for making a permanent magnet since its retentivity is high.

    Hence, the correct answer is (a).

36. As per the pair property of magnets, when a magnet is broken into two parts, both the parts behave like two magnets with two poles.

    Hence, the correct answer is (c).

37. In the electrical method of magnetization, if the current flows in clockwise direction, then south pole is formed.

    Hence, the correct answer is (b).

38. The working of an electric bell involves magnetic induction, attractive property of magnets and electromagnetism.

    Hence, the correct answer is (d).

39. The angle of declination changes from place to place even along magnetic equator.

    Hence, the correct answer is (c).

40. Ewing's molecular theory was able to explain saturation point of magnetism and existence of two poles in a magnet. But it was not able to explain the difference between paramagnetic, diamagnetic and ferro magnetic substances.

    Hence, the correct answer is (c).

41. Gold is a diamagnetic substance and it is repelled by magnets.

    Hence, the correct answer is (c).

42. Permanent magnets are used in electric motor, generator and particle accelerator. An electromagnet, which is a temporary magnet, is used in telegraph system.

    Hence, the correct answer is (b).

43. A magnet, paramagnetic substance and a ferromagnetic substance are attracted by magnets.

    Hence, the correct answer is (d).

44. According to Ewing's molecular theory, in unmagnetized iron bar, the molecular magnets form closed chains.

    Hence, the correct answer is (c).

45. (a) Draw a line in the middle of a white paper fixed on a drawing board.

    (b) Place a bar magnet NS on the line such that its axial line coincides with the line on the paper and mark its boundary.

    (c) Take a plotting compass and place it such that its south pole is directed towards point 0 at the edge of the bar magnet and mark point 1 in the direction in which the north pole of the plotting compass points.

    (d) Repeat the procedures described above by shifting the compass and plot the points 2, 3, 4, etc.

    (e) Join the points 0, 1, 2, 3, ... by a smooth curve.

    Hence, the correct answer is (a).

46. (a) Write the given value of pole strength (m) of the magnet.

    (b) Write the required formula, ie magnetic moment (M) = $m \times 2\ell$.

    (c) Find the value of length (ℓ) of the magnet from the problem and convert it into SI unit.

    (d) Substitute the values in the above formula to get the value of M.

    Hence, the correct answer is (c).

47. (B) Keep the steel bar to be magnetized inside a long coil of insulated copper wire.

    (C) Pass a direct current through the coil for some time.

    (D) The specimen of the steel bar will get magnetized.

    (A) The end at which the current enters in an anti-clockwise direction will become the north pole and the other end becomes the South Pole.

    Hence, the correct answer is (b).

48. (B) Write the given value of pole strength '*m*' of the magnet.
(C) Find the value of length '*l*' of the magnet from the problem and convert it into SI unit.
(D) Write the required formula, magnetic moment (M) = $m \times 2l$
(A) Substitute the values in the above formula to get the value of M.

Hence, the correct answer is (c).

Level 2: Review your Concepts

Note: This is how you should frame your answer covering.

49. Is it possible to increase the strength of a magnet if the maximum number of molecular magnets are arranged in an orderly way?

50. What happens when a diamagnetic substance, a paramagnetic substance and a magnet are placed in an external magnetic field?

51. When a compass needle is brought near a bar of brass, it does not show any deflection as there is no attraction or repulsion. But, when the compass needle is brought near a unmagnetized iron, there will be an attraction for both the north and south poles due to induction. Finally, when the compass needle is brought near a permanent magnet, there will be an attraction when the unlike poles are near and there will be a repulsion when like poles are near.

52. Dip circle or inclinometer is an instrument for measuring the inclination or dip of the earth's magnetic field. If we position the instrument along the plane of the circle in the magnetic meridian of the earth, the needle points in the direction of earth's magnetic field (refer Page 9.12).

53. Will the molecular magnet align in the same direction when an iron bar is magnetized?

54. For magnet A:

Pole strength, $m_A = 5$ A m

Effective length, $2l_A = ?$

Magnetic moment, $M_A = 2l_A \times m_A$

For magnet B:

Pole strength, $m_B = 2$ A m

Effective length, $2l_B = 5 \text{ cm} = 5 \times 10^{-2}$ m

Magnetic moment, $M_B = 2l_B \times m_B$

$= 2 \text{ A m} \times 5 \times 10^{-2} \text{ m} = 0.1 \text{ A m}^2$

Given: $M_A = 2 M_B$

$\Rightarrow 2l_A\, m_A = 2 \times 2l_B\, m_B = 0.2 \text{ A m}^2$

$\Rightarrow 2l_A = 0.2/5 = 0.04 \text{ m} = 4 \text{ cm}$

55. (i) What is net magnetic field at the centre of the ring?
(ii) Compare the ability of soft iron to allow the magnetic lines of force to pass through it with that of air.

Which direction does a magnetic needle point in the absence of an external magnetic field?

56. (i) What factors affect the orientation of a bar magnet?
(ii) Find out the direction of magnetic fields due to each magnet.

What will the resultant magnetic field be?

Using the direction of resultant magnetic field, find the direction along which the magnet points.

57. Map the magnetic lines of force in the magnetic field of a bar magnet.

What is the direction of magnetic lines of force in the soft iron rod?

Identify the magnetic poles by using the directions of magnetic lines of force inside the iron bar.

58. Difference between geographical axis and geographical meridian. Difference between magnetic axis and magnetic meridian.

59. Let 2l and m be the effective length and pole strength of the given bar magnet.

Then its magnetic moment, M = 2l × m

Given, the bar magnet is cut into 12 equal parts, in a way that it was made 4 equal parts in a direction parallel to its axis and 3 equal parts in a direction parallel to its equatorial line.

Hence, the pole strength of the new piece will be m' = m/4

And, the new effective length of each piece, 2l' = 2l/3

Thus, the magnetic moment of each new piece,

$$M' = 2l' \times m' \frac{2l}{3} \times \frac{m}{4} = \frac{2lm}{12} = \frac{M}{12}$$

Hence, $\dfrac{M'}{M} = \dfrac{12}{1}$

60. The magnetic south of the earth is located nearer to the geographic north, and the magnetic north is nearer to the geographic south. So, a magnetic needle always points in geographic north-south directions, i.e., the magnetic north of the needle points towards the geographic north which is the magnetic south. Similarly,

the magnetic south of the needle points towards the geographic south which is the magnetic north. Therefore, if a traveller follows the direction shown by a magnetic needle, he would be able to reach the geographic north pole.

61. The smallest particle which can be obtained by dividing a magnet by physical process is a molecule.

62. (i) Definition of null point

(ii) The magnetic lines of force are directed from the north pole to south pole of a magnet. Null points are obtained when two magnetic fields cancel each other at a point.

63. What type of energy conversion takes places in a magnetic train?

How is the electrical energy converted into mechanical energy?

64. When two bar magnets are aligned coaxially, such that their like poles face each other, we get a null point on the axial line of the magnets in between the like poles. However, the position of the null point may not be exactly the mid-point of the line segment joining the centre of the two magnets. The position of the null point on the coaxial line depends on the relative magnetic moments of the two magnets. If M_1 and M_2 are the magnetic moments of the left and right magnets arranged coaxially as shown, then the null point will be exactly at the midpoint of the line joining the centres of the two magnets. If $M_1 > M_2$, then the null point will be closer to the second magnet on the axial line. If $M_1 < M_2$, then the null point will be closer to the first magnet on the axial line.

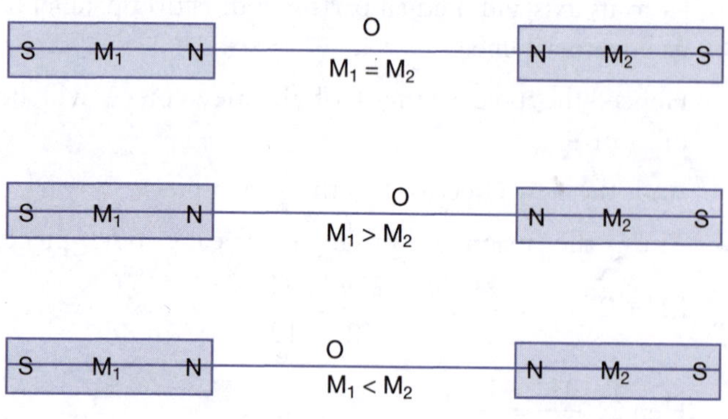

65. Pole strength decreases when the area of cross-section of the bar magnet is reduced and the crouding of iron pieces depends on the pole strength.

66. (i) What happens to the direction of magnetic field at a point if two magnetic lines of force intersect each other?

(ii) Will there be two directions for the magnetic field at such a given point?

Level 3: Assess Your Concepts

67. Alignment of the molecular magnet changes when an alternate current is passed through it.

68. Given length of the bar magnet, l = 4 cm.

∴ Effective length of the bar magnet,

2l = 8 cm = 0.08 m

Given pole strength of the bar magnet, m = 20 A m.

Magnetic moment of the bar magnet,

$M = 2l \times m = 0.08 \text{ m} \times 20 \text{ A m} = 1.6 \text{ A m}^2$.

69. Why does a freely suspended magnet lie in a particular direction if a strong magnet is fixed nearer to it?

70. What happens to an iron bar placed near a strong magnet?

Compare an iron bar placed in a strong magnetic field with an iron bar placed in a weak magnetic field.

71. Mapping of lines of force differ in the number of lines of force that are coming out or going into the magnetic poles of bar magnets. If the pole strength of the magnet is more then the number of lines of force will be more compared to a magnet whose pole strength is less. Since the lines of force interacting is more, the magnetism induced will be more.

72. Given, magnetic moment of the bar magnet, $M = 2l \times m = 4 \text{ A m}^2$, where 2l is the effective length and m is the pole strength

Pole strength, m = 10 A m

Therefore, $4 \text{ A m}^2 = 2l \times 10 \text{ A m}$

$\Rightarrow 2l = 0.4 \text{ m} = 40 \text{ cm}$

Hence, magnetic length of the bar magnet, l = ½ (2l) = ½ (40 cm) = 20 cm.

JEE-NEET Special Wing

Multiple-Answer Type Questions

1. Antimony is a diamagnetic substance and Nickel is a ferromagnetic substance.
Hence, the correct option is (c) and (d).

2. Knowledge based
Hence, the correct option is (a) and (d).

3. Self-induction and heating are processes used for destroying the magnetism of a magnet.
Hence, the correct option is (b) and (c).

4. The magnet which loses its magnetism once the current stops flowing through it, is
temporary magnet or electromagnet.
Hence, the correct option is (a) and (c).

5. A vertical plane passing through the magnetic axis of a freely suspended magnet is called magnetic meridian.
Hence, the correct option is (a), (b) and (c).

Comprehension-Based Questions

6. The correct order is D, B, A, C, E.
Hence, the correct option is (b).

7. The number of magnetic field lines passing perpendicularly through a certain area gives magnetic flux.
Hence, the correct option is (c).

8. Concept based
Hence, the correct option is (a).

9. At neutral point the resulting magnetic field is zero.
Hence, the correct option is (d).

10. Inside the magnet, the lines of force move from the South pole to the North pole.
Hence, the correct option is (a).

Match the Column

11. Choice (c) follows.
Some generally used artificial magnets are shown.
A - b, B - d, C - e, D - c, E - a

Electromagnetism

CHAPTER

10

Key Ideas

After completing this chapter, you should be able to:

- learn about the magnetic field produced due to straight conductor and circular conductor.
- understand Ampere's right-hand grip rule and Maxwell's right-hand rule.
- learn about electromagnets and their applications.
- discuss electromagnetic induction, direct current, alternating current and their applications.

Remember

Before beginning this chapter, you should be able to:

- define electricity, magnetism and terms related.
- discuss magnetic effects of electricity.
- understand magnetic field lines and their properties.

Scientific Crypt

A Tribute to Michael Faraday (1791-1867)

Michael Faraday was an English scientist who contributed to the study of electromagnetism and electrochemistry. His main discoveries include the principles underlying electromagnetic induction, diamagnetism and electrolysis. He was one of the most influential scientists in history. Faraday established the concept of the electromagnetic field in physics by his research on the magnetic field around a conductor carrying a direct current. His demonstrations established that a changing magnetic field produces an electric field; this relation was modelled mathematically by James Clerk Maxwell as Faraday's law, which subsequently became one of the four Maxwell equations. His inventions of electromagnetic rotary devices formed the foundation of electric motor technology, and it was largely due to his efforts that electricity became practical for use in technology. As a chemist, Faraday discovered benzene, investigated the clathrate hydrate of chlorine, invented an early form of the Bunsen burner and the system of oxidation numbers, and popularised terminology such as 'anode', 'cathode', 'electrode' and 'ion'. The SI unit of capacitance is named in his honour: the farad.

Crossword

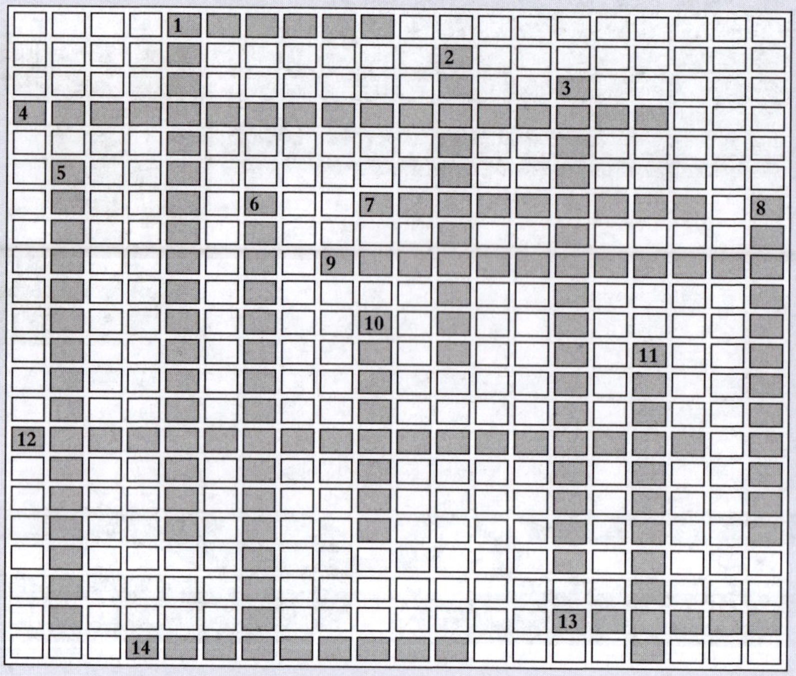

Across

1. A small generator used to light the lamp of a bicycle.
4. The orientation of iron filings in the magnetic field due to a straight current-carrying conductor.
7. Which property of magnetic field can be found using Ampere's swimming rule?
9. A device which converts electrical energy into sound energy.
12. The current produced by an electric generator.
13. The type of transformer that increases the voltage.
14. A current-carrying solenoid resembles.

Down

1. In Maxwell's right-handed corkscrew rule, the direction of motion of the screw gives.
2. The input coil in a transformer.
3. A device that converts mechanical energy into electrical energy.
5. A DC motor converts electrical energy into.
6. The basic principle involved in the telegraph system.
8. A device which is used to detect current in a circuit.
10. An insulated conducting wire wound around a cylindrical tube having a length greater than its diameter.
11. An electric device that steps-up or steps down the voltage in an electric energy distribution system.

INTRODUCTION

Before the 18th century, the subjects of electricity and magnetism were thought to be different and studied separately. The discovery of a link between the two subjects was accidental.

Magnetic Field

A German physicist Hans Christian Oersted was demonstrated to his students in his laboratory, that a magnetic needle placed near a conductor showed a deflection whenever an electric current was passed through the conductor.

Fig. 10.1(a) shows a magnetic compass placed below a straight conductor with the length of the wire along the north-south direction. The magnetic needle of the compass is also along the north-south direction as shown in Fig. 10.1(a). Now, if we pass some electric current through the conductor along south-north direction as shown in Fig. 10.1(b), the magnetic needle will be deflected towards west as shown in the figure.

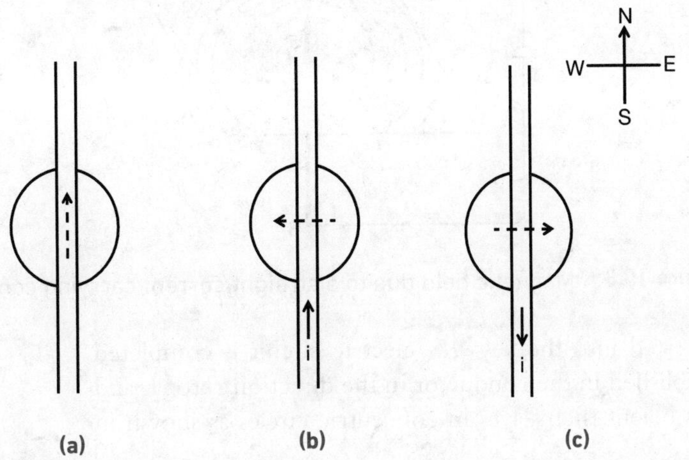

Figure 10.1 (a), (b) & (c) Showing the direction of current in the conductors and the deflection of magnetic needle in the compass

If the direction of the current is reversed and it is now allowed to pass through the conductor along north-south direction, then the deflection of the magnetic needle in the compass, placed below the conductor, is towards east as shown in Fig. 10.1(c). Deflection in the needle can also be observed, if the compass is placed above the conductor. If the length of the conductor is along the north-south direction, the compass is placed above the conductor and current is passed through the conductor in south-north direction then the deflection of the needle is towards east as shown in Fig. 10.2(a). If the direction of current is reversed and is allowed to flow through the conductor in north-south direction, then the deflection of the needle is towards the west as shown in Fig. 10.2(b).

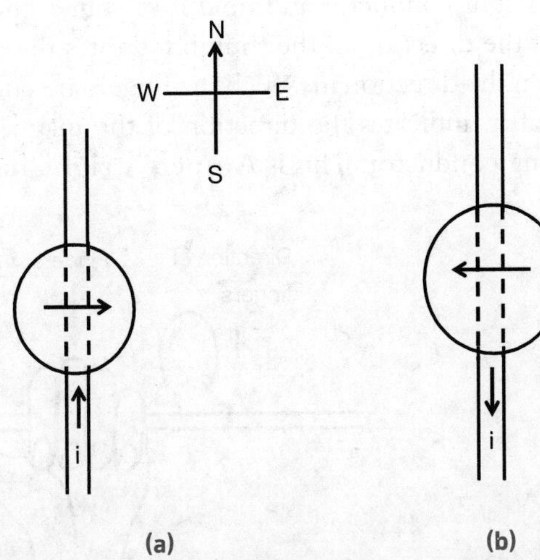

Figure 10.2 Showing the deflection of a magnetic needle placed

Consider a straight conducting wire carrying current. Place a small magnetic needle close to the current–carrying wire. In the absence of electric current the needle would orient itself in the north-south direction. But when a current flows through the wire, the needle would deflect. To know the direction of deflection, imagine a person swimming in the direction of the electric current and facing the magnetic needle. The needle would deflect in the direction of the swimmer's stretched left hand. This is referred to as **'Ampere's Swimming Rule'**.

Konnect

The Ampere's swimming rule helps in finding the direction of deflection of the magnetic needle.

A Demonstration to Show Magnetic Field Due to Straight Conductor

Take a plane rectangular card board. Stick a white paper to it. Make a small hole at its centre. Hold the cardboard in a horizontal position and pass a straight conductor '*AB*' through the hole at its centre such that the length of *AB* is perpendicular to the plane of the cardboard. Sprinkle some iron fillings on the cardboard. Connect the ends of the conductor (*A* and *B*) to a source of electricity like a cell through a plug key '*K*' as shown in the Fig. 10.3.

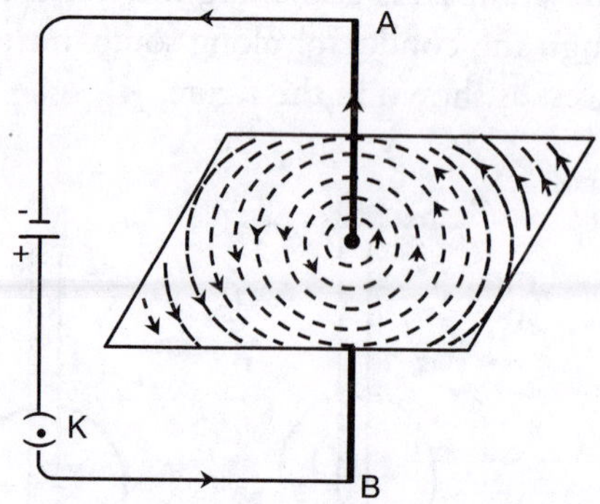

Figure 10.3 Magnetic field due to a straight current carrying conductor

As soon as the plug is inserted into the key '*K*', electric circuit is completed and an electric current is established in the conductor in the direction *B* to *A*, and immediately, the iron fillings orient themselves in concentric circles as shown in Fig. 10.3.

Info Bytes!

The direction of the magnetic field due to the current in the conductor is given by either Ampere's right hand grip rule or the Maxwell's right handed cork-screw rule.

Ampere's Right-hand Grip Rule

Take a long straight conductor and hold it in your right hand as a grip, as shown in Fig. 10.4. If the direction of the thumb indicates the direction of current in the conductor, then the direction in which the fingers are curled around the conductor to have grip of it, indicates the direction of the magnetic field produced by the current carrying conductor. This is **Ampere's right-hand grip rule**.

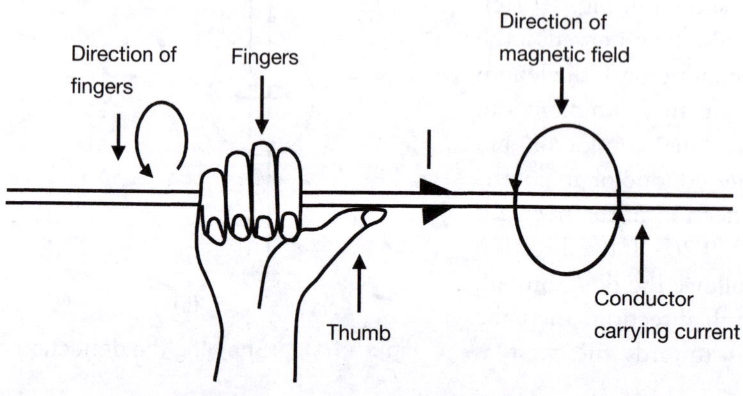

Figure 10.4 Ampere's right-hand grip rule

Maxwell's Right-handed Cork-Screw Rule

Consider a right-handed screw as shown in the figure 10.5. As observed from the top surface of the head of the screw, if the screw is rotated in the clockwise direction, it advances forward into a cork. If a straight conductor is taken with its length parallel to the axis of the screw, and if the direction of advancement of the screw indicates the direction of flow of current in the conductor, then, the direction in which the screw is rotated for its advancement indicates the direction of the magnetic field produced by the current carrying conductor. This is known as **Maxwell's right-handed cork-screw rule**.

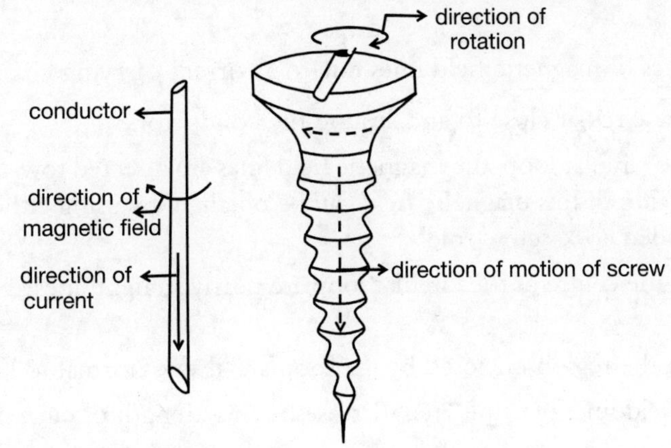

Figure 10.5 Maxwell's right-hand cork screw rule

The following are the properties of magnetic lines of force due to a straight current carrying conductor:

1. The magnetic lines of force are in the form of concentric circles with their centre at the centre or axis of the current carrying conductor.
2. The plane containing the lines of force around a straight current carrying conductor is perpendicular to the length of the conductor.
3. Within a given radius, in a plane perpendicular to the length of the conductor, the number of lines of force increase with an increase in the strength of the current in the conductor.
4. Assuming that the length of the conductor is normal to the plane of this page, the direction of magnetic field lines is in the anti-clockwise direction and in the plane of the page if the current in the conductor is flowing in a direction out of the page. If the direction of current is reversed, i.e., the current is flowing in a direction into the page, the direction of magnetic field lines is in the clockwise direction and in the plane of the page.

Konnect

A magnetic field can be understood by the field lines or the magnetic lines of force.

A Demonstration to Show Magnetic Field Due to A Circular Conductor

Take a rectangular cardboard *ABCD*. Place it horizontally and paste a white sheet to the board such that the plane having white sheet faces upwards. Make two holes on the board at *Q* and *S*, pass a circular loop *PQRST* through the two holes of the board and connect the terminals of the loop to an electric cell via a plug key '*K*'. Sprinkle some iron filings on the cardboard. Now insert the key in the plug to close the circuit. As soon as the circuit is closed as shown in figure we observe that the iron filings rearrange themselves in concentric circles as shown in Fig. 10.6.

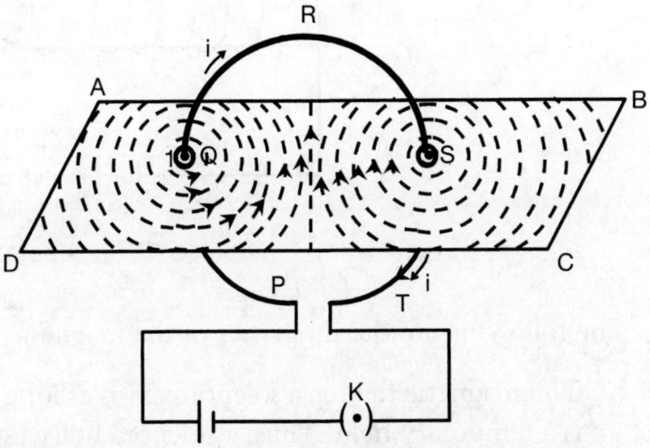

Figure 10.6 Direction of lines of force due to a circular current carrying conductor

The current in the circular loop flows along *PQRST* direction. Looking towards the loop from the edge *DC* of the cardboard, the current flows in clockwise direction. If a small magnetic needle is kept on the board between the holes Q and S, the needle points north towards the edge *AB* of the cardboard. This implies that the current carrying circular loop acts as a magnet with its north pole towards edge *AB* of the cardboard and a south pole towards the edge *DC* of the cardboard. If we observe the loop from the edge *AB* of the cardboard, we see that the current in the circular loop is in the anti-clockwise direction. Hence, for a circular conductor carrying some electric current a magnetic north pole is formed on that side of the conductor from where the direction of current in the conductor appears to be in anti-clockwise direction and a magnetic south pole is formed on the side from where, the direction of current in the conductor appears to be in clockwise direction.

The following are the properties of magnetic field lines due to a current carrying circular loop or coil:

1. The magnetic field lines are circular close to and around the conductor.
2. In the space enclosed by the circular loop, the magnetic field lines are directed towards the side where a net magnetic north is formed. The direction of this magnetic field can be obtained by using either Ampere's right hand grip rule or the Maxwell's right-handed cork-screw rule.
3. The magnetic field lines at the centre of the circular loop are nearly straight lines and are parallel forming a uniform magnetic field.
4. The magnetic field lines in the region enclosed by the loop are always normal to the plane of the loop.
5. The number of magnetic field lines per unit area increases as the strength of current in the loop increases.

Solenoid

We have just seen how a current carrying loop behaves like a magnet. Now, take certain length of conducting wire and wind it around a plastic tube having a uniform diameter.

Connect the two terminals of the wire (now in the form of a coil) to the terminals of a battery via a plug key as shown in Fig. 10.7. Now the coil conducting electric current acts like a magnet with the end *P*, where the current is in anti-clockwise direction, as the north pole and the end Q, where the current is in the clockwise direction as the south pole. This kind of coil made of an insulated conducting wire, wound around a cylindrical tube having length greater than its diameter and behaving like a magnet when an electric current flows through it is known as a **'solenoid'**. Each circular loop of the solenoid acts like a tiny magnet with north and south poles formed, adjacent to each other as shown in Fig. 10.7. As a result, a net south pole and a net north pole are formed at the two ends of the solenoid.

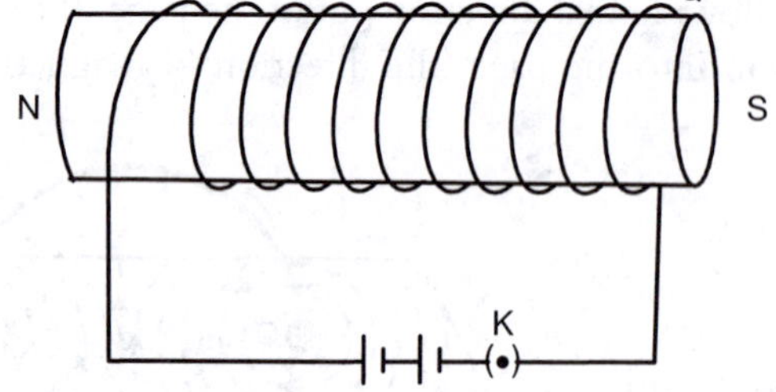

Figure 10.7 A solenoid

Konnect

A solenoid can be used to convert electrical energy into mechanical energy, often used in things like door locks and valves.

The following are the properties of the magnetic field set up in a solenoid:

1. The magnetic field in a solenoid exists as long as there is electric current in the solenoid. Hence, this magnetic field is a temporary field. Thus, a solenoid behaves like temporary magnet.
2. The strength of the magnetic field in the solenoid depends on the strength of the current in the coil. Higher the magnitude of the current in the coil, stronger is the magnetic field in the solenoid.

3. The magnetic field within the region of the solenoid is formed with magnetic field lines parallel to each other.
4. The magnetic field within the solenoid is always normal to the plane of the loops of the coil or it is along the axis of the cylinder.
5. The strength of the magnetic field also depends on the nature of the material on which the coil is wound. The magnetic field is maximum when the coil is wound around a soft iron core.
6. A solenoid with a soft iron core constitutes an **electromagnet**. It is a temporary magnet and its magnetism lasts as long as the electric current exists in it.

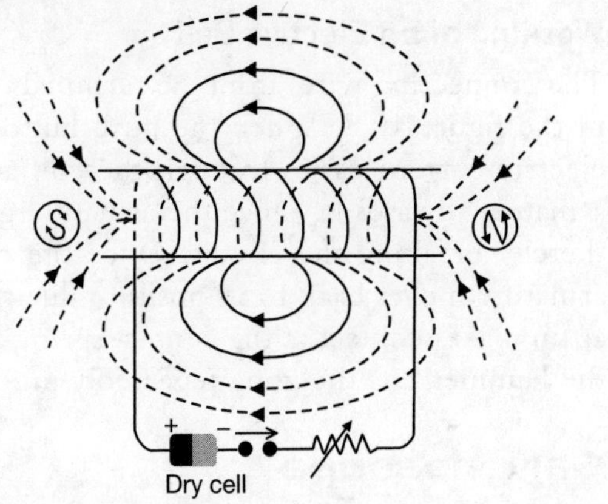

Figure 10.8 Magnetic field lines in a solenoid

Applications of Electromagnets

There are many applications of electromagnets. Some of them are as follows:

1. Electromagnets are used in electrical appliances like, electric bells, fans, motors, etc.
2. Electromagnets are used in electric generators where strong magnetic fields are required.
3. They are used in devices like picture tubes of televisions to produce deflection of electron beams.
4. They are used to separate magnetic ores like iron ore from other substances.
5. They are used in preparation of strong permanent magnets.
6. Electromagnets are also used in the field of medicine for diagnosis and treatment of certain diseases.

Electric Bell

An electric bell works on the principle of an electromagnetism. It consists of the following essential parts.

1. **Electromagnet:** A U-shaped rod made of soft iron with each of its arms mounted on a wooden reel is taken. An insulated copper wire is wound around each wooden reel to make the electromagnet. One end of the wire of the electromagnet is connected to the terminal 'T_1' and the other end is connected to the brass stud 'S'.
2. **Armature:** It is a soft iron bar fixed to the stud 'S' as shown in the figure. To this armature a steel hammer is attached which helps in striking the gong of the bell.
3. **Contact Spring:** To the other side of the armature, a steel strip is attached which acts as a spring and is used to make contact with the contact screw. The contact points are made of silver-cadmium alloy, which do not get oxidized easily due to sparking.
4. **Contact Screw:** The contact screw is made of brass material. The adjustment of the screw with the spring of the armature alters the frequency of ringing of the bell. The conducting wire from the contact screw is connected to terminal 'T_2' of the circuit.

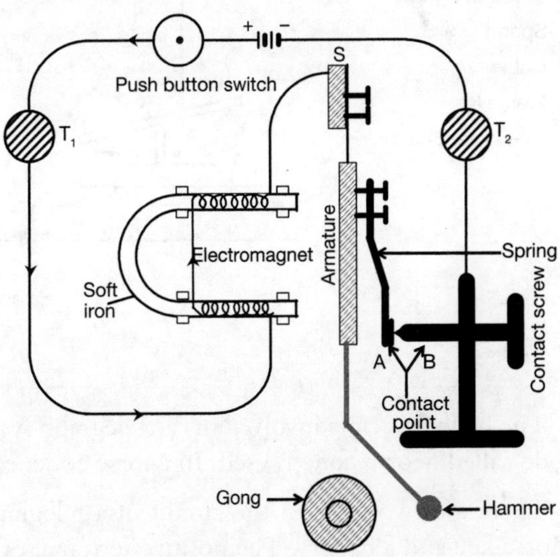

Figure 10.9 An Electric bell

Working of an Electric Bell

The connecting wires from the terminals T_1 and T_2 are connected to a battery via a push button switch as shown in the figure 10.8. When the push button is pressed, the circuit is closed and current passes through it. When electric current passes through the coil around the U-shaped soft iron core, it acts like magnet and attracts the armature towards it. Once the armature gets attracted towards the magnet, it breaks contact at the contact screw thereby breaking the circuit. Once the circuit is broken, the electromagnet loses its magnetism, and then the armature moves back to its position due to its spring action. Once the armature moves to its original position, it again makes contact at the contact spring and again conducts current. Thus, the armature oscillates to and fro and the hammer hits the gong repeatedly producing the ringing sound.

Galvanoscope

It is a device which is used to detect current in a circuit. It consists of a magnetic compass in which a small magnetic needle, pivoted at the centre is enclosed in a brass box with glass top. When a magnetic needle is kept near a current carrying conductor, it deflects. The working of a galvanoscope is based on this property.

When in use, the two terminals or ends of an insulated copper wire which is wound over the box are connected in a circuit (as shown in the figure 10.10). If current flows through the circuit, the needle deflects. Thus, the galvanoscope is used to detect current in a circuit.

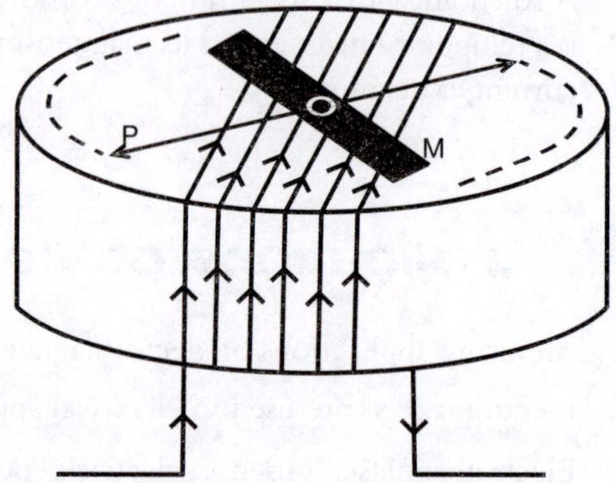

Figure 10.10 Galvanoscope showed by 'M' and Magnetic needle by 'P pointer'

Telegraph

It is one of the oldest (primitive) instruments used in the field of communication. It is used to send messages to distant places in a short time in the form of electric pulses through conducting wires. The circuit of a telegraph is as shown in the figure below:

A -Sender
B -Receiver
M -Electromagnet
S -Spring
C -Cable
K -Morse Key
k_1, k_2 -Contact Keys

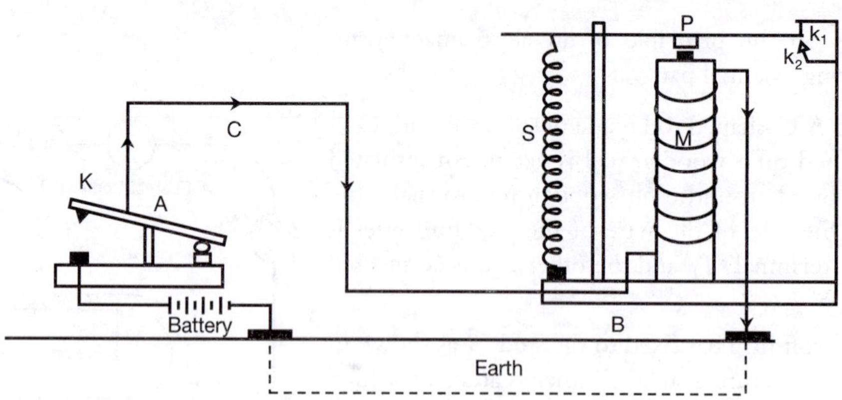

Figure 10.11 Telegraph

The basic principle involved in the telegraph system is electromagnetism. In communication through telegraph a special code called Morse code is used. In Morse code, each letter is represented by a group of dots and lines.

There are two parts in the circuit of a telegraph. One part is at the sender who sends a message. This consists of a Morse key and a battery. The positive terminal of the battery is connected to the Morse key and its negative terminal to earth. The other part of the circuit is at the receiver who receives the message. The receiver part of the circuit consists of an electromagnet (*M*), an armature (*P*) and a contact rod (k_1). The armature is supported by a vertical rod and a spring (*S*). The conducting wire wound around the electromagnet is connected to the earth (as shown in the above figure).

When the Morse key is pressed the conducting wire connected from the key to the electro-magnet conducts electricity and activates the electromagnet. Thus, the armature is attracted towards the electromagnet and thus it produces a 'click' sound on striking the rod 'k_2'. Once the Morse key is released, the circuit is broken and thus the armature moves to its original position, striking the rod 'k_1'. The contact time of the armature with 'k_2' is considered. If the contact time is short it is referred to as a dot, and if the contact time is more it is referred to as a line. Thus, by making and breaking the circuit using the Morse key, a series of dots and lines are transmitted to the receiver and thus message is transmitted using Morse code.

The main disadvantage of this telegraph is that a conducting wire connecting the sender and the receiver is compulsory and one has to learn the Morse code for decoding the messages received. The second disadvantage is that the mode of communication is only one way. If the receiver has to send a reply to the sender, he cannot do it with the same device. He has to employ one more telegraph instrument. This method of sending messages is not possible between two places where the two cannot be connected by a conducting wire.

Direct Current (D.C.) Motor

A DC motor is a device that converts electrical energy into mechanical energy. The schematic figure of a D.C. motor is as shown in Fig. 10.12. It consists of a coil ABCD wound around a soft iron core with a shaft at its centre. The length of the coil is parallel to the axis of the shaft. The ends of the coil are connected to two split rings S_1 and S_2. The split rings S_1 and S_2 are connected to the external circuit through the carbon brushes B_1 and B_2, respectively. The coil is placed in an external magnetic field that consists of concave shaped poles. In the external circuit we have a battery and a switch as shown in the figure below.

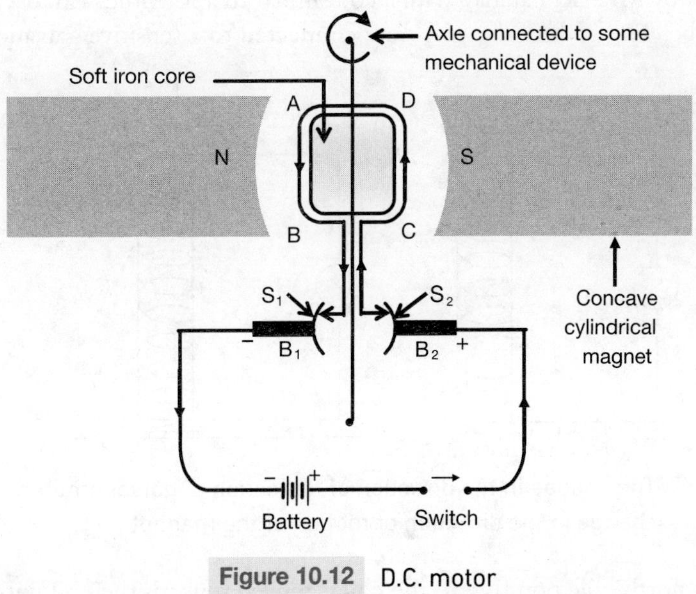

Figure 10.12 D.C. motor

When the circuit is switched on, electric current passes through the coil along CDAB and this produces a magnetic field. The electromagnetic field thus produced is superposed with the external magnetic field and thus the coil rotates such that the north pole of the electromagnet faces towards the south pole of the external magnetic field. When this happens, the slip rings S_1 and S_2 interchange their connections with brushes B_1 and B_2 and due to this the current in the coil now passes along $BADC$. This continues to produce turning effect in the coil in one direction. Along with the coil, the shaft also rotates and thus, electrical energy is transformed into mechanical energy. The speed of rotation of the coil, or the number of revolutions per minute (rpm) of the coil depends on the strength of the external magnetic field, the current in the coil and the number of turnings in the coil.

Electromagnetic Induction

So far, we have discussed about the magnetic effect of electricity and its applications, where basically a current carrying conductor produces a magnetic field around it. Alternately, it was found that when there is a relative motion between a magnet and a conductor, an electric current is induced in the conductor. This phenomenon is known as **electromagnetic induction**. The phenomenon is more clearly understood by the following demonstration.

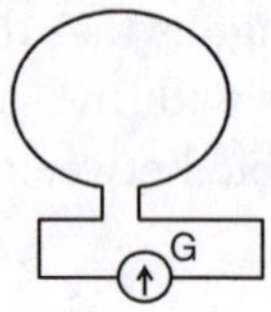

Figure 10.13 Zero Induced EMF

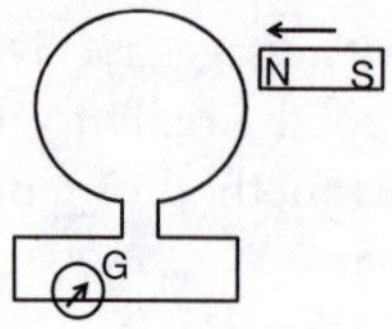

Figure 10.14 Increase in induced emf due to increase in magnetic flux

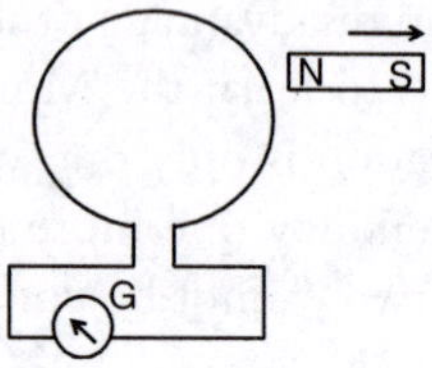

Figure 10.15 Increase in induced emf due to decrease in magnetic flux

Take a circular conductor connected to the terminals of a galvanometer as shown in the Fig. 10.13. Take a bar magnet and move the magnet towards the coil in a direction perpendicular to the plane of the coil as shown in Fig. 10.14. While the magnet is moving towards the coil, the galvanometer shows a deflection indicating that there exists an electric current in it. The deflection is zero when the magnet is brought near the coil and remains stationary. While the magnet recedes from the coil, the deflection in the galvanometer is in opposite direction to that in the previous case, as shown in the Fig. 10.15. Thus, the change in the magnetic field associated with the closed loop induces an electric current within it. Similar experiments were done by Michael Faraday with a coil similar to a solenoid. Faraday took an insulated copper coil wound around an insulated tube. The ends of the coil were connected to a sensitive galvanometer as shown Fig. 10.16.

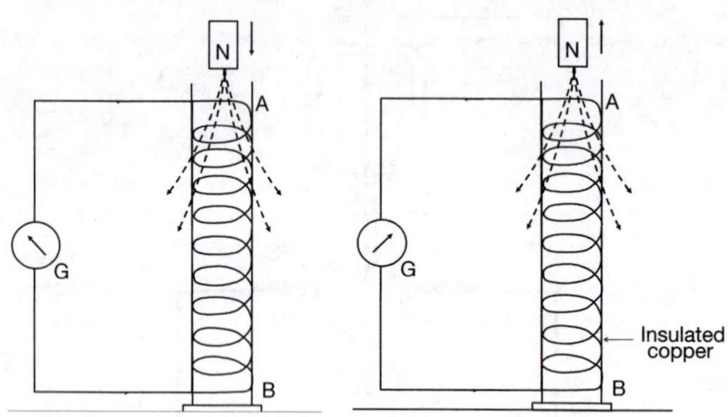

Figure 10.16 The change in the direction of deflection of galvanometer due to the change in the direction of motion of the magnet

When a bar magnet with its north pole pointing to the coil is moved towards the coil with its axis parallel to the axis of the coil, the galvanometer shows a deflection in one direction (say towards left) and similarly when the magnet is moved away from the coil, the galvanometer shows a deflection in the opposite direction (towards right) as shown in Fig. 10.16.

The following are the observations and conclusions from the experiments made by Faraday:

1. Only the relative motion between the coil and the magnet produces deflection in the galvanometer. If the relative motion ceases, i.e., if the magnet is stationary with respect to coil, the galvanometer shows no deflection. From this we may conclude that change in magnetic field associated with the coil induces current in the coil showing deflection in the galvanometer.
2. The deflection increased when a strong magnet is used in the experiment instead of a weak magnet. This indicates that the induced current is more when the rate of change of magnetic field is more.

3. The deflection in the galvanometer changes its direction when the direction of motion of magnet is reversed. This implies that induced current is alternating in nature, i.e., changes with rate of change in the magnetic field. So, the current so produced is called **alternating current (A.C.)**.
4. The deflections in the coil are momentary, i.e., for a short duration. This indicates that the induced current is instantaneous in nature, and flows only as long as the magnet is in motion.

The electromagnetic induction is the phenomenon in which a changing magnetic field associated within a closed coil induces an alternating current in it. In this phenomenon the kinetic energy of the magnet or the coil is converted into electrical energy.

Electric generator or dynamo and transformer are two applications of electromagnetic induction that are discussed below.

Electric Generator

Electric generator is a device that converts mechanical energy into electrical energy through the phenomenon of electromagnetic induction. An electric generator consists of an insulated copper coil *ABCD* wound over a soft iron core as shown in Fig. 10.17. The core consists of an axle that passes through its centre and is connected to a prime rotor. The coil is placed between two concave cylindrical magnetic poles that produce an intense radial magnetic field. The free ends of the coil are connected to two slip rings that maintain continuous contact with the external circuit through two metallic brushes. These metallic brushes are held tight to the slip rings with the help of springs (not shown in the figure). The connecting wires from the brushes are connected to an external load (a resistance) across which electric current produced is drawn.

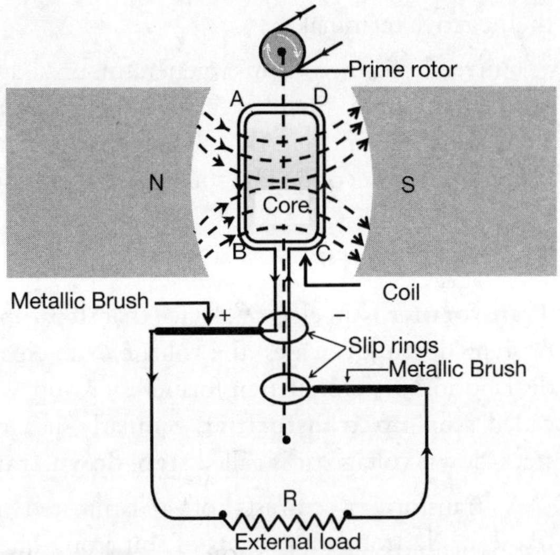

Figure 10.17 An electric generator

The prime rotor on rotating, rotates the coil in the magnetic field. Thus, the magnetic field associated with the coil changes and this produces an induced current in the coil. The induced current is alternating in nature, i.e., in one complete rotation of the coil, the current flows along one direction, say *ABRCD* in the first half rotation and then in the opposite direction, i.e., along *DCRBA* in the next half rotation. The magnitude of the induced current produced depends on the number of turns in the coil, the strength of external magnetic field and the speed of rotation of the coil.

Dynamo

Dynamo is a small generator used to light the lamp of a bicycle. The coil of the generator is connected to the wheel of the bicycle so that it rotates along with the wheel. The muscular energy of the cyclist is converted into electrical energy. Dynamo is also used in motor vehicles for charging the battery continuously. As the coil is connected to the axle of the wheels it generates electricity when the wheels rotate. Here, the chemical energy of petrol or diesel is converted to electrical energy.

Electric Power Stations

Electric power stations generate alternating current on large scale. Their working is based on electromagnetic induction. Following are the types of power stations:

1. Hydroelectric power station.
2. Thermal power station
3. Nuclear power station.

In a hydroelectric power station, the kinetic energy of falling water is used to rotate the coil of a generator, which is also called turbine. In a thermal power station, the heat generated by burning of coal is used to boil water and steam is generated. This steam is used to rotate the coil in a generator. In a nuclear power station, coal is replaced by nuclear energy. Electricity is also generated on a limited scale by tapping the mechanical energy of wind and tidal waves.

Direct and Alternating Electric Current

Flow of electrons through a conductor constitutes electric current. Current can flow through a conductor in two ways. When conductor is connected to a cell or a battery, current flows through it in one direction, i.e., from positive to negative terminal of the battery. Such a current which flows in one direction only is called **direct current, 'D.C.'**. The source of 'D.C.', i.e., a cell is represented by in a circuit diagram. Positive terminal of battery is represented by the longer line while the shorter line represents the negative terminal.

Konnect

Direct current in a cell is generated when chemical energy is converted into electricity.

Current obtained from a generator or a dynamo reverses its direction at regular intervals of time. Such a current which changes its direction alternately is called alternating current or 'A.C.'. The electric current which is supplied to our houses is A.C. and reverses its direction 50 times in every second. The source of an alternating current is represented by (~) in a circuit diagram.

Transformer

Transformer is an electric device that steps-up (increases) or steps-down (decreases) the voltage in an electric energy distribution system. If transformer steps-up voltage, it is called **step-up transformer**. Similarly, if a transformer steps-down voltage, it is called **step-down transformer**.

A transformer consists of a laminated rectangular frame made from thin sheets of soft iron. The sheets are insulated from each other. The two sides of the frame two insulated copper coils are wound having different number of turnings. One of the two is called **primary coil** and the other one is called **secondary coil**. The primary coil is connected to a source of alternating current and is called input of the transformer as shown in figure 10.18.

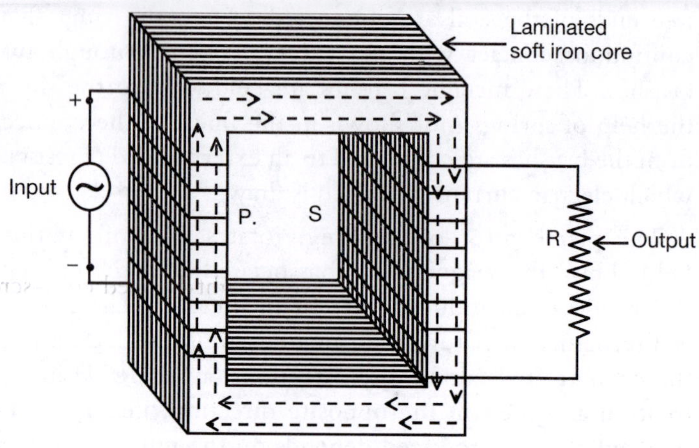

Figure 10.18 A Transformer

When an alternating current passes through the primary coil, an alternating magnetic field is produced in it and thus the magnetic field associated with the secondary coil too changes with time. This change in magnetic field associated with the secondary coil induces an electric current which is also alternating in nature and is called output. This output is collected across an external load resistance connected to the secondary coil.

The cause of induced current in the secondary coil is the electromotive force (emf) induced in it and is called **induced emf**. The relation between emf and number of turnings in each coil are given by,

$$\frac{\text{Current in primary coil } (I_p)}{\text{Current in Secondary coil } (I_s)} = \frac{\text{EMF}(\text{secondary coil})}{\text{EMF}(\text{primary coil})}$$

$$= \frac{\text{Number of turns in secondary coil } (N_s)}{\text{Number of turns in primary coil } (N_p)} \text{ or } \frac{V_s}{V_p} = \frac{N_s}{N_p}$$

Hence, if $N_s > N_p$, then $EMF_s > EMF_p$ and so the transformer is a step-up transformer. Alternately, if $N_s < N_p$, then $EMF_s < EMF_p$ and then the transformer is a step-down transformer.

At the power generating stations, step-up transformers are used to increase the voltage, thereby reducing the current. This reduces the power loss in transmission. At the electric substations, step-down transformers are used to reduce the voltage and supply to the domestic users.

POINTS TO REMEMBER

- ✔ If the direction of the thumb indicates the direction of current in the conductor, then the direction in which the fingers are curled around the conductor to have grip of it, indicates the direction of the magnetic field produced by the current carrying conductor. This is Ampere's right-hand grip rule.
- ✔ If the direction of advancement of the screw indicates the direction of flow of current in the conductor, then, the direction in which the screw is rotated for its advancement indicates the direction of the magnetic field produced by the current carrying conductor. This is known as Maxwell's right-handed cork-screw rule.
- ✔ Electric power stations generate alternating current on large scale.
- ✔ Galvanometer is a device which is used to detect current in a circuit. It consists of a magnetic compass in which a small magnetic needle, pivoted at the centre is enclosed in a brass box with glass top.
- ✔ A solenoid with a soft iron core constitutes an electromagnet. It is a temporary magnet and its magnetism lasts as long as the electric current exists in it.
- ✔ An electric bell works on the principle of an electromagnet.
- ✔ Galvanoscope is a device which is used to detect current in a circuit.
- ✔ D.C. Motor is a device that converts electrical energy into mechanical energy.
- ✔ When there is a relative motion between a magnet and a conductor, an electric current is induced in the conductor. This phenomenon is known as electromagnetic induction.
- ✔ Electric generator is a device that converts mechanical energy into electrical energy through the phenomenon of electromagnetic induction.
- ✔ Dynamo is a small generator used to light the lamp of a bicycle.
- ✔ Electric power stations generate alternating current on large scale. Their working is based on electromagnetic induction.
- ✔ Flow of electrons through a conductor constitutes electric current.
- ✔ Transformer is an electric device that steps-up (increases) or steps-down (decreases) the voltage in an electric energy distribution system. If transformer steps-up voltage, it is called step-up transformer.

CLASSROOM WING

PRACTICE QUESTIONS

Very Short Answer Type Questions

Directions for questions from 1 to 8:
Fill in the blanks.

1. The direction of deflection of a magnetic needle due to an electric current in a conductor is determined by __________, which is based on imagining a person swimming in the direction of the current.
2. According to Ampere's right-hand grip rule, if the thumb indicates the direction of current, the __________ indicates the direction of the magnetic field.
3. In Maxwell's right-handed cork-screw rule, the direction of the magnetic field is indicated by the __________ of the screw when it is rotated to advance in the direction of the current.
4. If work done in bringing a bar magnet near the coil of radius 10 cm, is 25 J, the electric energy generated in the coil assuming 60% efficiency in energy conversion is __________.
5. If the current in a coil as observed is anti-clockwise, then that face of the coil would become _____ pole.
6. The A.C. which is supplied to our houses has a frequency of ____.
7. Electric power stations generate _____ current.
8. Detection of small currents can be done by ________.

Directions for questions from 9 to 25:
Answer the following questions briefly.

9. State the following
   (a) Ampere's swimming rule.
   (b) Right hand grip rule
10. What is Maxwell's right handed cork-screw rule?
11. What type of energy transformation takes place in an electric generator?
12. What is (a) solenoid (b) electromagnet?
13. If the strength of electric current in a circular loop increases, does the magnetic field produced due to the current increase?
14. What are different types of electric power stations?
15. If an electric current flows in a clock-wise direction in a circular loop, facing towards you, which magnetic pole is observed by you?
16. What is an electric generator?
17. If a straight conductor is held normal to this page and current is flowing into the page, what is the direction of the electromagnetic field produced?
18. On increasing the current through a solenoid, the magnetic field produced by it at its centre
19. What is the shape of the magnetic field lines due to a straight current carrying conductor?
20. Two solenoids, 'P' and 'Q' are taken. The coil in solenoid 'P' is wound over a wooden cylindrical core and the coil in solenoid 'Q' is wound over a soft iron core. In which solenoid is the magnetic field stronger?
21. Define
   (a) alternating current.
   (b) direct current.
22. What is the use of (a) galvanoscope (b) telegraph?
23. What is the basic principle on which an electric bell works?
24. What is a transformer?
25. What is an electric motor?

Short Answer Type Questions

26. Explain Ampere's Swimming Rule in the context of magnetic field direction determination.
27. The number of turns in the primary coil of a transformer are 100 and that in the secondary coil are 200. What type of transformer is it? If the input voltage in the primary coil of the transformer is 200 V, find the output voltage in the secondary coil of the transformer.
28. Mention the properties of magnetic field lines due to a straight current carrying conductor.
29. How do the magnetic field lines behave near and inside a current-carrying circular loop?
30. The ratio of number of turns in the primary to secondary coil of a transformer is 3:2 and the total number of turns in both the coils put together is 300. The output voltage is 200 V. Find the number of turns in each coil and the input voltage.
31. Explain Maxwell's right handed cork-screw rule.
32. What is a transformer? How many types of transformers are there and what are they?
33. The input voltage and output voltage in the primary and secondary coils of a transformer are 250 V and 5 V, respectively. If the number of turns in the primary coil of the transformer is 1000, find the number of turns in its secondary coil. Also mention, whether the transformer is a step-up one or a step-down one?
34. Write the properties of magnetic field lines due to circular current carrying conductor.
35. Illustrate the magnetic field produced due to a straight current carrying conductor.
36. Illustrate the magnetic field produced due to a circular loop carrying an electric current.
37. Write the properties of magnetic field lines formed due to a solenoid.
38. Draw a neat labelled diagram of a transformer.
39. In an electromagnetic induction, what is the source of electric energy that causes induced current?
40. Mention the applications of electromagnets.
41. Is the magnetic field formed in a solenoid uniform or non-uniform?
42. What is the significance of alternating current (A.C.) and how is it different from direct current (D.C.)?
43. Explain why the deflection in a galvanometer is momentary during electromagnetic induction experiments.
44. Is electromagnetic field a vector or a scalar?
45. Mention two applications of electromagnetic induction.

Essay Answer Type Questions

46. Explain alternating and direct current.
47. With the help of a neat diagram, explain the construction and working of a D.C. Motor.
48. With the help of a neat-labeled diagram, explain the construction and working of an electric bell.
49. Explain how a DC motor transforms electrical energy into mechanical energy.
50. Discuss the principle and working of an electric generator, highlighting how it converts mechanical energy into electrical energy.

COMPETITION WING

PRACTICE QUESTIONS

Level 1: Apply your Concepts

Directions for questions 1 to 12:
State whether the following statements are true or false.

1. The strength of the magnetic field around a bar magnet decreases with increase in distance.
2. Mechanical energy cannot be converted into electrical energy by moving a magnet inside a coil.
3. A solenoid with a soft iron core is used in electrical appliances like electric bells, fans, motors, etc.
4. Magnetic field has neither magnitude nor direction.
5. Electromagnetic induction is not used in the devices which convert mechanical energy into electrical energy.
6. Each loop of a solenoid acts like a tiny magnet with north and south poles.
7. In step down transformers, the number of turns in primary is less than that in the secondary
8. The magnetic lines of force around a straight current carrying conductor are circular in nature.
9. The angular speed of the coil of a motor is independent of the number of turns in the coil.
10. Magnetic effect of current gives rise to mechanical forces.
11. An electric bell, works on the principle of electromagnetic induction.
12. Electricity and magnetism are two separate branches of physics, which are not related to each other.

Directions for questions 13 to 19:
Fill in the blanks.

13. In a solenoid, when the current flows in an __________ direction at one end, it behaves as the north pole, and when it flows in a __________ direction at the other end, it acts as the south pole.
14. The strength of the magnetic field inside a solenoid depends on the __________ of the current in the coil and the __________ of the material around which the coil is wound.
15. A __________ with a soft iron core constitutes an electromagnet, and its magnetism lasts as long as the __________ exists in it.
16. In a telegraph ______ is connected to positive terminal of a battery and the negative terminal of the battery is connected to ______
17. The frequency of the ringing of the bell in an electric bell can be altered by ______ adjustment.
18. In a D.C. motor, concave cylindrical magnets produce a __________ magnetic field.
19. When there is a _____ between a magnet and a conductor, an EMF is induced in the conductor.

Directions for question 20:
Match the entries in Column A with the appropriate ones in Column B.

20.

Column A	Column B
A. Ampere's rule	a. When the direction of advancement of the screw is in the direction of flow of current, the direction of rotation of the screw head gives the direction of magnetic field.
B. Galvanoscope	b. To produce turning effect in the coil in one direction.
C. Maxwell's rule	c. Production of magnetic field
D. Direction of magnetic field lines is in the anti-clockwise direction, in the plane of the page	d. Swimmer's stretched left hand points the direction of deflection of the needle.
E. Solenoid	e. No deflection in the galvanometer.

Column A	Column B
F. Electromagnet	f. Direction of current is out of the page.
G. Telegraph	g. Morse code
H. Split rings	h. To light a lamp in a bicycle

Directions for questions 21 to 35:
For each of the questions, four choices have been provided. Select the correct alternative.

21. What happens to the magnetic needle of a compass when it is placed above a conductor carrying current in the south-north direction?
(a) Deflects towards east
(b) Deflects towards west
(c) Remains unchanged
(d) Deflects downwards

22. How does the pattern of iron filings change around a straight current-carrying conductor?
(a) Straight lines parallel to the conductor
(b) Random orientation
(c) Concentric circles
(d) Radial lines away from the conductor

23. If a current carrying circular loop is observed from a point where the current flows clockwise, where is the magnetic south pole located?
(a) Towards the observer
(b) Away from the observer
(c) On the right side of the observer
(d) On the left side of the observer

24. What determines the direction of the magnetic poles in a solenoid?
(a) The length of the solenoid
(b) The direction of the electric current
(c) The diameter of the solenoid
(d) The type of the battery used

25. Magnetic field lines inside a solenoid
(a) are parallel to each other.
(b) are convergent.
(c) are divergent.
(d) None of the above

26. A coil is moved towards a stationary magnet. The voltage induced in the coil depends on _____
(a) area of the coil.
(b) the speed with which the coil is moved towards the bar magnet.
(c) number of turns of the coil.
(d) All the above.

27. If a bar of steel is placed in a solenoid, then it changes to _________.
(a) an electric bell
(b) an electromagnet
(c) a dynamo
(d) a permanent magnet

28. The work done in bringing a bar magnet near a coil of radius 14 cm is 50 J. The electric energy generated in the coil if only 45% of the work is converted into electric energy is _____ J.
(a) 50 (b) 25
(c) 22.5 (d) 45

29. The observations made by Faraday from the experiments on electromagnetic induction is (are) that:
(A) the deflection in the galvanometer increases when a strong magnet is used.
(B) the induced current in the coil is alternating in nature
(a) Only A is true
(b) Only B is true
(c) Both A and B are true
(d) Both A and B are false

30. The strength of magnetic field due to a straight current carrying conductor, at a given distance increases with increase in the
(a) temperature of the conductor.
(b) length conductor.
(c) strength of the current.
(d) Both (a) and (c)

31. The magnetic lines of force around a current carrying straight conductor are in the form of
(a) coaxial cylinders
(b) concentric circles
(c) parallel lines
(d) concentric spheres

32. In the phenomenon of electromagnetic induction, _____ energy of the coil or magnet is converted to _____ energy.
(a) magnetic, electric
(b) electric, magnetic
(c) electric, kinetic
(d) kinetic, electric

33. What kind of voltage is induced across the terminals of the copper coil in an electric generator when it is rotated in a magnetic field?
(a) Alternating voltage
(b) Step down voltage
(c) Step up voltage
(d) Direct Voltage

34. Which of the following is true regarding solenoid?
(A) Strength of the magnetic field is independent of the material on which the coil is wound.
(B) When the coil is wound around a soft iron core, it behaves like a temporary magnet.
(a) Only A
(b) Only B
(c) Both A and B
(d) None of the above

35. A transformer contains 250 and 150 turns in its primary and secondary coils, respectively. The transformer is a _______.
(A) Step up transformer
(B) Step down transformer
(a) Only (A) is true
(b) Only (B) is true
(c) Both (A) and (B) are true
(d) Both (A) and B are false

Level 2: Review your Concepts

36. A magnet and a coil are taken. In which of the following cases, emf is induced in the coil?
(a) magnet is moving, coil is at rest.
(b) magnet is at rest and the coil is moving.
(c) both magnet and coil are moving with equal velocities.
(d) magnet is moving with greater velocity than that of coil.

37. Two wires A and B are placed parallel to each other in a vertical plane such that A carries 5 A and B carries 2 A of current in W-E direction. If a magnetic compass is placed mid-way between A and B such that it is free to rotate in horizontal plane, then in which direction, would it deflect? If the direction of current in A and B is reversed, in which direction would it deflect?

38. Why electrical energy is transmitted at high voltage and low current?

39. Can we use Ampere's right hand rule to determine the deflection of a magnetic needle placed near a current carrying conductor? Explain.

40. A straight conductor carrying current produces a magnetic field around it. Does it possess a north or a south pole similar to a bar magnet?
What shape should be given to the conductor so as to have magnetic poles?

41. The work done in bringing a bar magnet near a coil of radius 14 cm is 50 J. What is the electric energy generated in the coil if only 45% of the work is converted into electric energy?

42. What happens if earthing is not proper in a telegraph?

43. What causes the rectangular coil in a D.C. motor to rotate? Explain.

44. Two, current carrying conductors are placed parallel to each other. Explain if there is attraction or repulsion between them when the current flowing through them is in the
(i) same direction
(ii) opposite direction.

45. A transformer has 250 primary turns and 500 secondary turns. If 200 V electric potential is applied to the primary resulting in a current of 5 mA, find the secondary voltage and current.

46. Explain how a galvanoscope can be modified to measure current.

47. The frequency of sinusoidal A.C. voltage is 50 Hz. How many times does the voltage become zero in 5 s?

48. In an electromagnetic induction, what is the source of electric energy that causes induced current?

49. A spring made of copper is moved towards a stationary bar magnet. What are the changes observed in the spring when
(i) the two ends of the spring are connected.
(ii) the two ends of the spring are not connected.

50. How can you locate a conductor concealed in a wall carrying D.C. current?

51. The input voltage and output voltage in the primary and secondary coils of a transformer are 250 V and 5 V, respectively. If the number of turns in the primary coil of the transformer is 1000, find the number of turns in its secondary coil. Also mention, whether the transformer is a step-up one or a step-down one?

Level 3: Assess Your Concepts

52. Can a transformer be used to step up or step down a D.C. voltage? Explain.

53. A magnet is dropped vertically downwards along the axis of the aluminium loop of wire lying horizontally. Will there be any difference in the time of fall if the wire is at room temperature and heated to below its melting point? If so, explain. (Hint: Resistance of a conductor is directly proportional to its temperature).

54. To detect electric current using a galvanoscope, the plane of the coil is placed along magnetic meridian. What happens if the plane of coil is along east-west direction?

55. Explain why on increasing the number of turns per unit length in a solenoid, the magnetic field strength increases.

56. Why are magnets with concave shaped poles used in a D.C. motor? What happens if magnets with flat poles are used in it?

AT

JEE-NEET SPECIAL WING

PRACTICE QUESTIONS

Multiple-Answer Type Questions

Directions for questions 1 to 5:

Select one or more correct alternative(s) from the given choices.

1. The direction of the magnetic field due to the current in the conductor is given by
   (a) Ampere's right-hand grip rule.
   (b) Maxwell's right-hand corkscrew rule.
   (c) Fleming's right-hand rule.
   (d) Fleming's left-hand rule.

2. For a step - up transformer,
   (a) $N_S < N_P$ (b) $V_S < V_P$
   (c) $N_S > N_P$ (d) $V_S > V_P$

3. The device used to detect current in a circuit is
   (a) Voltmeter (b) Galvanometer
   (c) Galvanoscope (d) Electroscope

4. Which of the following are the properties of magnetic field lines due to current carrying coil?
   (a) Magnetic field lines at the centre of the loop are nearly straight lines.
   (b) Magnetic field lines are always normal to the plane of the loop.
   (c) Magnetic field lines are cylindrical along the conductor.
   (d) Number of magnetic field lines per unit area determines the strength of current in the loop.

5. When there is a relative motion between a magnet and a conductor
   (a) electric current is induced.
   (b) resistance is induced
   (c) force is induced.
   (d) emf is induced.

Comprehension-Based Questions

Directions for questions 6 to 10:

These questions are based on the following information.

Electromagnetic Induction:
The phenomenon of inducing emf and thereby current in a coil due to the relative motion between a magnet and a coil is called electromagnetic induction. This was discovered by Michael Faraday through his experiments. There are two types of induction namely mutual induction and self-induction.

6. The energy conversion involved with the phenomenon of electromagnetic induction is
   (a) magnetic energy to electrical energy.
   (b) kinetic energy to electrical energy.
   (c) kinetic energy to magnetic energy.
   (d) magnetic energy to kinetic energy.

7. The device used to light the lamp of a bicycle is
   (a) Transformer (b) Generator
   (c) Dynamo (d) Motor

8. If a weak magnet is replaced by a strong magnet, then the deflection
   (a) increases
   (b) decreases
   (c) becomes zero
   (d) remains unaffected

9. The magnitude of the induced current does not depend on
   (a) number of turns in the coil.
   (b) strength of the external magnetic field.
   (c) speed of rotation of coil.
   (d) area of cross section of the coil.

10. Identify the application of electromagnetic induction
    (a) Optic fibre
    (b) Transformer
    (c) Speakers
    (d) both (b) and (c)

Match the Column

Directions for question 11:

The question is based on the following information.

Solenoid:

We now know that a current carrying loop behaves like a magnet. Thus, we have a coil of insulated wire wound around a cylindrical tube having length greater than its diameter and behaves as a magnet called the solenoid. Solenoid works on the principle of electromagnetism. Solenoids are frequently used in locking mechanisms and in many locking applications. A solenoid with a soft iron core constitutes an electromagnet.

11. Match the values in List - I with those in List - II:

List - I	List - II
A. Electromagnet	a. Morse code
B. Armature	b. Split rings
C. Contact spring	c. Temporary magnet
D. D C Motor	d. Soft iron bar
E. Telegraph	e. Silver cadmium alloy

(a) A - b, B - c, C - a, D - e, E - d
(b) A - c, B - d, C - e, D - b, E - a
(c) A - d, B - c, C - e, D - a, E - b
(d) A - a, B - b, C - c, D - d, E - e

ANSWER KEYS

Crossword

Across

1. Dynamo 4. Concentric Circles 7. Direction 9. Electric Bell
12. Alternating Current 13. Step up 14. Bar Magnet

Down

1. Direction of Current 2. Primary Coil 3. Electric Generator
5. Mechanical Energy 6. Electromagnetism 8. Galvanoscope 10. Solenoid 11. Transformer

Classroom Wing

Very Short Answer Type Questions

1. Ampere's Swimming Rule 2. Fingers' curl 3. Rotation 4. 15 J
5. North 6. 50 Hz 7. Alternating 8. Galvanoscope

Short Answer Type Questions

30. 300 V 33. 20

Competition Wing

Level 1: Apply your Concepts

1. True 2. False 3. True 4. False 5. False
6. True 7. True 8. True 9. False 10. True
11. False 12. False 13. Anticlockwise, clockwise 14. Strength, nature
15. Solenoid, electric current 16. Morse Key, earth 17. Contact screw 18. Radial
19. Relative motion 20. A : d, B : j, C : a, D : f, E : c, F : i, G : g, H : b, I : e, J : h 21. (a)
22. (c) 23. (a) 24. (b) 25. (a) 26. (d)
27. (d) 28. (c) 29. (c) 30. (c) 31. (b)
32. (d) 33. (a) 34. (b) 35. (b)

Level 2: Review your Concepts

41. 22.5 J 45. 2.5 mA

JEE-NEET Special Wing

Multiple-Answer Type Questions

1. (a) and (b) 2. (c) and (d) 3. (b) and (c) 4. (a), (b) and (d) 5. (a) and (d)

Comprehension-Based Questions

6. (b) 7. (c) 8. (a) 9. (d) 10. (d)

Match the Column

11. (b)

For complete answer key of Classroom wing and Competition wing, refer to Hints and Solutions

Hints and Explanations

Classroom Wing

Very Short Answer Type Question

1. Ampere's Swimming Rule
2. Fingers' curl
3. Rotation
4. 15 J
5. North
6. 50 Hz
7. Alternating
8. Galvanoscope
9. The needle deflects towards the direction of the swimmer's stretched left hand if the person is imagined to swim along the direction of flow of current.

   Hold a straight conductor in the right hand such that the thumb is directed along the direction of flow of current, then the direction in which the fingers are curled around the conductor gives the direction of magnetic lines of force.
10. The direction of current is the direction in which the tip of the screw advances and direction of rotation of the head of the screw gives the direction of magnetic lines of force.
11. Electric generator is a device used to produce electrical energy from mechanical energy.
12. A current carrying conductor when wind over a plastic tube, behaves as a magnet as each loop behaves as a magnet. When current carrying conductor is wind over a magnetic material like soft iron it gets magnetized.
13. Yes
14. Electrical energy is produced in different power stations from the mechanical energy of water, heat energy and nuclear energy.
15. If current through a coil flows in clockwise direction when observed from a face of a coil that face behaves as south pole and if current flows in anticlockwise direction that face of the coil behaves as north pole.
16. Electric generators are used to produce electrical energy from mechanical energy.
17. The tangent drawn at any point on the magnetic line of force gives the direction of magnetic field.
18. Decreases in strength.
19. Magnetic lines of force around a conductor are concentric circles.
20. Wood is a non magnetic substance whereas soft iron is a magnetic substance.
21. The direction and magnitude of alternating current and direct current.
22. (a) To detect the flow of electric current.

    (b) To send messages from one place to another.
23. Electromagnet is the main component used in electric bell and it behaves as a magnet when electric current passes through it.
24. Transformers are used to increase or decrease the voltage.
25. Electric motor is used in electric fan and it produces mechanical energy from electrical energy.

Short Answer Type Questions

Note: This is how you should frame your answer covering.

26. Ampere's Swimming Rule is a visualization tool to determine the direction of a magnetic field around a conductor carrying current. Imagine a person swimming along the direction of the electric current; the magnetic field will deflect towards the swimmer's stretched left hand. This rule aids in intuitively understanding the relationship between current direction and magnetic field orientation.
27. $\frac{N_P}{N_s} = \frac{V_P}{V_s}$
28. Shape, direction and relation between the strength of current and number of lines of force.

29. Close to the circular loop, the magnetic field lines are circular around the conductor. Inside the loop, these lines are directed towards the net magnetic north, which is determined based on the direction of the current in the loop. Near the centre of the loop, the lines are nearly straight, forming a uniform magnetic field, and always normal to the plane of the loop.

30. $\frac{n_p}{n_s}=\frac{3}{2}, n_p+n_s=300 \Rightarrow \frac{3}{2}n_s+n_s$

$=300 \Rightarrow \frac{5}{2}n_s=300 \Rightarrow n_s=\frac{600}{5}=120,$

$\therefore\ n_p=\frac{3}{2}n_s=\frac{3}{2}\times 120=180$

Given, the output voltage $=200V \Rightarrow V_s=200V$

$\frac{n_p}{n_s}=\frac{V_p}{V_s} \Rightarrow V_p=\frac{n_p}{n_s}\times V_s=\frac{3}{2}\times 200V=300V$

31. The direction of flow of current is along the direction of advancement of tip of the screw and the direction of rotation of head of the screw is the direction of magnetic field.

32. They can be used to increase or decrease the voltage. To increase and to decrease two different kinds of transformers are used.

33. $\frac{N_P}{N_S}=\frac{V_P}{V_S}$

$N_s=20$, it is a step-down transformer.

34. Direction, shape of magnetic lines of force at the centre of circular loop, shape of magnetic lines of force around the loop and relation between the strength of the current and number of magnetic lines of force.

35. Square shaped cardboard, hole in the middle, conducting wire, battery, iron filings and connecting wires.

36. Rectangular cardboard with two holes, circular loop through the holes, connecting wires, battery and iron filings.

37. The properties of magnetic lines of force change due to a bar magnet. A solenoid behaves like a bar magnet.

38. Core, primary and secondary coils.

39. (i) Cause of change in magnetic field
(ii) Loses

40. Electromagnets can be used to separate magnetic materials. Electromagnets can be used in devices when strong temporary magnetic field is required. For example electric bell, telegraph etc.

41. A solenoid behaves similar to a bar magnet. The strength of the magnetic field around a bar magnet decreases with increase in distance, so it is non-uniform.

42. Alternating current (A.C.) is significant as it changes its direction periodically, unlike direct current (D.C.) which flows in only one direction. This property of A.C. makes it ideal for efficient transmission over long distances and for use in various electrical appliances. D.C., being unidirectional, is typically used in batteries and electronics.

43. The deflection in a galvanometer is momentary during electromagnetic induction experiments because the induced current is instantaneous and flows only as long as there's motion between the magnet and the coil. Once the relative motion ceases, the magnetic field becomes stable, ceasing the induction of current and thus the deflection in the galvanometer.

44. Construct your answer by defining of vector quantity and scalar quantity. Magnetic field has both magnitude and direction.

45. Construct your answer by defining phenomenon of electromagnetic induction is used in the devices which convert mechanical energy into electrical energy.

Essay Answer Type Questions

Note: This is how you should frame your answer covering.

46. The direction and magnitude of alternating and direct current.

47. Soft iron core, cylindrical coil, split rings, metallic brushes, battery, switch, connecting wires, shaft and concave cylindrical magnet.

48. Gong, armature, horse-shoe soft iron core, copper wire, conducting wires, plug key and battery.

49. In a DC motor, the conversion of electrical energy into mechanical energy is achieved through the interaction between magnetic fields and electric current. When the current flows through the coil of the motor, placed within an external magnetic field, it generates an electromagnetic field. This field interacts with the external field, causing the coil to experience a force and rotate. The coil is connected to a shaft, which also rotates, converting the electrical energy into rotational mechanical energy. The direction of the current in the coil is periodically reversed by the split rings functioning as a commutator, ensuring the coil spins in a consistent direction. The speed and efficiency of this conversion are influenced by factors like the strength of the external magnetic field, the current in the coil,

and the number of turns in the coil. This ingenious design allows for a simple yet effective transformation of energy forms, harnessing electromagnetic principles for practical mechanical work.

50. An electric generator operates on the principle of electromagnetic induction, where mechanical energy is converted into electrical energy. It consists of an insulated copper coil wound over a soft iron core placed between magnetic poles. As the prime rotor rotates, it also rotates the coil within the magnetic field, changing the magnetic field associated with the coil. This change induces an alternating current (A.C.) in the coil. The direction of the induced current alters with each half rotation of the coil, exemplifying the characteristics of A.C. The magnitude of this induced current depends on factors like the number of coils turns, the strength of the magnetic field, and the speed of the coil's rotation. This process demonstrates the conversion of kinetic (mechanical) energy into electrical energy, underlying the fundamental operation of electric generators used in various applications, including power generation.

Competition Wing

Level 1: Apply your Concepts

21. The deflection is determined by the direction of the electric current with respect to the compass. When the current is south-north, and the compass is above the conductor, the deflection is towards east.

Hence, the correct answer is (a).

22. The magnetic field around a straight current-carrying conductor is in the form of concentric circles centred at the conductor.

Hence, the correct answer is (c).

23. For a circular conductor, if the current direction appears clockwise, the magnetic south pole is formed on the side facing the observer.

Hence, the correct answer is (a).

24. The magnetic poles of a solenoid are determined by the direction in which the electric current flows through the coil.

Hence, the correct answer is (b).

Level 2: Review your Concepts

Note: This is how you should frame your answer covering.

36. (i) Relative motion between coil and the magnet.

(ii) Varying magnetic field–Induced emf.

37. The given situation is depicted in the figure. The compass is placed at the point P, mid-way between the conductors A and B carrying current 5 A and 2 A respectively in the same direction (West to East) as shown. The magnetic field strength due to a straight current carrying conductor at a point which is at a distance 'r' from the

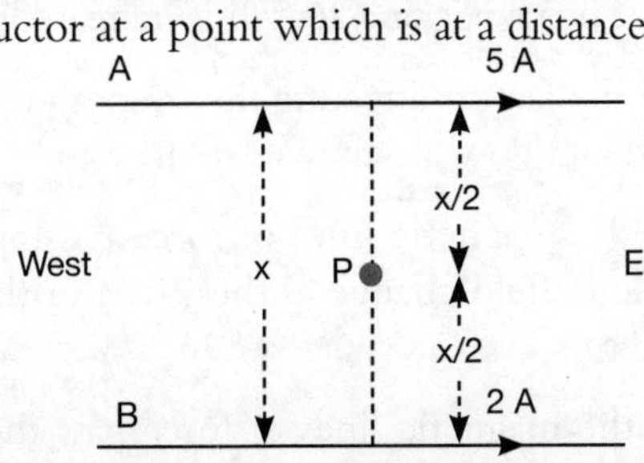

conductor is given by $B = \dfrac{\mu_0 i}{2\pi r}$

$$\therefore B_A\left(at\ P\right) = \frac{\mu_0 5}{2\pi\left(\frac{x}{2}\right)} = k5 \rightarrow (1) \text{ where } k = \frac{\mu_0}{\pi x}$$

$$B_B\left(at\ P\right) = \frac{\mu_0 2}{2\pi\left(\frac{x}{2}\right)} = k2 \rightarrow (2)$$

Comparing equations 1 and 2, we have $B_A > B_B$

The direction of B_A at P is obtained by applying right hand grip rule, and it is into the plane of the paper, that is south to north.

The direction of B_B at P is obtained by applying right hand grip rule, and it is out of the plane of the paper, that is north to south.

Hence, the direction of the net magnetic field strength will be in the direction of B_A the greater field, which is the direction of , that is, into the plane of the paper, that is south to north.

If the direction of current in both the conductors A and B is reversed, then the direction of the net field would also be reversed, that is, it will be then out of the plane of the paper, that is north to south.

38. (i) $P \propto i^2$

(ii) Heat energy $\propto i$

39. Will the compass needle deflect when it is placed near a current carrying conductor?

If so, in what direction will it deflect?

How do you determine the direction of deflection of a magnetic needle if the direction of external magnetic field is given?

40. Build your answer by giving the definition of magnetic poles. We know that in case of bar magnet, its strength is concentrated at its ends. You can compare magnetic lines of forces due to a bar magnet and a current-carrying conductor. Also, you must write about the shape of magnetic lines force, how it changes when current-carrying conductor is bent to form a circular coil.

41. The work done in moving the magnet towards the coil, W = 50 J

The part of the work done which is converted to electricity = 45%

Hence, the electrical energy generated in the coil =

$$45\% \text{ of } 50\text{ J} = \frac{45}{100} \times 50 = \frac{45}{2} = 22.5\,J$$

42. How does the electric circuit get closed between two places in a telegraph? Will earth conduct electricity? Is it possible to send the messages from one place to another if the circuit is not closed?

Is it possible to receive messages if earthing is not proper?

43. Do the two vertical sides of the coil of a DC motor?

What is the direction of the forces acting on

Do the forces acting on the vertical sides constitute a couple?

What is the effect of the couple?

44. Identify the direction of magnetic field produced by each wire when current flows through them.

Identify whether the force is attractive or repulsive when the magnetic fields are in the same direction and opposite direction?

45. $n_p = 200$; $n_s = 500$; $V_p = 200$ V, $i_p = 5$ mA, $V_s = ?$, $i_s = ?$

$$\frac{n_p}{n_s} = \frac{V_p}{V_s} = \frac{i_s}{i_p}$$

$$\frac{n_p}{n_s} = \frac{V_p}{V_s} \Rightarrow V_s = \frac{V_p \times n_s}{n_p} = \frac{200V \times 500}{250} = 400\ V$$

$$\frac{V_p}{V_s} = \frac{i_s}{i_p} \Rightarrow i_s = \frac{V_p \times i_p}{V_s} = \frac{200V \times 5\ mA}{400V} = 2.5\ mA$$

46. How is the strength of the electric current related to the deflecting angle of a galvanoscope?

Is it possible to calibrate a galvanoscope to measure current?

47. (i) Change of sign in one cycle.

(ii) Is it possible to increase the strength of a magnet if the maximum number of molecular magnets are arranged in an orderly way?

48. How is the induced current developed when a magnet moves towards the coil?

What happens to the mechanical energy that is used to move the magnet?

49. (i) Requirement for current to flow.

(ii) Difference between geographical axis and geographical meridian.

(iii) Change in the length of the spring.

(iv) Pole strength decreases when the area of cross-section of the bar magnet is reduced and the

50. (i) Current carrying wire-magnetic field.

(ii) Compass needle.

51. $n_p = 1000$; $n_s = ?$; $V_p = 250$ V, $V_s = 5$ V

$$\frac{n_p}{n_s} = \frac{V_p}{V_s} \Rightarrow n_s = \frac{V_s \times n_p}{V_p} = \frac{5V \times 1000}{250V} = 20$$

As $V_s < V_p$, the transformer is a step-down transformer.

Level 3: Assess Your Concepts

Note: This is how you should frame your answer covering.

52. What is the principle of the working of a transformer?

What is the basic difference between A.C. voltage and D.C. voltage?

How do the induced emf develop in the secondary coil?

53. (i) Change in the magnetic field.

(ii) Dependence of induced current on resistance of the coil.

(iii) Dependence of resistance on temperature

(iv) Force between induced current and magnet.

(v) Dependence of fall in amount of current induced.

54. Will the magnetic needle show any deflection if the magnetic field produced due to the flow electric current is along the same direction as the earth's magnetic field?

How do you detect the flow of electric current in such cases?

55. What happens to the total length of the wire when the number of turns per unit length is increased?

What are the factors affecting the strength of the magnetic field and how are they related?

56. How do the magnetic lines of force passing through the magnetic field change as the shape of the magnet changes?

How do the magnetic lines of force pass through the magnetic field if the magnetic poles are flat?

How should the magnetic lines of force pass through a magnetic field to produce more turning effect in an armature?

JEE-NEET Special Wing

Multiple-Answer Type Questions

1. Maxwell Right-handed screw Rule: If a screw held in the right hand is turned so that it moves in the direction of the conventional current, its direction of rotation will indicate the direction of the magnetic field.
Ampere Right-hand thumb rule: If the conductor carrying current is held in the right hand such that the thumb points to the direction of current, then the direction of rotation of curled fingers gives the direction of the magnetic field.
Hence, the correct option is (a) and (b).

2. Step-up transformer: The voltage produced in the secondary coil should be greater than that in the primary coil. $v_s > v_p$. which is made possible by making a greater number of turns in secondary coil compared to primary coil.
$N_s > N_p$.
Hence, the correct option is (c) and (d).

3. A galvanometer is a device that measures a small current by deflection of a moving coil.
Galvanoscopes detect current by measuring deflection of needle in a field included by current.
Hence, the correct option is (b) and (c).

4. The magnetic field lines are in the form of concentric circles along the length of the conductor.
Hence, the correct option is (a), (b) and (d).

5. Whenever there is a change in the magnetic flux in the coil, an induced EMF is generated (EMF is voltage).
If the coil with changing magnetic flux is closed then an induced current is produced,
Hence, the correct option is (a) and (d).

Comprehension-Based Questions

6. In this phenomenon, the kinetic energy of the magnet or coil is converted into electrical energy.
Hence, the correct option is (b).

7. Dynamo is a device which converts mechanical energy to electric energy.
Hence, the correct option is (c).

8. When the rate of change of magnetic field is more, the induced current is also more and more the deflection.
Hence, the correct option is (a).

9. The Induced Current produced in a coil depends upon
   - The number of turns of coil.
   - The rate of change in magnetic flux.
   - The strength of magnet used.

   Hence, the correct option is (d).

10. Knowledge based.
Hence, the correct option is (d).

Match the Column

11. **Choice (b) follows.**
The direction of current in DC motors needs to be changed for every half rotation of the coil. Split rings, which act as commutators, are used
Morse code: A language used by people to communicate with each other, through telegrams or satellites.
An electromagnet is called a temporary magnet because it produces a magnetic field as long as current flows in it.
Armature is made up of an iron bar, it can be magnetized and demagnetized very easily.
Silver cadmium alloy does not get oxidised easily even in sparkling, hence they are used as contact spring in electric bells.

Sources of Energy

CHAPTER
11

Key Ideas

After completing this chapter, you should be able to:

- learn about renewable and non-renewable sources of energy.
- understand uses of different sources of energy.
- study about fossil fuels and their uses.
- recognize causes and preventive measures of air pollution.

Remember

Before beginning this chapter, you should be able to:

- define energy and its types.
- discuss forms of energy such as light, sound, etc.

Scientific Crypt

A Tribute to James Watt (1736-1819)

James Watt was a Scottish inventor, mechanical engineer, and chemist. Watt became interested in the technology of steam engines while he was working as an instrument maker. Watt introduced a design enhancement, the separate condenser, which avoided this waste of energy and radically improved the power, efficiency, and cost-effectiveness of steam engines. In trying to understand the thermodynamics of heat and steam, James Watt carried out many laboratory experiments and his diaries record that in conducting these, he used a kettle as a boiler to generate steam. James Watt's improvements to the steam engine were one of the main causes of the Industrial Revolution. He invented and constructed machines for copying sculptures and medallions which worked very well. Watt was much honoured in his own time. In 1784, he became a fellow of the Royal Society of Edinburgh. As Watt developed the concept of horsepower, the SI unit of power, the watt, was named after him.

Crossword

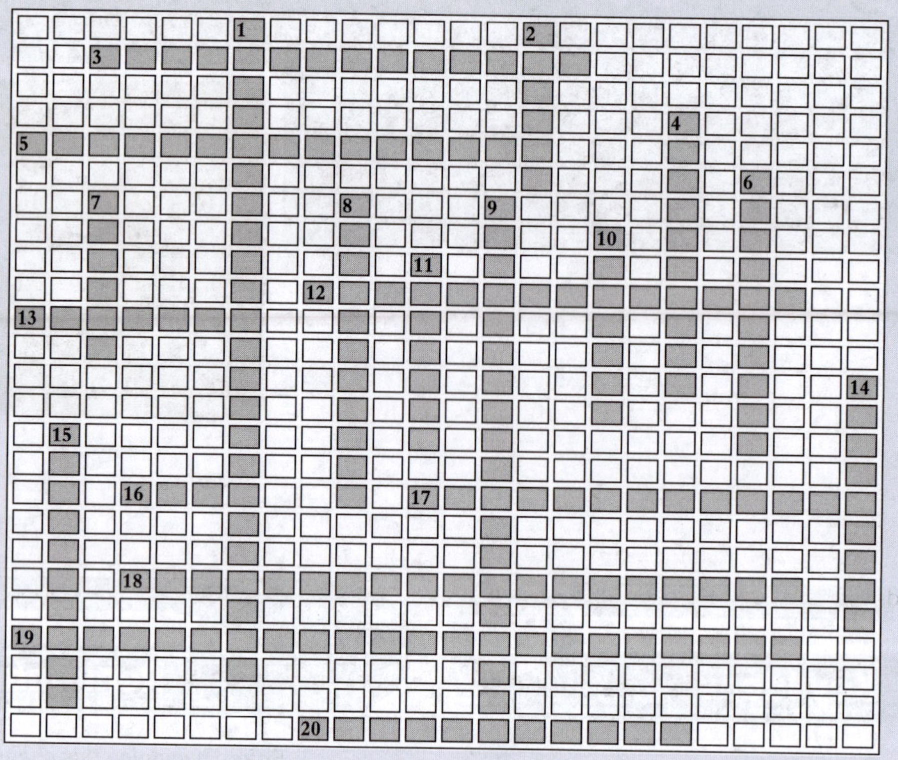

Across

3. The process in which a heavy nucleus of an atom is split into two atoms of lighter nuclei.
5. A device in which a controlled nuclear fission reaction takes place.
12. The quantity of heat liberated by completely burning a unit mass of fuel.
13. The main constituent of biogas.
16. A source from which energy is derived in the form of heat.
17. The substance whose resistivity lies between those of conductors and insulators.
18. The phenomenon of ejection of electrons from a metallic surface when light of suitable radiation falls on the metallic surface.
19. The process of extracting derivatives from crude oil in their gaseous state.
20. Energy possessed by moving water.

Down

1. The process of burning of material in the absence of oxygen.
2. The process of adding impurities to a semi-conductor.
4. The materials that pollute the air.
6. The process of deriving heat energy by burning fuels.
7. The paths in which the electrons revolve around the nucleus.
8. The energy possessed by the moving water of tides and ocean currents.
9. The temperature at which the combustion takes place.
10. The central part of an atom.
11. The remains of dead plants and animals that are buried under the Earth and preserved by nature for thousands of years.
14. Photoelectric cell.
15. The energy possessed by moving air.

INTRODUCTION

The word energy is derived from its Greek origin 'energia' meaning 'at work' or 'in work'. Thus, energy is linked with doing work and is defined as the capacity to do work. In physics, work is said to be done when a net force acts on a body and the body undergoes displacement.

Energy and its Sources

As we know, in physics we define **energy** as the capability to do work. In the process of doing work, energy is transformed from one form to another. For example, when water is lifted into an overhead tank using a motor, electrical energy supplied to the motor is converted into mechanical energy in the pump, which in turn is converted into potential energy (energy possessed by a body by virtue of its position) of the water stored in the overhead tank. When the water stored in the tank flows through the pipes connected to the tank, the potential energy of water is converted into its kinetic energy (energy possessed by a body by virtue of its motion).

In general, electrical energy is produced at

1. hydel power plants, where electricity is derived from flowing water.
2. thermal power plants, where electricity is derived from heat produced by burning coal or any other substance, generally called fuel.

Any fuel from which energy is derived can be termed as a **'source of energy'**. Thus, energy in any form is derived from a 'source' and is transformed from one form to another. Thus, the total amount of energy remains constant and is said to be conserved. This is known as the **law of conservation of energy.** In other words, it states that energy can neither be created nor be destroyed but can only be transformed from one form to another. There are several sources of energy available in nature. The current chapter deals with different types of sources of energy and their related topics.

There are various sources of energy available in nature on which we are dependent for our energy requirements. These sources of energy can be broadly classified into two categories, namely non-renewable and renewable sources of energy. The sources of energy which, once used up, cannot be replenished are termed **'non-renewable sources of energy'**. Coal, petroleum, etc., are some of the examples of non-renewable sources of energy. The sources of energy which can be replenished after usage are termed **'renewable sources of energy'**. Wind, water, solar energy are some of the examples of renewable sources of energy. Before proceeding to learn in detail about these sources of energy, let us briefly study the characteristics of a good source of energy.

1. **High Ratio of Output to Input Energy:** If a log of wood is to be burnt to derive heat energy, we should supply energy in the form of fire. So, in order to derive energy from a source, some amount of work has to be done or, in other words, some energy must be spent. Such energy spent initially is referred to as an input energy and the total energy derived from the source is referred to as an output energy. The output energy should be more than the input energy. The difference in the output and input energy is referred to as net output energy. For a good source of energy, the net output energy should be sufficiently large.
2. **Easy Availability:** The source of energy selected should be available over a long period of time and supply energy at a steady rate, eg., solar energy.
3. **Risk Free:** The energy available should be safe and convenient for use. For example, nuclear energy cannot be used for cooking food.
4. **Convenient for Storage and Transportation:** A source of energy should be convenient for storage and transportation. For example, petroleum and natural gas compressed to a liquid state are transported using tankers mounted over truck bodies.
5. **Economical to Use:** A source of energy should be economical for the consumers who use it.

Non-Renewable (Conventional) Sources of Energy

Fuel

A source from which energy is derived in the form of heat is called **fuel**. Fuels are available in the three states of matter, namely, solids, liquids and gases. Wood, charcoal, coal, cowdung cakes, etc., are some examples of solid fuels. Petroleum and its derivatives like petrol, diesel, kerosene, etc., are some examples of liquid fuels. Compressed natural gas (CNG), liquefied petroleum gas (LPG), etc., are some examples of fuels in gaseous state.

Info Bytes!

Fuels that have very low ignition temperature, like petrol, catch fire easily and thus cannot be used for domestic purposes as their use is highly risky.

Heat energy is derived by burning fuels and this process of burning is called **combustion**. Usually, combustion of fuels takes place in the presence of oxygen in atmosphere. Combustion can also take place in the absence of oxygen. For example, magnesium can undergo combustion in the presence of chlorine gas. In general, oxygen acts as a supporter of combustion.

The key components of a combustion process are

1. a combustible substance, i.e., the fuel;
2. a supporter for the combustion process; and
3. the temperature at which the combustion takes place, called **ignition temperature**.

The above characteristics discussed are applicable for fuels in addition to other sources of energy. In addition to the above feature that characterize a good fuel, another important feature that is considered is the amount of heat liberated by burning completely a unit mass of the fuel. The quantity of heat liberated by completely burning a unit mass of a fuel is called its **calorific value** and is measured in calories per gram or joule per gram or multiples of these units.

Konnect

A good fuel should have a high calorific value so that minimum amount of fuel is utilized to gain large amount of heat energy.

When solid, liquid, and gaseous fuels are compared, it is found that gaseous fuels have the highest calorific value. Also, it is found that the cause of much higher calorific values of gaseous fuels is the presence of hydrogen in them. Thus, the greater the percentage of hydrogen in a fuel, the greater is its **calorific value**.

Table 11.1 The following table gives a comparison between calorific values of different fuels:

Type of Fuel	Fuel	Calorific value (kJ Kg^{-1})
Solid fuels	Cowdung cake	6000-8000
	Wood	17000-22000
	Coal	25000-33000
Liquid fuels	Ethanol	30000
	Kerosene	45000
	Petrol	47000
Gaseous fuels	Biogas	35000-40000
	LPG	55000
	Methane	55000

Fossil Fuels

Fossils refer to the remains of dead plants and animals that are buried under the Earth and preserved by nature for thousands of years. Fuels like coal, petroleum, etc., are formed as a result of fossils, and hence, these are referred to **fossil fuels**. Coal is the fossilised remains of plants that have been buried in the Earth's crust for millions of years and formed as a result of burning of the buried material in the absence of oxygen due to the heat present in the Earth. This process of burning of material in the absence of oxygen is known as '**destructive distillation**'. The conditions that led to the formation of coal and petroleum do not prevail now on the Earth. Thus, once these sources are used up, they cannot be replenished, and hence, fall under the category of non-renewable sources of energy.

Coal

The main constituent of coal is carbon. Some other derivatives obtained from coal are coke, coal gas and coal tar. Coke is obtained from coal by heating coal in the absence of air. In the process, coal gas and an oily liquid called coal tar are obtained as by-products. The quality of coal depends on the percentage of carbon in it. The following table depicts the major types of coal and the percentage of carbon in them.

Table 11.2 Major types of coal and the percentage of carbon

Type of Coal	Percentage of Carbon
Peat	27%
Lignite	28% to 30%
Bituminous	78% to 87%
Anthracite	94% to 98%

Coke, obtained from coal, is used as a reducing agent in the extraction process of some metals from their ores and also used in making steel. High grade coke is used as fuel in blast furnaces. Combustion of coal gives out oxides of carbon like carbon dioxide, some of which pollute the air.

Info Bytes!

Carbon percentage in coke is higher than that in coal.

Petroleum

The word petroleum is derived from the Greek words, '*petra*' meaning rocks and '*oleum*' which means oil. Thus, petroleum is oil derived from rocks, i.e., earth. Petroleum is also referred to as crude oil; and it falls under the category of non-renewable source of energy. Petroleum deposits are formed from the dead remains of plants and animals buried under the sediments of the Earth's crust millions of years ago and thus are referred to as fossil fuels. Due to immense heat and high pressure, they get converted into petroleum. Petroleum consists of complex compounds of two major elements namely, hydrogen and carbon, generally referred to as hydrocarbons.

The major derivatives of petroleum are kerosene, diesel, petrol, lubricating oil, petroleum wax, etc. These derivatives have different boiling points. This property of the derivatives is used to

(i) separate them from the crude oil, and
(ii) extract them in the gaseous state by a process called **fractional distillation**. The crude oil is taken in a huge chamber and is heated to its boiling point thus converting it into gaseous state. Then, it is cooled in the chamber at different stages to obtain different derivatives at their respective condensation points.

Gaseous Fuels

Petroleum gas and natural gas are two major gaseous fossil fuels that are used. Petroleum gas is obtained as a byproduct in the process of refining petroleum. It consists mainly of hydrocarbons like butane and small fractions of ethane and propane. Butane is also the main constituent of liquified petroleum gas (LPG) that is used for domestic purposes.

When the valve of an LPG cylinder is opened, butane vapourises due to decrease in pressure and the gas flows to the burner of the stove. One mole of butane yields 2900 kJ of heat energy when it is heated.

Konnect

Liquification of gases by compressing them under high pressure makes their transportation easy and convenient.

Natural gas mainly consists of methane and is obtained from earth either in isolation or along with petroleum deposits. The transportation of natural gas is made convenient by compressing it under high pressure, and it is referred to as compressed natural gas (CNG). CNG is generally used in industries for production of electricity through generators and also used as fuel in automobiles.

Nuclear Energy

Many years ago, atom was believed to be the most fundamental and indivisible entity of matter. Later on, it was discovered that atom too is divisible and it consists of elementary particles like protons, neutrons and electrons. Protons, that are considered to be positively charged and neutrons that do not possess any charge are contained in the central part of an atom called **nucleus**, where the mass of the atom is concentrated. Electrons that are considered to be charged negatively revolve around the nucleus in their specified paths called **orbits.**

In the formation of atom from its constituents, energy is released and thus, energy transactions are related to the reactions that are linked with the nuclei. These reactions are called **nuclear reactions**. There are broadly two types of nuclear reactions: nuclear fission and nuclear fusion.

Nuclear fission is a process in which a heavy nucleus of an atom is split into two atoms of lighter nuclei by bombarding it with slow moving particles like neutrons resulting in the release of a huge amount of energy. The energy released in the fission process is in the form of heat and can be conveniently utilized to produce electricity using turbines.

Konnect

The energy from the sun and other stars is based on the nuclear fusion phenomenon whereas energy released in the explosion of atom bombs is based on nuclear fission.

Nuclear fusion is a process in which two lighter nuclei combine to form heavy nucleus with release of energy. It is a process in which two lighter nuclei, like hydrogen, are combined at high temperatures to form a single atom having heavier nucleus like helium. In nuclear fusion, an enormous amount of energy which is greater than that produced in a fission reaction is released. For fusion to take place a very high temperature of the order of 107 K is required. Energy released per unit mass in fusion is greater than the energy released per unit mass in fission.

Nuclear reactor is a device in which a controlled nuclear fission reaction takes place. The nuclear fuel, either uranium 235 or plutonium, is bombarded with slow moving neutron and this releases energy in the form of heat and radiation. The fission reaction producing neutrons is controlled in the reactor, and hence, the energy is released at a constant rate. The heat energy obtained during fission reaction is absorbed by the coolant (water) and the water is converted into steam. The steam is used to rotate the turbine placed between two strong magnetic poles. This in turn generates electricity. Nuclear waste obtained from fission reaction is radioactive and it gives out radiations which cause hazards to the living beings, diseases such as cancer, leukaemia, etc. Some of the nuclear power plants in India are at Tarapur, Kota, Kalpakkam, Narora, etc.

The working of a nuclear reactor is based on the phenomenon of nuclear fission. In a nuclear reactor, the fission reactions that take place can be controlled and the energy derived from it is harnessed into productive applications. But in the case of fusion reactions, the energy released cannot be harnessed into productive applications as the fusion reactions cannot be controlled. A hydrogen bomb is based on a nuclear fusion reaction. The reason for the controlled fusion reactions that take place in the sun and stars is yet to be established.

Renewable Sources of Energy

Solar Energy

Nuclear fusion phenomenon that takes place continuously in the interior of the sun causes incessant release of energy from it. It is estimated that the Earth directly receives only 4.58×10^{-8} per cent of the total output of solar energy.

Directly or indirectly every form of energy manifested on the Earth is dependent on solar energy. The various transformations that can occur from solar energy can be understood by the figure 11.1.

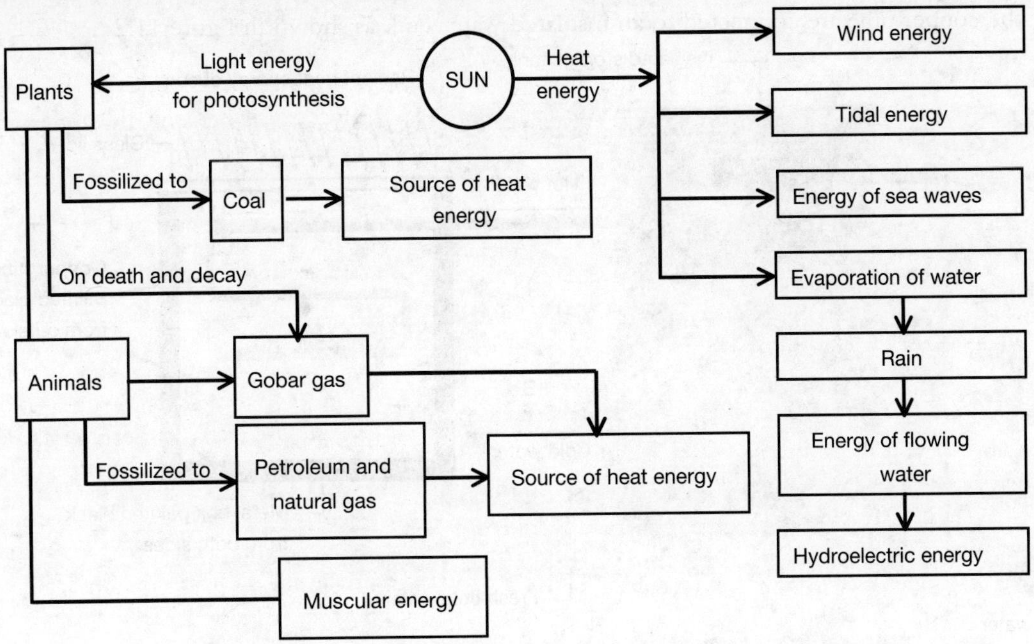

Figure 11.1 Block diagram of transformation of solar energy

The demand for fuels to meet the needs of increasing population and depletion of the non-renewable sources of energy gives rise to the necessity of harnessing solar energy as an alternative to the existing non-renewable fossil fuels. Solar energy can be harnessed either directly by using devices like solar cookers, solar heaters, etc., or indirectly by using energy by wind, flowing water, etc.

Energy received from the sun is abundant but some percentage of this energy is reflected by the atmosphere and the energy reaching the Earth is scattered. Consequently, the solar energy received per unit area per second on the Earth's surface is very small (0.64 kg m^{-2} s^{-1}). In order to increase the intensity of the incident solar energy, flat plate collectors are used.

The intensity of the harnessed solar energy is enhanced by the following procedures:

1. The surface which has to collect solar energy is painted black since black is a good absorber of radiation.
2. The collector is placed in an insulated box with a glass top. The insulated box prevents the flow of heat due to conduction, convection and radiation and the glass covering allows the solar energy to pass through it and it traps the infrared radiation. This increases the temperature of the blackened surface.
3. Solar energy is collected over a large area and is focused to a small area by the reflectors. Plane mirror or a concave mirror can be used as a reflector.

Solar Furnace

Solar furnace consists of a huge concave reflector which is made up of a number of plane mirrors. The material to be melted is placed in a crucible and the crucible is placed at the principal focus of the reflector. The reflector focuses the solar energy on the crucible when turned towards the sun and the temperature of the material rises up to 4000°C which is sufficient to melt the material.

The principle of solar furnace may have been known in ancient times. The Greek scientist Archimedes is said to have offered resistance to the attacking ships by setting them on fire with a burning glass that may have been formed by an array of mirrors.

Solar Water Heater

Solar energy can also be used to heat water. In this the solar energy is collected by a collector. The collector consists of an insulated box and inside the box a copper pipe is laid.

The ends of the copper pipe are connected to an insulated water tank as shown in figure 11.2.

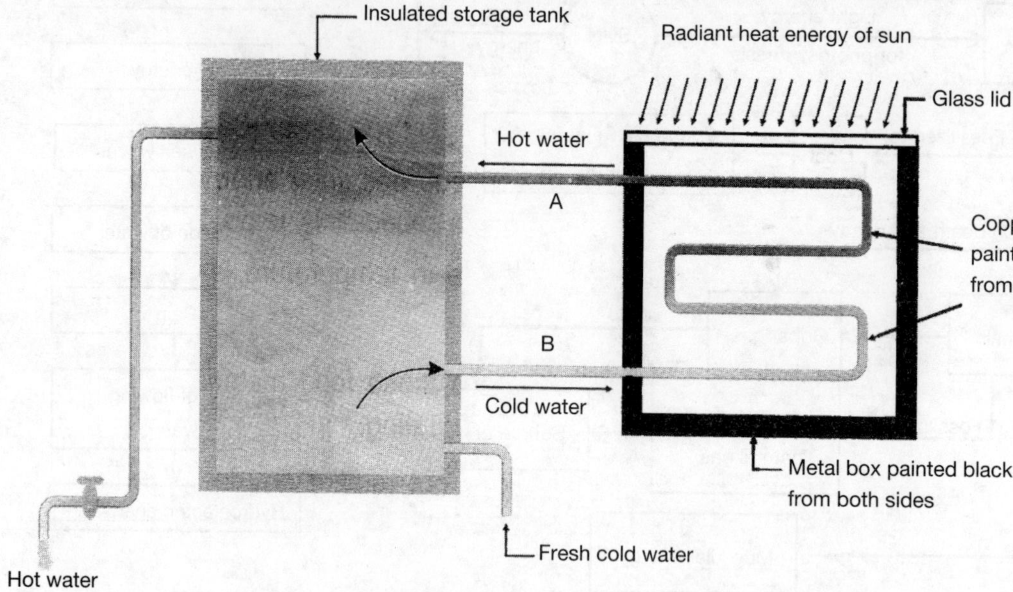

Figure 11.2 Solar water heater

The inner side and the outer side of the insulated box, and the outer surface of the copper pipe are painted black to absorb solar radiation. The top of the insulated box is covered with glass which traps radiation of longer wavelength and the heat energy is absorbed by the cold water flowing from the tank through the copper pipe and the hot water rises up to take its place, fresh cold water flows from the tank. Hence, a convection current is set up and the hot water is collected in the tank.

Solar Drier

There are many types of solar driers which are alternatives to direct sun drying. The two types of solar drier are direct type and indirect type. The direct solar dryer is a closed insulated box in which sun rays are collected and the drying takes place in the same box.

The indirect solar dryer has a flat plate collector and a separate drying chamber. The air is preheated in the flat plate collector and the hot air rises to the drying chamber to dry cereals, fruits, vegetables, etc., which are kept in perforated trays. The indirect dryer is more efficient than the direct dryer. The agricultural products which are dried by solar dryers are not attacked by insects or pests. This reduces the loss of agricultural products. The cereals and vegetables dried in the solar dryers are hygienic.

Solar Cooker

Cookers that use solar energy are solar cookers. Two types of solar cookers are generally used. One is a box type solar cooker and another is a reflector type solar cooker.

Box Type Solar Cooker

It consists of a cuboidal wooden box, lined inside with a heat insulating material like thermocol or glass wool and the inner walls are painted black as shown in Figure 11.3. Black surfaces absorb as well as radiate more heat compared to other coloured surfaces. A plane mirror is clamped at the top of the box so as to adjust its inclination and allow sunlight to be reflected into the box. A glass cover is placed at the top surface of the box. The glass cover allows solar energy to pass through it into the box but not out of the box. This property of glass helps to trap solar energy in the box thus resulting in the food items in the box being cooked.

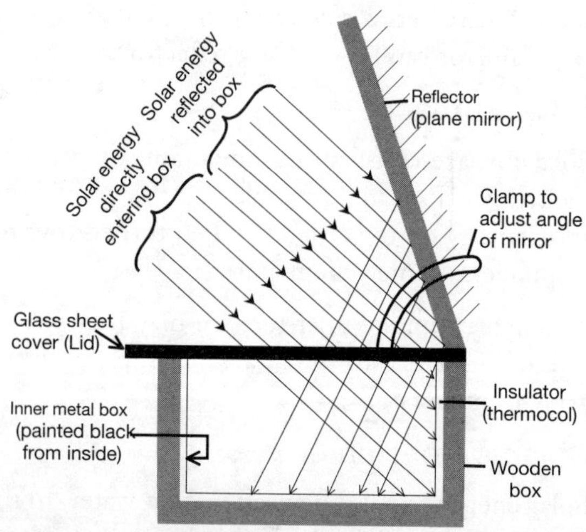

Figure 11.3 Solar cooker

Reflector Type Solar Cooker

In this type of solar cooker, the solar radiation is made incident on a concave reflector, which after reflection is focussed at a point. The items that are to be cooked are placed in a vessel and the vessel is then kept at the focal point by an arrangement as shown in the figure below. The advantage of this type of cooker is that temperatures upto 180°C can be obtained in this cooker and thus is more effective than a box type solar cooker.

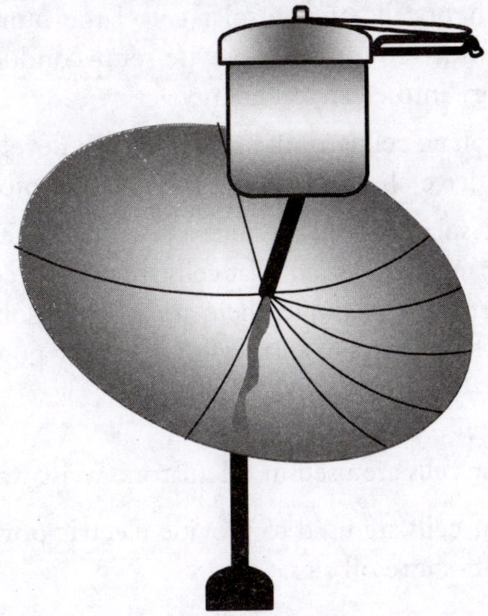

Figure 11.4 A reflector type solar cooker concentrates solar energy on a small area

Solar Power Plant

It consists of a parabolic or a concave reflector which focusses solar energy on a copper pipe and the water flowing through the copper pipe is heated and is converted into steam. The generated steam is used to drive a turbine which is placed between the poles of a strong magnet. The mechanical energy of the turbine is converted to electrical energy.

Solar Cells

Solar cell is a photoelectric cell, which converts light energy into electrical energy. They work on the principle of photoelectric effect. **Photoelectric effect** is the phenomenon of ejection of electrons from a metallic surface when light of suitable radiation falls on the metallic surface.

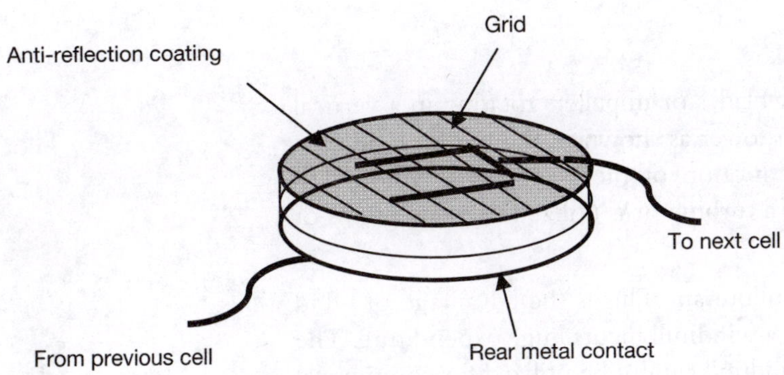

Figure 11.5 Solar cell

Info Bytes!

Solar panels can still generate energy when it's cloudy, although at a reduced efficiency.

Solar cell was first discovered by two British scientists. They produced current by exposing selenium to sunlight, but the conversion of solar energy to light energy was just 0.6%. Later Bell laboratory of USA discovered silicon solar cells which had efficiency of 5%. Nowadays we have solar cells which are more efficient and economically cheaper.

Solar cells are made up of semi-conductors. **Semi-conductors** are substances whose electrical properties like resistivity and conductivity lies between those of conductors and insulators. Germanium and silicon are some of the examples of semi-conductors. Conductivity of a semi-conductor can be increased by adding impurities. This process of adding impurities to a semi-conductor is called **doping**. If an impurity atom like boron or aluminium is added to germanium or silicon the semi-conductors, have more affinity to attract electrons and this type of semi-conductor is called ***p*-type semi-conductor**. If an impurity like phosphorus or arsenic is added to a germanium or a silicon semi-conductor crystal, large amount of electrons are obtained and this semi-conductor is known as ***n*-type semi-conductor**.

A typical solar cell consists of a *p*-type and an *n*-type semi-conductor sandwiched by a special technique. This sandwiched semi-conductor is fixed to a metal base. The metal base has a lead and a U-shaped metal grid is placed on the sandwiched semi-conductor. The grid has another lead which is used to connect to another cell in series. The upper layer of a semi-conductor is coated with a material which does not reflect light.

When light falls on the solar cell, large number of electrons are produced in the n-type semi-conductor and these electrons move towards the p-type semi-conductor causing electric current. Thus, solar cell is a device which converts light energy into electrical energy.

Photovoltaic cell is a solar cell. This cell develops its own potential difference, i.e., this cell does not require an external source to drive charges. Hence, the name photovoltaic cell (photo = light, voltaic = potential difference).

A single solar cell can produce a potential difference of less than a volt and a current of the order of few milliampere. But in a solar panel many such solar cells are connected in series and parallel arrangements to obtain large potential difference and large current. For example, there are arrays of solar cells on satellites which are used to supply electric power to its electrical systems. These arrays of solar cells can supply power even to a house for domestic usage.

Uses

1. Solar cells are used in calculators, wrist watches, street lights, etc.
2. Solar cells are used to provide electric power to houses, to provide electrical energy in satellites and provide power to off-shore oil rigs.

Wind Energy

Moving air is wind and thus wind possesses kinetic energy. This kinetic energy of wind is converted into mechanical energy and further into other forms by using a windmill. Uneven heating of the Earth's atmosphere causes a pressure difference in air, between one region and another. This difference in atmospheric pressure causes motion of air. Thus, the root cause of energy due to wind is the solar energy. The speed of wind is not equal at all altitudes. It usually increases with altitudes. The speed of wind is also high over seas and coastal regions.

Windmill

A windmill comprises a set of three to four blades or impellers rotating in a vertical plane fixed to a shaft erected at the top of a tower as shown in the figure. It appears similar to a fan. The mechanical rotatory motion of the blades of a windmill is converted into electrical energy by running a turbine or is utilized to grind grains or to pump water from a connected well.

The energy from a windmill does not pollute air. This is the advantage of wind energy. But the construction and erection of a windmill incurs huge expenditure. The electricity generated by means of a single windmill cannot be utilized for commercial purposes as the magnitude of electricity produced by a single windmill is quite small. Thus, a large number of windmills erected over a considerable area, collectively called wind farm, are used for generation of electricity on a large scale.

Figure 11.6 Wind mill

Hydel Energy

Energy obtained from moving water is referred to as **hydel energy**. Dams are constructed across rivers and water is accumulated in the reservoirs of the dams. When the level of water in a reservoir reaches the maximum limit, water is let out of the reservoir and allowed to fall on the blades of a turbine which generates electricity.

Thus, moving water is a source of energy. It is a renewable source of energy. The power plants which generate electricity using running water are called **hydroelectric power plants.**

Kinetic energy of the water is converted into rotational kinetic energy of the blades of turbine. As the turbine blades rotate between the poles of a strong magnet, their rotational kinetic energy is converted to electrical energy.

Limitations of Hydel Energy

To convert hydel energy to electrical energy, vast amount of water is required and moreover the dams or the reservoir should be constructed in place where it does not disturb the human habitat and eco-system.

The minimum height required to store water from the turbine is 34 m in order to convert potential energy of water to electrical energy. Hence, the construction of reservoir is not economical.

Pumped Storage Plant

It is a type of hydro electric power plant. The turbines whose direction of rotation can be reversed are used in this type of plants. The turbine can be used either for power generation or for pumping water.

Thermal Power Plants

Coal is used in thermal power plants. The heat obtained from the fossil fuel is used to generate steam, the steam generated is used to rotate a turbine which in turn generates electric power.

Bicycle Dynamo

In a dynamo, mechanical energy is converted into electrical energy. A dynamo consists of an armature coil placed in a magnetic field. When the bicycle wheel rotates, the armature coil is set into rotation in the magnetic field. This gives rise to electrical energy in the form of induced current and makes the bulb glow. Hence, dynamo works on the principle of **electromagnetic induction**.

Tidal Energy

Tidal energy is obtained by the moving water of tides and ocean currents. Energy from the tides can be extracted in two ways:

1. from kinetic energy of the moving water of the tides.
2. from potential energy, which is due to the difference in the height between high and low tides.

The efficiency of tidal power station depends on the height of the rise and fall of the tides. Tidal energy is extracted by building a small dam near a narrow bay where the amplitudes of the tide is very high. During the rise of tide, the sea water is trapped by the dam by opening the gates of the dam. When the water level outside the barrier or dam decreases, i.e., during the fall of the tide the gates of the dam are closed and as a result sea water is collected at a higher level in the dam or the barrage. This potential energy of the water is used to drive a turbine which in turn generates electric power.

Info Bytes!

The largest tidal power station is installed on river Rance in France which can generate electrical energy of 600 GWh per annum.

Biogas

This is the most preferred renewable source of energy, specially in rural areas where the raw materials required to produce biogas are readily available. Agricultural waste and animal dung mixed with water form the raw material for the production of biogas. This raw material is called slurry and is fed into a tank called **digester tank**. In the digester tank, that lies below the ground level, biogas, is produced by a special process called **anaerobic fermentation**. **Biogas** is a mixture of methane, carbon dioxide, hydrogen and a small amount of hydrogen sulphide. Methane is the main constituent of biogas. The fermentation of biogas takes place in the absence of air and in the presence of bacteria present in the dung. Hence, this is called **anaerobic fermentation**. For better yield of biogas, the fermentation should take place at 35°C with large amount of water. Any decrease in the quantity of water or the temperature will effect the yield of the biogas. The gas that is produced is collected over the top of the tank with the help of pipes and is supplied to homes for domestic use. This is called **biogas plant**. The material that is left behind after the production of biogas is used as a manure in agriculture.

Biogas Plant

This is also called **gobar gas plant**. The fixed-dome type plant consists of a digester tank, slurry mixing tank and spent slurry tank. All these tanks are constructed with bricks and cement. Digester tank and spent slurry tank are below the ground and the slurry tank is placed above the ground as shown in the figure below.

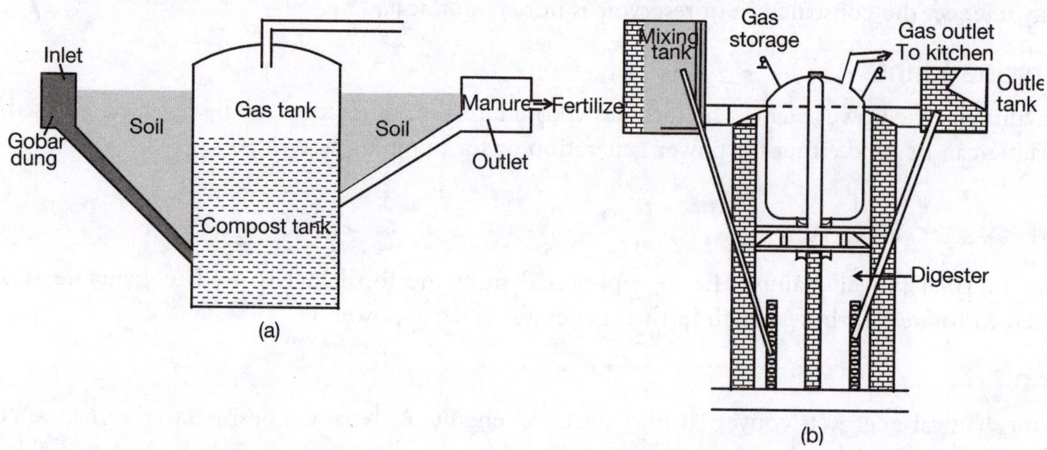

Figure 11.7 Schematic view of two designs of biogas plants: (a) Fixed dome type (b) Floating gas-holder type

The slurry tank in which animal dung, human excreta, farm waste, leaves and water is mixed in proper proportion is connected to the digester. Thus, the slurry flows into the digester tank. Here anaerobic fermentation takes place and this releases biogas. The biogas thus released collects in the dome of the digester. As more and more slurry flows into the digester tank the biogas collects under pressure. When the pressure of the biogas exceeds certain limit it pushes the slurry into the spent slurry tank or the over flow tank and the biogas flows through the outlet pipe and this gas is supplied to homes for domestic use. The spent slurry is removed periodically and is used as manure after drying.

The production of biogas is cheaper as the raw materials are available easily. Biogas has large calorific value, and can be easily supplied through pipe lines. It pollutes air but to a lesser extent when compared to other fuels.

Air Pollution

Injudicious consumption of fuels and increase in population are the two major factors that lead to air pollution to an alarming level. The release of smoke and micro sized dust particles from industries and automobiles are the major contributors to air pollution. The materials that pollute the air are called **pollutants**. Carbon monoxide, hydrogen sulphide, nitrogen dioxide and chlorofluoro carbons (CFCs) are the major air pollutants.

Causes for Air Pollution

1. Wind carries dust and sand particles which pollute air.
2. When volcano eruption takes place it releases sulphur dioxide and ash into the air.
3. Factories and industries release smoke.
4. Burning of wood, coal, kerosene, petrol and forest fire releases large amount of smoke, carbon monoxide and nitrogen oxide to air.
5. Burning of petrol and diesel in vehicles gives hydrocarbons, lead, carbon monoxide and smoke particles which pollute the air.
6. Smoke given out by cigarettes and burning of plastic bags adds to the air pollution.
7. Cutting down trees and deforestation affects the ecological balance and aggravates the atmospheric pollution.
8. Use of insecticides and pesticides causes air pollution.

Hazards of Air Pollution

1. Dust and carbon monoxide when deposited in lungs causes respiratory disorders.
2. Sulphur dioxide when inhaled is converted into sulphuric acid and this acid destroys the nocuous membrane of lungs.
3. Sulphur dioxide reacts with moisture of air to form sulphuric acid. This causes acid rains and the acid rains destroy buildings and monuments.

   Example: sulphur dioxide given out by an industry in Mathura poses a threat to the famous monument, Taj Mahal.
4. Carbon monoxide reacts with red blood corpuscles (R.B.C.) to form carboxy haemoglobin. This lessens the capacity of R.B.C. to carry oxygen and leads to respiratory disorders. Also carbon monoxide destroys the ozone layer of the atmosphere.

Konnect

Planting trees can act as a natural air filter, capturing pollutants and releasing oxygen.

Measures to Control Air Pollution

1. Improved stoves should be used instead of chulhas which give out smoke and ash.
2. Biogas should be used for cooking.
3. Electrostatic precipitators should be installed by cement and other industries which produce smoke and ash.
4. Sulphur dioxide and nitrogen dioxide given out by thermal power plants and other industries should be eliminated by passing them thorough water before letting them to atmosphere. Sulphur dioxide and nitrogen dioxide dissolve in water producing the corresponding acids.
5. Vehicles which run on petrol and diesel eject smoke and other harmful gases. These vehicles should be provided with catalytic converters or vehicles should be run using CNG.
6. Planting large number of trees called afforestation helps in the control of pollution. Trees absorb harmful gases.

Info Bytes!

Switching to renewable energy sources can significantly reduce the strain on natural resources, mitigating aspects of the energy crisis.

Energy Crisis

Fossil fuels like coal, petroleum and natural gas are extensively used in large scale to meet out demands. The rate at which we use fossil fuels would deplete their reserves at a very fast rate. Hence, energy sources should be used judiciously.

POINTS TO REMEMBER

- ✔ A source from which energy is derived in the form of heat is called fuel.
- ✔ Fuels are availablein the three states of matter, namely, solids, liquids and gases.
- ✔ The temperature at which the combustion takes place, called ignition temperature.
- ✔ Fuels like coal, petroleum, etc., are formed as a result of fossils, and hence, these are referred to fossil fuels.
- ✔ Petroleum is also referred to as crude oil; and it falls under the category of non-renewable source of energy.
- ✔ Petroleum gas and natural gas are two major gaseous fossil fuels that are used. Petroleum gas is obtained as a byproduct in the process of refining petroleum.
- ✔ Natural gas mainly consists of methane and is obtained from earth either in isolation or along with petroleum deposits.
- ✔ Nuclear fission is a process in which a heavy nucleus of an atom is split into two atoms of lighter nuclei by bombarding it with slow moving particles like neutrons resulting in the release of a huge amount of energy.
- ✔ Nuclear fusion is a process in which two lighter nuclei, like hydrogen, are combined at high temperatures to form a single atom having heavier nucleus like helium.
- ✔ Solar energy can be harnessed either directly by using devices like solar cookers, solar heaters, etc., or indirectly by using energy by wind, flowing water, etc.
- ✔ Moving air is wind and thus wind possesses kinetic energy. This kinetic energy of wind is converted into mechanical energy and further into other forms by using a wind mill.
- ✔ Energy obtained from moving water is referred to as hydel energy.
- ✔ Tidal energy is obtained by the moving water of tides and ocean currents.
- ✔ Semi-conductors are substances whose electrical properties like resistivity and conductivity lies between those of conductors and insulators.
- ✔ Agricultural waste and animal dung mixed with water form the raw material for the production of biogas.
- ✔ The release of smoke and micro sized dust particles from industries and automobiles are the major contributors to air pollution.
- ✔ Fossil fuels like coal, petroleum and natural gas are extensively used in large scale to meet out demands.

CLASSROOM WING

PRACTICE QUESTIONS

Very Short Answer Type Questions

Directions for questions 1 to 8:
Fill in the blanks.

1. The fuel used in blast furnaces is _____.
2. The type of energy utilized by humans and animals to carry out their life activities is ___________.
3. Wood is a ___________ source of energy.
4. _____ is higher in coke than in coal.
5. The decomposition of matter that takes place in the absence of oxygen is called ___________.
6. The percentage of carbon is least in ____ type of coal.
7. Anthracite consists of ___________.
8. ___________ is the chief source to all forms of energies.

Directions for questions 9 to 25:
Answer the following questions.

9. What is photoelectric effect?
10. What are the constituents of natural gas?
11. What is a solar cooker? Mention the types of solar cookers?
12. Define a source of energy?
13. What is a solar cell? Mention its uses.
14. What is a non-renewable source of energy?
15. State law of conservation of energy.
16. Define a fuel and give some examples of solid, liquid and gaseous fuels.
17. What causes wind (motion of air)?
18. Define calorific value.
19. What is a wind mill?
20. What is a nuclear reactor?
21. What is LPG and what is its chief constituent?
22. What is an orbit in an atom?
23. What is nuclear fission?
24. What is biogas?
25. What is nuclear fusion?

Short Answer Type Questions

26. What are *p*-type and *n*-type semi-conductors?
27. What are the qualities of a good fuel? Discuss.
28. What are the constituents of biogas?
29. What are the advantages and disadvantages of producing hydroelectricity by building dams on rivers? Explain.
30. Why hydel energy is not generally preferred?
31. What are the advantages and limitations of using wind energy?
32. What is meant by 'calorific value of a fuel is 8000 kJ kg^{-1}?
33. Explain how air pollution can be minimised.
34. Name the process that converts solar energy into chemical energy naturally. What is the ultimate source of energy contained in wood?
35. What is the working principle of dynamo? Explain it.
36. Mention the hazards of air pollution.

37. Explain the limitations in harnessing solar energy.

38. What is the full form of CNG. Mention its uses.

39. How can the harness of solar energy be enhanced?

40. State the energy transformations that take place in:
(i) Battery cell (ii) Plant cell
(iii) Muscle cell (iv) Solar cell

Essay Answer Type Questions

41. Explain the working of bicycle dynamo.

42. Explain briefly the working of biogas plant.

43. What are the characteristics of a good energy source?

44. What is a photovoltaic cell? Briefly explain the working of a solar cell.

45. Describe the construction and working of
(a) box type solar cooker and
(b) reflector type solar cooker

COMPETITION WING

PRACTICE QUESTIONS

Level 1: Apply your Concepts

Directions for questions 1 to 7:
State whether the following statements are true or false

1. When the fast moving wind rotates the blades of a windmill its shaft rotates the armature inside the generator producing electric current.
2. Coal is a renewable source of energy.
3. Ignition temperature is the temperature above which the material cannot catch fire.
4. The unit of calorific value is J g^{-1} $°C^{-1}$.
5. The process of burning a material in the absence of oxygen is called destructive distillation.
6. Solar cell is a device which converts light energy into electrical energy.
7. Bituminous coal is the finest quality of coal.

Directions for questions 8 to 19:
Fill in the Blanks.

8. Carbon percentage in coke is ________than that in coal.
9. The heat in solar radiation is due to __________.
10. __________ is the main constituent of biogas.
11. __________, __________, __________ and __________ are the major air pollutants.
12. Biogas is a mixture of ____, ____and ____.
13. The sources of energy, which cannot be replenished after usage are termed as ________.
14. ________ is the energy liberated when its unit mass is burnt completely.
15. Fuels that have ________ catch fire easily.
16. Volcanic eruption pollutes air, by releasing ______ and ______ into the air.
17. The group of solar cells connected in specific pattern to produce definite potential difference and current is known as ________.
18. ______ destroys the ozone layer of the atmosphere.
19. The device which converts light energy into electrical energy and generates its own potential difference is ________.

Directions for question 20:
Match the entries given in Column A with appropriate ones in Column B.

20.

	Column A		Column B
A.	Hydel power plants	a.	Percentage of hydrogen in a fuel.
B.	Renewable source of energy	b.	Solar reactions
C.	Good source of energy	c.	Deforestation
D.	High calorific value for gaseous fuels	d.	Electricity from flowing water
E.	Fossil fuels	e.	Afforestation
F.	Nuclear fission	f.	Wind
G.	Nuclear fusion	g.	Remains of dead plants and animals.
H.	Ecological balance	h.	Energy crisis
I.	Absorption of harmful gases	i.	Nuclear reactor
J.	Non-judicious use of energy sources	j.	Germanium

Directions for questions 21 to 35:
For each of the questions, four choices have been provided. Select the correct alternative.

21. When the coils of an electric generator rotate in a magnetic field,
    (a) the mechanical energy changes into electric energy.
    (b) the thermal energy changes into electric energy.
    (c) the solar energy changes into electric energy.
    (d) the wind energy changes into electric energy.

22. The fuels that cannot be replenished, once they are used, are called ________.
    (a) renewable sources
    (b) non-renewable sources
    (c) ultimate sources
    (d) accessible sources

23. Industries which produce smoke and ash should be installed with ______ to minimise air pollution.
    (a) electric precipitators
    (b) magnetic precipitators
    (c) electrostatic precipitators
    (d) All of the above

24. The harmful gases present in the exhaust should be removed by using ______ in vehicles.
    (a) analytic convertor
    (b) pollutant convertor
    (c) subtractive convertor
    (d) catalytic convertor

25. Respiratory disorders are caused when the capacity of R.B.C. to carry oxygen is lessened. This happens when ______ is inhaled.
    (a) sulphur dioxide
    (b) nitrogen trioxide
    (c) carbon dioxide
    (d) carbon monoxide

26. The essential(s) for combustion is (are)
    (a) a combustible material.
    (b) the presence of oxygen.
    (c) ignition temperature of the substance.
    (d) All the above

27. The energy possessed by steam produced by geothermal energy is _______.
    (a) potential energy
    (b) kinetic energy
    (c) hydroelectric energy
    (d) Both (a) and (b)

28. Which of the following statements is/are true regarding hydel energy?
    (A) Moving water is a source of energy.
    (B) It is a renewable source.
    (C) Construction of reservoir is not expensive.
    (a) A and B
    (b) A and C
    (c) A, B, C
    (d) None of the above

29. **Statement 1:** Combustion or burning takes place only in the presence of oxygen.
    Statement 2: Oxygen is a supporter for combustion.
    (a) Statements (1) and (2) are true
    (b) Statement (1) is true and statement (2) is false
    (c) Statements (1) and (2) are false
    (d) Statement (1) is false and statement (2) is true

30. A wind energy farm converts __________.
    (a) solar energy to wind energy
    (b) wind energy to mechanical energy
    (c) electrical energy to wind energy
    (d) wind energy to solar energy

31. The main constituent of petroleum gas is
    (a) ethane (b) propane
    (c) methane (d) All the above

32. The power of a solar panel depends on
    (A) the arrangement of the solar cells in it
    (B) the extent of surface area of the solar cells.
    (a) Only A is true.
    (b) Only B is true.
    (c) Both A and B are true
    (d) Both A and B are false.

33. **Statement A:** For nuclear fusion to take place a very high temperature is required.
    Statement B: Hydrogen bomb is based on a nuclear fusion reaction.
    (a) Both statements A and B are true.
    (b) Statement A is true. Statement B is false.
    (c) Statement A is false, statement B is true.
    (d) Both statements A and B are false.

34. In a nuclear reactor, the energy is released by borm- barding uranium nucleus with _____
(a) fast moving neutrons
(b) slow moving α-particles
(c) fast moving electrons
(d) slow moving neutrons

35. Which of the following has the highest calorific value?
(a) LPG (b) CNG
(c) Hydrogen (d) Petrol

Level 2: Review your Concepts

36. Discuss-'Hydrogen gas which is easily available on the Earth is going to be the next promising fuel'.

37. In a residential colony, it is estimated that the inci- dent solar radiation is 1000 W/m^2. The efficiency of installed solar panels is 42%. Assuming that the energy from solar panels of area 100 m^2 is completely used for heating, calculate the quantity of water (in litre) that can be heated from 10 °C to 40 °C in one hour. Take specific heat capacity of water as 4.2 J g^{-1} °C^{-1}.

38. A solar panel containing 1500 solar cells each of sur- face area 5 cm^2 arranged in parallel combination, is used to supply electrical energy for domestic needs. The efficiency of a solar cell is 35% and 600 J of energy is incident on one square metre area in one second, find the electrical energy generated in one hour.

39. How much energy will 1 kg mass of wood yield on complete combustion if its calorific value were 18 kJ g^{-1}?

40. Among the given fuels, justify which one is a good fuel?

Fuel	Calorific value	Ignition temperature
A	150 kJ g^{-1}	5°C
B	60 kJ kg^{-1}	30°C
C	10 kJ g^{-1}	45°C

41. Some renewable sources of energy are given below: Solar energy, tidal energy, biogas energy, hydel energy, OTEC, wind energy, geothermal energy, ocean wave energy. Which of the given sources are more reliable and consistent in availability.

42. What is the principle of a solar furnace? How this principle can be used to attack enemy ships?

43. The flame of a candle or kerosene stove is sometimes yellow and sometimes blue. What do these colours indicate?

44. What is doping? Why is it done for semiconducting materials?

45. The heat produced on complete combustion of 20 g of a fuel could raise the temperature of 1.5 kg of water from 25°C to 75°C. Calculate the calorific value of the fuel if the specific heat capacity of water is 4.2 J g^{-1}°C^{-1}. Assume that the heat absorbed by the container is negligible.

46. What are the advantages and disadvantages of using nuclear energy?

47. 60 MJ energy is produced on combustion of 2 kg of coal. Find how much energy is produced on burning 0.5 kg of coal. Also find the calorific value of coal.

48. What are the advantages and disadvantages of using charcoal as a fuel as compared to wood?

49. A piece of cloth is soaked in kerosene and another piece in water. When both are lighted with a match stick, which one will burn easily? Why?

50. What is the source of energy for an artificial satellite? Can this source of energy be used to run vehicles on the Earth?

51. Why is kerosene preferred over petrol as a domes- tic fuel? Why is hydrogen preferred over kerosene as rocket fuel but not as domestic fuel?

52. Find the mass of the fuel required to raise the temperature of 2 kg of water in a copper container of mass 1 kg by 88°C. Given calorific value of fuel is 48 MJ kg^{-1}, specific heat capacity of water is 1 cal g^{-1} °C^{-1} and specific heat capacity of copper is 0.095 cal g^{-1} °C^{-1}.

53. A surface of area 1 m^2 kept perpendicular to the sun rays absorbs 3 MJ of solar energy in one hour.

(a) What is the amount of solar energy absorbed by a solar heater when a surface of area 9 m^2 is exposed perpendicular to the sun rays for 4 hours.

(b) What is the amount of time taken by this heater to boil 12 kg of water at 40°C if its efficiency is 60%? Specific heat capacity of water = 4200 J kg^{-1} $°C^{-1}$

54. State the energy transformations that take place in:

(i) Battery cell

(ii) Plant cell

(iii) Muscle cell

(iv) Solar cell

Level 3: Assess Your Concepts

55. Why do gaseous fuels have high calorific values?

56. Every form of energy manifested on the Earth is dependent on solar energy either directly or indirectly. Is this true in case of fossil fuels.

57. How does the water in a solar water heater get heated up?

58. Why is it not possible to use solar cell panels to meet all our domestic energy needs?

59. At a place, the solar energy incident in one second is 640 J, on an area of one square metre. Assuming that all the solar energy is absorbed by 10 kg water, incident on its surface of area 400 cm^2, how much time will it take to raise its temperature by 70°C? (specific heat capacity of water is 4.2 J g^{-1} $°C^{-1}$)

60. In a thermal power plant, the electricity generated from burning coal is 4800 kW h per metric ton. In a nuclear power plant, the electricity generated from controlled nuclear fission of U-235 is 24,000 kW h per gram. How many times is the efficiency of U-235 compared to coal in electricity generation?

JEE-NEET SPECIAL WING

PRACTICE QUESTIONS

Multiple-Answer Type Questions

Directions for questions 1 to 5:
Select one or more correct alternative(s) from the given choices.

1. Which of the following are the characteristics of a good source of energy?
   (a) low ratio of output to input energy
   (b) easy availability
   (c) Economical
   (d) Convenient for storage and transportation.
2. Calorific value is measured in
   (a) $g\ J^{-1}$ (b) $J\ Kg^{-1}$
   (c) $cal^{-1}\ g$ (d) $cal\ g^{-1}$
3. Identify the uses of solar cell
   (a) Calculators (b) Street light
   (c) Wrist watch (d) Lift system
4. Energy conversion involved in hydroelectric power plants are
   (a) Kinetic energy to potential energy
   (b) Kinetic energy to rotational kinetic energy
   (c) Rotational kinetic energy to electrical energy.
   (d) Potential energy to electrical energy.
5. The fixed - dome type biogas plant consists of
   (a) Dispenser tank
   (b) Rotor blade
   (c) Digester tank
   (d) Spent slurry tank

Comprehension-Based Questions

Directions for questions 6 to 10:
These questions are based on the following information.

Solar Energy

Solar energy is the cleanest and most abundant renewable energy source available in the world. It is the radiation from the sun which produce heat that can result in chemical reactions or electricity generation. Since it does not emit any chemicals or gases, it is eco - friendly and helps to reduce global warming and ozone depletion. While conducting experiments about photography, Edmond Becquerel discovered the principle behind solar energy. As long as sun is present we can harness solar energy. Henceforth it is the most efficient and infinite form of energy.

6. The photoelectric component which convert light energy into electrical energy is
   (a) Solar cell (b) Dynamo
   (c) LED (d) Leclanché cell
7. Solar cell are made up of
   (a) Conductors (b) Insulators
   (c) Semi - conductors (d) Opaque objects
8. When phosphorus is added to germanium crystal, the crystal obtained is
   (a) Pure semi – conductors
   (b) Conductors
   (c) p - type semiconductors
   (d) n - type semiconductors
9. In a solar water heater, the inner and outer side of insulated box is painted black to
   (a) radiate radiation (b) Absorb radiation
   (c) Reflect radiation (d) Focus radiation
10. A device powered by solar energy that helps in agriculture is
    (a) Solar cooker (b) Solar cell
    (c) Solar drier (d) Solar furnace

Match the Column

Directions for questions 11:

The question is based on the following information.

Non – Renewable Sources of Energy

Non - renewable energy sources are those which cannot be replaced immediately once they are depleted. They are abundant, cost effective and easier to produce and use. Non - renewable sources are extracted directly from the Earth. The leading non - renewable source of energy across the world is fossil fuels. There are four major types of non - renewable sources like oil, nuclear energy, coal and natural gas. We must use them wisely as once they exhaust then there is no more of them for human use.

11. Match the values in List - I with those in List - II:

List - I	List - II
A. Fossil fuels	a. Fractional distillation
B. Coal	b. Butane
C. Petroleum	c. Uranium 235
D. Natural gas	d. Destructive distillation
E. Nuclear energy	e. Carbon

(a) A - e, B - d, C - b, D - a, E - c
(b) A - c, B - e, C - b, D - d, E - a
(c) A - d, B - a, C - b, D - c, E - e
(d) A - d, B - e, C - a, D - b, E - c

ANSWER KEYS

Crossword

Across

3. Nuclear Fission 5. Nuclear Reactor 12. Calorific Value 13. Methane 16. Fuel
17. Semiconductor 18. Photoelectric Effect 19. Fractional Distillation
20. Hydel Energy

Down

1. Destructive Distillation 2. Doping 4. Pollutants 6. Combustion
7. Orbits 8. Tidal Energy 9. Ignition Temperature 10. Nucleus
11. Fossils 14. Solar cell 15. Wind Energy

Classroom Wing

Very Short Answer Type Questions

1. Coke 2. Bioenergy 3. Non-renewable 4. Carbon percentage
5. Anaerobic degradation 6. Peat 7. 94%–98% carbon 8. Solar energy

Competition Wing

Level 1: Apply your Concepts

1. True 2. False 3. False 4. False 5. True
6. True 7. False 8. higher 9. sun 10. methane
11. Carbon monoxide, hydrogen sulphide, nitrogen dioxide and chlorofluoro carbons (CFCs)
12. CH_4, CO_2 and hydrogen 13. Non-renewable source of energy 14. Calorific value
15. Low ignition temperature 16. SO_2, ash 17. Solar panel 18. CO
19. Photo voltaic cell 20. A : d, B : f, C : j, D : a, E : g, F : i, G : b, H : c, I : e, J : h 21. (a)
22. (b) 23. (c) 24. (d) 25. (d) 26. (d)
27. (d) 28. (a) 29. (d) 30. (b) 31. (c)
32. (c) 33. (a) 34. (d) 35. (c)

Level 2: Review your Concepts

37. 1200 litre 38. 567 kJ 39. 18 MJ 45. 15.75 kJ g^{-1}
47. 30 kJ g^{-1}, 15 MJ 52. 16.3 g 53. 567 kJ

Level 3: Assess Your Concepts

59. 31.9 hour 60. 5×10^6 times

JEE-NEET Special Wing

Multiple-Answer Type Questions

1. (b), (c) and (d)
2. (b) and (d)
3. (a), (b) and (c)
4. (b) and (c)
5. (c) and (d)

Comprehension-Based Questions

6. (a)
7. (c)
8. (d)
9. (b)
10. (c)

Match the Column

11. (d)

For complete answer key of Classroom wing and Competition wing, refer to Hints and Solutions

Hints and Explanations

Classroom Wing

Very Short Answer Type Questions

1. Coke
2. Bioenergy
3. Non-renewable
4. Carbon percentage
5. Anaerobic degradation
6. Peat
7. 94%–98% carbon
8. Solar energy
9. Methane.
10. Ejection of electrons from a metallic surface when light of suitable radiation falls on the metallic surface.
11. (i) Cookers that use solar energy.
    (ii) Box type solar cooker, reflecter type solar cooker.
12. A fuel from which energy can be produced.
13. (i) Photoelectric cell, which converts light energy into electrical energy.
    (ii) Used in calculators, street lights, etc.
    Used to provide electric power to houses, satellites etc.
14. Sources of energy, which cannot be replenished after usage.
15. Law of conservation of energy: The energy can neither be created nor be destroyed but can only be transformed from one form to another.
16. A source from which energy is produced in the form of heat.
    Solid fuels–Wood, coal.
    Liquid fuels–Petrol, kerosene
    Gaseous fuels–LPG, CNG
17. (i) Uneven heating of the earth's atmosphere.
    (ii) Pressure difference in air between two regions.
18. The quantity of heat liberated by completely burning a unit mass of a fuel.
19. Comprises a set of three to four blades rotating in a vertical plane—used to produce wind energy.
20. A nuclear reactor is a device in which a controlled nuclear fission reaction takes place.
21. (i) Liquefied petroleum gas—By product in the process of refining petroleum.
    (ii) Butane.
22. The path in which the charged electrons revolve around the nucleus is called an orbit.
23. Heavy nucleus of an atom is split into two or more lighter nuclei.
24. Gas produced from biological wastes.
25. Two lighter nuclei combine at high temperature to form a single heavy nucleus.

Short Answer Type Questions

Note: This is how you should frame your answer covering.

26. (i) Silicon or germanium doped with boron or aluminium.
    (ii) Silicon or germanium doped with phosphorus or arsenic.
27. Discuss the qualities of good fuel regarding
    (i) calorific value,
    (ii) pollution,
    (iii) storage and transportation,
    (iv) availability and cost effectiveness.
28. Biogas is a mixture of methane, carbon dioxide, hydrogen and a small amount of hydrogen sulphide. Methane is the main constituent of biogas.
29. (i) Advantages and disadvantages in building dams.
    (ii) Is water a free and renewable source of energy?
    Do dams help in flood control and irrigation?
    Can a huge hydroelectricity is possible to generate?
    Is it economical to build dams on rivers?
    Does it destroy the natural fauna and flora?
    Is it possible to build dams in any area?
30. Characteristics of a good source of energy.

31. Is the wind farming technology cost effective?

Is wind energy a dependable source?

Does it produce pollution?

Is it available all through the year?

What is the minimum wind speed at which the wind energy can be harnessed?

Is net energy output satisfactory?

Is the source available free of cost and is it a renewable source?

32. Heat energy liberated when 1 kg of fuel is burnt.

33. Chimneys, filters, precipitators, good source of fuel.

34. (i) Plants convert solar energy into chemical energy.

(ii) What is meant by photosynthesis?

What type of changes are observed in plants after photosynthesis?

Do plants become trees after some years?

So, solar energy is converted into chemical energy.

Then, is solar energy not the ultimate source of energy in wood?

35. Dynamo works on the principle of electromagnetic induction. A dynamo consists of an armature coil placed in a magnetic field. When the bicycle wheel rotates, the armature coil is set into rotation in the magnetic field. This gives rise to electrical energy in the form of induced current.

36. (i) Respiratory disorders.

(ii) Destroy buildings and mountains.

37. Is it possible to generate solar energy in nights and during cloudy days?

Is the cost of solar cells high or low?

Do the rotation of earth affect the production of solar energy?

What is the effect of changes in seasons on solar energy?

38. (i) Compressed natural gas.

(ii) Used in industries for production of electricity through generators, as a fuel in automobiles.

39. The intensity of the harnessed solar energy is enhanced by the following procedures:

(i) The surface which has to collect solar energy is painted black since black is a good absorber of radiation.

(ii) The collector is placed in an insulated box with a glass top. The insulated box prevents the flow of heat due to conduction, convection and radiation and the glass covering allows the solar energy to pass through it and it traps the infrared radiation. This increases the temperature of the blackened surface.

(iii) Solar energy is collected over a large area and is focused on a small area by the reflectors. Plane mirror or a concave mirror can be used as a reflector.

40. (i) In a battery cell, chemical energy gets transformed into electrical energy.

(ii) In a plant cell, light energy gets transformed into chemical energy.

(iii) In a muscle cell, chemical energy gets transformed into mechanical energy.

(iv) In a solar cell, light energy gets transformed into electrical energy.

Essay Answer Type Questions

Note: This is how you should frame your answer covering.

41. Circular magnet, coil, shaft, wheel attachment.

42. Animal waste, huge pit, compost tank, water inlet, outlet.

43. (i) High ratio of output to input energy

(ii) Easy availability

(iii) Risk free

(iv) Economical to use

44. (i) A solar cell

(ii) Develops its own potential difference

Working:

(i) Light incident on a solar cell.

(ii) Produces large number of electrons in n-type semi-conductor.

(iii) Move towards p-type semi-conductor causing electric current.

45. (i) Wooden box, thermocol, black paint, glass lid, plane mirror.

(ii) Concave surface, plane mirrors, cooking material at focus.

Competition Wing

Level 2: Review your Concepts

Note: This is how you should frame your answer covering.

36. (i) Calorific value of hydrogen gas. Advantages and disadvantages of hydrogen gas as a fuel.

(ii) Find the calorific value of hydrogen as a fuel.

Find the pollutants released due to the combustion of hydrogen.

Is steam (water vapour) a toxic substance?

Can a technology in which hydrogen is used as fuel be developed?

Is it already in use?

How are rockets sent into outer space?

37. Incident solar radiation = 1000 W/m^2

Efficiency of solar panels = 42 %

Useful solar radiation = 42/100 × 1000 W/m^2

= 420 W/m^2

Area of Solar panels = 100 m^2

Total useful solar radiation = 420 × 100 W

Using, 1 W = 1 J/1 s,

420 × 100 W means, 420 × 100 J of solar energy for every 1 s.

Now, useful solar energy for 1 hour = 420 × 100 × 3600 J (1)

(1 h = 3600 s)

Let 'x' litre of water be heated in 1 h.

Density of water = 1 g/cm^3

Hence, mass of 'x' litre of water = 1000 × x g

Initial temperature of water, t_1 = 10 °C

Final temperature of water, t_2 = 40 °C

Change in temperature, Δt = 40 °C – 10 °C = 30 °C

Using, Q = m s Δt,

The quantity of heat gained by 'x' litre of water,

Q = 1000 × x × 4.2 × 30 J (2)

Now, (2) = (1)

1000 × x × 4.2 × 30 J = 3600 × 420 × 100

x = (3600 × 420 × 100) / (1000 × 4.2 × 30)

x = 1200 litre.

38. (i) Efficiency $= \dfrac{\text{Energy utilized}}{\text{Energy supplied}}$

(ii) 567 kJ

39. (i) Definition and formula for calorific value.

(ii) Find the amount of mass of fuel (*m*) and its calorific value (*s*).

Convert the calorific value in terms of J kg^{-1}.

Then, the amount of heat energy (Q) released will be Q = *ms*.

Substitute the values of '*m*' and '*s*' and find the value of 'Q'.

(iii) 18 MJ

40. Characteristics of a good fuel.

41. From among the given sources of energy find those which are available throughout the year irrespective of climatic changes.

Are the remaining sources of energy of no advantage?

42. The principle of solar furnace is to concentrate incident solar energy at its principal focus to produce high temperatures.

Solar furnace consists of a huge concave reflector which is made up of several plane mirrors. The reflector focuses the solar energy at the position of principal focus and the temperature of a material at the principal focus raises up to 4000°C which is sufficient to melt the material.

The principle of solar furnace can be used to attack the enemy ships by setting them on fire by focusing the solar energy on them.

43. (i) Factors affecting the combusting of a substance.

(ii) Adequate or inadequate supply of oxygen or fuel for combustion.

(iii) Complete and incomplete supply of oxygen

44. The process of adding impurities to a semiconductor is called doping.

When a suitable impurity is added to a semiconducting material, either the semiconductor gets more affinity to attract electrons (*p*-type) or a large number of electrons (*n*-type) which increases the conductivity of the semiconductor.

45. (i) Formula for calorific value, Q = *ms*Δθ.

(ii) Find the amount of heat energy required to increase the temperature of 1.5 μg of water from 25°C to 75°C using the formula Q = *ms* (1)

Let '*s*' denote specific heat capacity of water and 'Δθ' denote change in the temperature.

Is this heat energy released due to complete combustion of 20 g of a fuel?

Then, the formula related to combustion of fuel is $Q = m.k.$ (2)

$Q = m.k = mwst$, since heat released in combustion is absorbed by water.

Thus, find the value of 'k'.

(iii) 15.75 kJ g^{-1}

46. Is nuclear wastage hazardous?

Is it possible to produce nuclear isotopes?

Is nuclear radiation harmful to biological life?

Is nuclear technology cheap or expensive?

Is current produced by nuclear reactors less expensive?

Find various uses of nuclear isotopes?

47. (i) Definition of calorific value.

(ii) Calorific value is constant for a given substance.

(iii) $Q = mc$

(iv) $Q \propto m$

(v) 30 kJ g^{-1}, 15 MJ

48. Characteristics of a good fuel.

49. (i) Ignition temperature of a substance.

(ii) Cloth soaked in kerosene

50. Artificial satellites use solar cells as their main source of energy.

51. The temperature at which the combustion takes place is called ignition temperature. The ignition temperature of petrol is quite low compared to kerosene. Thus, petrol is very inflammable, catches fire easily and thus cannot be used for domestic purposes, as its use is highly risky. Hence, kerosene is preferred over petrol as a domestic fuel.

The quantity of heat liberated by completely burning a unit mass of a fuel is called its calorific value. The calorific value of hydrogen is nearly 2.5 times that of kerosene. Hence, hydrogen is preferred over kerosene as rocket fuel. However, due to very high combustion rate, it is difficult to store and transport hydrogen. Hence, hydrogen is not preferred as domestic fuel.

52. (i) Energy supplied is utilized to raise the temperature of both water and container.

(ii) Definition of calorific value.

(iii) $Q = m_w s_w \Delta t_w + m_c s_c \Delta t_c$

(iv) $Q = mc$

(v) 16.3 g

53. (i) $Q = ms\Delta t$ (ii) 567 kJ

54. (i) In a battery cell, chemical energy gets transformed to electrical energy.

(ii) In a plant cell, light energy gets transformed to chemical energy.

(iii) In a muscle cell, chemical energy gets transformed to mechanical energy.

(iv) In a solar cell, light energy gets transformed to electrical energy.

Level 3: Assess Your Concepts

Note: This is how you should frame your answer covering.

55. (i) Reason for high calorific value of a fuel.

(ii) Presence of hydrogen

56. (i) Meaning of fossil fuels.

(ii) Their formation.

57. The collector of a solar water heater consists of an insulated box and inside the box, a copper pipe is laid. The ends of the copper pipe are connected to an insulated water tank. The inner side and the outer side of the insulated box, and the outer surface of the copper pipe are painted black to absorb solar radiation. The top of the insulated box is covered with glass which traps radiation of longer wavelengths and the heat energy is absorbed by the cold water flowing from the tank through the copper pipe and the hot water rises up to take its place, and fresh cold water flows from the tank. Hence, a convection current is set up and the hot water is collected in the tank.

58. (i) Drawbacks of solar energy.

(ii) Is the efficiency of energy conversion (light to electricity) low or high, when compared to other methods of electricity generation?

Is the power output low for solar cells?

Do solar cell panels work only during day?

Find, what happens during nights and on cloudy days?

Is this technology cost effective?

59. (i) Total energy = (Energy incident per unit area) (× total area) × (total time)

$$Q = ms\,\Delta\theta$$

(ii) Find the change in temperature.

Find the mass of water and its surface area over which light is made to be incident from the given data.

Convert surface area in S.I system.

Find the solar energy incident in one second per square metre?

Find the amount of heat energy (Q) required to raise the temperature of water from formula $Q = ms\Delta\theta$. (1)

Find the amount of solar energy incident in one second on water surface.

Is it equal to (640 × 0.04)? (2)

Then find the time taken to produce Q amount of heat by solar energy which can be found out by dividing (1) by (2).

(iii) 31.9 hour

60. Electricity generated from burning one metric ton of coal is 4800 kW h.

1 metric ton = 1000 kg

Hence, electricity generated from burning 1 kg of coal

= 4800/1000

= 4.8 kW h

Electricity generated from controlled nuclear fission of 1 g of U-235 is 24,000 kW h.

$1\text{ g} = 10^{-3}\text{ kg}$

Hence, electricity from controlled nuclear fission of 1 kg of U-235 = $24000/10^{-3} = 24000 \times 10^{3}$ kW h.

Efficiency of U-235 compared to coal in electricity generation = $(24000 \times 10^{3})/4.8 = 5 \times 10^{6}$.

Hence, the efficiency of U-235 is 5×10^{6} times compared to coal in electricity generation.

JEE-NEET Special Wing

Multiple-Answer Type Questions

1. For a good source of energy, the net output energy should be sufficiently large.
Hence, the correct option is (b), (c) and (d).

2. Calorific Value: It is the amount of heat released when unit mass of substance is completely burnt.
$C = \frac{\text{Heat}}{\text{mass}}$.
Units of heat are calories(cal) and joules (J).
Units are $\frac{\text{cal}}{\text{gm}}, \frac{J}{kg}$
Hence, the correct option is (b) and (d).

3. Solar cells are not used in lift system.
Hence, the correct option is (a), (b) and (c).

4. Kinetic energy of water is converted into rotational kinetic energy of blades of a turbine. When turbine rotates, rotational kinetic energy is converted into electrical energy.
Hence, the correct option is (b) and (c).

5. Digester Tank: It is large sealed tank used for storing organic manure for the action of bacteria to produce methane gas
Spent Slurry Tank: It is on the right side of the digester tank, which is constructed below ground level.
Hence, the correct option is (c) and (d).

Comprehension-Based Questions

6. Solar cells work based on the photoelectric effect. They utilize semiconductors to convert light energy into electric energy.
Hence, the correct option is (a).

7. Semi-conductors: They are non-ohmic conductors whose resistance decreases with the increase in temperature.
Hence, the correct option is (c).

8. Phosphorus is a pentavalent impurity with a valency of 5 electrons. When it is added to germanium, which has four electrons in its valency shell, its four electrons get paired, leaving one electron of phosphorus unpaired. This results in the creation of n-type semiconductor germanium, with large number of excess electrons.
Hence, the correct option is (d).

9. Black bodies are good absorbers of heat, they absorb large amount of heat from the sunlight which is incident on it.
Hence, the correct option is (b).

10. Solar dryers are devices that accumulate solar radiation and transfer it in the form of heat energy. This heat energy is then transferred to the product for dehydration.
Unlike sun dehydration, solar dryers have a dedicated structure that regulates the dehydration
Hence, the correct option is (c).

Match the Column

11. **Choice (d) follows.**
(A) Fossil Fuels: Destructive distillation of fossil fuels (coal) gives coal tar and coke.
(B) Coal: The major constituent of coal is carbon.
(C) petrol: It is obtained from fractional distillation of crude oil.
(D) Natural gas: Butane is one of the components of natural gas.
(E) Nuclear Energy: Uranium-235 is a naturally occurring radioactive element. When it undergoes fission, it releases a large amount of energy.